THE SOCIOLOGY OF
HEALTH, ILLNESS, AND HEALTH CARE
IN CANADA

A CRITICAL APPROACH

Lisa Strohschein
University of Alberta

Rose Weitz
Arizona State University

NELSON

NELSON

The Sociology of Health, Illness, and Health Care in Canada:
A Critical Approach

by Lisa Strohschein and Rose Weitz

Vice President, Editorial Higher Education:
Anne Williams

Acquisitions Editor:
Maya Castle

Marketing Manager:
Terry Fedorkiw

Developmental Editor:
Toni Chahley

Photo Researcher:
Melody Tolson

Permissions Coordinator:
Melody Tolson

Content Production Manager:
Christine Gilbert

Production Service:
Cenveo Publisher Services

Copy Editor:
Julia Cochrane

Proofreader:
Anandhan. S

Indexer:
BIM Indexing Services

Manufacturing Coordinator:
Ferial Suleman

Design Director:
Ken Phipps

Managing Designer:
Franca Amore

Interior Design:
Greg Devitt

Interior Images:
Flower (top) – Sylvie Bouchard/ Shutterstock

Cover Design:
Greg Devitt

Cover Image:
Flower (top): Sylvie Bouchard/ Shutterstock; Echinacea flower: oksana2010/Shutterstock

Compositor:
Cenveo Publisher Services

Library and Archives Canada Cataloguing in Publication

Strohschein, Lisa, 1966–

The sociology of health, illness, and health care in Canada : a critical approach / Lisa Strohschein, Rose Weitz.

Includes bibliographical references and index.
ISBN 978-0-17-651417-4

1. Social medicine—Canada—Textbooks. 2. Medical care—Canada—Textbooks. I. Weitz, Rose, 1952– II. Title.

RA418.3.C3S77 2013
306.4'610971   C2012-907797-6

ISBN-13: 978-0-17-651417-4
ISBN-10: 0-17-651417-1

*For anyone who thinks the world ought to be a better place
than it is and lives to make it so.*

BRIEF CONTENTS

CONTENTS

Part IV
Health Care Systems, Professions, Settings, and Technologies

I entered university in the late 1980s, brimming with intellectual curiosity and eager to make a positive difference in the world, but with little sense of what I actually wanted to do with my life. That changed after I took a course in medical sociology (as it was called back then) taught by Judith Golec at the University of Alberta. Spellbound by the material and Judith's inimitable teaching style, I subsequently registered in every course on health and illness offered in the department. These courses, coupled with an opportunity to conduct a research project in my final year of undergraduate studies, convinced me to pursue further studies in the sociology of health and illness. Graduate studies took me to York University in Ontario, where I was mentored by Peggy McDonough (now at the University of Toronto), and later to McMaster University and the Institute for Human Development, Life Course and Aging at the University of Toronto, where I respectively completed my PhD (supervised by Margaret Denton) and a postdoctoral fellowship (with Blair Wheaton). The training and guidance I received from them and many others at these institutions both broadened and deepened my knowledge of the discipline and nurtured what has become a lifelong passion.

In 2004, I accepted a faculty position at the University of Alberta, bringing my life full circle with the rare pleasure of having as departmental colleagues those who had once been my teachers. Hoping to inspire the next generation of students, I began teaching courses on the sociology of health and illness and chose Rose Weitz's text over others, including the small number of available Canadian texts, because her book excelled in at least three ways: It was more comprehensive in its coverage than most, it followed a format that paralleled how I structured my course, and its emphasis on a critical approach (to be described in more detail shortly) was compelling. Each time I taught the course, however, I found myself offering the same apology to my students: The textbook was wonderful, but it was not Canadian. That excuse sounded feeble to me after a while, and when Maya Castle from Nelson Education approached me in the spring of 2011 about adapting Weitz's text for Canada, I quickly accepted her invitation.

The critical approach, as Rose Weitz defines it, means using the "sociological imagination" to question previously taken-for-granted aspects of social life. For example, it is largely believed that doctors define illness according to objective biological criteria. It is only when we begin to question this assumption that we catch a glimpse of the political and social forces that underlie the process of defining illnesses. Similarly, rather than accept existing power relationships as the way things are, a critical approach invites us to probe beneath the surface to evaluate the sources, nature, and health consequences of these relationships. Thus, a critical approach motivates sociologists to pay attention to how doctors gained control over health care and to question how the power of industrialized nations has affected health in developing nations. In short, while other disciplines may focus their research on identifying the social factors that create risk for heart disease or exploring the reasons patients might lie to their doctors, such endeavours are merely the starting point for sociologists, who in applying a critical approach examine the structural forces that bring these relationships into being. As such, my sentiments about a critical approach closely correspond with Rose's—we both have an interest in digging into issues around health and illness as a means of bringing greater scrutiny to the ways in which our societies are organized.

A CANADIAN EDITION

For those who might wonder if adapting a textbook for a Canadian audience simply means inserting Canadian data and research in place of U.S. data and research, let me be clear that this is not the case at all. I have retained the scaffolding (overall organization, critical approach, and many of the pedagogical features) of the U.S. text, but addressed the revision with two overarching goals: first, to improve upon its breadth and depth, and second, to achieve greater integration between theory and research. Along the way, I have infused the text with content that reflects the specific interests and circumstances of Canadians.

Although Canadians and Americans may have much in common, they also differ in many ways. For example, the life expectancy of Canadians is on average higher than it is in the United States, the leading cause of death in Canada is cancer whereas in the United States it is heart disease, and income inequality (the size of the gap between a country's poorest and wealthiest citizens) is greater in the United States than in Canada. Similarly, whereas greater government control over health care is considered a threat to medical dominance in both countries, it unfolds in very different ways in Canada. These observations make it imperative that a Canadian textbook focus on the Canadian context.

At the same time, there are lessons to be learned by contrasting the Canadian situation with what occurs in the United States and other countries. Most Canadians already know that their health care system operates on completely different principles than the market-oriented health care system of the United States; however, few may have an exhaustive understanding of these differences. For example, many probably do not realize that prescription drugs generally cost less in Canada than in the United States because provincial governments leverage their buying power when negotiating with pharmaceutical companies to achieve significant cost reductions. Chapter 11 provides a comprehensive framework for evaluating the performance of a health care system, and students will come away with a better understanding of how both the Canadian and U.S. health care systems rank in terms of equity, cost, efficiency, and responsiveness. Similarly, some common influences shaped how bioethics came to be institutionalized in Canada and the United States. Noting these similarities as well as points of divergence in Chapter 14 helps to clarify the relative strengths and weaknesses of the Canadian system. When it comes to evaluating the impact of bioethics on Canadian research, medical education, and clinical practice, however, the discussion is squarely focused on the Canadian context.

In terms of breadth, the Canadian edition contains three new chapters, with each filling important gaps.

- **Chapter 5—Work and Family Life** evaluates how and why roles associated with work and family life are linked to patterns of health and well-being, moving beyond the nearly exclusive focus of the U.S. textbook on factors related to social status (e.g., age, sex and gender, race/ethnicity, and socioeconomic position). Given the ways in which work and family life are rapidly changing, raising important questions about how these changes may be influencing contemporary patterns of health and illness, this chapter is a timely addition.
- **Chapter 9—The Body and the Pursuit of Health** focuses on growing sociological interest in health as a phenomenon in and of itself. To the extent that health is more than the absence of disease, this chapter explores how Canadians accomplish the imperative of health in the twenty-first century. This chapter also describes and assesses how new social forces, combined with rapid advances in medical technology, are leading us into uncharted territory, where the ability to modify and transform bodies, brains, and behaviours is unleashing fundamental questions about what the human species is and might become.

- Finally, as might be expected for the Canadian edition, **Chapter 10—A History of Health Care in Canada** details the history and current challenges of the Canadian health care system.

The Canadian edition also digs more deeply into topics that received only cursory attention in the U.S. text. For example, to cover the literature on the social determinants of health in a way that is comprehensive, incorporates the latest advances, and recognizes the intersectionality of different social factors, a single chapter on the social distribution of disease in the U.S. text was divided in two for the Canadian edition. Differences in illness and death according to age, sex and gender, and race/ethnicity are now found in one chapter (Chapter 3), and socioeconomic inequalities in health are covered in another (Chapter 4).

Depth of coverage has also been accomplished in other ways. For example, the chapter on illness and death in the developing world (Chapter 6) has been almost entirely rewritten in the Canadian edition, expanding on both emerging health problems (the rise of non-communicable disease and road traffic accidents) and the underlying causes of the greater health burden of low- and middle-income countries. In addition, the United Nations Millennium Development Goals (MDG) are used as a reference point for assessing what has been accomplished to date and which goals remain unfulfilled. Similarly, Chapter 11 provides a more thorough description of indicators used to evaluate health care performance, showing specifically how Canada's health care system compares with those in other high-income countries.

Finally, although the U.S. text makes the connection between theory and research, I have attempted to articulate these linkages more consistently and thoroughly in the Canadian edition. As in the U.S. text, Chapter 1 outlines a sociological perspective of health and illness, differentiating the interests of sociologists from those in other health-related disciplines. The Canadian edition, however, goes beyond these distinctions to describe the range of theories that fall under the umbrella of a sociological perspective and then draws on these theories at various points in the text to reveal new insights on a given topic. For example, a sociology of the body perspective has become critical to understanding the limitations of both a medical model approach to disability and a social model of disability, and has instigated new ways of thinking about disability (Chapter 8). Similarly, postmodernism helps us to understand the growing popularity of body projects in contemporary society (Chapter 9), whereas the ongoing phenomenon of specialization in medicine is interpreted from both a structural-functionalist and a conflict perspective (Chapter 12).

To achieve greater integration, some chapters have been reorganized for the Canadian edition. To highlight that the struggle for power among health care occupations occurs across the entire hierarchy, the Canadian edition combines two chapters that dealt separately with the medical profession and other health care providers into a single chapter (Chapter 12). Similarly, some of the material that once constituted a separate chapter on mental illness has been shifted to other chapters. For example, discussion on the rise and fall of the mental asylum now appears in the chapter on health care settings (Chapter 13), so that the shifting of care from the institution to the community and home setting can be seen as a shift that occurred for both mental and physical illness, even though these have historically been treated in different institutional settings (asylum versus hospital).

Despite these changes, much remains the same. First, Rose and I share the belief that sociology neither can nor should exist in isolation but must be informed by and in turn inform other related fields. Accordingly, most chapters include a historical overview. For example, the chapter on the meanings of illness discusses how people throughout history have explained and responded to illness and ill persons (Chapter 7), the chapter on Canada's health care system describes how it came into being and emphasizes the importance of its history in shaping current challenges (Chapter 10), the chapter on health care professions outlines the history of several different health care occupations (Chapter 12), and the chapter on health care settings and technologies discusses the political and social forces that led to their development (Chapter 13). These discussions provide a context to help students understand the current status and future trends in each of these areas.

As is the case with the U.S. edition, considerable effort went into evaluating and interpreting the available research findings and figuring out how to pull these findings together into a coherent "story" in each chapter. Telling these stories in a manner that would engage students—whether in sociology classes, medical schools, or nursing schools—and stimulate active learning and independent thinking guided the entire writing process.

Most importantly, the Canadian edition attempts to raise critical questions about health, illness, and health care by encouraging students to question their own assumptions. By taking a critical approach, students are encouraged to acquire for themselves the tools needed to see the world around them in a new way.

UP-TO-DATE COVERAGE OF ALL TOPICS

Throughout the textbook, the statistics provided are the most recently available. In addition, topical issues (like the health consequences of divorce, progress on the MDG, emerging technologies such as 3-D bioprinters, and ongoing efforts to reform health care) reflect what is currently known. As a result, even though the Canadian edition retains reference to the "classics," more than two-thirds of the references are from 2000 or later and more than 20% are from 2010 or later. The reader can assume that all statistics, policy summaries, and legal information were the latest available as this book went to press.

ORGANIZATION OF THE TEXT

As one of the largest fields in the discipline, the sociology of health and illness is vibrant, theoretically rich, and diverse. Its historical roots have been traced back to the final decade of the nineteenth century; however, medical sociology only came of age in the middle of the twentieth century, having secured a niche for itself that did not place it subordinate to the interests of medicine. Early contributions helped to establish that social factors were as critical to understanding the causes of disease and death as biological factors, enriching both sociology and medicine. As the field matured, a new set of interests and sociological debates shifted attention to framing illness as a social category and deconstructing health so that it was no longer placed in binary opposition to disease. These strands within the sociology of health and illness are still discernible today, as the field can be broadly categorized into three areas: the social patterning of disease and death, the meanings and lived experience of illness, and the social organization of health care.

These areas are thoroughly covered in three of the five parts, forming the core of the Canadian text, bookended by an introductory part, which provides students with the sociological theories and tools they will need to understand the rest of the book, and a concluding part on issues in bioethics. Each of the three core areas gets almost equal treatment in the text. That is, four chapters make up the part on the social patterning of disease and death, with three chapters and four chapters, respectively, devoted to the meanings and lived experience of illness and the social organization of health care. These are described in more detail in the following paragraphs, with specific attention paid to how the Canadian edition has been written for a Canadian audience.

Within each of the five parts described above, each chapter has its own area of focus. **Part I** comprises two chapters and introduces students to basic theories and concepts in the sociology of health and illness. **Chapter 1: The Sociology of Health, Illness, and Health Care** distinguishes between a medical model approach and a sociological approach, followed by a description of the range of sociological theories that inform research on health and illness. Canadian content includes a new opening vignette and a review of Canadian academic journals and government agencies that are oriented around health. **Chapter 2: The Social Sources of Disease and Death** introduces students to basic concepts in epidemiology, offers a brief history of disease in the Western world, and evaluates the contribution of medicine to substantial improvements in population health over the past two centuries. The last half of the chapter reviews the health belief model and health lifestyle theory, the population health model, fundamental cause theory, and stress process as different ways of thinking about how social factors influence health and illness, illustrating how each uniquely perceives the social causes of disease by using obesity as a case study. Canadian content is used throughout, and, in addition, an opening vignette on SARS and a box on the Canadian Institute for Advanced Research (CIfAR) draw on the experiences and efforts of Canadians in dealing with challenges to population health.

Part II comprises four chapters that systematically review what is known about the influence of social factors on the health of the population. **Chapter 3: The Social Determinants of Health and Illness – Age, Sex and Gender, and Race/Ethnicity** focuses on the influence of age, sex and gender, and race/ethnicity on patterns of disease and death in the Canadian population. Students are also encouraged to think about the ways that negative perceptions of the aging process, which emphasize decline and dependency, contribute to the view that growing demand among Canada's aging population will one day overwhelm its health care system. Similarly, Chapter 3 provides a comprehensive discussion of the different ways in which biological and social factors can produce gender differences in death and disease, and notes the increasing relevance of adopting a sex- and gender-based approach to understanding what makes men and women ill. Finally, Chapter 3 draws on critical race theory to address the structural barriers that keep Canada's Aboriginal peoples from achieving better health and also describes the healthy immigrant effect from a Canadian perspective. In addition to providing Canadian statistics and research, the opening vignette and each of the three boxes refer to issues relevant to the Canadian context.

Chapter 4: Socioeconomic Inequalities of Health turns to the issue of socioeconomic inequalities in health. The chapter begins by providing comprehensive evidence of socioeconomic inequalities in health in Canada at each stage of the life course using different measures of socioeconomic position (income, education, homeownership, neighbourhood income) and health (mortality, morbidity, and health behaviours). This is followed by a review of different explanations for the association, including the latest advances in theory and research, such as biological embedding and the cumulative advantage hypothesis. Chapter 4 also addresses issues related to the income inequality hypothesis and introduces the concept of intersectionality, whereby different aspects of one's social location are seen as multiplying or offsetting risks to health. The opening vignette on At Home/Chez Soi, a research demonstration project on homelessness and health, highlights leading-edge Canadian research, and two boxes that respectively focus on the health consequences of food banks and the Great Recession also centre on the Canadian context.

Chapter 5: Work and Family Life – The Influence of Social Roles on Health and Illness moves beyond markers of social position to examine the ways in which work and family roles are linked to health. The chapter draws on both a life course approach and stress process, illustrating how changing patterns of work and marital behaviour in Canadian society are affecting health and well-being, with a case study on the health effects of divorce. Importantly, the chapter includes statistics drawn from the 2011 Canada Work Stress and Health survey, which not only shows how work and family life are dynamically linked to health but also highlights the contribution of Canadian researchers to this area.

Finally, **Chapter 6: Illness and Death in the Developing World** systematically documents patterns of death and disease around the world, evaluates efforts to improve health in low- and middle-income countries, and provides explanations for their greater health burden. Although the focus is on countries outside Canada, the contribution of Canadian researcher Prabhat Jha, lead investigator of the Million Deaths Study in India, is highlighted in one of the boxes.

Part III shifts attention to the social construction of health and illness, that is, the ways in which societies frame and respond to issues around health and illness as well as the meaning-making activities of those with a lived experience of disease or disability. **Chapter 7: The Social Meanings of Illness** investigates responses to disease and abnormality as a powerful form of social control. This involves showing how different conditions have evoked different social responses over time, exploring medicalization as a process that converts the problems of living into diseases to be treated with medical intervention, and evaluating how the sick role regulates the behaviour of those who have been labelled ill. In addition to citing the work of Canadian researchers in this area, the chapter includes two boxes with Canadian content: The first describes government-sponsored websites such as www.stupid.ca that denigrate cigarette smokers and the backlash it has produced from smokers' rights groups, whereas a second box addresses the issue of direct-to-consumer advertising in Canada.

Chapter 8: The Experience of Disability, Chronic Pain, and Chronic Illness evaluates the lived experience of individuals with life-threatening disease, disability, and chronic illness, describing how such individuals come to terms with their changed circumstances, navigate structural barriers, and combat the negative perceptions of others. The Canadian edition also provides a thorough critique of both the medical model of disability and the social model of disability, revealing new insights gained from a sociology of the body perspective. The work of Canadian sociologist Arthur Frank on narrative reconstruction is given particular attention, as is the contribution of Rick Hansen, whose life story is described in one of the boxes.

Chapter 9: The Body and the Pursuit of Health, new to the Canadian edition, addresses an emerging area in the sociology of health and illness that focuses on how individuals subjectively interpret and pursue what it means to be healthy in contemporary society. Drawing on both postmodernism and a sociology of the body perspective, the chapter poses questions about the type of future we are ushering in as medical technologies, commodification, and medicalization together offer opportunities and enticements to radically transform human bodies far beyond their present capabilities. The chapter ends with a systematic evaluation of the social and ethical implications of these new enhancement technologies. An opening vignette draws on a Canadian father's experiences with his severely disabled son as he contemplates the implications of what choices he might have made had he been able to take advantage of new fetal DNA testing products. In addition, Canadian research is highlighted in a case study on the practices of body modification, and two boxes discussing issues that transcend national borders, one on menstrual suppression and another on attempts by a biotechnology company to patent a gene for breast cancer, emphasize how these are connected to the experiences of Canadians.

Part IV comprehensively covers the sociological aspects of health care. **Chapter 10: A History of Health Care in Canada** focuses specifically on the Canadian health care system, describing its history and current challenges. The opening vignette draws on the highly publicized and controversial story of Shona Holmes, an Ontario woman who travelled to the United States to receive what she called life-saving treatment, offering the opportunity to explore a question asked by many Canadians: How good is our health care system? Organized around the belief that to understand our health care system's problems, we must know its history, this brand new chapter provides a systematic account of its origins right up to and including details and analysis of the new 2014 health accord. The chapter includes two boxes, one on the debate over safe injection sites and the other on the delisting of sex reassignment surgery, which both highlight ongoing controversies in Canadian health care.

Chapter 11: Health Care in Other Countries reviews basic indicators of health care performance and then uses these to compare the Canadian health care system to those in other high-income countries. The chapter also provides an overview of the health care systems of the United States, Germany, the United Kingdom, and China. **Chapter 12: Health Care Professions** describes the hierarchical nature of health care professions, beginning with medical doctors, who sit atop that hierarchy. After detailing how Canadian allopaths achieved medical dominance in the twentieth century, discussion turns to evaluating whether and how the state, the public, other professions, and internal division pose a threat to medical dominance. The chapter also contains a brief section on the socialization of physicians, before describing the struggles of several other Canadian health care occupations to achieve, maintain, or regain professional status. The chapter has been extensively rewritten to focus on the status of these professions from the Canadian standpoint. The opening vignette contains an excerpt from a well-known book written by Vincent Lam, an award-winning Canadian novelist and emergency physician. **Chapter 13: Health Care Settings and Technologies** focuses on health care settings and technologies and has also been extensively revised so that it is relevant to the situation in Canada. The three boxes in this chapter address timely Canadian issues.

Part V contains a single chapter, on bioethics (**Chapter 14: Issues in Bioethics**). Historical examples of what would now be considered egregious violations of ethics from Nazi Germany, the United States, and Canada are used to show how each acted as pivotal turning points in the emergence of bioethics as a field of study and the regulation of ethical principles in medical research, teaching, and clinical practice in Canada. The opening vignette describes the story of Canadian medical doctor and researcher Dr. Nancy Olivieri, who was censured by her own university when she simply tried to fulfill her ethical duty to warn others about the harmful side effects of an experimental drug she had been researching and using in her lab. A case study on the issue of medical futility highlights two recent and emotionally wrenching Canadian stories: the short life of baby Joseph, who died in September 2011, and the ongoing struggle of the family of Hassan Rasouli to keep him alive in spite of medical advice to remove life support.

SPECIAL FEATURES

Opening Vignettes

Each chapter opens with an engaging vignette chosen to spark students' interest in the topic. Some of the vignettes demonstrate that the topic has real consequences for real people—that, for example, technologies such as DNA testing offer new opportunities for understanding the risk for future disease for oneself or one's unborn child, but create moral quandaries for those who wonder about what such tests say about the value of a human life. Other vignettes speak to the lived experience of battling cancer (Dionne Warner) and coming to terms with a degenerative condition (Nancy Mairs), whereas still others recount personal experiences in the health care setting, such as participating in one's first autopsy in medical school.

Learning Objectives

Immediately following the opening vignette, each chapter contains a box outlining the major learning objectives of that chapter. With anywhere between four and eight learning objectives, students are able to recognize in advance the major concepts and issues with which they must become familiar.

Key Concepts Boxes

These boxes are designed to help students understand particularly important or complex topics, such as the nature of stressors, explanations for socioeconomic inequalities in health, or the strengths and weaknesses of the sick role model. For example, Chapter 9 includes a Key Concepts box that provides a useful summary of the major ethical concerns and questions arising as a result of the proliferation of enhancement technologies.

"In the News" Boxes

A number of chapters include a boxed discussion of a relevant topic taken from current newspapers. Topics include the debate over whether the smallpox virus should be destroyed, the plight of the community of Kashechewan, the health effects of the Great Recession, the participation of Oscar Pistorius in the 2012 Olympics, attempts to patent genes for breast cancer, and the death of Ashley Smith. Most, but not all, of these boxes deal with events and situations that are specific to Canada. For example, the story of Ashley Smith, a young woman who killed herself while prison officials looked on, vividly demonstrates how the mentally ill in Canada are falling through the cracks and failing to receive the help they need. Because the details of her story received so much media attention and launched several judicial inquiries, there is some hope that the story will one day bring about change in the treatment of the mentally ill.

Other boxes draw attention to historic moments that touch us all, transcending national interests and boundaries and reshaping how we view the world around us. Those who watched Oscar Pistorius sprint down the track in London as the first double-amputee to compete in the Olympics could not help but be amazed at his performance—an unforgettable achievement that was the culmination of a protracted struggle to be allowed to compete as a disabled person in the Olympics. These boxes should spark student interest while helping them to make connections between textbook topics and the world around them.

Ethical Debate Boxes

These boxes demonstrate that ethical dilemmas pervade health care. The debates are complex enough that students must use critical thinking skills to assess them; teachers can use these debates for classroom discussions, group exercises, or written assignments. Each is presented in a way that does not presuppose that there is an easy solution: Many of these dilemmas reveal a tension between conflicting social values. For example, Chapter 13 discusses the issue of a right to die in light of the decision of the British Columbia Supreme Court in June 2012 to overturn the ban on physician-assisted suicide. At issue is whether individuals have the right to determine what happens with their own bodies or whether the sanctity of life demands that it always be preserved.

"Changing the World" Boxes

To help students see how sociological knowledge can translate into effective social action, some chapters include boxes describing the work of individuals and non-profit organizations that are using sociological insights to change the world of health and health care. For example, Rick Hansen is profiled for his inspiring life story and ongoing efforts to raise money and awareness as a means of improving the lives of those with disabilities.

Implications Essays

Each chapter ends with a brief essay that discusses the implications of the chapter and points the reader toward new questions and issues. These essays should stimulate critical thinking and can serve as the basis for class discussions.

Chapter Summaries

All chapters include a detailed, bulleted summary that appears immediately after the implications essay. Importantly, each item in the chapter summary is linked to the learning objectives introduced at the beginning of each chapter.

Glossary

The book includes an extensive Glossary that defines all important terms used in the book. Each term in the Glossary is printed in bold and defined the first time it appears in each chapter. To assist those who skip some chapters, each term is printed in bold without a definition if it appears in any subsequent chapter, alerting students that they can find a definition in the book's Glossary.

Review Questions and Critical Thinking Questions

Each chapter contains both Review Questions, which take students through the main points of the chapter, and Critical Thinking Questions, which push students to extrapolate from the chapter to other issues or to think more deeply about issues discussed within the chapter.

CHANGING THE WORLD

Rick Hansen and the Man in Motion World Tour

Born in 1957 in Port Alberni, British Columbia, Rick Hansen grew up wanting to be part of a great adventure. A few months before his sixteenth birthday, Rick was thrown from the back of a truck on his way home from a fishing trip, sustaining a spinal cord injury that left him paralyzed from the waist down. Undaunted by his injury, Rick became the first person with a physical disability to graduate with a degree in physical education from the University of British Columbia. He went on to enjoy a stellar career as an athlete by competing in wheelchair marathons, winning the world title four times.

Supported by a close-knit family and inspired by mentors and friends, including Terry Fox, Rick began to plan his big adventure. On March 21, 1985, Rick and his team launched the Man In Motion World Tour [...] a distance of 40,598 kilometres in [...]

IMPLICATIONS

The language of illness and disease permeates our [...] living in a "sick" society or about the "disease" of vio[...] labelling anyone who behaves in a way we don't under[...]

This metaphoric use of language reveals the true nat[...] or situations that powerful groups find disturbing and b[...] or psychological roots. In other times or places, the same [...] might have been ignored, condemned as sin, or labelled [...] a social construction and a moral status.

In many instances, using the language of medicine [...] doctors offers a more humanistic option than the altern[...] strated, medical social control also carries a price. For e[...] positively changed the lives of some who have ment[...] legally imperative for all who have mental illness. In [...] increased our personal mobility in exchange for hi[...] adopting the language of illness and increasin[...] and costs. Still, nothing stays the same forev[...] weakening how medicine wields so[...] [...] of health to pervade al[...]

In sum, importing the [...] behaviour to broader social structur[...] for public issues rather than personal tri[...]

GLOSSARY

acculturation:
The process by which immigrants increasingly adopt the lifestyles and habits of their host country. (p. 67)

actuarial risk rating:
A system in which insurers try to maximize their financial gain by identifying and insuring only those populations that have low health risks. (p. 269)

acute illness:
Any illness that strikes suddenly and disappears rapidly (within a month or so). Examples include chicken pox, colds, and influenza. (p. 18)

advanced practice nurses:
Individuals who, after becoming registered nurses, additionally receive specialized postgraduate training. Includes nurse-midwives and nurse-practitioners. See *registered nurses*. (p. 30)

[...] surgery. (p. 210)

SUMMARY

1. Epidemiology refers to the distribution of disease [...] rely on concepts such as life expectancy, mortality an[...] prevalence to describe the health of the population.
2. Epidemics refer to any significant increase in the number [...] first appearance of a new disease. Pandemics diseases are en[...] endemic diseases are those that continue to appear in a pop[...] rate.
3. Devastating epidemics accompanied the rise of cities in medie[...] early eighteenth century, however, life expectancy began to inc[...] improved living and working conditions, later and less frequen[...] in military strategies that separated soldiers and civilians.
4. Life expectancy increased further in the nineteenth century, pr[...] improvements in nutrition and public hygiene, with both cont[...] advances in terms of importance. Still, as in previous eras, the m[...] infectious and parasitic diseases.
5. The shift from a society characterized by low life expectancy an[...] diseases to one characterized by high life expectancy and chro[...] as the epidemiological transition. Although Canada and other [...] experienced the epidemiological transition, infectious illness [...] significant health concerns in the latter half of the twentieth [...] overuse of antibiotics, changing physical environments, an[...]
6. Although proposed several centuries earlier, germ theory [...] for understanding the causes of infectious disease in [...] was understood that microscopic living organisms [...] disease patterns shifted, germ theory was found to [...] the causes of chronic disease, initiating a searc[...]

14. What str[...] the 1990s?
15. How did CHST in 199[...] health care? How did these [...] respective jurisdictions?
16. What are the implications of the [...] federal government and the provi[...]
17. What are the implications of lawsu[...] for health services offered in the pub[...] rights?

CRITICAL THINKING QUESTIONS

1. Given what you now know about Ca[...] you were to read in the newspaper t[...]
2. On what basis should the decision [...] according to one's ability to pay? [...] of need, and, if so, how will nee[...] on the basis of potential bene[...] guarantee provision? Wh[...]

ANCILLARIES

Instructor Ancillaries

The Nelson Education Teaching Advantage (NETA) program delivers research-based instructor resources that promote student engagement and higher-order thinking to enable the success of Canadian students and educators.

Instructors today face many challenges. Resources are limited, time is scarce, and a new kind of student has emerged: one who is juggling school with work, has gaps in his or her basic knowledge, and is immersed in technology in a way that has led to a completely new style of learning. In response, Nelson Education has gathered a group of dedicated instructors to advise us on the creation of richer and more flexible ancillaries that respond to the needs of today's teaching environments.

In consultation with the editorial advisory board, Nelson Education has completely rethought the structure, approaches, and formats of our key textbook ancillaries. We've also increased our investment in editorial support for our ancillary authors. The result is the Nelson Education Teaching Advantage and its key components: *NETA Engagement, NETA Assessment,* and *NETA Presentation.* Each component includes one or more ancillaries prepared according to our best practices, as well as a document explaining the theory behind these practices.

NETA Assessment relates to testing materials: Under *NETA Assessment,* Nelson's authors create multiple-choice questions that reflect research-based best practices for constructing effective questions and testing not just recall but also higher-order thinking. Our guidelines were developed by David DiBattista, a 3M National Teaching Fellow whose recent research as a professor of psychology at Brock University has focused on multiple-choice testing. All Test Bank authors receive training at workshops conducted by Prof. DiBattista, as do the copyeditors assigned to each Test Bank. A copy of *Multiple Choice Tests: Getting beyond Remembering,* Prof. DiBattista's guide to writing effective tests, is included with every Nelson Test Bank/Computerized Test Bank package.

The Test Bank was written by Rose Ricciardelli of York University. It includes over 490 multiple-choice questions written according to NETA guidelines for effective construction and development of higher-order questions. Also included are over 40 short answer and 30 essay questions. Test Bank files are provided in Microsoft Word format for easy editing and in PDF format for convenient printing, whatever your system.

FOSTERING CONVERSATIONS ABOUT TEACHING SOCIOLOGY IN CANADA

We invite you to join *Fostering Conversations about Teaching Sociology in Canada,* a virtual community site built by sociology educators for sociology educators. A dynamic, continually evolving blog that houses dozens of self-reflexive pieces about various aspects of teaching—including student engagement, assessment, course preparation, and teaching with technology—*Fostering Conversations* is an educator's tool kit and a virtual home for sharing teaching ideas, practices, and complexities. Housing contributions by educators from across the country, including universities and colleges, large and small, *Fostering Conversations* provides a framework for cross-institutional conversations about the craft of teaching in the twenty-first century. Join the conversation today! Visit **http://community.cengage.com/Site/fosteringconversations/**

Student Ancillaries

The Companion Website for *The Sociology of Health, Illness, and Health Care in Canada* provides students with interactive learning tools, including

- quizzes
- flashcards
- and more

Visit **www.sociologyofhealth1e.nelson.com** and access it today.

ACKNOWLEDGMENTS

In revising this textbook and adapting it for a Canadian audience, I benefited greatly from the assistance of several research assistants—Hamda Ali and Farhia Aden, who compiled the references, and Katherine Childs, whose careful work helped me pull all the pieces together at the end. In addition, these three research assistants, who were drawn from my undergraduate course on the sociology of health and illness, along with their 2011–12 classmates and Ariane Hanemaayer, who was the teaching assistant, provided valuable feedback on topics and issues that were of interest to them. I am also grateful to those who gave me permission to tell their stories and use their pictures in the opening vignettes of the various chapters. Their personal journeys firmly connect personal troubles with public issues, breathing light and life into these pages.

This text is also much improved through the comments and suggestions of the following reviewers:

Brent Berry, University of Toronto

Steven Prus, Carleton University

Eric Mykhalovskiy, York University

Kim Shuey, Western University

Gerry Veenstra, University of British Columbia

I would like to express heartfelt appreciation to Maya Castle and Toni Chahley for their unflagging support and enthusiasm even as I consistently missed the deadlines they set for me, as well as the rest of the team at Nelson, with a special note of thanks to Julia Cochrane, whose work as copyeditor made me look like a much better writer than I really am. Finally, to my husband Frank, who had to look harder than usual over the course of the past year to find me amidst the stacks of books and journal articles strewn about my office, thanks for being the best friend I have ever had.

Lisa Strohschein

Lisa Strohschein

Lisa Strohschein is an associate professor in the department of sociology at the University of Alberta. Drawing on a life course approach and stress process, her work involves examining the social determinants of health and well-being across the lifespan. Her specific interests lie in understanding the consequences of divorce and widowhood for the health and well-being of children and adults; investigating the relative influence of poverty and parenting behaviour on child health and development; and exploring how caring, as it takes place both within families and in extra-familial social networks, operates as a form of social capital that affects the well-being of families and family members. Internationally recognized for her research, she publishes regularly in top-ranked journals and has received generous funding and financial support from SSHRC; CIHR; and other government agencies, including HRSDC and Statistics Canada. In her spare time, Lisa enjoys cooking, gardening, and travelling the world with her husband.

Rose Weitz

Rose Weitz received her doctoral degree from Yale University in 1978. Since then, she has carved an exceptional record as both a scholar and a teacher. She is the author of numerous scholarly articles, the book *Life with AIDS* (Rutgers, 1991), and the book *Rapunzel's Daughters: What Women's Hair Tells Us about Women's Lives* (Farrar, Straus and Giroux, 2004). She is also coauthor of *Labor Pains: Modern Midwives and Home Birth* (Yale University Press, 1988) and editor of *The Politics of Women's Bodies: Appearance, Sexuality, and Behaviour* (Oxford University Press, 2009). Prof. Weitz has won two major teaching awards at Arizona State University, as well as the Pacific Sociological Associations Distinguished Contributions to Teaching Award, and she has been a finalist for other teaching awards numerous times.

LIST OF OPENING VIGNETTES AND BOXES

	Opening Vignette	Ethical Debate Boxes	In the News Boxes	Key Concepts Boxes	Changing the World Boxes	Boxes
CHAPTER 1 **The Sociology of Health, Illness, and Health Care**	Never Leave Your Wingman					Useful Internet Sources
CHAPTER 2 **The Social Sources of Disease and Death**	Canada's Twenty-First Century Epidemic		Deciding the Future of the Smallpox Virus	The Health Belief Model; Health Lifestyle Theory; Nature of Stressors		Canadian Institute for Advanced Research (CIfAR)
CHAPTER 3 **The Social Determinants of Health and Illness: Age, Sex and Gender, and Race/ Ethnicity**	Isolation and Assimilation: An Apology from the Government of Canada		Kashechewan: A Community at Risk			Sex- and Gender-Based Analysis (SGBA) in Health Research; It's Movember!
CHAPTER 4 **Socioeconomic Inequalities in Health**	At Home/ Chez Soi: A Research Demonstration Project		How Is the Great Recession Affecting the Health of Canadians?	The Black Report: Potential Explanations for Social Class Differences in Mortality and Morbidity		Are Food Banks Good for Your Health?
CHAPTER 5 **Work and Family Life: The Influence of Social Roles on Health and Illness**	The Modern Dad's Dilemma					Time for a Pedicure?; Why Study the Health of Same-Sex Couples?
CHAPTER 6 **Illness and Death in the Developing World**	Kibera School for Girls	The Ethics of Sex Preselection			Médecins Sans Frontières/ Doctors Without Borders	Million Deaths Study
CHAPTER 7 **The Social Meanings of Illness**	Is Being Short a Disease?			Medical and Sociological Models of Illness; Strengths and Weaknesses of the Sick Role Model		Negative Social Sanctions against Cigarette Smokers: A Step Too Far?; Direct-to-Consumer Advertising

	Opening Vignette	Ethical Debate Boxes	In the News Boxes	Key Concepts Boxes	Changing the World Boxes	Boxes
CHAPTER 8 **The Experience of Disability, Chronic Pain, and Chronic Illness**	Nancy Mairs	The Ethics of the Sale of Human Organs	South Africa's Blade Runner	Some Factors Predicting Illness Behaviour; The Health Belief Model and Medical Compliance	Rick Hansen and the Man in Motion World Tour	
CHAPTER 9 **The Body and the Pursuit of Health**	Measuring a Life: Choosing Walker		Patenting the Breast Cancer Gene	Ethical Concerns Associated with Enhancement Technologies		Off-label Use of Oral Contraceptive Pills
CHAPTER 10 **A History of Health Care in Canada**	Health Care in Crisis?	Insite and the Ethics of a Safe Injection Site		Four Principles of the Medical Care Act, 1966		Delisting Sex Reassignment Surgery
CHAPTER 11 **Health Care in Other Countries**	The Accident	Is There a Right to Health Care?	The Death of Deamonte Driver	Four Indicators for Evaluating the Performance of a Health Care System		
CHAPTER 12 **Health Care Professions**	The Autopsy: Training to Be Doctors	Truth Telling in Health Care				Nurse-Practitioners
CHAPTER 13 **Health Care Settings and Technologies**	The Care-Cost Dilemma	A Right to Die?	Ashley Smith and Transinstitutionalization			CT Scans
CHAPTER 14 **Issues in Bioethics**	Dr. Nancy Olivieri: Whistleblower		Guinea Pigging		Choosing Your Career	Principles of the Nuremberg Code

Part I

Sociological Approaches to Health and Illness

Illness is a fact of life. Everyone experiences illness sooner or later, and everyone must eventually cope with illness and death among close friends and relatives.

To the ill individual, illness can seem a purely internal and personal experience. Yet illness is also a social phenomenon, with social roots and social consequences. Learning to think about health and illness through a sociological lens and recognizing the importance of the social causes of illness and death are the major objectives of the first section.

In Chapter 1, we begin by outlining the key assumptions of a medical model approach that constitute our prevailing ideas about health and illness, before introducing the theoretical perspectives used by sociologists. We will draw upon these sociological perspectives in subsequent chapters to help us understand issues related to health, illness, and health care. Chapter 2 provides a brief history of illness in the Western world, including the epidemiological transition, and includes an evaluation of the relative contribution of medical advances to changing patterns of illness and death. The recognition that what makes people healthy or ill depends just as much on their social context as on their biological characteristics has produced differing ways of thinking about the pathways through which social factors influence health and illness. We discuss the health belief model and health lifestyle theory, the population health model, fundamental cause theory, and stress process.

The Sociology of Health, Illness, and Health Care

Dionne Warner

Dionne and Graham Warner

Never Leave Your Wingman

Returning from her honeymoon at 30 years of age, Dionne was shocked to hear her doctor say that she had breast cancer. After sharing the devastating news with her husband and her family, Dionne told her work colleagues about her diagnosis. One co-worker remembers the moment. "I was 28. I didn't know anyone who had cancer. We were all crying and she was consoling us. She told us not to worry, that it was going to be okay." Dionne's prediction about being okay seemed to come true at first. She underwent a lumpectomy (removal of the tumour from her breast), radiation, and chemotherapy, and a year later, she was back at work full-time. Seven months after her return to work, however, Dionne had a seizure while talking on the phone to a friend. At the hospital, she learned that she had brain cancer. For a second time, Dionne had to cope with losing her hair, although this time not as a result of chemotherapy but because it was shaved in preparation for surgery. After two painful surgeries, she had survived both breast and brain cancer, but her life was changed forever. Dionne

was told that she shouldn't have children because her cancer was affected by her hormones. The news was the final strain on her marriage.

Happily, a short time later, Dionne started dating a man she had known for 16 years, and, after a whirlwind romance, Graham proposed to her and convinced her to move from her home in Ontario to live with him in Saskatchewan. Three months into their new life together, Dionne experienced a sharp pain in her side one afternoon and, after going to a doctor, was told that she had liver cancer. Telling her fiancé was one of the most memorable events of her life. "I told him that he didn't have to marry me. I would go back to Ontario and I'd be okay. He didn't have to take all of this on himself. Graham, drawing on his experiences as a pilot, responded immediately 'You never leave your wingman. I'm not going anywhere. We'll get through this together.'"

Few doctors held out any hope for Dionne, but eventually Dionne found a surgeon who would operate on her, and, soon after, half of her liver and her gall bladder were removed. A second liver cancer diagnosis came the following year, but time was given for Dionne and Graham to get married. She recovered and began to give back by volunteering her time at the Allan Blair Cancer Centre in Regina. Responding to the surprise of others who wonder why she volunteers at the cancer centre when she's dealt with so much cancer, she says, "I enjoy giving back, after all I have been through. I want to help others as they go through their journeys." She also began to speak publicly about her experiences and to participate in cancer fundraising activities such as Relay For Life.

In December 2009, Dionne was told that her cancer had metastasized to her spine, pelvic area, ribs, liver, and lungs and that her condition was Stage IV and not operable. This diagnosis only temporarily slowed her down. Dionne continues to maintain her positive attitude, volunteering for Relay For Life and other cancer fundraisers and encouraging those around her, showing up for her weekly chemotherapy appointments dressed in creative costumes with Graham, who remains by her side.

Adapted from: Deana Driver, *"Never Leave Your Wingman: Dionne and Graham Warner's Story of Hope,"* 2011.

LEARNING OBJECTIVES

In this chapter, students should be able to:

LO-1 **Identify** topics that are of interest to sociologists of health and illness.

LO-2 **Understand** the major assumptions behind a medical model approach and **explain** how these assumptions shape medical practice and what is seen as illness.

LO-3 **Identify** a sociological perspective and **understand** what sets sociologists apart from other health and social researchers.

LO-4 **Recognize** the range of different perspectives taken by sociologists on health and illness.

LO-5 **Distinguish** between a sociology *in* medicine and a sociology *of* medicine.

LO-6 **Evaluate** the quality of printed and online sources.

THE SOCIOLOGY OF HEALTH, ILLNESS, AND HEALTH CARE: AN OVERVIEW

Dionne's story demonstrates the diverse ways that illness affects individuals' lives. It also offers a window into the diverse range of topics that sociologists of health, illness, and health care can study.

First, sociologists can study how social forces promote health and illness and why some social groups suffer more illness than others do. For example, people who are poor are much more likely to die when diagnosed with cancer than more affluent people. The pattern is observed in both Canada and the United States, even though Canada has a universal health care system that allows its citizens to receive care regardless of cost. If access to health care is not an explanation, then why are poor Canadians more likely to die from cancer than wealthier Canadians? Sociologists are interested in understanding how and why poverty makes it difficult for people to stay healthy and to get better when they become ill.

Second, instead of studying broad patterns of illness, sociologists can study the experiences of those, like Dionne, who live with illness on a day-to-day basis—exploring, for example, how illness affects individuals' sense of identity, relationships with family and friends, or ideas about what causes illness. Similarly, sociologists can study the experiences of health care providers. Some sociologists have analyzed how doctors' status and power have shifted over time, and others have investigated how power affects interactions between doctors, nurses, and other health care workers. Still others have examined interactions between health care workers and patients, asking, for example, how doctors maintain control in discussions with patients or whether doctors treat male and female patients differently.

Finally, sociologists can analyze the health care system as a whole. Sociologists have examined how health care systems have developed, compared the strengths and weaknesses of different systems, and explored how systems can be improved. For example, what obstacles might Dionne have encountered if she lived in the United States, where access to health care would depend on her level of insurance, or in a country like Haiti, where the inability of the state to invest in its health care system means that advanced medical treatments are not readily available. Would Dionne be better served in a health care system where doctors are paid on a fee-for-service basis, as they are in Canada, or where doctors are salaried employees of the government, as is the case in Britain?

Just as there are a wide range of topics related to health and illness that are of interest to sociologists, there are a number of sociological perspectives and theories that sociologists draw upon. In the remainder of this chapter, we will examine the prevailing and taken-for-granted view that illness is properly understood as a biological condition and briefly introduce some of the theoretical perspectives used by sociologists to show that illness is never simply a biological condition. In the final pages of this chapter, we provide an overview of the book, explain the types of sources used in researching it, and offer some pointers for evaluating those and other sources.

A MEDICAL MODEL APPROACH

The medical model approach refers to what doctors typically mean when they say something is an illness. The **medical model of illness** is not unquestioningly accepted by all doctors; conversely, not all sociologists reject the medical model outright. Medical doctors, who daily confront the limits of medicine, are generally aware of the shortcomings of a medical model approach, even though many are constrained from moving beyond it. Importantly, a sociological analysis of the medical model is not intended to be a critique of what medical doctors do, but rather is a way of identifying and describing how we as a society are predisposed to think about and respond to illness.

There are four operating assumptions of a medical model approach. The first assumption, **biological reductionism**, says that illness is an objective biological condition. Physicians are trained to focus their clinical gaze on the bodies of their patients, but not to examine the social context in which illness occurs. For example, a doctor will order tests and explore treatment options for a woman who has a repetitive strain injury in her wrists, but not question a workplace environment that requires her to spend long hours at a computer station. The **doctrine of specific etiology** states that for every disease, there is a specific cause. The idea that illness is caused by a specific mechanism or agent not only further concentrates attention on the body, but often leads to a **magic bullet approach** that assumes that curing illness is just a matter of finding the right drug or therapy. Moreover, what a person reports to their physician is taken to be less important than the diagnostic tests doctors use to detect illness. Parents who tell the doctor that their five-year-old son is always thirsty and goes to the bathroom a lot may provide helpful clues, but it is the test revealing high blood sugar levels that will provide a definitive diagnosis of diabetes. That patients are passive recipients of care whose perspectives may be considered irrelevant by the physician is also reinforced in the third assumption of a medical model approach. **Mind-body dualism** reflects the work of Descartes, who described bodies and minds as uniquely different entities (bodies have a material presence, but minds do not) that have a limited ability to interact. Although our minds can direct our bodies to speak and to move, we cannot order our hearts to beat nor can we stop ourselves from breathing. Because this means that illness can exist in the body independent of the patient's awareness or ability to control it, the physician is the one who achieves cures and receives the credit when a patient is healed. For example, in an environment where depression is increasingly viewed as a biochemical disorder in the brain and treatment is primarily directed toward altering the behaviour of neurotransmitters rather than psychotherapy or counselling, patients who

medical model of illness:

The belief that illness is a biological condition that occurs exclusively within the sphere of the human body, with the direct implication that one need look no further than the individual to determine cause and cure.

biological reductionism:

One of four operating assumptions of a medical model approach that postulates that illness is an objective biological condition that is located within the body.

doctrine of specific etiology:

One of four operating assumptions of a medical model approach asserting that for each disease there is a specific cause.

magic bullet approach:

To prevent or cure illness by attacking one specific etiological factor, usually with drugs.

mind-body dualism:

One of four operating assumptions of a medical model approach that refers to the Cartesian philosophy that bodies and minds are uniquely different entities in that bodies have a material presence, but minds do not.

are treated for depression may come to believe that it is the treatment that is responsible for any improvement in mood and that a cure lies outside their own efforts. Moreover, patients who report symptoms or signs of discomfort that cannot be verified by a diagnostic test run the risk of having their physician treat them as if they are malingering (faking symptoms for personal gain) or have hypochondria (an illness that is in the patient's mind but not his or her body).

The final assumption of a medical model approach is that the body is comparable to a machine with unique functioning parts that can be fixed or replaced when broken. The assumption of **body as machine** gives physicians confidence that when an intervention works in one instance it can be successfully applied in similar situations. Moreover, it is the basis for innovative medical surgeries that allow patients to be transplanted with organs and body parts that have been donated or synthesized in a laboratory. Beyond these advances, however, there are other implications of treating the body like a machine. There is a tendency to place greater emphasis on the body part that is receiving treatment and overlook the impact on the rest of the body. In a hospital setting, it is the rendered medical services that are the most valued, not only in terms of cost but in garnering praise when the procedure is successful. Yet the practical food and laundry services that offer critical protection to the recovering patient not only have less prestige attached to them, but almost never receive credit for assisting in the patient's recovery. Moreover, if bodies operate like machines, then responses to treatment should occur in a similar fashion, with an average rate of recovery or response to treatment. Patients who take longer than the average patient may face unwanted consequences. For example, in the early 1990s, the Society for Obstetricians and Gynaecologists of Canada recommended that the average length of stay in hospital for newborns following birth should be two days. A report several years later showed that the average length of stay subsequently decreased from 4.1 to 2.7 days; however, the report also revealed that provinces with the shortest average length of stay for newborns also had the highest readmission rates (Liu et al., 2000). The most common reasons for readmission were jaundice, dehydration, and inadequate weight gain, suggesting that blind adherence to the recommended average was resulting in rushed discharges that jeopardized the health of some babies. (Home-visiting programs that were put in place afterwards appear to have resolved the situation.)

Together, the four assumptions of a medical model approach inform us that illness is a biological condition that occurs exclusively within the sphere of the human body. The problem is that when we direct all our attention to what happens within individual bodies, we fail to see that illness is also a social phenomenon, with social roots and social consequences. Hence, a medical model approach serves to both **individualize** (by focusing attention on the individual) and **depoliticize** (by hiding or minimizing the social context) the problem of illness. In contrast, sociologists and other disciplines with an interest in health contend that our understanding of health and illness is limited if we only see illness as a biological condition, pointing instead to the myriad ways in which social context matters. We will revisit the differences between a medical model approach and sociological perspectives in later chapters. For now, we turn to a brief discussion of a sociological perspective on health and illness.

A SOCIOLOGICAL PERSPECTIVE

Using a **sociological perspective** means focusing on social patterns rather than on individual behaviours. Whereas a psychologist might help a battered wife develop a greater sense of her own self-worth so she might eventually leave her abusive husband, a sociologist would likely consider therapy a useful but inefficient means of addressing the root causes of wife abuse. Most battered wives, after all, do not have the time, money, or freedom to get

body as machine:
One of four assumptions of a medical model approach that contends that the body is comparable to a machine with unique functioning parts that can be fixed or replaced when broken.

individualize:
To define a situation in a way that focuses attention only on the individual.

depoliticize:
To define a situation in a way that hides or minimizes the political and social context of that situation.

sociological perspective:
A perspective regarding human life and society that focuses on identifying social patterns and grappling with social problems rather than on analyzing individual behaviour and finding solutions for personal troubles.

help from psychologists. Moreover, even when therapy helps, it takes place only after these women have experienced physical and emotional damage. The sociologist would not deny that individual personalities play a role in wife battering, but would find it more useful to explore whether social forces can explain why wife battering is more common than husband battering, or why battered wives so often remain with abusive husbands. Consequently, whereas the psychologist hopes to enable the individual battered wife to eventually leave her husband, the sociologist hopes to uncover the knowledge needed by policymakers, social workers, activists, and others to prevent abuse in the first place. As such, much of the work that sociologists do has the potential to bring about positive social change.

As this example demonstrates, using a sociological perspective means framing problems as *public issues,* rather than simply *personal troubles.* According to C. Wright Mills (1959: 8–9), the sociologist who first drew attention to this dichotomy:

> [*Personal*] *troubles* occur within the character of the individual and within the range of his immediate relations with others; they have to do with his self and with those limited areas of social life of which he is directly and personally aware. Accordingly, the statements and the resolutions of troubles properly lie within the individual as a biographical entity and within the scope of his immediate milieu.… [In contrast, *public*] *issues* have to do with matters that transcend these local environments of the individual and the range of his inner life. They have to do with the organization of many such milieux into the institutions of an historical society as a whole.

For example, whenever a child dies from leukemia, it is a tragedy and a personal trouble for the child's family. If, on the other hand, several children in a neighbourhood die of leukemia during the same year, it could suggest a broader public issue such as toxic contamination of the neighbourhood water system. A sociologist would be likely to look for such a pattern, and to explore why, for example, polluting industries are more likely to build factories in poor minority neighbourhoods than in affluent neighbourhoods. A sociological perspective, then, departs radically from the popular belief that individuals create their own fates.

A sociological perspective can help us identify critical research questions that might otherwise go unasked. For example, in the book *Forgive and Remember: Managing Medical Failure,* sociologist Charles Bosk (2003: 62–63) described a situation he observed one day on "rounds," the time each day when recently graduated doctors (known as residents) and more senior doctors jointly examine the patients on a service, or ward:

> Dr. Arthur [the senior doctor] was examining the incision [surgical cut] of Mrs. Anders, a young woman who had just received her second mastectomy. After reassuring her that everything was fine, everyone left her room. We walked a bit down the hall and Arthur exploded: "That wound looks like a walking piece of dogshit. We don't close wounds with continuous suture on this service. We worked for hours giving this lady the best possible operation and then you screw it up on the closure. That's not how we close wounds on this service, do you understand? These are the fine points that separate good surgeons from butchers, and that's what you are here to learn. I never want to see another wound closed like that. Never!" Arthur then was silent, he walked a few feet, and then he began speaking again: "I don't give a shit how Dr. Henry [another senior doctor] does it on the Charlie Service or how Dr. Gray does it on Dogface; when you're on my service, you'll do it the way I want."

Dr. Arthur and the residents he supervised undoubtedly viewed this situation as a personal trouble, requiring a personal solution—the residents seeking to appease Dr. Arthur, and Dr. Arthur seeking to intimidate and shame the residents into doing things the way he considered best. Similarly, depending on their viewpoint, most non-sociological observers would probably view this as a story about either careless residents or an autocratic senior doctor. Sociologists, however, would first ask whether residents and senior doctors typically interact like this. If they do, sociologists would then look for the social patterns underlying such interactions, rather than focusing on the personalities of these particular individuals. So, for example, based on his observations in this and other cases, Bosk discovered that cultural expectations within the medical world regarding authority; medical errors; and the importance of personal, surgical experience gave Dr. Arthur and the other supervising doctors power and allowed them to humiliate residents publicly and to set policies based more on personal preferences than on scientific data.

In sum, a sociological perspective shifts our focus from individuals to social groups and institutions. One effect of this shift is to highlight the role of power. **Power** refers to the ability to get others to do what one wants, whether willingly or unwillingly. Power is what allows factories with a history of emissions violations to settle unimpeded in vulnerable communities and allowed Dr. Arthur to treat his residents so rudely. Because sociologists study groups rather than individuals, the sociological analysis of power focuses on why some social groups have more power than others, how groups use their power, and the consequences of unequal access to power, rather than on how specific individuals get or use power. For example, sociologists have examined why doctors as a group proved more successful than nurses did in obtaining the power to control their working conditions and how recent changes in the health care system have limited doctors' power. Similarly, sociologists have explored how *lack* of power exposes poor persons and disadvantaged minorities to conditions that promote ill health, while limiting their access to health care.

It is also the case that sociologists of health and illness rely on a range of different sociological perspectives. These perspectives will be referred to throughout this book, and we briefly introduce them here, grouping them broadly into three categories: structural-functionalism, conflict theories, and social constructionism. These distinctions are important to the extent that the issues that sociologists of health and illness pay attention to often depend on the perspective they are using. For example, conflict theorists frequently focus their attention on social inequalities in health, believing that higher rates of depression among the poor are the result of social class struggle, whereas many social constructionists would dispute whether depression can even be said to have an objective existence in the world.

Structural-Functionalism

A structural-functionalist approach to health represents the earliest efforts of sociologists to view illness as more than a biological condition. Structural functionalists view society as a harmonious system consisting of interdependent functioning parts that become more complex as societies themselves become more developed. Talcott Parsons, a leading proponent of **structural-functionalism** during its height from the 1940s to early 1960s, theorized that illness was a potential threat to the social order because it prevented individuals from performing their unique and critical function in society. To deal with the threat, the **sick role** emerged as an institutionalized mechanism in which illness became recognized and legitimated through the interaction of doctor and patient, allowing the sick person to step away from his or her responsibilities for a temporary period to recover from illness. Although Parsons has been harshly criticized for accepting the power of the physician at face value, some of his later ideas, particularly his assertion that health exists and has value insofar as it

power:
The ability to get others to do what one wants, whether willingly or unwillingly.

structural-functionalism:
The view that society is a harmonious system consisting of interdependent functioning parts that become more complex as societies themselves become more developed.

sick role:
An institutionalized mechanism in which illness becomes recognized and legitimated through the interaction of doctor and patient, allowing the sick person to step away from their responsibilities for a temporary period to recover from illness.

can be used to achieve particular goals, belie a prescient awareness of transformations that were beginning to ripple through the field of sociology and society itself (Frank, 1991). As such, Parson's work continues to generate scholarly interest and debate (Williams, 2005).

Conflict Theories

conflict theory:
The view that society is held together by power and coercion, with dominant groups imposing their will on subordinate groups.

Rather than viewing society as based on consensus and harmony, **conflict theory** holds as a basic premise that society is composed of diverse groups that struggle for resources and power. Powerful social groups exploit and download risk to those with less power, with the consequence that weaker social groups are more frequently exposed to threats to their health and well-being. From here, sociologists diverge by identifying different fault lines that separate the powerful from the weak. A political economy approach contends that under a capitalist regime there is an ongoing tension between the pursuit of profit and the pursuit of health. The concerns of Engels, who, in the eighteenth century, decried the damp, dark rooms in which impoverished young girls produced fine lace for the ladies of the bourgeoisie and suffered consumption and blindness for their efforts, do not appear markedly different from the concerns of twenty-first century sociologists who find that a high proportion of assembly line workers in the manufacturing industry experience repetitive strain injuries from completing the same tasks repeatedly under time pressure. Feminist theories point to the effects of living in a patriarchal society that differentially distributes health risks to men and women. Critical race theory contends that racism, which is seen as pervasive but unacknowledged in our societies, poses a threat to the health and well-being of those whose skin colour is not white. More recently, sociologists from a Bourdieusian perspective have attempted to show how subjectivity (how one thinks and feels about oneself at the microlevel) is related to social structure (the macrolevel forces that reflect the social organization of our societies). In essence, Bourdieu's work addresses a central problem for sociologists: how do macrolevel processes such as class struggle affect choices, behaviours, and health at the individual level? For a sociologist applying a Bourdieusian perspective, the answer is that social structure influences health by creating bodies that bear the mark of social class through the lifestyles and tastes that are differentially taken up by the lower and upper social classes. As an example, to the extent that the lower classes are more likely to have an instrumental orientation to their bodies and the upper classes view their bodies as an aesthetic project, the lower classes will choose foods that are cheap and filling whereas privileged classes will choose foods that are light and health-giving (Williams, 1995). Consequently, obesity and its accompanying illnesses occur disproportionately among the lower classes.

Social Constructionism

social constructionism:
The view that reality is socially defined and created through meaning-making and interpretive practices.

Social constructionism covers a range of different theories that contend that reality is socially defined and created through meaning-making and interpretive practices. From this viewpoint, illness is recognized as being real through social interaction rather than the objective identification of disorder in the body. Symbolic interactionism posits that people are social actors and that their performance of who they are (or who they believe themselves to be) changes depending on who is observing them. In this vein, Goffman, a Canadian-born sociologist and social interactionist, wrote about the process through which mental hospitals socialized newcomers into the role of patient and convinced them that they were mentally ill. Goffman argued that although this served the system well, by creating docile patients who were unlikely to disturb the status quo, it also meant that mental patients became lifelong inhabitants of the institution, judged incapable of living outside its walls. From Foucault, sociologists of health and illness have come to appreciate surveillance and normalization as new forms of power that influence perceptions of health and illness. Record-keeping in the eighteenth century brought into visibility the characteristics of populations (their life expectancy, rates of disease) that are described in statistical terms. Improving the health of the population began to be recognized as an important goal, and, over time, the practices of surveillance (record-keeping) and normalization (comparison to the average) became internalized so that people scrutinize their own bodies by comparing their experiences to the statistical average and then conform their behaviour to new norms of healthy living, thereby improving the health of the population. One consequence of this process, however, is that it becomes increasingly difficult to be certain that one is healthy and normal. Similarly, postmodernism questions the notion of truth, rationality, and progress, placing greater value on subjectivity than objectivity. Thus, while modernity privileged the knowledge of physicians, postmodernity posits that patients and doctors hold different but equally valid perspectives, putting them on a level playing field. A postmodern approach to health and illness also contends that societies are no longer organized around the production of goods, but rather around the logic of consumption. This shift means that health is no longer judged in terms of a body's ability to work, but rather in terms of its capacity to consume and receive stimulation (Bauman, 1998). Thus, health and illness no longer refer to conditions in the body, and indeed cease to exist, to the extent that they have been replaced by a consumer-driven simulation of the good life (Frank, 1991). Finally, a sociology of the body perspective is concerned with embodiment, taking issue with theories that focus on illness but ignore the materiality of the body. These theorists argue for bringing the body back in because it is the site upon which oppressive practices take place (it is workers' bodies that are strained and injured in assembly line work), and, in illness, a body that fails to behave as it should assumes particular importance for shaping self and identity (Kelly and Field, 1996).

A CRITICAL APPROACH

As can be observed from the different sociological perspectives presented in the last section, the concept of power is a common theme; however, not all sociologists emphasize power in their research and writing. Instead, some essentially take for granted the way power is distributed in our society, examining the current system without questioning why it is this way or how it might be changed. Those sociologists, on the other hand, who do not take for granted existing power relationships and who instead focus on the sources, nature, and consequences of power relationships can be said to use a critical approach. Critical sociologists recognize that, regardless of how power is measured, men typically have more power than do women, adults more power than do children, Caucasians more power than do those from other ethnic backgrounds, heterosexuals more power than those who identify as gay, lesbian, or transgendered, and so on. Critical sociologists who study health, illness, and health care have raised such questions as how this differential access to power affects the likelihood that members of a social group will live in healthy conditions and have access to quality health care. They also emphasize how social institutions and popular beliefs can reflect or reinforce the existing distribution of power. Most basically, these sociologists have questioned the very terms *health, illness,* and *disability* and have explored whether such terms reflect social values more than they reflect objectively measurable physical characteristics. In any sociological field, therefore, those who adopt a critical approach will ask quite different research questions than will others. Within the sociology of health, illness, and health care, this approach translates largely to whether sociologists limit their research to questions about social life that doctors consider useful—a strategy referred to as **sociology in medicine**—or design their research to answer questions of interest to sociologists in general—a strategy referred to as the **sociology of medicine** (Straus, 1957). Research using

sociology in medicine: An approach to the sociological study of health, illness, and health care that focuses exclusively on research questions of interest to medical doctors.

sociology of medicine: An approach that emphasizes using the area of health, illness, and health care to answer research questions of interest to sociologists in general. This approach often requires researchers to raise questions that could challenge medical views of the world and power relationships within the health care world.

the latter strategy often challenges both medical views of the world and existing power relationships within health care.

To understand the difference between sociology *in* medicine and sociology *of* medicine, consider the sociological literature on patients who do not follow their doctors' advice. Because doctors typically define such patients as problems, over the years many sociologists (practising sociology *in* medicine) have adopted this view and so have sought to determine how to get patients to comply with medical advice. In contrast, sociologists *of* medicine have looked at the issue of compliance through patients' eyes. As a result, they have learned that patients sometimes ignore medical advice not out of stubbornness or foolishness but because their doctors have not clearly explained how or why to follow the prescribed regimens. In other circumstances, patients have ignored medical advice because the emotional or financial costs of following that advice seem to outweigh the potential health benefits. Similarly, whereas those practising sociology *in* medicine have studied various aspects of the experience of *patienthood,* those practising sociology *of* medicine have instead studied the broader experience of *illness,* which includes but is not limited to the experience of patienthood. The growing emphasis on sociology of medicine and on the critical approach has led to a proliferation of research on the many ways illness affects everyday life and on how ill individuals, their families, and their friends respond to illness.

CHAPTER ORGANIZATION

This textbook demonstrates the breadth of topics included in the sociology of health, illness, and health care. The text covers both microlevel issues (those occurring at the level of interactions among individuals and small groups) and macrolevel issues (those occurring at the level of the society as a whole). In Part I (which includes this chapter), we discuss differences between medical and sociological perspectives of health and illness. In Chapter 2, we debate the relative contribution of medicine and social factors to improvements in human health, describing the major causes of illness and death in the western world and how patterns of health and illness have changed over time. This chapter introduces different models, such as the population health model, fundamental cause theory, and stress process, that describe different theories about how social factors operate on human health. Building on this basis, in Part II we take a closer look at the varied social factors that are responsible for the social patterning of illness and disease. In Chapter 3, we describe patterns and explanations for differences in health and illness by age, sex and gender, and race/ethnicity, whereas in Chapter 4 we discuss how socioeconomic position and income inequality account for the social distribution of illness in the population. In Chapter 5, we discuss the health consequences of social roles embedded in work and family life and how work–life balance influences health and well-being. Finally, in Chapter 6, we explore the nature and sources of illness in the poorer countries of Asia, Africa, and Latin America.

Part III contains an analysis of the meaning and experience of illness and disability. In Chapter 7, we explore what people mean when they label something an illness, as well as how people explain why illness occurs. This chapter also looks at the social consequences of defining behaviours and conditions as illnesses. In Chapter 8 we first explore the meaning of disability, and then offer a sociological overview of the experience of living with chronic pain, chronic illness, or disability, including the experience of seeking care. In Chapter 9, we explore the implications of living in a society where medical advances potentially offer endless possibilities for enhancing the capacity of the human body, transforming what it means to be healthy.

Part IV moves the analysis to the macrolevel. Chapter 10 provides an overview of the history of Canada's health care system, showing how power struggles between allopathic physicians and the state set the stage for the present system. We then critically evaluate the claim that Canada's health care system is in crisis. In Chapter 11, the health care system in Canada is compared with health care systems in the United States, Germany, the United Kingdom, and China. In Chapter 12, we describe the history and social position of different health care professions in the hierarchy of the Canadian health care system. Although allopathic physicians have historically held the most power, their privileged position cannot be taken for granted—challenges have emerged on several fronts. Similarly, there have been shifts in the relative power and prestige of other health care professions, and examples of professions that have both improved and fallen in their standing in recent years are discussed. Lastly, we consider whether complementary and alternative medicine (CAM) still retains its outsider status. In Chapter 13, we examine the settings in which health care takes place, providing a social analysis of the technologies used in those settings.

Finally, Chapter 14, the lone chapter in Part V, is an overview of bioethics: the study of ethical issues involved in the biological sciences, health, and health care. In the chapter, we discuss how bioethics can inform sociological debate and how sociology can inform bioethical debate. (Reflecting the importance of bioethics to understanding health, illness, and health care, many of the preceding chapters also include an ethical debate on a topic related to that chapter.)

The glossary at the end of the book defines all essential terms used in the book. The first time a term appears in the book, it is defined and set in boldface type. In case professors assign the chapters out of sequence, each term also appears in boldface type (without a definition) the first time it appears in any subsequent chapter. In addition, "Key Concepts" tables throughout help explain particularly complex and important topics.

Each chapter begins with Learning Objectives and concludes with a Chapter Summary, and each (except this one) ends with a discussion of its implications. In addition, each chapter includes Review Questions and Critical Thinking Questions designed to provide an overview of the chapter. Readers who can answer these questions should feel confident that they understand the material. Finally, to link abstract concepts directly to what is happening in our world, each chapter includes boxes that highlight either an ongoing issue or an ethical debate related to health and illness in Canadian society or describe an individual or organization that has fought successfully to prevent illness or to improve the lives of those who experience illness or disability.

A NOTE ON SOURCES

Printed Sources

This book is based primarily on data from three types of printed sources: medical journals, sociological journals and books, and government and United Nations statistics. Before readers can evaluate this book and the conclusions drawn in it, they need to know how to evaluate these sources.

The most influential American medical and public health journals are the *Journal of the American Medical Association,* the *New England Journal of Medicine,* and the *American Journal of Public Health.* The comparable British journals are the *British Medical Journal* and *Lancet.* In Canada, the most prestigious journals are the *Canadian Medical Association Journal* and the *Canadian Journal of Public Health.* These journals are most influential for several reasons. Each has been in existence for several decades, proving its worth through its longevity. Each has a large readership, indicating that doctors take it seriously enough to pay for subscriptions. Finally, each accepts for publication only a small percentage of submitted manuscripts, so these journals publish only the best articles.

The most influential journals in the sociology of health and illness are the *Journal of Health and Social Behavior, Sociology of Health and Illness, Social Science and Medicine,* and *Social Theory and Health.* Many of the sociological articles cited in this book come from these sources. Sociologists widely respect these journals for the same reasons that doctors widely respect the medical journals noted earlier.

Although all these journals—especially the medical journals—sometimes print articles based on only a few cases, most of the articles cited in this book draw on large samples that can be used to make inferences about the population. As a result, the conclusions presented in these articles are more likely to reflect trends among the population as a whole than to reflect individual idiosyncrasies. In addition, many of the articles cited in this book use statistical techniques to **control** for the impact of extraneous factors on any observed relationships. For example, people who smoke cigarettes are more likely than non-smokers to get lung cancer. But poor people are more likely both to smoke *and* to get cancer. Perhaps poverty rather than smoking causes lung cancer. To control for the possible impact of poverty on lung cancer, researchers must divide their sample into poor and non-poor, and then see whether in *both* groups smokers are more likely than non-smokers to get cancer. (Researchers have, in fact, found that smokers are more likely than non-smokers to get lung cancer regardless of their income but have also found that *poor* smokers are more likely to get cancer than are wealthy smokers, suggesting that both poverty *and* smoking can somehow lead to lung cancer.)

Finally, this book draws heavily on statistics collected by the Canadian government and by the World Health Organization (WHO), a branch of the United Nations. Because these statistics are collected by non-partisan bureaucrats whose employment typically continues regardless of shifts in the political climate, rather than by groups with a particular political agenda, they are generally regarded as the most objective data available.

This brief discussion of sources suggests several questions students should keep in mind while reading this book. First, ask if the data come from a reputable source. Second, ask whether the data were peer-reviewed or in some other way checked for quality or potential bias. Third, ask about the size and nature of the study's sample as well as whether the study controlled statistically for possible confounding factors. Fourth, ask what questions the researchers asked in collecting their data and what questions they *should* have asked. For example, countries that define infants who die during the first week after birth as stillborns will appear to have fewer infant deaths than will countries that define these as infant deaths. Finally, ask if the data presented are sufficient to justify the conclusions. If not, ask what additional data are needed to reach a firmer conclusion and how one might obtain that information from reputable sources.

control:
A process through which researchers statistically eliminate the potential influence of extraneous factors.

Internet Sources

In addition to using printed sources, some of the information used in this book was obtained through the Internet. The Internet can be an excellent source for current statistics and an efficient way of learning about many topics. However, the vast wealth of materials available via the Internet and the ease with which anyone can post materials make it crucial for users to evaluate these sources critically.

When evaluating materials garnered through the Internet, readers can use the same principles used to evaluate printed materials. Most important, users must determine whether a reputable source provided the information; most of the information used in this book and obtained through the Internet came from either Canadian government sources or the World Health Organization. Box 1.1 lists the websites for the federal agencies that cover issues related to health and illness in Canada as well as other long-standing and useful Internet sources

BOX 1.1
Useful Internet Sources

Here are several online sources you may find useful when reading this book:

www.cihi.ca: Established in 1994, The Canadian Institute for Health Information is an independent not-for-profit corporation that is funded by the federal, provincial, and territorial governments to collect data and report on the state of Canada's health care system and the health of Canadians.

www.statcan.gc.ca: The Statistics Canada website provides vast amounts of information about Canadians. Here you can obtain statistics for life expectancy, learn how many non-smokers are exposed to second-hand smoke in the home, discover factors associated with medication errors in Canadian hospitals, and compare the operating costs of residential care facilities by province. Much of this information comes from surveys conducted by Statistics Canada, including cross-sectional surveys such as the Canadian Community Health Survey that provide a snapshot of the health of Canadians at regular intervals and longitudinal surveys such as the National Longitudinal Survey of Children and Youth that track children as they are growing up and make it possible to determine how social factors are linked to child health and well-being over time.

www.hc-sc.gc.ca: Health Canada is a federal agency whose tasks include making sure that provinces operate their health care systems in compliance with the Canada Health Act, providing health services to First Nations and Inuit people, regulating and approving pharmaceuticals and medical devices, and setting standards for food safety.

www.phac-aspc.gc.ca: The Public Health Agency of Canada is a federal agency that was created in 2004 in response to the SARS outbreak. This agency is responsible for emergency preparedness and response as well as preventing and controlling infectious disease.

www.who.int: Run by the World Health Organization, this website provides a vast array of information about health, illness, and health care around the world.

scholar.google.com: This branch of the Google search engine takes viewers only to scholarly journal articles, on health as well as on other topics. This is an excellent starting point for finding reputable information on any topic.

for health issues. Keep in mind that websites found through search engines such as Yahoo and MSN.com are often sponsored by drug companies or other for-profit companies (Green, Kazanjian, and Helmer, 2004).

SUMMARY

LO-1 1. Topics covered in Chapter 1 include the nature of the health care system; how social forces promote health and illness; the experience of living with illness or disability; and the status, power, training, and values of health care providers.

LO-2 2. A medical model approach represents how our society tends to think about and respond to the problem of illness. The four assumptions that underpin a medical model approach (biological reductionism, doctrine of specific etiology, mind-body dualism, and body as machine) serve to *individualize* illness by assuming that the cause and solution to disease can be found solely within the confines of the body and *depoliticize* illness by neglecting to take into account the social context in which illness occurs.

LO-3 3. The sociological perspective sets sociologists apart from other health and social researchers. This perspective focuses on explaining social patterns rather than individual behaviour and on identifying and resolving public issues rather than personal problems.

LO-4 4. Sociologists employ a range of different perspectives that fall loosely into three categories: structural-functionalism, conflict theories, and social constructionism.

LO-5 5. Sociology *in* medicine refers to sociological research that essentially takes for granted the way power is distributed in our society and attempts to answer questions that doctors consider useful. Sociology *of* medicine focuses on how power affects health, illness, and health care. Sociology of medicine is a branch of critical sociology, which focuses more generally on the sources, nature, and consequences of power.

LO-6 6. To evaluate printed or online sources, readers must ask if their data come from a reputable source, were peer-reviewed or otherwise checked for quality and bias, were based on a representative sample of reasonable size, and were controlled statistically for possible confounding factors. In addition, readers should question what important information is omitted from the source.

REVIEW QUESTIONS

1. What are the assumptions of a medical model approach?
2. How do the questions sociologists ask differ from the questions asked by psychologists or by health care workers?
3. How would a structural-functionalist, a conflict theorist, and a social constructionist respond if asked to comment on the power and authority of the medical profession in today's society?
4. What does this textbook mean by a critical approach?
5. What are some ways a reader can tell if a journal article or Internet website is a reliable source of data?

CRITICAL THINKING QUESTIONS

1. Write three research questions about the causes of cancer. The first should be a question that a doctor might ask, the second a question a psychologist might ask, and the third a question that a sociologist might ask.
2. Imagine that you have found a website that argues that vitamin C is the best cure for the common cold. List three questions you would want to ask before deciding whether to believe the website or not.

KEY TERMS

biological reductionism (p. 4)
body as machine (p. 5)
conflict theory (p. 8)
control (p. 12)
depoliticize (p. 5)
doctrine of specific etiology (p. 4)
individualize (p. 5)
magic bullet approach (p. 4)
medical model of illness (p. 4)

mind-body dualism (p. 4)
power (p. 7)
sick role (p. 7)
social constructionism (p. 8)
sociological perspective (p. 5)
sociology in medicine (p. 9)
sociology of medicine (p. 9)
structural-functionalism (p. 7)

2

The Social Sources of Disease and Death

CP PHOTO ARCHIVE/J.P. Moczulski

Canada's Twenty-First Century Epidemic

New glass walls went up in the intensive care unit of Scarborough Hospital in the winter of 2003. The floor-to-ceiling enclosures barricade each bed, separating one patient from another, keeping the sick from the healthy. If every war has its monument, these walls now stand as a symbolic victory to the only goal that mattered the winter that SARS hit Canada: containment.

Before the battle, Scarborough's multisite facility in Toronto's east end was known best for its two acute-care community hospitals, where women delivered babies, the elderly recovered from falls, and doctors performed surgeries. But after SARS appeared unannounced at Scarborough's Grace division in March 2003, the hospital

earned a less enviable reputation as the epicentre of an outbreak that crippled Canada's largest city.

SARS killed 38 men and women in the Toronto area over a four-month period, 44 in all. More than 250 fell sick and around 10,000 were forced into quarantine. Local public health officials, like those in the rest of the world, knew little about their new microbial enemy when it hit. But what precious intelligence they did gather came largely from the devastation it wreaked first at Scarborough Hospital, the epidemiological root of nearly all of Toronto's cases.

The virus struck Scarborough Hospital twice, first at its Grace division and then in a demoralizing second wave at its General site. In all, 100 staff members fell ill, many of them seriously, forcing the hospital to close and plunging those left standing into the surreal horror of caring for sick colleagues, working under quarantine, worrying for themselves and their families, and all the while serving the patients who remained in their wards.

Paul Caulford, Scarborough Hospital's chief of family medicine and community services, said the experience represented the greatest challenge of their professional careers, but at the same time offered profound lessons about solidarity. "I always wondered how you can be in a war and the guy in front of you gets shot and somehow the next guy just steps up and keeps going," he said. "But we had a common enemy, we didn't panic. Everyone worked, under incredible strain, from the administration to the cleaners, who would scrub one area and a little while later come back and scrub it again."

Source: World Health Organization, *SARS: how a global epidemic was stopped*, Pg. 126, 2006.

LEARNING OBJECTIVES

In this chapter, students should be able to:

LO-1 **Describe** measures used to assess patterns of disease and death in the population.

LO-2 **Describe** how patterns of death and disease have changed over time, from the Middle Ages to the present day, and **evaluate** the role of medical intervention in facilitating increases in life expectancy over the past few centuries.

LO-3 **Understand** that the transition from infectious diseases to chronic and degenerative diseases required scientists to formulate new overarching theories about the cause of disease, such that germ theory was eventually replaced by social epidemiology/social determinants of health.

LO-4 **Recognize** that social epidemiology is an umbrella term for a number of different ways of viewing the social causes of disease and death, and that not all of these ways take a critical approach.

LO-5 **Describe** the principles of a health belief model, a population health model, fundamental cause theory, and stress process, and **evaluate** how these can provide insight into the causes of disease in the present age.

SARS was the first new virus to emerge in the twenty-first century. When epidemiologists discovered that it was both deadly and highly contagious, the news generated widespread panic and disbelief around the world. Several months later, the SARS outbreak had killed hundreds, sickened thousands, and quarantined tens of thousands, before disappearing almost as quickly as it came.

Throughout history, new diseases have appeared and old diseases have disappeared. In this chapter, we begin with an overview of some basic concepts used to talk about disease patterns. Then we provide a brief history of how patterns of disease have shifted over time, from the great epidemics of the past, to the late-nineteenth-century decline of infectious diseases, to their modern re-emergence. We also evaluate the contribution of medicine in improving the health of the population over the past few centuries. The final section focuses on different ways that sociologists theorize about the social determinants of health.

AN INTRODUCTION TO EPIDEMIOLOGY

There are several essential terms to understand as we begin to take a closer look at patterns of disease and illness. To researchers working in health care, **disease** refers to a biological problem within an organism. In contrast, **illness** refers to the social experience and consequences of having a disease. So, for example, an individual who is infected with the poliomyelitis virus has the *disease* we call polio. When we refer, however, to subsequent changes in that individual's sense of self and social relationships, we should properly refer to these changes as consequences of the *illness* known as polio, not the disease. (In Chapter 7, we will discuss the meaning of illness in more detail.)

The study of the distribution of disease within a population is known as **epidemiology**. This chapter and the next few chapters focus more specifically on **social epidemiology**, defined as the distribution of disease within a population by social factors (such as social class or gender) rather than biological factors (such as blood pressure or genetics). An equally valid term for this type of research is the **social determinants of health**. Whereas medical researchers might evaluate whether heart disease is more common among those with high versus low cholesterol levels, those who investigate the social determinants of health or who call themselves social epidemiologists might conduct research to determine whether heart disease is more common among those with high versus those with low incomes.

What do we mean when we say that a certain disease is "more common" among one group than another? One way is to look at how many people in each group have the disease. Relying

disease:
A biological problem within an organism.

illness:
The social experience of having a disease.

epidemiology:
The study of the distribution of disease within a population.

social epidemiology:
The study of the distribution of disease within a population according to social factors rather than biological factors. Equivalent to the term *social determinants of health*.

social determinants of health:
The study of the range of social factors that influence the health status of individuals or populations. Equivalent to the term *social epidemiology*.

on raw numbers, however, can distort our picture of a population's health. For example, during 2005–2006, more than 900,000 Brazilians were infected with HIV/AIDS, but fewer than half as many persons were infected in Botswana (Population Reference Bureau, 2007). On the surface, these numbers suggest that HIV/AIDS was a much greater problem in Brazil. However, Brazil's population is much larger than that of Botswana. To take this difference into account, epidemiologists typically look at the *rate* rather than the number of HIV/AIDS cases in a population. **Rate** refers to the *proportion* of a specified population that experiences a given circumstance. We use the following formula to calculate the rate of any event (whether disease, disability, birth, or death):

$$\frac{\text{Number of events in a given period}}{\text{Specified population during that period}} \times 100$$

rate:
The proportion of a population that experiences a given condition or certain circumstance.

Using this formula, we find that the rate of adults infected with the virus that causes HIV/AIDS (calculated as the number of infected persons in a country divided by that country's population and then multiplied by 100) was 5 per 1,000 adults in Brazil compared to *240* per 1,000 adults in Botswana (Population Reference Bureau, 2007). This tells us that HIV/AIDS affected a much greater proportion of the population in Botswana than in Brazil in 2005–2006 (24% versus 0.5%) and demonstrates the advantage of using rates rather than raw numbers.

Note that some rates are typically presented in a specific format. For example, infant mortality rates are generally reported as the rate per 1,000 live births. This avoids reporting fractions where an infant mortality rate of 4.0 deaths per 1,000 live births is more readily understood than 0.4 deaths per 100 live births. Rates for rare diseases may even be given per 100,000 in the population.

Two particularly useful types of rates are incidence and prevalence rates. **Incidence** refers to the number of *new* occurrences of an event (disease, births, deaths, and so on) within a specified population during a specified period. **Prevalence** refers to the *total* number of cases within a specified population at a specified time—both those newly diagnosed (incidence) and those diagnosed in previous years but still living with the condition under study. So, for example, to calculate the *incidence* rate of lung cancer per 100,000 persons in Canada this year, we would use the formula

incidence:
The number of new cases of an illness or health problem occurring within a given population during a given time period.

prevalence:
The total number of cases of an illness or health problem within a given population at a particular point in time.

$$\frac{\text{Number of new cases of lung cancer diagnosed this year in Canada}}{\text{Population of Canada this year}} \times 100{,}000$$

To calculate the *prevalence* rate of lung cancer, we would use the formula

$$\frac{\text{Number of persons living with lung cancer in Canada this year}}{\text{Population of Canada this year}} \times 100{,}000$$

acute illness:
Any illness that strikes suddenly and disappears rapidly (within a month or so). Examples include chicken pox, colds, and influenza.

chronic illness:
Illness that develops in an individual gradually or is present from birth and that will probably continue at least for several months and possibly until the person dies.

In general, incidence better measures the spread of acute illnesses. **Acute illnesses**, such as chicken pox and cholera, strike suddenly and disappear quickly—sometimes killing their victims, sometimes causing only a mild illness. Incidence also better measures rapidly spreading diseases such as HIV/AIDS. For example, to see how HIV/AIDS has spread, we would compare its incidence in 1981 to its incidence today. Prevalence, on the other hand, better measures the frequency of **chronic illnesses**. Chronic illnesses are those illnesses that typically last for many years, such as muscular dystrophy, asthma, and diabetes.

Two technical terms often used in epidemiology are *morbidity* and *mortality*. **Morbidity** refers to symptoms, illnesses, and impairments; **mortality** refers to deaths. To assess the

morbidity:
Symptoms, illnesses, or impairments.

mortality:
Deaths.

overall health of a population, epidemiologists typically calculate the rate of serious morbidity in a population (that is, the proportion suffering from serious illness) and **life expectancy** (the average number of years individuals born in a certain year can expect to live). Epidemiologists are also interested in the health of different segments of the population. Deaths that occur in the first year of life relative to the number of live births are used to estimate the **infant mortality rate**, with the understanding that risks tend to be greatest in the earliest period of the life course. The infant mortality rate is often taken to be a very sensitive indicator of the overall health of the population. Thus, populations with a low infant mortality rate are deemed to be in overall better health than those with high infant mortality rates. Similarly, because complications during pregnancy and childbirth have historically been a leading cause of death, epidemiologists also track **maternal mortality**, defined as the death of a woman who was pregnant or within 42 days of termination of pregnancy, and whose death was caused or aggravated by the pregnancy or its management.

Making comparisons between populations on these different health indicators is an important task in epidemiology; however, what if one population is much older than another? Since younger people have very different health risks than do older people, it is misleading to compare these populations without taking this into account. For example, Alberta's population is younger on average than Québec's, so we would expect Alberta to have more deaths from drunk driving and fewer from heart disease than would Québec. To deal with this issue, epidemiologists use **age-adjusted rates**. These rates are calculated using standard statistical procedures that, as Chapter 1 described, **control** for the effect of age differences among populations.

In the next section, we use epidemiological concepts and data to describe how patterns of disease have changed over time.

A BRIEF HISTORY OF DISEASE

The European Background

The modern history of disease begins during the Middle Ages (approximately 800–1300 CE), as commerce, trade, and cities began to swell (Kiple, 1993). These shifts sparked a devastating series of epidemics. The term **epidemic** refers to any significant increase in the numbers affected by a disease *or* to the first appearance of a new disease. In the fledgling European cities, people lived in close and filthy quarters, along with rats, fleas, and lice—perfect conditions for transmitting infectious diseases such as bubonic plague and smallpox. In addition, because city dwellers usually disposed of their sewage and refuse by tossing them out their windows, typhoid, cholera, and other waterborne diseases that live in human waste flourished. Simultaneously, the growth of long-distance trade helped epidemics spread to Europe from the Middle East, where cities had long existed and many diseases were **endemic** (that is, established within a population at a fairly stable prevalence).

The resulting epidemics ravaged Europe. Waves of disease, including bubonic plague, leprosy, and smallpox, swept the continent. The worst of these was bubonic plague, popularly known as the "Black Death." Between 1347 and 1351, bubonic plague killed at least 25 million people—between 25% and 50% of Europe's population and as much as two-thirds of the population in some areas (Gottfried, 1983; J. Kelly, 2005).

Although the great **pandemics** (worldwide epidemics) began diminishing during the fifteenth and sixteenth centuries, average life expectancy increased only slightly, for malnutrition continued to threaten health (Kiple, 1993). By the early 1700s, however, life expectancy began to increase. This change cannot be attributed to any developments in health care, for folk healers had nothing new to offer, and medical doctors and surgeons (as will be described in more detail in Chapter 10) harmed at least as often as they helped.

life expectancy:
The average number of years that individuals in a given population and born in a given year are expected to live.

infant mortality rate:
The number of deaths of babies under 1 year of age per 1,000 live births.

maternal mortality:
The death of a woman who was pregnant or within 42 days of termination of pregnancy, and whose death was caused or aggravated by the pregnancy or its management.

age-adjusted rates:
Epidemiological data that have been manipulated, using standard statistical techniques, to eliminate any effects that arise because some populations include more older or younger persons than do others.

epidemic:
Either a sudden increase in the rate of a disease or the first appearance of a new disease.

endemic:
Referring to diseases that appear at a more or less stable rate over time within a given population.

pandemic:
A worldwide epidemic.

If advances in medicine did not cause the eighteenth-century decline in mortality, what did? Historians commonly trace this decline to a combination of social factors (Kiple, 1993). First, changes in warfare moved battles and soldiers away from cities, protecting citizens from both violence and the diseases that followed in soldiers' wakes. Second, the development of new crops and new lands improved the nutritional status of the population and increased its ability to resist disease. Third, women began to have children less often and at later ages, increasing both women's and children's chances of survival. Fourth, women less often engaged in long hours of strenuous fieldwork, increasing their chances of surviving the physical stresses of childbearing. Infants, too, more often survived because mothers could more easily keep their children with them and breastfeed. (This lifestyle, however, would change soon for those women who became factory workers.)

Disease in the New World

As these changes were occurring in Europe, colonization by Europeans was decimating the Indigenous peoples of the New World (Kiple, 1993). The colonizers brought with them about fourteen new diseases—including influenza, measles, smallpox, scarlet fever, yellow fever, cholera, and typhoid—that had evolved in the Old World and for which Indigenous peoples had no natural immunities. These diseases ravaged the Indigenous population, in some cases wiping out entire tribes (Crosby, 1986). Conversely, life expectancy *increased* for those who emigrated from Europe to the colonies, for the vast lands and agricultural resources of the New World protected them against the malnutrition and overcrowding common in Europe.

The Epidemiological Transition

tuberculosis:
An infectious, airborne disease caused by the bacillus *Mycobacterium tuberculosis,* which attacks and destroys lung tissue.

As industrialization and urbanization increased, mortality rates rose, especially among the urban poor. The main killer was **tuberculosis**, followed by influenza, pneumonia, typhus, and other infectious diseases. By the late nineteenth century, however, deaths from infant mortality, child mortality, and infectious diseases began to decline rapidly. In 1900, life expectancy in Canada was 50 years for women and 47 years for men; by 1926, both women and men had increased their life expectancy by 10 years (Statistics Canada, 2008ab). In subsequent years, life expectancy rates increased steadily but at a more shallow rate, such that women increased their life expectancy by nearly 23 years between 1926 and 2005, with men gaining an additional 20 years in the same timeframe.

As infant mortality declined, families no longer felt obligated to have many children to ensure that one or two would survive long enough to become workers and bring income into the household. At the same time, the national economy continued to shift from agriculture to industry, reducing the need to have children to work on the family farm. Similarly, employers increasingly offered pensions and other social benefits, so fewer couples needed children to care for them in their old age. Taken together, these trends produced a sharp decline in family size. Consequently, families could devote more resources to each child, further increasing their children's chances of survival.

As infectious diseases declined in importance, chronic and degenerative diseases, which can affect only those who live long enough for them to develop, gained importance. Cancer, heart disease, and stroke became major causes of mortality, while arthritis and diabetes emerged as major sources of morbidity. Increasingly, too, conditions such as heart disease, stroke, and hypertension shifted from being primarily diseases of the affluent to being disproportionately diseases of the poor.

The shift from a society characterized by infectious and parasitic diseases and low life expectancy to one characterized by degenerative and chronic diseases and high life expectancy is referred to as the **epidemiological transition** (Omran, 1971). This transition seems to occur around the world once a nation's mean per capita income reaches a threshold level (in 2010 U.S. dollars) of about $8,400 (Wilkinson, 1996). In Chapter 6, we explore health in countries that have not fully made or are currently experiencing the epidemiological transition.

Contrary to conventional wisdom, medical interventions such as vaccinations, new drugs, and new surgical techniques played little role in the epidemiological transition (Leavitt and Numbers, 1985; McKeown, 1979; McKinlay and McKinlay, 1977). In a series of dramatic graphs showing how mortality from several important diseases declined over time, both McKeown and his colleagues, using data from the United Kingdom (McKeown, Record, and Turner, 1975), and McKinlay and McKinlay (1977), analyzing data from the United States, demonstrated that most of these declines *preceded* the introduction of effective medical interventions. For example, McKinlay and McKinlay (1977) showed that the death rate for tuberculosis declined steadily from about 3.5 per 1,000 persons in 1860 to 0.34 per 1,000 in 1946 (see Figure 2.1). Yet the first effective treatment for tuberculosis was not introduced until 1947.

If medical intervention was not the main contributing factor, how then can we explain the epidemiological transition? The answer appears to lie in changing social conditions. McKeown and his colleagues argued that the main contributing factor was improved nutrition. Nutrition improved because agricultural knowledge and technologies facilitated a stable and growing food supply and advances in transportation such as railways allowed for a wider and more rapid distribution of food to the population (McKeown, Brown, and Record, 1972). Second, even though doctors at the time misunderstood the causes of various diseases, public health measures such as the development of clean water supplies and sanitary sewage systems virtually eliminated many waterborne diseases, such as typhoid. These measures also reduced the number of minor infections individuals acquired, increasing their overall health and reducing their risks of dying from diseases such as pneumonia and tuberculosis. McKeown

epidemiological transition: The shift from a society burdened by infectious and parasitic diseases and in which life expectancy is low to one characterized by chronic and degenerative diseases and high life expectancy.

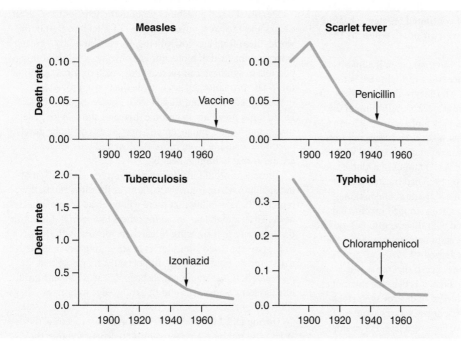

FIGURE 2.1 The Fall in The Standardized Death Rate (per 1,000 Population) for Four Common Infectious Diseases in Relation to Specific Medical Measures

Source: John B. McKinlay & Sonja J. McKinlay, "The questionable effect of medical measures on the decline of mortality in the United States in the twentieth century," *Milbank Memorial Fund Quarterly*, Vol. 55, Pg. 422, 1977. Reprinted by permission of Blackwell Publishers.

and his colleagues contended that medical intervention was third in order of importance, ranked behind improvements in both nutrition and hygiene. This immensely popular thesis, generated at a time when faith in the power of medical intervention to cure disease was high, continues to provoke debate among scientists. Indeed, these ideas were recently taken up by Markle and McCrea (2008), whose book titled *What if Medicine Disappeared?* similarly finds that medical intervention has played a relatively modest role in improving the health of the population.

The New Rise in Infectious Disease

By the second half of the twentieth century, many had come to believe infectious diseases were under control, fuelled in part by the widely heralded success of eliminating the smallpox virus from the human population. (Box 2.1 highlights ongoing debate as to whether the

---

BOX 2.1

IN THE NEWS

Deciding the Future of the Smallpox Virus

In May 2011, the World Health Organization (WHO) deferred yet again a decision on what to do with the remaining stockpiles of the smallpox virus. Currently, only two laboratories in the world are authorized to have the virus: the United States Centers for Disease Control in Atlanta and a remote laboratory in Siberia, Russia. Both facilities are highly secure and access to the virus is extremely limited: research on the virus must undergo rigorous review and is only approved if it has direct health benefits. Both the United States and Russia have been reluctant to destroy their remaining stockpiles, and their continued resistance has successfully delayed a decision since a proposal to destroy the virus was first made in 1990.

In existence for at least 3000 years, smallpox is a highly contagious viral disease that once had a mortality rate of about 30 percent and left many who survived the disease with disfiguring facial scars and blindness. The eradication of the smallpox virus is one of the hallmark global health achievements of the twentieth century: it is the first disease in history to be eliminated from the human population. Armed with an easily administered vaccine, the WHO launched a global vaccination program in 1966, and by 1977 had tracked the last case of smallpox to Somalia. Following the confirmation of its eradication in 1980, most countries stopped vaccinating their citizens from smallpox, and with the exception of the two approved facilities noted above, all remaining samples of the smallpox virus were ordered destroyed.

Despite this, there is ongoing concern that the world remains vulnerable to the virus. First, it is believed that not all countries complied with the directive to destroy their stockpiles or that some countries or terrorist organizations acquired the virus illicitly from one of the two approved labs. For example, there is some evidence to suggest that some countries, such as North Korea, have the virus, although these allegations have been denied. On the basis of faulty intelligence, the United

States went to war with Iraq in 2003 to destroy its stockpile of viruses, believing that the smallpox virus was among them. Second, it is now known that the two approved labs have made attempts to weaponize the smallpox virus. Russia's efforts to develop the virus for biological warfare were exposed by high-level defectors from the country during the collapse of the Soviet Union. In 2002, the United States admitted that some of its collection has been combined with other viruses to create new types of viruses. This behaviour suggests that the virus could be released intentionally by either country as an act of war at some point in the future.

Despite the real possibility that other countries have secret caches and that weaponized versions of smallpox exist in the world, these fears are slowly being overshadowed by a greater worry. As the field of biotechnology advances, it is becoming possible to synthesize or recreate the smallpox virus. Although the WHO prohibits any lab outside the two approved labs in the United States and Russia from possessing smallpox DNA, it has no ability to enforce this regulation. With genetic manipulation and enhancement, new strains could be developed that would be even more virulent and pose an even greater threat to human health.

Those who would like to see the complete elimination of the smallpox virus argue that as long as the virus exists, there remains the possibility that there will be an accidental release of the virus and the potential for others to obtain it. Moreover, they contend that allowing researchers to work with the virus in the two approved laboratories is generating new knowledge that could be used for harm. Importantly, they note that the proclamation that smallpox has been defeated remains unfulfilled as long as the virus and the knowledge to synthesize it are allowed to exist.

Having failed to reach a decision at its last meeting, the WHO will not have an opportunity to debate whether the smallpox virus will be consigned to oblivion until the next World Health Assembly, which is scheduled for 2014.

risk of smallpox has disappeared entirely and whether it should have.) Yet, such confidence proved to be misplaced. In 1981, the first cases of what would become known as HIV/AIDS were identified. Since then, other new infectious diseases (such as Ebola hemorrhagic fever and SARS) have been identified; previously known diseases (such as cholera and strepto-coccus) have become deadlier; and previously harmless microbes (such as the virus that causes avian influenza, or "bird flu") have caused important disease outbreaks, including the H1N1 swine flu virus that spread worldwide in 2009.

The renewed dangers posed by infectious disease partly reflect basic principles of natural selection. Just as natural selection favours animals whose camouflaging coloration hides them from predators so they can survive long enough to reproduce, natural selection favours those germs that can resist drug treatments. As doctors prescribed antibiotics more widely, often under pressure from patients who feel "cheated" if they do not receive a prescription at each visit (Vuckovic and Nichter, 1997), the drugs killed all susceptible variants of disease-causing germs while allowing variants resistant to the drugs to flourish. Similarly, drug-resistant tuber-culosis is rising in nations where both HIV/AIDS and poverty leave individuals both more susceptible to infection and less able to afford consistent, effective treatment. The growing use of antibiotics in everything from cutting boards to kitty litter, chicken feed, and soaps also encourages the rise of drug-resistant bacteria.

Other forces also promoted the rise in infectious diseases (Oldstone, 2010). In the same way that population growth and the rise of cities once fostered the spread of infectious dis-eases in Europe, they now are causing new epidemics in the rapidly growing cities of Africa, Asia, and Latin America (as we will discuss in Chapter 6). Meanwhile, older cultural tradi-tions often erode among those who move to these cities, making health-endangering activities such as tobacco smoking and sexual experimentation more likely. At the same time, as indus-trial sites and cities replace forests and farmlands and drive out animal populations, some microbes that had previously infected only animals are now infecting humans.

All these factors have been heightened by **globalization**, the process through which ideas, resources, people, and trade increasingly operate in a worldwide rather than local frame-work. The erosion of cultural traditions in Asia, Africa, and Latin America reflects, among other things, the increasingly global spread of Western ideas by tourists, the mass media, businesspeople, and non-governmental organizations such as the United Nations and the International Monetary Fund (IMF). Similarly, environmental changes that encourage dis-ease partly stem from actions taken by Western-based industries and corporations, which have found it increasingly easy to operate around the world due to new free trade agreements (such as NAFTA, the North American Free Trade Agreement). Finally, the globalization of business investment and tourism has globalized disease simply by increasing the number of people travelling from one region to another (Oldstone, 2010). It took just one highly conta-gious traveller to bring SARS from China to Canada, and international travel allowed SARS to infect 8,000 people in 29 countries within a few short months (World Health Organiza-tion, 2005).

The Emergence of HIV/AIDS

HIV/AIDS provides the premier example of the new rise in infectious disease. Beginning in 1979, a few doctors in New York, San Francisco, and Los Angeles had noticed small out-breaks in young gay men of rare diseases that typically affect only persons whose immune systems have been damaged by disease or chemotherapy. Within a few years, however, people around the world would learn to their horror that a deadly new infectious disease, HIV/AIDS, had taken root. By 1982, the U.S. Centers for Disease Control and Prevention (CDC) had officially coined the term *acquired immunodeficiency syndrome (AIDS)* to describe what

globalization:
The process through which ideas, resources, and persons increasingly operate within a worldwide rather than a local framework.

HIV/AIDS:
The term that summarizes all stages of disease in humans caused by HIV infection. The disease harms individuals' health by gradually destroying their body's immune system.

HIV (human immunodeficiency virus):
The virus that causes AIDS.

we now know is the last, deadly stage of infection with **human immunodeficiency virus (HIV)**.

HIV/AIDS is spread through sexual intercourse, through sharing unclean intravenous needles, through blood transfusions or blood products, or from mother to child via breast milk or during birth. It cannot be spread through any form of non-intimate contact, such as spitting, sneezing, hugging, or food preparation (Stine, 2005).

The rapid spread of HIV/AIDS since 1981 reflects political decisions as much as biological realities. A handful of changes could have virtually halted its spread: testing the blood supply for infection, using latex condoms and spermicide with sexual partners, and using clean needles when injecting drugs. Unfortunately, early in the epidemic when intervention would have been most effective, most governments treated HIV/AIDS as a distasteful moral issue rather than as a medical emergency. Thus, some of the more controversial measures of the 48 policy recommendations made in a report by the Royal Society of Canada were never implemented by the Canadian government (Duffin, 1994). These measures included free needles, syringes, and condoms for vulnerable populations such as IV drug users and inmates of penitentiaries. While critics of these measures contended that drug use was an illegal activity and that prisoners shouldn't be having sex, such arguments failed to recognize the reality of the situation and undoubtedly contributed to the growing rates of infection among these populations.

Current trends in HIV/AIDS also illustrate the social sources of illness. For many Canadians, risk is associated with residence in poor, marginalized neighbourhoods where infection is common (Singh-Setia et al., 2009). In these neighbourhoods, poverty has led many to seek escape through illegal drugs and has kept people hungry, ill, and less able to fight off infections of all sorts. Anyone who lives—and finds their sexual partners—in these neighbourhoods fights elevated risks of HIV/AIDS even if they do not use drugs and have few sexual partners.

Today's Top Killers

Despite the recent re-emergence of infectious diseases, however, these diseases still play a relatively small role in Canadian mortality rates. Table 2.1 shows the top eight causes of death in Canada in 2008 (the latest data available) and illustrates how these causes have changed since 1921.

TABLE 2.1 Leading Causes of Death in Canada, 1921 and 2008

Rank	1921	2008
1	Cardiovascular and renal diseases	Cancer
2	Influenza, bronchitis, pneumonia	Heart disease
3	Diseases of infancy	Cerebrovascular disease (stroke)
4	Tuberculosis	Chronic lower respiratory diseases
5	Cancer	Accidents
6	Gastritis, duodenitis, enteritis, colitis	Diabetes
7	Accidents	Alzheimer's
8	Communicable diseases (e.g., diphtheria, measles, scarlet fever, typhoid fever)	Influenza, pneumonia

Source: Statistics Canada, *Historical Statistics of Canada*. Ottawa: Ministry of Industry, Series B35-50, Pg. 12, 1983; Statistics Canada, *Leading Causes of Death in Canada*. Cat. No. 84-215-XWE, Table 1-1, 2011.

As the table demonstrates, many of the top killers in 1921 are not the same as those in 2008. Although some of this reflects variability in categorization (bronchitis is now considered a chronic lower respiratory disease), for the most part, the infectious diseases that were the leading causes of death in 1921—tuberculosis and other communicable diseases, such as diphtheria, whooping cough, scarlet fever, measles, and typhoid fever, are no longer represented in the leading causes for 2008. The exceptions are influenza and pneumonia—assigned the second leading cause in 1921 and the eighth leading cause in 2008.

As infectious diseases have receded in importance and infant mortality rates have declined, the leading causes of death in contemporary Canadian society have shifted to chronic diseases—cancer, heart disease, and stroke—primarily associated with middle-aged and older populations. These diseases now far outpace infectious diseases as causes of death.

Table 2.1 also illustrates the greater role that social factors such as health behaviours play in mortality rates. Accidental deaths mostly stem from motor vehicle accidents (many of them linked to alcohol use), while tobacco use is the main cause of chronic lower respiratory disease and is a common contributor to heart disease, cancer, and cerebrovascular disease (strokes). Similarly, diabetes largely reflects diet and exercise patterns. Each of these causes of death reflects the accumulation of unhealthy behaviours that over time may lead to disease.

As we have described the transition from infectious disease to chronic disease, an astute student may have observed that there has been a corresponding shift in conceptualizing the causes of mortality and morbidity. At the end of the nineteenth century, scientists learned that conquering infectious disease involved identifying single microbial agents in the controlled setting of the laboratory. Thus, when Robert Koch conclusively demonstrated that a healthy specimen developed symptoms of tuberculosis once exposed to the tubercle bacillus cultured in the laboratory from an infected host, scientists unanimously endorsed **germ theory** as the cause of infectious disease (Susser and Susser, 1996). With germ theory as the unifying framework, medical doctors and public health officials were able to implement a standard set of interventions that included limiting transmission of identified microbial agents, isolating people who were infected from the rest of the population, and attacking the agent with antibiotics.

germ theory:
A theory that proposes that infectious diseases are caused by the activity of microorganisms invading the human body.

This approach was successful for dealing with infectious disease, but once the burden of illness shifted to chronic and degenerative diseases, germ theory lost much of its force. Consequently, researchers had to devise new ways of thinking about the causes of diseases, eventually replacing germ theory with what is now recognized as social epidemiology or the social determinants of health. The principles underlying social epidemiology/social determinants of health are quite different from those of germ theory. First, rather than a single cause of disease model, social epidemiology posits a "web of causation" in which multiple risk factors place individuals at risk for multiple health problems. For example, heart disease is not caused by a single agent that invades the body; rather, age; sex; socioeconomic position; and health behaviours such as smoking, physical inactivity, and high-fat diets are all identified as contributing risk factors. Moreover, these risk factors not only increase the risk for heart disease but are implicated in many other diseases as well.

Second, whereas the length of time from exposure to a microbial agent to the emergence of the symptoms of disease is governed by the life cycle of the microbial agent, social epidemiologists recognize that the latency period between exposure and the onset of disease is too variable to be estimated. For example, it takes between ten and twelve days to develop measles after one has been exposed to the virus. In contrast, the length of time between exposure to cigarette smoking and heart disease cannot be determined with any precision.

Third, whereas infectious disease involves specifying the pathways through which pathogens infect humans, social epidemiologists merely posit that multiple social risk factors operate as a "black box," which means that exposure to these risk factors can be linked to diseases without the need to trace the biological pathways through which they have their influence (Susser and Susser, 1996). Consequently, rather than identifying microbial agents in a controlled laboratory setting to determine the cause of a disease, social epidemiology relies on statistical analyses with data gathered on the characteristics of large numbers of people, allowing researchers to parse out the relative influence of many different factors simultaneously.

Although social epidemiology/social determinants of health is currently the dominant paradigm for thinking about the causes of mortality and morbidity, it is important to recognize that this umbrella term covers many different theoretical perspectives. As Nancy Krieger (2001) has noted, shared observations do not necessarily translate into common understandings of cause. That is, social epidemiologists unanimously recognize that gender is a risk factor for depression but may offer very different explanations for why this association exists. Similarly, the finding that health behaviours are a causal factor in many of the leading causes of death in the Canadian population is also subject to different interpretation.

To illustrate the different ways in which social epidemiologists theorize about health behaviours as risk factors for morbidity and mortality, we turn to the results of a recent report produced for the Province of Ontario and jointly published by the Institute for Clinical Evaluative Sciences and Public Health Ontario. (Students who are interested may download the full report at http://www.oahpp.ca/sevenmoreyears.html.) Bearing the title *Seven More Years,* the report alludes to the main finding that five health behaviours together reduce the average life expectancy of residents of Ontario by 7.5 years (Manuel et al., 2012). These five health behaviours are smoking, unhealthy alcohol consumption, inadequate diet, physical inactivity, and stress. Given the list we presented earlier of the top eight causes of death in 2008 for Canada as a whole, identifying these health behaviours as a cause of poorer health and shorter life expectancies should not be entirely surprising.

This report, which draws on a social epidemiology/social determinants of health approach, would generally be viewed very positively by some social epidemiologists, but would likely be roundly criticized by those sociologists who take a critical approach. One of the main critiques would be that the report conforms to a **medical model of illness** approach because it serves to both **individualize** and **depoliticize** the causes of mortality and morbidity in the population. We can see this more clearly if we take a closer look at the conceptual model the authors of the report are using for their analysis (reproduced in Figure 2.2). The authors identify the five health behaviours as distal factors that first act to increase body mass index, which leads to problems in blood pressure, lipid levels, and glucose levels, which in turn increase the probability of disease and death. Assigned as background risk factors are age, sex, immigrant status, education, and socioeconomic position. These background risk factors

FIGURE 2.2 Spectrum of Risk Factors Leading to Disease Outcomes

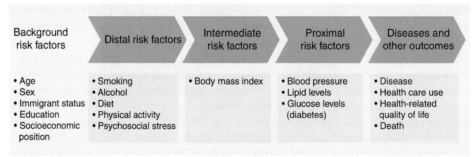

Source: D. G. Manuel, R. Perez, C. Bennett, L. Rosella, M. Taljaard, M. Roberts, R. Sanderson, T. Meltem, P. Tanuseputro, H. Manson, "Seven More Years: The impact of smoking, alcohol, diet, physical activity and stress on health and life expectancy in Ontario," An ICES/PHO Report, Toronto: Institute for Clinical Evaluative Sciences and Public Health Ontario, Exhibit 4, Pg. 24, 2012.

are treated as having little substantive importance in the model, other than to act as **control** variables.

The net consequence of focusing our attention on only the five health behaviours is that we fail to see the social context in which these health behaviours occur, assuming instead that these behaviours are nothing more than the result of bad choices on the part of those individuals who engage in them. Sociologists would not disagree that there is a role for individual choice, but they would give at least equal attention to the social and structural contexts in which these choices are made. By focusing only on individual behaviours and failing to critically examine the background risk factors as a causal influence on health behaviours themselves, the conceptual model presented in this report is necessarily individualizing and depoliticizing and thus falls squarely within a medical model approach.

What are the implications of only looking at individual risk factors for disease and death? In a widely cited article titled "A Case for Refocusing Upstream," sociologist John McKinlay (1994) offered the following oft-told tale as a metaphor for the implications of looking only at the immediate picture:

> Sometimes it feels like this. There I am standing by the shore of a swiftly flowing river and I hear the cry of a drowning man. So I jump into the river, put my arms around him, pull him to shore and apply artificial respiration. Just when he begins to breathe, there is another cry for help. So I jump into the river, reach him, pull him to shore, apply artificial respiration, and then just as he begins to breathe, another cry for help. So back in the river again, reaching, pulling, applying, breathing, and then another yell. Again and again, without end, goes the sequence. You know, I am so busy jumping in, pulling them to shore, applying artificial respiration, that I have no time to see who the hell is upstream pushing them all in. (McKinlay, 1994: 509–510)

Unfortunately, researchers and the public have generally looked only far enough upstream to see how individual psychological or biological characteristics make some people more susceptible than others to disease. For example, an increasing number of medical researchers now focus on identifying genes that might cause alcoholism. Moreover, many psychologists focus on understanding the psychodynamic forces that lead individuals to adopt unhealthy behaviours such as smoking and unsafe sex. Similarly, the popular media often focus on how individual "lifestyle choices" such as dieting, smoking, and using a seat belt affect the likelihood of health or illness.

Sociologists recognize that biological and psychological factors affect health. But they also note that these factors do not operate in a vacuum. For example, adolescents' decisions regarding whether to drink alcohol are affected significantly by the attitudes of their friends, family, and culture in general. Similarly, the high rates of diabetes found among contemporary First Nations, Inuit, and Métis partially reflect individual decisions regarding exercise and diet, but they also reflect the effects of living on-reserve with ready access to fatty and sugary foods, limited access to fresh fruits and vegetables, and high rates of poverty, which can lead to poor nutrition and in the long run to diabetes. In both cases, to blame unhealthy behaviour patterns on individual choices seems overly simplistic. As these examples suggest, truly refocusing upstream requires us to look beyond individual behaviour and characteristics.

Importantly, it is difficult to sustain the notion that individuals make choices to engage in unhealthy behaviours when these behaviours themselves are socially patterned. If choices were truly made freely, then we should find that they are randomly distributed in the population. To the extent that unhealthy behaviours are concentrated among certain segments of the population, there is some question as to how freely the choice was made to engage in that behaviour, even if the people who make these unhealthy choices perceive their actions to be of their own free will.

As such, the message of this report that people simply need to engage in healthy behaviour to improve their life expectancy rings somewhat hollow. That is, the report is operating on the assumption that people need only be educated about the health consequences of their behaviours and, armed with this information, that they will respond accordingly by making better choices. But if these behaviours are not freely chosen, then simply conveying this message does little to empower individuals to make better choices.

Let's look at this from a different angle. The authors of the report note that the biggest gains in life expectancy will come when the poorest residents of Ontario change their health behaviours, explicitly recognizing that it is the poor who are most likely to engage in unhealthy behaviours. The authors then state that "half the differences in life expectancy and health-adjusted life expectancy across socioeconomic position could be attributed to higher levels of risk behaviour among people in low socioeconomic position" (Manuel et al., 2012, p. 34). While the authors clearly intended this statement to reflect the position that the poor have much to gain by changing their behaviour, what is left unsaid is that half the difference in life expectancy between the wealthy and the poor remains unexplained. Stated plainly, even if the poor did abandon these five unhealthy behaviours, they would still experience shorter life expectancies than those who are more financially advantaged. This finding would lead a sociologist with a critical approach to conclude that the report has a misplaced focus on health behaviours and that there is a need to pay greater attention to poverty as an upstream social factor.

THEORIZING THE SOCIAL DETERMINANTS OF HEALTH

In this section, we provide a broad overview of different ways of thinking about the causes of mortality and morbidity from a social determinants of health perspective. We discuss in turn the health belief model and health lifestyle theory, the population health model, fundamental cause theory, and stress process.

The Health Belief Model

health belief model:
A model predicting that individuals will follow medical advice when they (1) believe they are susceptible to a particular health problem, (2) believe the health problem they risk is a serious one, (3) believe compliance will significantly reduce their risk, and (4) do not perceive any significant barriers to compliance.

The **health belief model** was developed by Irwin Rosenstock (1966) and extended, most importantly, by Marshall Becker (1974, 1993). Its original purpose was to explain why healthy individuals adopt preventive health behaviours. According to the model, four factors affect these decisions (see Key Concepts 2.1): Individuals must believe (1) that they are susceptible to a particular health problem, (2) that the problem is serious, (3) that adopting preventive measures will reduce their risks significantly, and (4) that no significant barriers make it difficult for them to adopt these measures. For example, people are most likely to adopt a low-fat diet if they believe that otherwise they will face high risks of heart disease; that heart disease will substantially decrease their life expectancy; that a low-fat diet will substantially reduce their risk of heart disease; and that adopting such a diet will not be too costly, inconvenient, or unpleasant. In turn, according to the health belief model, these four factors are affected by demographic variables (such as the individual's gender and age), psychosocial variables (such as personality characteristics and peer group pressures), structural factors (such as access to knowledge about the problem and contact with those who experience the problem), and external cues to action (such as media campaigns about the problem or doctors' advice).

KEY CONCEPTS 2.1   The Health Belief Model

People are Most Likely to Adopt Healthy Behaviours When They:	Example: Adopting Healthy Behaviours Likely	Example: Adopting Healthy Behaviours Unlikely
Believe they are susceptible	Forty-year-old smoker with chronic bronchitis who believes he is at risk for lung cancer.	Sixteen-year-old boy who believes he is too healthy and strong to contract a sexually transmitted disease.
Believe risk is serious	Believes lung cancer would be painful and fatal and does not want to leave his young children fatherless.	Believes that sexually transmitted diseases can all be easily treated.
Believe compliance will reduce risk	Believes he can reduce risk by stopping smoking.	Doesn't believe that condoms really prevent sexual diseases.
Have no significant barriers to compliance	Friends and family urge him to quit smoking, and he can save money by doing so.	Enjoys sexual intercourse more without condoms.

Although this model incorporates the possibility that social factors as well as individual psychological factors affect health decision-making, in practice the model is most often used to identify why individuals make the choices they do. In other words, researchers who use this model tend to emphasize **agency**—individual free will to make choices—over **structure**—social forces that limit the choices individuals truly have available to them (Cockerham, 2005). As a result, such researchers, along with most policymakers, more often promote policies such as educating consumers about the dangers of smoking than policies such as banning smoking in public places. The debate over the relative importance of agency and structure—sometimes referred to as "life choices" versus "life chances"—is at the centre of many theoretical discussions within sociology and, even more so, between sociology and other fields, such as psychology and medicine.

All human behaviour is affected by both agency and structure. No one blindly follows every social rule and expectation. Nor is anyone fully free of socialization, cultural expectations, and social limitations on what options are truly available. Nevertheless, knowing to which social groups an individual belongs allows us to predict the likelihood that they will adopt various health behaviours: Lower- or working-class citizens are far more likely than upper- or leisure-class citizens to smoke, men are far more likely than women to drink heavily, and so on. Consistent patterns such as these prompted sociologist William Cockerham, who drew heavily on a Bourdieusian perspective (described in the previous chapter), to propose a new **health lifestyle theory** that acknowledges both agency and structure but emphasizes group rather than individual behaviours. Compared to the health belief model, this new theory offers a more comprehensive analysis of why healthy behaviours are or are not adopted.

Cockerham (2005: 55) defines health lifestyles as "collective patterns of health-related behaviour based on [life] *choices* from options available to people according to their life *chances*." (Emphasis is ours.) According to this theory (see Key Concepts 2.2), decisions about healthy and unhealthy behaviour begin with demographic circumstances, cultural memberships, and living conditions. These factors affect individuals' experiences and socialization

agency:
The ability of individuals to make their own choices, free of any limitations placed on them by other people, culture, or social forces. Similar to the concept of free will.

structure:
The social forces around us, including cultural pressures; economic standing; gender expectations; presence or absence of resources (time, money, prestige); and so on. When used as the opposite of agency, refers to the concept that individual choices are limited by all these social forces.

health lifestyle theory:
A theory that attempts to predict why groups adopt patterns of healthy or unhealthy behaviour by showing how demographic circumstances and cultural memberships combine with socialization and experiences to produce both life chances and life choices. These life chances and choices in turn lead to habitual dispositions toward healthy or unhealthy behaviours, which then lead to actual behaviours.

regarding how to think about healthy and unhealthy behaviours—whether, for example, their parents abstain from drinking and consider all alcohol use immoral or their parents consider alcohol just another beverage and have wine with dinner nightly. These factors also *directly* affect individuals' life *chances* (such as whether they have the education needed to avoid physically dangerous jobs) and, through their effect on socialization and experiences, *indirectly* affect their life *choices* (such as the decision to seek dental care). For example, someone who grew up middle class likely learned early to consider dental checkups important and likely has the money to purchase dental care as an adult. In turn, life choices affect life chances, and vice versa. Those who choose to drive safely are more likely to avoid injury and have better chances to get ahead in life, while those who have better chances to get ahead are more likely to try to avoid injury because they are looking forward to the future. As this theory suggests, life choices and life chances come together to create habitual dispositions toward health behaviours—routine, almost instinctual ways of thinking about whether certain behaviours are or are not worth adopting. These dispositions are crucial to the health lifestyles individuals and groups adopt. Finally, Cockerham notes that not only do dispositions affect health lifestyles, but health lifestyles affect dispositions. As people's ways of thinking about behaviours such as smoking change, so do their behaviours. And as their behaviours change, so do their dispositions.

KEY CONCEPTS 2.2   Health Lifestyle Theory

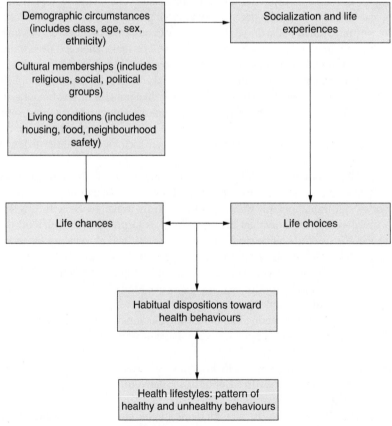

Source: Adapted from: William Cockerham, "Health lifestyle theory and the convergence of agency and structure," *Journal of Health and Social Behavior*, Vol. 46, Pg. 51, 2005.

The Population Health Model

Canada has a long history of shaping how the rest of the world thinks about the social determinants of health. In 1974, the Canadian government published the Lalonde Report, named after federal health minister Marc Lalonde, which presented an innovative framework for thinking about how to improve the health of the Canadian population (O'Neill and Pederson, 1994). One of its main ideas was to suggest that the health of the Canadian population should not be treated as equivalent to the quality of its medical care because medical care was only one determinant of health. Rather, the report suggested that health was influenced by four factors: human biology, lifestyle, environment, and health care. Even though this statement might seem commonsensical to us today, at the time it was a radical proposition. Up until this point, previous government reports had nearly always pivoted around the interventions of medical doctors and the health care system. The Lalonde Report, however, made it clear that the health care system could only treat people when they became ill, and, as such, a more expansive framework was needed, one that was focused on helping people to prevent illness and achieve better health. (As we will see in Chapter 9, the implications of the shift from treating disease to the loftier, more intangible goal of pursuing health are tremendous.) In fact, the Lalonde Report was the first time a major industrialized country had recognized in an official policy document that social and environmental conditions played a vital role in fostering health.

The Lalonde Report was also the first to introduce the term **health promotion**. In the report, health promotion referred to efforts to reduce the risks to health by encouraging individuals to accept greater responsibility for their health and to become more active in making positive lifestyle choices. The health promotion model would soon become the premier model for thinking about the social determinants of health. In 1986, health researchers and policy-makers from around the world came to Ottawa to attend a meeting sponsored by the World Health Organization. The meeting culminated in the Ottawa Charter, which adopted the major tenets of the health promotion model. The health promotion model was defined in the following way in the Charter:

> Health promotion is the process of enabling people to increase control over, and to improve, their health. To reach a state of complete physical, mental and social well-being, an individual or group must be able to identify and to realize aspirations, to satisfy needs, and to change or cope with the environment. Health is, therefore, seen as a resource for everyday life, not the objective of living. Health is a positive concept emphasizing social and personal resources, as well as physical capacities. Therefore, health promotion is not just the responsibility of the health sector, but goes beyond healthy life-styles to well-being. (WHO, 1986)

Although the health promotion model was widely praised and implemented around the world, critics of the model were quick to point out its limitations. Some suggested that the health promotion model used the rhetoric of empowerment, but that its overarching purpose was to compel individuals to act for themselves in attaining optimal health. By emphasizing individual responsibility for health, the health promotion model ensured that health continued to be regarded primarily as an individual matter. Some even argued that the health promotion was inherently disempowering because it constrained individuals to be responsible for their own health by endlessly expanding the scope of behaviours and choices over which they must exert control (Bunton, Nettleton, and Burrows, 1995). Moreover, in a health promotion model, the influence of upstream social factors on health remained invisible.

health promotion:
The process of enabling people to increase control over, and to improve, their health.

population health model:

A theory that posits that health and illness are determined by the full range of individual and collective factors and involve a complex interplay between biological, psychological, environmental, social, economic and political factors.

These discontents and the formation of a new Canadian research institute, the Canadian Institute for Advanced Research (CIfAR), led by a forward-thinking physician named Fraser Mustard, prompted a subsequent round of intensive efforts to create a new theoretical framework for a social determinants of health perspective. (See Box 2.2 to learn more about the past achievements and current focus of health-related research at CIfAR.) These efforts culminated in a book titled *Why Are Some People Healthy and Others Not?* (Evans, Barer, and Marmor, 1994). In the book, the authors described a new theoretical framework for understanding the causes of disease, called the **population health model** (see Figure 2.3).

The population health model accepts many of the concepts introduced in health promotion but expands these ideas in three major ways. First, the population health model corresponds to health promotion in that both situate health and disease as unique constructs, where health is more than the absence of disease. Both also posit that the health care system can influence

BOX 2.2

Canadian Institute for Advanced Research (CIfAR)

Founded in 1982, the Canadian Institute for Advanced Research (CIfAR) has played a critical role in advancing theory and knowledge about the social determinants of health. As a world-renowned non-profit research institute supported through public and private donations, CIfAR brings teams of researchers together to address what are considered the big questions in a given field of research. In 1987, it launched the Population Health program, which brought together Canadian and international researchers from a range of disciplines, including economics, epidemiology, public policy, child development, and sociology. Their task, to better understand how social and economic status affects health, resulted in the landmark book called *Why Are Some People Healthy and Others Not?*, which gave the population health model its theoretical moorings.

The population health model was also integral to the efforts of the concurrently operating program in Human Development at CIfAR that investigated the determinants of health from a developmental perspective and culminated in an equally influential book titled *Developmental Health and the Wealth of Nations* (Keating and Hertzman, 1999). The central premise of their book was that the wealth of nations in the Information Age may depend on how well

they promote the developmental health of their populations. Focused on how to create learning societies, the authors also linked their work to and expanded the theoretical framework of the population health model by positing different pathways through which exposure to social and environmental conditions at critical periods early in the life course can influence developmental processes that produce social inequalities in health and well-being during adulthood.

In 2003, CIfAR concluded both the Population Health and Human Development programs but has subsequently launched three new programs that are broadly connected to the social determinants of health. Successful Societies has as its mandate to understand how communities and individuals develop resilience when confronted with "shocks" to their well-being. The second program, Experience-Based Brain and Biological Development, is seeking to understand how gene–environment interactions influence health and human development over time. Finally, researchers with the Social Interactions, Identity and Well-Being program are exploring the ways in which a sense of identity that comes from belonging to groups and from having control over one's outcomes and surroundings leads to improved health and well-being.

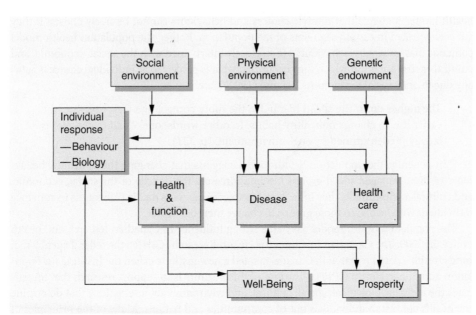

FIGURE 2.3 The Population Health Model

Source: Robert G. Evans, Morris L. Barer, & Theodore R. Marmor, *Why are Some People Healthy and Others Not?*, New York: Aldine de Gruyter. Pg. 53, Figure 2.5, 1994.

disease outcomes but has little association with how individuals pursue health and well-being. Yet the population health model takes an important step beyond health promotion. Whereas advocates of health promotion merely argued that there is more to health than health care, proponents of the population health model postulated that pouring resources into the health care system may have diminishing returns on the health of the population and may in fact damage health by diverting resources away from more important factors contributing to health (Evans et al., 1994). By including a causal link between the health care system and a nation's overall economic prosperity (see Figure 2.3), the population health model also posits that countries that spend too much on health care may damage their own economies. Thus, a population health model takes a much stronger position than health promotion for limiting the amount of money that is spent on health care.

Second, the population health model takes a much broader perspective on the social determinants of health by focusing attention on the cultural, social, and economic factors that influence the health not just of individuals but of entire populations (J. W. Frank, 1995). Thus, advocates of the population health model have often cited the contrasting examples of Japan and Russia. Japan has the highest life expectancy in the world, spends less on its health care system than other major industrialized countries, and is characterized by great wealth and a relatively equal distribution of income. In contrast, Russia experienced economic upheaval and political restructuring during the 1990s that resulted in declining life expectancies over this time period. Thus, the potential for improving health necessarily depends on larger social forces that are beyond the ability of individuals to control.

An important implication of the population health model is its emphasis on social inequality. Because our societies are hierarchically organized, with resources and power unequally distributed across the population, a population health model suggests that how a society distributes these resources determines the health of the population. We will examine this interesting and provocative relationship in more detail in Chapter 4.

Finally, the population health model differs from health promotion in terms of how it conceptualizes the lifestyle choices and behaviours of individuals. In particular, the population health model contends that lifestyle choices and behaviours cannot be freely chosen if they are concentrated in certain segments of the population. Rather, the population health model contends that unhealthy behaviours are so closely intertwined with the social, economic, and cultural environments in which they occur that what is perceived as individual choice is actually due to one's social location. As Renaud (1994) states:

> The higher up in the social hierarchy, the more control one feels over life, the easier it is to change unhealthy habits. In other words, one's "will to change" is largely predetermined by one's environment. (p. 321)

Consequently, the population health model suggests that changing the unhealthy behaviours of disadvantaged social groups lies in addressing the deficits of the social, economic, and cultural environments they inhabit rather than using mass media campaigns to convince individuals who belong to these groups to change their behaviour.

The population health model has had a strong influence in Canadian research and health policy. In 2000, The Canadian Institutes for Health Research (CIHR), the federal agency that funds health-related research in Canada, created a new institute called the Institute for Population and Public Health (IPPH). The aim of this institute is to support research that investigates the complex biological, social, cultural, and environmental interactions that determine the health not just of individuals but of communities and nations. Many of the principles of health promotion (strategies aimed at encouraging healthier behaviour) have been subsumed into the mandate of IPPH, but, importantly, the institute also has as one of its goals the task of funding research that can identify and ameliorate social inequalities in health.

Nonetheless, there are critics of the population health model. Some have criticized the population health model for treating wealth creation and economic growth as policy priorities, suggesting that this reflects a free-market ideology rather than any genuine concern with the social and structural determinants of health (Labonte, 1995; Poland et al., 1998). Along these lines, Armstrong and Armstrong (1998) argue that the population health model has only been implemented insofar as it has been used to justify cutbacks to the health care system. Ironically, they suggest that these cuts contribute directly to higher levels of inequality and reinforce an individualized perception of health by shifting the burden of care from the public to the private sphere. Finally, critics have charged that the population health model places too much emphasis on structural factors and is unable to connect the macrolevel (social, economic, and cultural environments) with agency (how real people think, feel, and act to change their environments and improve their health) at the microlevel (Coburn et al., 2003).

Fundamental Cause Theory

In the mid-1990s, two American sociologists proposed fundamental cause theory as a new way of thinking about the social determinants of health. Link and Phelan suggested that the standard approach of identifying risk factors, operating at the level of individuals and/ or at the societal level, was of limited benefit because researchers were too often lulled into exploring proximal risk factors rather than upstream social factors (Link and Phelan, 1995, 2002). Importantly, Link and Phelan posited that researchers continued to overlook a key insight: social conditions have persistent effects on health even as intervening risk factors themselves fluctuate with time.

To demonstrate their point, the authors present a figure (reproduced in Figure 2.4) depicting the observed increase in life expectancy between 1800 and 2000, a phenomenon that we discussed earlier in this chapter. Yet, looking beyond this trend, Link and Phelan (2002) draw attention to the constant difference in the life expectancy between those who are most and least advantaged, even as both social groups saw increases in their average life

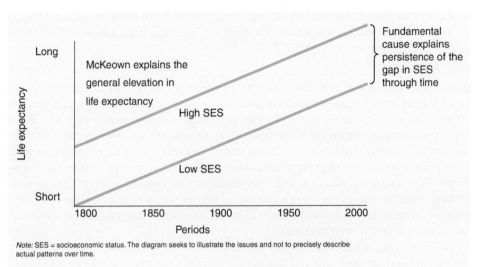

FIGURE 2.4
Fundamental Cause Theory of Disease

Note: SES = socioeconomic status. The diagram seeks to illustrate the issues and not to precisely describe actual patterns over time.

Source: Bruce G. Link & Jo C. Phelan, "McKeown and the Idea That Social Conditions are the Fundamental Causes of Disease," *American Journal of Public Health*, Vol. 92, Pg. 731, Fig. 1, 2002.

expectancy. Similarly, the authors note that while disease patterns have shifted from infectious disease to chronic and degenerative diseases during this same time period, disparities in the risk for disease between the wealthy and the poor have also persisted.

The reason for the consistent gap in health outcomes between the rich and the poor over the past few centuries, according to Link and Phelan, is that risk factors are influenced by social conditions: they are social products that are created as a direct result of efforts to understand the causes of disease. Thus, even as researchers and scientists uncover the risk factors for disease and make their findings known to the public, some social groups are much better able than others to exploit this information for their own health benefit. Which social groups are most adept? The answer is those who have at their disposal a range of flexible resources that can be readily deployed to protect and enhance health while minimizing exposure to risk. These resources include money, power, knowledge, prestige, and social connections. Resources thus create opportunities to become aware of emerging risks to health and provide supports that make it easier to avoid those risks. For example, Phelan, Link, and Tehranifar (2010) suggest that as new technologies to screen for cancer became available, those who had early knowledge and resources to pay for these services were most likely to go for screening. Consequently, these screening technologies became a new intervening mechanism through which the more advantaged were better able to avoid mortality from cancer. Consistent with fundamental cause theory, the association between economic resources and cancer mortality persists, and it is the intervening mechanisms (new technologies to detect cancer) that change.

To be identified as a **fundamental cause**, the social condition must (1) influence a wide range of health conditions, (2) operate through a number of different intervening mechanisms, (3) be associated with resources that can be used to protect health, and (4) maintain a persisting association with health over time even as intervening mechanisms are replaced and new ones take their place (Link and Phelan, 1995; Phelan et al., 2010). Thus, **socioeconomic position**, a measure of one's relative location within the stratified structure of society based on access to economic and social resources, operates as a fundamental cause of disease. Because race/ethnicity and gender are intertwined so tightly with resources, these may also be regarded as fundamental causes, although the term is primarily used to understand how

fundamental cause:
Any social condition that (1) influences a wide range of health conditions, (2) operates through a number of different intervening mechanisms, (3) is associated with resources that can be used to protect health, and (4) maintains a persisting association with health over time even as intervening mechanisms are replaced and new ones take their place.

socioeconomic position:
A measure of one's relative location within the stratified structure of society based on access to valued resources such as money, power, knowledge, prestige, and social connections.

socioeconomic position influences health outcomes. We will revisit fundamental cause theory in Chapter 4, when we turn to the issue of socioeconomic inequalities in health.

The Stress Process

Stress is a natural, unavoidable, and sometimes beneficial part of life. For thousands of years, hunters experienced stress as they anxiously prepared to track wild animals, and farmers experienced stress as they wondered whether their crops would get enough rain. That emotional stress put physical stress on their bodies, but it also kept their minds focused on their tasks. If, for example, a wild animal suddenly attacked, a hunter might have survived because the emotional stress resulted in the physical stress response known as the fight-or-flight syndrome. The same quick heartbeat and heavy breathing we experience while fighting with a friend could have saved the life of someone fighting or fleeing from a lion, because these physical changes help our bodies produce additional energy and oxygen and hence respond more quickly and effectively to threats.

The fight-or-flight response is highly adaptive for dealing with sudden threats, such as rampaging lions, speeding cars, and last-minute quizzes. Over the long run, however, constantly responding to stress wears down the body. Stress can affect the immune system, leaving the body less able to fight off infection or illness—from herpes to asthma to heart disease. It can also lead to mental disorders such as depression and post-traumatic stress disorder and to conditions that straddle the border between mental and physical (such as insomnia, migraines, and colitis). In addition, stress can lead individuals to adopt unhealthy behaviours, including smoking tobacco, driving too fast, and participating in unsafe sexual activity. Finally, stress can impair the healing process, making it difficult to recover quickly from injury or illness.

One of the major influences on the current field of stress research can be traced back to the mid-1960s, when two psychiatrists, Thomas Holmes and Richard Rahe (1967), began to systematically investigate the effects of life events on mental illness. They developed an inventory, named the Social Readjustment Rating Scale, consisting of 43 life events ranging from the most stressful (death of a spouse) to the least stressful (minor violations of the law). Each life event had a number assigned to it, with higher values representing a more stressful event that would require a greater amount of adjustment. For example, death of a spouse was assigned a score of 100 and minor violations of the law received a score of 11. This inventory was used in survey research to ask participants how many of these 43 events they had experienced in the past year, producing a scale in which higher values represented overall greater upheaval in one's life over the past year. What the psychiatrists found was that higher scores on the Social Rating Readjustment Scale were associated not only with greater risk for mental illness but also with a range of physical health outcomes. This research, replicated in numerous studies by others who were drawn to this rapidly growing field, led to two major conclusions (Thoits, 2010). First, negative events (losing a job, bankruptcy, personal injury) had a much stronger effect on health outcomes than positive events (marriage, vacation, Christmas). Second, it appeared that the higher the scores on the Social Readjustment Rating Scale, the greater the risk for physical and mental illness. These findings steered researchers away from investigating positive life events and generated interest in developing a more rigorous theoretical framework for thinking about how negative stressful life events exert damaging effects on health.

Out of this has come a theoretical model known as stress process (Pearlin et al., 1981). The stress process differentiates among three major components: stressors, moderators, and health outcomes. Having briefly mentioned health outcomes above, we turn our attention to the nature of stressors and moderators.

Stressors

Stressors refer to the broad range of problematic conditions and experiences that challenge the adaptive capabilities of individuals (Pearlin, 2010a). Building on the work of Holmes and Rahe, researchers now separate stressors into one of two categories: stressful life events and chronic strains (see Key Concepts 2.3). **Stressful life events** are discrete: they have an identifiable moment of onset. Extending far beyond the original inventory of the Social Readjustment Rating Scale, these events range among being a victim of a violent crime, experiencing a natural disaster, job loss, divorce, and death of a spouse. Life events that are most damaging to health are those that are undesired, unexpected, uncontrollable, and non-normative (Thoits, 2010).

KEY CONCEPTS 2.3 Nature of Stressors

Types of Stressors	Description	Examples
Stressful life events	Discrete events that have an identifiable moment of onset.	Victim of a violent crime or a natural disaster, job loss, divorce, or death of a spouse.
Chronic strains	Enduring stressors that have no specific moment of onset, but typically develop slowly over time.	Financial difficulties, living in overcrowded conditions, marital conflict, harassment in the workplace, and caregiver strain.

In contrast, **chronic strains** have no specific moment of onset, but typically develop slowly, lying beneath the surface until they are recognized as problematic aspects of people's environments or roles. Examples include financial difficulties, living in overcrowded conditions, marital conflict, harassment in the workplace, and caregiver strain. Among the wide range of chronic strains, researchers give greater attention to role strain because it is the challenge of enacting major social roles within the spheres of family and work where most difficulties arise. We will discuss these in greater detail in Chapter 5, but for now, we define **role strain** as any problem an individual experiences in fulfilling one of their social roles, including one's role as worker, parent, student, and so on.

Researchers who work in the area of stress process contend that making distinctions between stressful life events and chronic strains leads to important insights about causal relationships as well as their dynamic and interrelated nature. That is, in making the distinction between events that involve exiting a role from the problematic aspects of occupying a given role, researchers can determine which has the greater influence on health outcomes. For example, as noted earlier, the death of a spouse is considered one of life's most stressful events. The outpouring of grief as one responds to the crisis of losing a life partner may increase the risk for a number of health conditions, including depression, and it has been shown to be associated with increased mortality (Elwert and Christakis, 2008; Lillard and Waite, 1995). It is also the case that occupying the role of widow(er) is one that holds little social value and has few rewards attached to it. Widow(er)s are generally viewed as socially dependent: they lack a spouse for companionship and may need assistance from others, particularly if they are older. The question is: does poorer health among those who are widowed derive from the more problematic aspects of occupying the role or is it attributable to the loss experience itself? To address this issue, Strohschein and her colleagues (2005) analyzed longitudinal data from the Canadian National Population Health Survey to compare changes in distress over time between those who experienced no change in marital status and those who experienced a

stressors:
The broad range of problematic conditions and experiences that challenge the adaptive capabilities of individuals.

stressful life events:
Discrete events that have an identifiable moment of onset. Examples include being a victim of a violent crime, experiencing a natural disaster, job loss, divorce, and death of a spouse.

chronic strains:
Enduring stressors that have no specific moment of onset, but typically develop slowly, lying beneath the surface until they are recognized as problematic aspects of people's environments or roles.

role strain:
Any problem that individuals experience in fulfilling one of their social roles, including one's role as worker, parent, student, and so on

change in marital status over a four-year period. This allowed them to identify those who were widowed at initial interview and remained in this role throughout the study as well as those who experienced bereavement over the course of the study, making the transition from married to widowed. What the authors found was that *being* a widow(er) was not associated with changes in distress levels over the course of the survey; in contrast, *becoming* a widow(er) was associated with significant increases in distress. Thus, the event of spousal death matters more for mental health than occupying the role of widow(er), suggesting that efforts to improve mental health would be best focused in the time period immediately after spousal death.

Moreover, stressful life events and chronic strains are often linked to one another in a temporal sequence that illuminates the dynamic aspects of the stress process (Pearlin, 1989). First, stressful events can be followed by chronic strains. For example, losing one's job is a stressful life event that may lead to chronic strains of financial hardship and tension in family relationships. Similarly, chronic strains may precipitate a stressful life event such as occurs when ongoing marital conflict eventually culminates in divorce. Finally, stressful life events and chronic strains provide meaning contexts for one another. That is, conditions that precede or follow a stressful life event may influence the extent to which an event is experienced as stressful. For example, some have shown that widow(er)s whose spouse suffered and was in great pain prior to death were more likely to struggle with anxiety and intrusive thoughts in the period after bereavement than those whose spouse died without pain or suffering (Carr, 2003).

Moderators

The second component of the stress process refers to moderators. **Moderators** are the resources that can be mustered to combat the health effects of stressors. Moderators are an important component of the stress process because not everyone who encounters a stressor will experience a change in health as a result. Indeed, the likelihood that a stressful life event or chronic strain will affect health depends in part on the type and amount of resources that one can draw on to minimize the impact of the stressor. Two types of resources are of critical importance. Coping refers to the psychological and other personal resources that an individual has to deal with stress, whereas social support refers to the emotional support and assistance that one can obtain from others.

One aspect of coping is the way in which one appraises the stressor. Those who are not daunted by the headwinds of life and choose to find meaning in stressful situations will respond more positively than those who are easily rattled when things don't turn out as planned. Similarly, those who have high levels of mastery, that is, those who feel that they are in control of their life and able to direct their own circumstances, will be less swayed by stressors than those who have low levels of mastery and feel powerless and unable to control their life.

Similarly, those who are surrounded with a strong, supportive network may ward off the health-damaging effects of stressful conditions more easily than those who have few friends or whose friends hold different values and thus fail to be supportive. Thus, the characteristics of one's social networks also come into play. Some social networks rally around the person who is experiencing a stressful event, maintaining support throughout the ordeal; still other social networks will initially respond, but exhaust their resources and be unable to provide long-term support, eventually leaving the person to deal with the situation on their own.

As this brief review suggests, there are a number of ways in which coping and social support can act to minimize the impact of stressors. We use the example of a student struggling with poor academic performance to further illustrate the moderating impact of coping and social support. Poor school performance may be far more stressful for a student who could lose a scholarship as a result than it might be for a student who has no such fears. It may also

moderators:
Resources that can be mustered to combat stressors and minimize their impact on health.

be less stressful if the student copes by quickly seeking out a good tutor, rather than by going out for a drink or blaming poor performance on incompetent teachers. One might also ask: Has the student learned from a young age to turn to alcohol as a coping measure? Do his or her friends encourage the student to continue trying or to drop out? Does he or she have the funds needed to hire a tutor and the contacts needed to find a good one? The answers to each of these questions will affect whether this stressor influences the student's health.

In sum, stress process has both its strengths and its weaknesses. Its advantages lie in being able to outline a temporal process, by which stressful conditions are linked to health outcomes, that can be empirically tested. Moreover, by showing that stressors themselves are socially patterned such that stressful events and chronic strains are more likely to occur among those who have the fewest resources in society (Turner, Wheaton, and Lloyd, 1995), stress process offers a way to link broader social structural conditions to the microlevel aspects of individuals' lives. At the same time, stress process cannot explain why any one individual does or does not become ill as a result of exposure to a stressor, nor can it address the issue of why some social groups are more prone to certain types of health outcomes (Thoits, 2010). Thus, stress process cannot tell us why women are more likely to respond to stressors with depression and other mood disorders, whereas men are more likely to turn to drugs and alcohol.

As with the other social determinants of health perspectives we have reviewed, stress process offers unique insight into the causes of disease but on its own is incapable of providing a complete account of the causes of disease and death. Thus, researchers may draw on multiple perspectives in offering explanations for the risk factors they find. We turn to the example of obesity to understand how these different perspectives may together enhance our understanding of this complex phenomenon.

Case Study: Thinking about the Social Determinants of Obesity

Mirroring trends worldwide, rates of obesity in Canada have skyrocketed in recent decades (Shields, Carroll, and Ogden, 2011). Currently, nearly one in four adults and nearly one in ten children aged 6 to 17 in Canada are obese (Canadian Institute for Health Information/ Public Health Agency of Canada, 2011). Obesity is of concern because it is a risk factor for many diseases, including diabetes, heart disease, and some forms of cancer. In addition, life is more difficult for those who are overweight. In contemporary society, overweight persons are not only considered less attractive but also assumed to be less intelligent, less responsible, and even less moral than others. Heavier persons—especially if they are female—are less likely to get dates, job promotions, marriage proposals, and so on. Physically, too, above a certain weight life becomes more difficult. Chairs and clothes don't fit, exercise becomes less fun or even impossible, and finding the energy for life's daily tasks and pleasures becomes more difficult.

Why has body weight increased over the last generation in Canada and elsewhere? To answer this question, we need to look at how biology and social factors interact (Critser, 2003). Biologically, humans have a natural craving for sweet and fatty foods and a natural desire to seek food of all sorts for survival. In past eras, when food was scarce, these cravings were healthy. Now, however, most Canadians have plentiful access to food and eat more calories than their bodies can use, leading in the long run to weight gain. In addition, the rapid adoption by food manufacturers of high-fructose corn syrup (an inexpensive sweetener) and palm oil (an inexpensive fat) has spurred rapid weight gains, for the former is metabolized by the body differently than are other sugars, and the latter is an especially saturated fat (Critser, 2003).

To these changes in *what* Canadians eat were added changes in *how much* they eat. Longer work weeks, lowered costs for eating out, and the increase in two-earner and single-parent families have led Canadians to eat out more than ever before, and restaurant foods typically include far more fat and sugar than do homemade meals. Moreover, restaurants typically offer a wider variety of foods at any given meal, on appetizer plates, buffet tables, and in packaged "value meals." In addition, since the 1970s, restaurants have increasingly "supersized" portions as a way to increase sales and profits. Unfortunately, few individuals can regulate themselves when presented with large portions of varied foods, and so both these trends increased calorie consumption. As a result, the rise in eating away from home has increased calorie consumption by an average of 1,400 calories per person per week (Critser, 2003: 33). Eating at fast-food restaurants is particularly problematic. For example, teenage boys who eat at fast-food restaurants three or more times a week consume 800 more calories *per day* than do those who eschew fast food (French et al., 2001).

Food manufacturers and the fast-food industry have used advertising to reinforce the tendency toward eating a sweet, fatty, high-calorie diet. Because food manufacturers earn far less money by selling healthy foods (such as fruits, vegetables, and grains) than by selling highly refined products loaded with fat, sugar, and salt (such as candy, soft drinks, and convenience foods), they spend more than 30 times as much to advertise the latter foods (Nestlé, 2002: 22). That advertising has grown increasingly insidious and now pervades every sphere of our society—especially those where children can be found. Soft-drink companies, for example, advertise to children not only on television, in magazines, and on the Internet but also by offering toys and clothing with brand logos, placing products in movies, sponsoring school sports teams, providing soft drink–vending machines to schools, and offering cash bonuses to schools based on how much pop their students purchase. Many schools have felt helpless against this onslaught, because signing deals with soft drink companies seems the only way they can replace funds lost to budget cuts and to meeting mandates to prepare students for required high-stakes tests. Consumption of sugar-sweetened soft drinks is directly and substantially related to obesity and diabetes among both adults and children (Apovian, 2004).

Meanwhile, as caloric consumption has increased, physical exercise has decreased. The same budget cuts and emphasis on test scores have led many schools to drop physical education as a required course. And at home, few children these days are allowed to spend their afternoons running free or playing non-organized sports. Instead, poor children are admonished to stay indoors to stay safe, and more-affluent children are shepherded from tutors to classes to the occasional sports activity. At the same time, physical activity is now an everyday part of life for only a small minority of children or adults, because very few commute by foot or bicycle to work, play, or shopping.

Now that we have reviewed some of the major biological and social factors that have been implicated in the obesity epidemic, we reconsider the problem of obesity through the lens of the various social determinants of health perspectives we have just presented to see what additional or unique insights each might provide. Whereas the health belief model would simply look at the balance of factors that come into play when individuals make decisions about what and how much to eat, health lifestyle theory posits that life choices and life chances come together to create class-related habitual dispositions toward food. As noted in Chapter 1, food preferences are shaped by the different objectives of different social classes, with those from the lower classes preferring foods that are cheap and filling, whereas more advantaged classes prefer foods that are light and fresh (Williams, 1995). As a consequence, those in the lower classes are at greater risk for obesity than those in more advantaged classes.

To combat the obesity epidemic, policies implementing a health promotion agenda would involve the use of mass media campaigns to encourage people to make healthier food choices and to become more physically active. In contrast, a population health model might examine social structural factors to address why obesity rates are soaring in North America, but increasing less rapidly in other industrialized countries. Cutler and his colleagues suggest that international differences in the uptake of new food technologies help to explain why obesity rates have risen more rapidly in North America than in Europe (Cutler, Glaeser, and Shapiro, 2003). The authors begin by showing that new technologies both inside the home (such as microwaves) and in commercial food production (better methods for enhancing the quality and taste of processed food) have reduced the length of time it takes to prepare food, encouraging people to eat more frequently during the day and consume a wider range of foods, which in turn contribute to growing rates of obesity. Yet countries differ in the extent to which these new technologies have been adopted: North Americans have generally been quick to embrace such technologies, whereas Europeans have acted more slowly. For example, the authors note that more than 80% of Americans own a microwave; in Italy, where rates of obesity are much lower than in North America, approximately 14% of households own a microwave.

Moreover, stricter regulation in Europe slowed the introduction of processed foods, whereas as relatively lax oversight in North America imposed few barriers and resulted in widespread availability of processed foods to the general public. Thus, whole societies can become more susceptible to obesity when new technologies alter the food habits of the population, with differences emerging between countries as a result of the unique practices and regulations that govern food technologies within their respective jurisdictions.

Fundamental cause theory would draw attention to the fact that, in past centuries, obesity was once more common among the wealthy. Having a large girth was a symbolic representation of one's wealth, reflecting the ability to feed oneself beyond a minimum level of subsistence at a time when the food supply was less stable than it is today. As food became more available and inexpensive, the dietary habits of the population shifted and overeating became a greater problem than an insufficient amount of food, with obesity emerging as a new risk factor for disease. Concomitantly, social perceptions of the ideal body shifted and the public no longer viewed the round and portly body as desirable, but instead preferred one that was slim and physically fit. Better positioned to make changes to their lifestyle to produce slim and fit bodies, the wealthy were first to shed excess pounds; conversely, obesity began to be concentrated among the lower classes. Consistent with fundamental cause theory, the advantaged classes have remained in better health than the poor, even though rates of obesity were once higher among those who were wealthy. When confronted with the information that obesity was a new risk factor for disease, the wealthy encountered fewer challenges in acquiring a healthy body weight, thereby maintaining the persisting association between socioeconomic position and health outcomes.

Finally, stress process would attempt to elucidate the ways in which stressful life events and chronic strains are linked to a greater risk for obesity. That is, researchers would hypothesize that stressors affect food choice by reducing the time one has available for food preparation and increasing one's desire for foods that are high in fat and dense in energy (Wardle et al., 2011). Although there are few longitudinal studies in this area, the evidence supports stress being associated with subsequent weight gain. For example, Gerace and George (1996) tracked firefighters over an eight-year period and found that those who had experienced divorce or who worried over their financial security gained more weight than those who did not report these stressors.

Clearly, the obesity epidemic is a complex phenomenon. It cannot be understood with reference to biological factors alone, and, as the above analysis reveals, substantial progress in identifying the causes of obesity depends on the combined insights and contributions of many different social determinants of health perspectives. In the following chapters, we will draw on many of these theoretical perspectives to better understand the causes of disease and death here in Canada and elsewhere, seeking always to take a critical approach to these issues.

IMPLICATIONS

Recent years have seen an increasing tendency to blame individuals for their own health problems, with many assuming that the unhealthy behaviours that underlie today's chronic diseases are the result of poor decision-making. Yet, as we have seen, patterns of disease stem from social conditions as much as, if not more than, they stem from individual behaviours or biological characteristics. Tapping into many of the ideas presented in this chapter, Marshall Becker writes:

> I would argue, first, that health habits are acquired within social groups (i.e., family, peers, the subculture); they are often supported by powerful elements in the general society (e.g., advertising); and they have proven to be extremely difficult to change. Second, for most people, personal behaviour is not the primary determinant of health status and it will not be very effective to intervene at the individual level without concomitant attempts to alter the broader economic, political, cultural, and structural components of society that act to encourage, produce, and support poor health. (1993: 4)

In sum, improving the health of the population will require us to look beyond individual behaviour to broader social structural issues—to look, in the words of C. Wright Mills (1959), for public issues rather than personal troubles.

SUMMARY

LO-1   1. Epidemiology refers to the distribution of disease in a population. Epidemiologists rely on concepts such as life expectancy, mortality and morbidity rates, incidence, and prevalence to describe the health of the population.

LO-1   2. Epidemics refer to any significant increase in the numbers affected by a disease *or* to the first appearance of a new disease. Pandemic diseases are worldwide epidemics, whereas endemic diseases are those that continue to appear in a population at a relatively stable rate.

LO-2   3. Devastating epidemics accompanied the rise of cities in medieval Europe. By the early eighteenth century, however, life expectancy began to increase, primarily due to improved living and working conditions, later and less frequent childbirth, and changes in military strategies that separated soldiers and civilians.

LO-2   4. Life expectancy increased further in the nineteenth century, primarily due to improvements in nutrition and public hygiene, with both ranked ahead of medical advances in terms of importance. Still, as in previous eras, the main causes of death were infectious and parasitic diseases.

LO-2   5. The shift from a society characterized by low life expectancy and infectious and parasitic diseases to one characterized by high life expectancy and chronic diseases is known as the *epidemiological transition*. Although Canada and other developed nations have experienced the epidemiological transition, infectious disease has re-emerged as a significant health concern in the final decades of the twentieth century, due in part to overuse of antibiotics, changing physical environments, and globalization.

LO-3   6. Although proposed several centuries earlier, germ theory became a unifying framework for understanding the causes of infectious disease in the late nineteenth century, once it was understood that microscopic living organisms invaded the body to cause disease. As disease patterns shifted, germ theory was found to be much less effective in elucidating the causes of chronic disease, initiating a search for a new theoretical framework.

LO-3   7.   The principles underlying social epidemiology/social determinants of health are quite different from those of germ theory. First, instead of a single agent that causes a specific disease, multiple social risk factors exert their influence on a range of chronic conditions.

LO-3   8.   Second, whereas germ theory can precisely determine the length of time between exposure and the onset of infectious disease, social epidemiologists are unable to predict how long it takes for exposure to known social risk factors to produce chronic illness.

LO-3   9.   Finally, from a social determinants of health perspective, risk factors are theorized to operate as a "black box," which means that exposure to these risk factors can be linked to diseases without the need to trace the biological pathways through which they have their influence. Consequently, whereas germ theory required the controlled environment of the laboratory to determine the causes of disease, the work of social epidemiologists typically involves data analysis of the characteristics of large populations in which the relative influence of different risk factors is tested simultaneously.

LO-4   10.   Although the methods of research are the same, social epidemiologists do not always interpret observed relationships similarly. Importantly, not all of these perspectives take a critical approach: theories that address the role of power in social models of disease causation are said to take a critical approach.

LO-5   11.   The health belief model predicts that individuals will be most likely to adopt healthy behaviours if they believe they are susceptible to a problem, believe the problem is serious, believe changing their behaviours will decrease the risk, and face no significant barriers to doing so. Health lifestyle theory offers a more comprehensive analysis of why healthy behaviours are adopted by emphasizing social structure as well as personal agency.

LO-5   12.   Although it was considered groundbreaking at the time because it challenged the long-held belief that health was what was provided for in the health care system, health promotion has been critiqued for focusing too much on changing individual behaviour to prevent disease. Attempting to overcome some of these shortcomings, the population health model seeks to improve the health of populations as a whole rather than target the behaviour of individuals, taking into account the complex interplay of biological, psychological, environmental, social, economic, and political factors.

LO-5   13.   Critics have questioned how the population health model has been implemented within Canada, suggesting that many of the structural issues that lie at the core of social inequalities in health continue to remain unaddressed.

LO-5   14.   According to Link and Phelan, some social conditions rise to the level of a fundamental cause of disease. To be a fundamental cause, the social condition must (1) influence a wide range of health conditions, (2) operate through a number of different intervening mechanisms, (3) be associated with resources that can be used to protect health, and (4) maintain a persisting association with health over time even as intervening mechanisms are replaced and new ones take their place. Socioeconomic position and to a lesser extent gender and race/ethnicity are considered fundamental causes.

LO-5   15.   Stress process has three components: stressors, moderators, and health outcomes. Stressors are divided into stressful life events that have a clear moment of onset and chronic strains that develop slowly over time before they are recognized as problematic. Moderators refer to those resources that can be mustered to combat stressors and minimize their impact on health. These include an individual's level of coping, such as their appraisal of stress and sense of mastery over their own life and social support, that is, the emotional support and assistance provided by social networks.

REVIEW QUESTIONS

1. What is the difference between morbidity and mortality, incidence and prevalence, and acute and chronic illnesses?
2. What is the epidemiological transition?
3. What factors caused the decline in mortality between the nineteenth and early twentieth centuries?
4. How do methods to determine the causes of disease differ for germ theory compared to social epidemiology/social determinants of health?
5. In what ways does the government report titled *Seven More Years* draw on a medical model approach?
6. In what ways does the health belief model neglect upstream factors in disease causation? How does health lifestyle theory take an upstream approach into consideration?
7. Describe three ways in which the population health model builds on health promotion.
8. What conditions does socioeconomic position satisfy to be identified as a fundamental cause?
9. How are stressful life events different from chronic strains? Describe how stressful life events can lead to chronic strains and vice versa.

CRITICAL THINKING QUESTIONS

1. How can knowing the history of disease help us to understand (a) current health problems and (b) how health patterns might change in the future?
2. What are the *political* consequences of focusing on how social factors cause illness rather than focusing on biological factors?
3. Tobacco and alcohol have been identified as two of the most important underlying causes of death in Canada. What upstream social policies would you recommend to modify these risk factors, and what response would you give to those who suggest that simply informing people they are making unhealthy choices is the best way to reduce mortality rates in Canada?
4. Think of something you do (or believe you should do) to protect your health: wearing seat belts, wearing bike helmets, drinking alcohol only moderately, eating five portions of fruits and vegetables daily, flossing your teeth, etc. Use the health belief model to explain why you do or do not take these precautions. (If you can't think of an example from your own experience, use an example from a friend or relative's life.) How would your understanding of your behaviour change if you were to take one of the other perspectives (health lifestyle theory, population health, fundamental cause theory, or stress process)?

KEY TERMS

acute illness (p. 18)
age-adjusted rates (p. 19)
agency (p. 29)
chronic illnesses (p. 18)
chronic strains (p. 37)
endemic (p. 19)

epidemic (p. 19)
epidemiological transition (p. 21)
epidemiology (p. 17)
disease (p. 17)
fundamental cause (p. 35)
germ theory (p. 25)

Part II

Social Factors and Illness

In Part II, we take a closer look at the social factors that underlie contemporary patterns of health and illness and explore why some social groups bear a greater burden of illness than others. In Chapter 3, we examine socially patterned differences in illness according to age, sex and gender, and race/ethnicity. In Chapter 4, we explore the ways in which socioeconomic position and income inequality account for the social distribution of illness in the population and demonstrate how a life course approach has improved our understanding of the dynamic relationship between socioeconomic position and health. We conclude the chapter with research questions that sociologists are just beginning to address as they develop theory to guide investigation into the intersections between socio-economic position, age, sex and gender, and race/ethnicity as they jointly influence health. In Chapter 5, we turn our attention to the social roles embedded in work and family life and consider how these each influence patterns of health and illness, and discuss the health implications of ongoing transformations in both of these spheres. Because the causes of disease and death in the developing world are different from those in more affluent countries, the last chapter of this part (Chapter 6) examines health and illness from a global perspective and discusses how social forces—from the low status of women to rapid urbanization—can foster illness in developing countries.

3

The Social Determinants of Health and Illness: Age, Sex and Gender, and Race/Ethnicity

Getty Images

Canadian Prime Minister Stephen Harper and National Chief of the Assembly of First Nations Phil Fontaine walk into the House of Commons on Parliament Hill June 11, 2008, in Ottawa, Canada. Harper delivered a formal statement of apology on behalf of the Federal Government and all Canadians to former students of Indian Residential Schools, who for decades were forcibly removed from their communities and sent to state-funded schools to be assimilated.

Isolation and Assimilation: An Apology from the Government of Canada

June 11, 2008, marked a historic day in Canada as Prime Minister Stephen Harper stood in the House of Commons and delivered a formal apology to the former residents of the Indian Residential School system and to the Aboriginal peoples of Canada. An excerpt of his speech appears below:

> In the 1870s, the federal government, partly in order to meet its obligations to educate aboriginal children, began to play a role in the development and administration of these schools. Two primary objectives of the residential school system were to remove and isolate children from the influence of their homes, families, traditions and cultures, and to assimilate them into the dominant culture. These objectives were based on the assumption that aboriginal cultures and spiritual beliefs were inferior and unequal. Indeed, some sought, as was infamously said, "to kill the Indian in the child".
>
> Today, we recognize that this policy of assimilation was wrong, has caused great harm, and has no place in our country. One hundred and thirty-two federally-supported schools were located in every province and territory, except Newfoundland, New Brunswick and Prince Edward Island.
>
> Most schools were operated as joint ventures with Anglican, Catholic, Presbyterian and United churches.
>
> The Government of Canada built an educational system in which very young children were often forcibly removed from their homes and often taken far from their communities.
>
> Many were inadequately fed, clothed and housed. All were deprived of the care and nurturing of their parents, grandparents and communities.
>
> First Nations, Inuit, and Métis languages and cultural practices were prohibited in these schools. Tragically, some of these children died while attending residential schools and others never returned home.
>
> The government now recognizes that the consequences of the Indian residential schools policy were profoundly negative

and that this policy has had a lasting and damaging impact on aboriginal culture, heritage and language.

While some former students have spoken positively about their experiences at residential schools, these stories are far overshadowed by tragic accounts of the emotional, physical and sexual abuse and neglect of helpless children, and their separation from powerless families and communities.

The legacy of Indian residential schools has contributed to social problems that continue to exist in many communities today.

It has taken extraordinary courage for the thousands of survivors who have come forward to speak publicly about the abuse they suffered. It is a testament to their resilience as individuals and to the strengths of their cultures.

Regrettably, many former students are not with us today and died never having received a full apology from the Government of Canada.

The government recognizes that the absence of an apology has been an impediment to healing and reconciliation. Therefore, on behalf of the Government of Canada and all Canadians, I stand before you, in this chamber so central to our life as a country, to apologize to aboriginal peoples for Canada's role in the Indian residential schools system. (Canada Parliamentary Debates, 2008)

The apology by the government of Canada has been one step in the healing process and is part of the larger agreement between the federal government and Aboriginal peoples. In addition to compensation, the federal government formed the Residential Schools Truth and Reconciliation Commission. Its purpose is to allow former students and other persons affected by the residential school system to share their individual experiences in a safe and culturally appropriate manner. These stories will be used to create a historical account of the residential school system, help people to heal, and encourage reconciliation between Aboriginals and non-Aboriginal Canadians. Today, the Commission continues to host events across the country to give voice to former residents and to raise awareness about the residential school system and its impact.

Source: Canada Parliament House of Commons, Edited Hansard. Vol. 142, No. 100, Session 2, 39th Parliament, Wednesday, June 11, 2008.

LEARNING OBJECTIVES

In this chapter, students should be able to:

LO-1 **Describe** age-related patterns of morbidity, mortality, and the causes of death in the Canadian population.

LO-2 **Explain** how and why the Canadian population is aging and **identify** key points in the debate over whether the aging population will pose a threat to Canada's health care system.

LO-3 **Understand** the differences between sex and gender and **describe** how sex and gender combine to affect health and illness in the Canadian population.

LO-4 **Recognize** that race is primarily a social construct rather than a biological construct.

LO-5 **Describe** differences in patterns of mortality and morbidity between Aboriginal peoples and the rest of Canada and **recognize** that colonization and the legacy of residential schools has had a lasting impact on the health of Aboriginal peoples.

LO-6 **Define** the healthy immigrant effect and **identify** potential explanations for why the effect varies by immigrant class and tends to disappear over time.

In the last chapter, we learned that social characteristics influence patterns of health and illness in the population. In this chapter, we look at how three social factors—age, sex and gender, and race and ethnicity—combine with biological forces to inequitably distribute illness, disability, and death in the population.

AGE

Overview and Evidence

Not surprisingly, age is the single most important predictor of **mortality** and **morbidity.** As noted in Chapter 2, deaths during the first year of life were common in North America and Europe prior to the twentieth century. Although far less common now, infant mortality remains an important issue because so many years of productive life are lost when an infant dies and because infant mortality is so often caused by preventable social and environmental conditions. Once individuals pass the danger zone during and immediately after birth, mortality **rates** drop precipitously. Those rates then begin to rise significantly after age 45. This pattern is clearly noted in Table 3.1, which shows that 5.4% of the 238,617 deaths in Canada in 2008 were among those aged 44 and younger. Thereafter, deaths by age accelerate such that the percentage of deaths among Canadians between the ages of 45 and 54 (6.1%) exceeds the percentage of deaths for all those 44 and younger. The highest percentage of deaths (31.7%) occurs for those over the age of 85.

The causes of death also vary across the life course (see Table 3.1). In the first year of life, death is often related to congenital anomalies and complications at birth. During childhood, accidents, cancer, and congenital anomalies are the leading causes of death, but from adolescence into middle adulthood, most deaths are due to accidents, cancer, and suicide. From age 45 to 64, chronic conditions begin to emerge as leading causes of death so that heart disease displaces suicide in the top three causes of mortality. The causes of death in later life also vary such that cancer and heart disease are the two leading causes of death from ages 65 to 84, with the third leading cause listed as chronic respiratory disease for those 65–74 and stroke for those aged 75–84. After the age of 85, heart disease supersedes cancer as the leading cause of death, with stroke in third place.

Patterns of morbidity also demonstrate a positive association with age, such that older Canadians are more likely to have a chronic illness. For example, very few Canadian young adults have been diagnosed with arthritis, but after age 35, rates begin to increase such that arthritis affects 7.7% of men and 7.2% of women aged 35 to 44 and rises to 33.1% for men and 51.0% for women over the age of 65 (Statistics Canada, 2012a). Similarly, high blood pressure is much more common among Canadians who are over the age of 65 (47.7%) compared to 35- to 44-year-olds (8.0%) (Statistics Canada, 2012b).

Despite this trend, it would be a mistake to assume that old age is necessarily characterized by illness and decline. For example, less than half of Canadian seniors are disabled and only one in four Canadians over the age of 65 say they are in fair or poor health (Raina et al., 1998; Turcotte and Schellenberg, 2007). Moreover, seniors are generally in better mental health: nearly half of Canadian adults aged 25–54 indicated that they felt sad or depressed in the past month compared to one-third of Canadians over the age of 65.

The Crisis of an Aging Population

The Canadian population is aging steadily, as seniors account for a growing proportion of the population. In 2011, 14.8% of Canadians were 65 or older, up from 7.7% in 1956, and by 2056, it is projected that seniors will make up between 25% and 30% of the Canadian population (Statistics Canada, 2010, 2012c). The aging population is due in part to increased life expectancy and declining fertility, a phenomenon that is happening worldwide. In addition, following World War II, a number of countries, including Canada and the United States, experienced a surge in births, creating a baby boom. The **baby boom generation**, defined as those born between 1946 and 1965 in Canada (Wister, 2005), started to reach the age of retirement in 2011, and by 2031, the entire baby boom generation will be over the age of 65.

baby boom generation:
Those born between 1946 and 1965 in Canada.

	Percent of Deaths within Age Group	Percent of all Deaths
Birth to Age 1		
Congenital malformations	21.7	
Disorders related to gestation and low birth weight	13.4	
Maternal complications of pregnancy	7.8	
Total number of deaths	1,911	0.8
Ages 1–14		
Accidents	28.8	
Cancer	16.2	
Congenital malformations	6.3	
Total number of deaths	712	0.3
Ages 15–34		
Accidents	35.3	
Suicide	20.3	
Cancer	10.8	
Total number of deaths	4,816	2.0
Ages 35–44		
Cancer	24.7	
Accidents	16.9	
Suicide	14.1	
Total number of deaths	5,456	2.3
Ages 45–54		
Cancer	38.6	
Heart disease	15.6	
Accidents	8.6	
Total number of deaths	14,438	6.1
Ages 55–64		
Cancer	46.8	
Heart disease	18.0	
Accidents	3.9	
Total number of deaths	25,940	10.9
Ages 65–74		
Cancer	44.5	
Heart disease	19.1	
Chronic lower respiratory diseases	5.0	
Total number of deaths	39,476	16.6
Ages 75–84		
Cancer	31.1	
Heart disease	21.7	
Stroke	6.3	
Total number of deaths	69,209	29.0
Ages 85 and older		
Heart disease	26.6	
Cancer	15.3	
Stroke	8.5	
Total number of deaths	75,654	31.7

TABLE 3.1 Top Three Causes of Death by Age in Canada, 2008

Note: Summing the percent of all deaths does not add up to 100% because age at death is unknown for 0.4% of all deaths in 2008.

Source: Adapted from: Statistics Canada, *Leading Causes of Death in Canada*, Cat. No. 84-215-XWE, Tables 1-1 to 1-10 & Table 2, Ottawa: Ministry of Industry, 2011.

These trends have fuelled concern that there will be too few workers in the labour market to support the health care needs of the elderly as the century progresses, throwing Canada's health care system into crisis.

Canada is also experiencing the **feminization of aging**—the steady rise in the proportion of the population who are female in each older age group, so that women make up a larger proportion of the elderly than of the young and middle-aged. This phenomenon occurs because women live on average longer lives than men. The trend is a concern to the extent that older women tend to have fewer health protective factors than older men. For example, older women are more likely to be poor, and because men generally marry women younger than themselves and are more likely to remarry if their spouses die, widows dramatically outnumber widowers. Consequently, the feminization of aging is also expected to increase the costs of providing health and social services to the elderly.

Yet some researchers have taken a more balanced approach to fears that Canada's health care system will be thrown into crisis as a result of the aging population. First, most projections find that aging will actually have a small to modest effect on health care costs (Anderson and Hussey, 2000; Chappell and Hollander, 2011; Canadian Institute for Health Information, 2008a) and poses little threat to the long-term economic stability of Canada (Ruggeri and Zou, 2007). Indeed, rather than Canadian seniors being a drain and dependent on government resources, most Canadian seniors will be contributing to government revenues as they pay taxes on the monies they withdraw from their retirement savings plans. Moreover, in many ways, Canadian seniors are aging better than ever before. For example, Canada's baby boomers already have lower rates of heart disease, hypertension, and arthritis than previous cohorts at similar ages. On the other hand, changes in sedentary lifestyles and poor eating habits imply that future generations of seniors may be at increased risk for obesity and related diseases. Diabetes is more common among today's seniors than in the past, although it is difficult to determine whether this reflects an increase in the prevalence of the disease or changes in diagnostic criteria (Menec, Lix, and MacWilliams, 2005). Finally, some suggest that health care costs are being driven more by the growing number of services that healthy seniors receive. It is possible that all seniors, including healthy seniors, are simply having more done for or to them than in the past (Chappell and Hollander, 2011; Evans, 2011). Taken together, these studies provide little evidence that an aging population is a burgeoning social problem that requires immediate health care reform. Nonetheless, fears that Canada's growing elderly population has the potential to imperil the health care system and bankrupt Canada continue to be expressed in the mainstream media and in academic journals (Sinha, 2011).

Frailty: A New Disease of Aging

As we have observed, aging is associated with accumulating impairment and vulnerability to disease and death; however, not all older persons are in poor health. The wide variability in health in later life prompted some medical researchers to search for a way to identify older people who are particularly vulnerable to poor health outcomes. These efforts have led to the emergence of a new condition called frailty. Over the past two decades, this disease gained rapid acceptance in the medical community, even though there remains little agreement on its definition. Bergman and colleagues (2007) focus on the lack of adaptive capacity of the individual by suggesting that frailty represents "increased vulnerability to stressors due to impairments in multiple, inter-related systems that lead to decline in homeostatic reserve and resiliency" (p. 731). Other definitions emphasize the social context by suggesting that frailty "occurs when there is diminished ability to carry out the important practical and social activities of daily living" (Brown, Renwick, and Raphael, 1995, p. 95). The diagnostic criteria for frailty are equally contested, with some quantifying frailty as the accumulation of deficits

feminization of aging:
The steady rise in the proportion of the population who are female in each older age group.

or chronic conditions across multiple domains (i.e., a frailty index), whereas others have attempted to establish a **phenotype** of frailty, such that the diagnosis is applied to seniors who meet three or more of the following criteria: weak grip strength, slow walking speed, exhaustion, weight loss, and inactivity (Fairfall et al., 2011).

From the perspective of most medical researchers, frailty is an objective medical condition that can be reliably associated with poor health outcomes. For example, a recent Canadian study that used a frailty index (defined as how many of 42 possible different chronic conditions a person currently had) reported that frailty increased concomitantly with age and was a significant predictor of death, institutionalization, and use of health care services over a twelve-year period (Rockwood, Song, and Mitnitski, 2011). Yet, other clinicians are cautious about frailty, suggesting that while the diagnosis may result in improved care for seniors, one of the consequences of labelling an older person with the diagnosis may be that it changes self-concept and the perceptions that others have of the older person and may lead to poor decision-making (Bergman et al., 2007).

From a social constructionist perspective, sociologists challenge frailty as an objective medical condition by questioning whether prevailing negative beliefs about the aging process make it easier to transform the problems of living experienced by older persons into medical fact. Gilleard and Higgs (2011) note the vagueness of symptoms such as weakness, slowness, and inactivity for defining frailty as a medical condition and suggest that these symptoms cannot be meaningfully distinguished from the aging process. Moreover, they contend that frailty represents not so much a disease as an unspecified risk category for experiencing undesirable events in the future. Thus, frailty speaks not to the current health status of the older person but rather to their capacity to live independently.

Because the diagnosis of frailty is used to make decisions about whether an older person is deemed capable of living independently, sociologists are also interested in the ways in which medicine exercises authority over the aging process and health care resources. First, the power to label frailty as an illness means that attention is often focused on the doctor's checklist of items rather than on the subjective experiences of the older person. Restricting their gaze in this way means that doctors may overlook the social and emotional experiences that often accompany functional changes in the body during later life and fail to recognize that older people may struggle more with the implications of a change than with the change itself. In addition, in an environment of finite health care resources, frailty operates as a necessary label to gain eligibility for services. In this way, the diagnosis is used to ration treatment to those at greatest risk, forcing older people to compete for scarce resources (Grenier, 2007).

In sum, the focus on age as a risk factor for poor health has often meant that seniors are subject to greater surveillance by the health care system than younger people. As such, while age is a strong predictor of both mortality and morbidity, social perceptions about older people and the aging process can lead us to overestimate the relationship between age and health.

SEX AND GENDER

Overview and Evidence

Both sex and gender strongly affect health status. **Sex** refers to the biological categories of male and female, to which we are assigned based on our chromosomal structure, genitalia, hormones, secondary sexual characteristics such as facial hair, and so on; those who have two X chromosomes and a vagina are sexually female, those with one X and one Y chromosome and a penis are sexually male. In contrast, **gender** refers to the social categories of masculine and feminine and to the social expectations regarding masculinity and femininity

phenotype:
The observable physical or biochemical characteristics of an organism, as determined by both genetic makeup and environmental influences.

sex:
The biological categories of male and female, to which we are assigned based on our chromosomal structure and physical appearance: those who have two X chromosomes and a vagina are sexually female, those with one X and one Y chromosome and a penis are sexually male.

gender:
The social categories of masculine and feminine and the social expectations regarding masculinity and femininity that we are expected to follow based on our assigned sex.

that we are expected to follow based on our assigned sex. Because these categories are social, they vary across time and across culture.

Basic epidemiological data show that both sex and gender affect health. For example, before the twentieth century, the life expectancies of men and women were fairly similar, with women having a slight advantage over men. Over the course of the twentieth century, however, the life expectancy of women began to increase more rapidly than it did for men so that by the 1950s Canadian women lived on average more than 4.5 years longer than their male counterparts and by the 1970s the gap was as large as 7 years (Trovato and Lalu, 2007). From its peak in the 1980s, the gap has since narrowed such that in 2005 Canadian women are expected to live only 4.7 years longer than men on average. This pattern of diverging, then converging, life expectancies for men and women has also been observed in other countries, including the United States and Sweden. The *differences* between men's and women's life expectancies suggest that sex may directly affect health, while the *changes* in these differences across time suggest that gender affects health, reflecting variations in women's social position, access to resources, and health behaviours.

But mortality differences tell us only part of the story. If we look only at life expectancies, we might conclude that women are biologically hardier than men. When we look at morbidity rates, however, the picture blurs. While at each age, including *in utero,* males have higher rates of mortality than females, women in general tend to have higher rates of morbidity and of non-fatal disease than men (Bird and Rieker, 2008). Thus, it appears that women live longer than men but experience more illness and disability, whereas men experience relatively little illness but die more quickly when illness strikes.

In recent years, however, the notion that "women get sicker, but men die quicker" has come under greater scrutiny. The assumption that chronic illnesses are more likely to befall women than men now requires qualification. For example, for some conditions, such as diabetes, men are significantly more likely to have the disease than are women (Tang, Chen, and Drewski, 2003). Other chronic conditions show variable gender differences across the life course. As noted in the discussion of age-related differences in chronic conditions, arthritis increases with age; however, at earlier ages, there are few gender differences in arthritis and it is only at older ages that rates of arthritis for women far exceed those for men (Statistics Canada, 2012b). Other conditions, such as asthma, are more prevalent among boys than girls in early life, but more common among girls than boys in adolescence, with gender differences thereafter dissipating with age (Chen et al., 2003; Walters, McDonough, and Strohschein, 2002). These varied patterns suggest that explanations for differences in health and illness between men and women, which we explore next, are complex and not easily understood.

Explanations for Gender Differences in Health

Differences in health between men and women stem from both the biological differences of sex and the socially reinforced differences of gender. Therefore, progress in understanding differences in health and illness between and among men and women requires a sex- and gender-based analysis (SGBA), described in greater detail in Box 3.1. Because patterns and explanations are specific to the health outcome, we will examine heart disease, injuries, and depression in turn.

Heart disease is the second leading cause of mortality after cancer in both Canadian men and Canadian women. Although deaths from heart disease in Canada have declined almost 30% between 1994 and 2004, they have been dropping more rapidly for men than for women. As a result, from 2000 onward, more women are dying of heart disease than men (Tu et al., 2009). These trends have brought greater attention to women's risk for heart disease, traditionally regarded as a male disease, with researchers identifying both biological and social factors.

From a biological standpoint, women appear to be protected from heart disease until they reach menopause. Although the exact mechanisms through which this works are unknown, some theorize that estrogen and other "female" hormones (which in fact also occur in males, but in different proportions) somehow protect the heart from heart disease. Because of the delayed risk, women with heart disease tend to be older and have other health problems compared to men. Men and women also differ in the symptoms and signs of a heart attack. Men tend to report chest and radiating arm pain, whereas women are more likely to report fatigue, nausea, shoulder or back pain, and shortness of breath (Low, Thurston, and Matthews, 2010). Sex differences in the symptoms of a heart attack and the long-standing assumption that heart disease is a male disease may help to explain why women are less likely to be diagnosed with heart disease and less likely to receive aggressive treatment.

Social factors also play a role in gender differences in heart disease. Women generally report higher levels of social support than men, and high levels of social support are protective against heart disease. The source of stress may also operate differently for men and women. Men appear to be more vulnerable to heart disease when they experience stress in their jobs, and women appear to be more vulnerable to heart disease when they experience stress in their interpersonal relationships (Low et al., 2010). Finally, there are gender differences in individual behaviours, such as smoking and physical inactivity, that are major risk factors for heart disease. Women are more likely than men to be sedentary, and although men are generally more likely to smoke than women, gender differences in smoking behaviour have been narrowing over time. Indeed, the increase in women's smoking behaviour over the latter half of the twentieth century is considered to be a contributing factor to the converging life expectancies of men and women noted earlier (Trovato and Lalu, 2007). As this short summary demonstrates, the ways in which sex and gender operate to affect risk for heart disease is extraordinarily complex, and there is much that researchers need to learn about the ways in which sex and gender operate to make substantial progress in understanding their precise effects on heart disease.

Injuries, both intentional and unintentional (accidents), are a major health problem. As noted in Table 3.1, accidents are the leading cause of death for those between the ages of 1 and 34. Many more Canadians survive their injuries but require medical care. Approximately 4.3 million Canadians (15% of the population) reported that they suffered an injury in the past twelve months that limited their daily activities in 2009–2010, and of these, more than half sought out medical care within forty-eight hours of sustaining the injury (Billette and Janz, 2011). Injuries are costly to society. In 2004, costs were estimated to be $19.8 billion as a result of the direct cost of providing health care and lost productivity due to hospitalization, disability, and death.

Injury rates vary across the life course, with rates highest in adolescence and generally declining throughout adulthood; however, gender differences in injury rates are not consistent over the life course (Table 3.2). In adolescence and for most of adult life, women are less likely than men to sustain an injury that is serious enough to limit daily activity. Gender and social constructions of masculinity appear to explain why men are more vulnerable to injury than women during this period of the life course. Men are more likely than women to use legal and illegal drugs, drive dangerously, participate in dangerous sports, or engage in violence and consequently are more likely to be injured as a result of these activities. Work, too, more often endangers men, who are more likely to be in dangerous occupations such as agriculture and commercial fishing.

Past the age of 65, gender differences in injury rates are reversed and women become more likely than men to report injury. Part of their vulnerability is because women experience

BOX 3.1
Sex- and Gender-Based Analysis (SGBA) in Health Research

Canadian researchers continue to make significant advances in understanding how sex and gender affect health and inequalities in health. This progress is due in part to policies established in Canada since 2003 that require the use of sex- and gender-based analysis (SGBA) in the development of health programs and in the funding of health research (Clow et al., 2009). These policies represent the successful efforts of women's health movements in the past fifty years to bring greater attention to the ways in which women's health problems were often reduced to their reproductive systems (i.e., pathologizing normal processes such as menstruation, pregnancy, and menopause) while ignoring the health impact of the social aspects of their lives (i.e., caring work, unequal treatment in the labour market). Yet, it is important to recognize that SGBA is not just about identifying the causes of illness and mortality among women as a means of improving their health status nor does it aim to document the differences between women and men. Rather, SGBA involves understanding the health needs and realities of both females and males and, as such, is constructed around four main principles: sex, gender, diversity, and equity. As noted earlier, sex refers to the biological characteristics that distinguish male and female, whereas gender reflects the social aspects of what it means to be male or female in a given society. Although sex and gender are treated as binary categories, both

may be better viewed as a continuum. For example, those who have an extra X or Y chromosome (i.e., XXX , XXY or XYY) do not fit neatly into either category; similarly, transgendered people see themselves as neither male nor female, and characteristics coded masculine are often used to describe women, and vice versa. Conceptualizing sex and gender as operating along a continuum more accurately represents human experience, highlights some of the challenges facing individuals who do not identify as female or male, and makes it imperative to understand how sex and gender matter for health and well-being. Diversity recognizes that each person's experience of sex and gender is specific to them; therefore, it is important to refrain from generalizing to all men or all women when conducting research on how sex and gender affect health. Instead, researchers need to pay attention to differences among groups of women and men, moving beyond initial questions about women's and men's health to consider how other variables or determinants of health affect different groups of women and men. Finally, equity refers to differences in health outcomes among and between men and women that are deemed to be unfair, avoidable, and changeable (Clow et al., 2009). This means translating research into effective policy that provides women and men, girls and boys, with equal opportunity and access to the conditions and services that enable them to achieve good health.

greater bone loss over their lifetime than do men. The rate of bone loss accelerates even more rapidly after menopause so that in later life, women are much more likely than men to have brittle bones. Thus, a fall is more likely to result in injury for older women than for older men. In sum, norms around masculinity create greater risk for injury for men over most of the life course, but in later life, biological differences between men and women emerge to create greater risk of injury for women.

Finally, depression is a mood disorder associated with a loss of interest or pleasure in life (anhedonia); feelings of hopelessness, worthlessness, and sadness; low energy; and difficulty concentrating. Depression has traditionally been viewed as a female problem, with women twice as likely as men to be diagnosed with the mental disorder. Depression first emerges as a significant health problem in adolescence, with adolescent girls at greater risk than adolescent boys (Wade, Cairney, and Pevalin, 2002). Depression peaks in young adulthood and thereafter declines with age; however, the gender gap in depression remains constant throughout the life course (Cairney and Krause, 2005; Clarke et al., 2011).

Feminists contend that psychiatry has historically viewed women's bodies and minds as deficient, equating femininity with sickness (Ehrenreich and English, 2005a). No more than a century ago, psychiatrists believed that women were hostage to their reproductive systems, which controlled and determined their mental states. For example, during menstruation women were encouraged by their doctors to excuse themselves from normal duties to rest their minds. Ironically, this cult of invalidism only applied to upper-class women, who could afford to disengage from everyday duties. Working-class women were not permitted time off from pregnancy or recovery from childbirth, let alone for menstruation (Ehrenreich and English, 2005a).

Although biological explanations for excess levels of depression among women still persist, researchers from a feminist perspective have successfully shifted attention to the differences in men's and women's social roles as potential explanations for gender differences in depression. Their efforts have shown that women encounter more strain in roles associated with employment and family than do men. Employment is associated with better mental health for both men and women, but throughout their lives, women are less likely to be employed than men, and receive less compensation for their work and have less autonomy in their working conditions than do men (McDonough and Strohschein, 2003). While women spend more of their lives in the labour market than in the past, they have not relinquished responsibilities in the home. Thus, women continue to spend more time than men taking care of children and performing household chores and consequently encounter greater time pressures than do men in trying to meet the competing demands of work and home. In addition, expectations around motherhood may also increase the pressure on women to spend time with their children and to feel guilty when they cannot. Recent research suggests that in dual-earner households where both parents potentially experience time pressures, subjective feelings of time strain with children are associated with lower psychological well-being among mothers but have no effect on fathers (Nomaguchi, Milkie, and Bianchi, 2005).

A feminist perspective also suggests that dominant conceptions of gender may shape how mental illness manifests in men and women (Rosenfield, 1999). To the extent that masculinity is associated with power and independence and has greater value than femininity, men may develop a sense of entitlement, control, and separateness that enables them to blame others for their difficulties, with the result that their expressions of mental disorder become directed outward. Women, who are often socialized to attend to the emotional responses of others and to be less assertive in acting on their own feelings, may internalize responses to

Age	Injuries	
	Male	Female
12–19	26.9	18.4
20–39	18.3	11.3
40–64	11.9	9.6
65–79	6.3	9.3
80+	7.8	11.5

TABLE 3.2 Gender Differences in Injuries in Canada, 2001.

Source: Adapted from: Katherine Wilkins & Evelyn Park, "Injuries," *Health Reports*, Vol. 15 (3), Pg. 43-48, Table A, 2004.

stress and begin to exhibit symptoms that correspond to a diagnosis of depression. A recent study on Canadian adults supports the argument that there are gender-specific manifestations of mental illness. Whereas 10.3% of women and 6.4% of men reported that they had been diagnosed with a mood or anxiety disorder, a higher proportion of men (4.3%) than women (1.7%) reported a substance abuse disorder (Rush et al., 2008). Others suggest that men may simply be less likely to admit to feelings of depression or to seek out help for depression because to do so would appear unmanly (Courtenay, 2000).

Our brief look at sex and gender differences in heart disease, injuries, and depression makes several points. First, each of these conditions reflects the complex, dynamic influences of both sex and gender. Importantly, as we have observed, in none of these instances do sex and gender operate in quite the same way. Understanding the risks to health for men and women thus requires a condition-specific approach rather than an evaluation of morbidity in general (although a condition-specific approach does not always produce its intended result either, as we illustrate in Box 3.2). Second, gender is not a static phenomenon. Ideas about what it means to be male and female have undergone significant transformation over time, and researchers need to be attuned to these historical variations to make sense of how gender influences health. Third, sex and gender differences in health need to be investigated in the context of other statuses. We have already seen how sex and gender differences in health fluctuate across the life course. Thus, gender differences in depression are fairly stable from adolescence onward, with nearly twice as many women as men diagnosed with depression at all ages, but the risks for heart disease and injuries switch from being greater in men to being greater in women as they age. In general, the risk for heart disease increases with age, whereas for injuries, older age is associated with decreased risk. In both instances, however, excess risk for men at younger ages gives way such that with increasing age, women experience greater risks for heart disease and injuries relative to men. Thus, sex and gender differences should not be investigated in isolation but should be viewed in the context of age as well as race/ethnicity, socioeconomic position, and other social roles. In doing so, we incorporate more fully a sex- and gender-based analysis, not just providing greater insight into differences in health between men and women, but uncovering variations in health among women and among men.

BOX 3.2
It's Movember!

Every November, men from around the world start the month clean shaven and compete with one another to grow their moustaches over the rest of the month. Their efforts are intended to raise money for prostate cancer research, to educate other men about their risk for the disease, and to encourage men to go for cancer screening on a regular basis. Begun nearly a decade ago in Australia, the "Movember" campaign now operates in more than a dozen countries, including Canada.

There are obvious parallels between prostate cancer awareness in Movember and the much more established breast cancer awareness campaigns that operate during the month of October. First, both conditions are common in the respective sexes. One in seven men in Canada will be diagnosed with prostate cancer in their lifetime, and one in twenty-eight will die of the disease. One in nine women in Canada will be diagnosed with breast cancer in their lifetime, and one in twenty-nine will die of the disease. Second, death rates from both prostate cancer and breast cancer have been declining over time. Moreover, treatments for both cancers are relatively successful. The five-year survival rate for breast cancer is 88% for women, whereas the five-year survival rate for prostate cancer is 96%.

There is another link between breast cancer and prostate cancer that is less well known: the growing concern that screening for prostate and breast cancer is not having the anticipated positive benefits. For example, screening for prostate cancer involves testing middle-aged male patients at periodic intervals for prostate-specific antigen (PSA), a chemical produced by the prostate. If a patient's PSA level has increased significantly, doctors then perform a biopsy—inserting a needle into the prostate to remove a few cells, which they then check for cancer. Unfortunately, PSA tests are highly inaccurate: About 30% of those who have cancer are not identified by the test, and about two-thirds of those tested are **false positives**: identified by the test as having cancer but in fact not having the disease. The test brings no benefits to those whose cancers are missed, while those who are falsely identified as having cancer suffer unnecessary emotional trauma, financial costs, and painful procedures.

If the biopsy suggests cancer, doctors usually perform a prostatectomy (that is, surgical removal of the prostate). The surgery succeeds in removing the cancer in about 80% of cases. Even in these cases, however, the risks of surgery can outweigh the benefits. Between 0.5% and 2% of patients die within a month of surgery, and another 5% experience serious and potentially deadly complications (Wilt et al., 2008). In addition, more than 30% experience serious difficulties in sustaining erections or controlling their urine. Perhaps most importantly, a number of studies have found no significant differences in survival rates between men who do and do not receive treatment, appar-

ently because the dangers of treatment balance out the benefits and because untreated prostate cancer rarely causes death (Wilt et al., 2008).

The situation appears to be the same for breast cancer, where regular screening for breast cancer also results in an excessive number of false positives as well as the overtreatment of breast cancers that pose minimal threat. The problem was succinctly summarized in an article published in the *Journal of the American Medical Association*. The authors stated:

> After 2½ decades of screening for breast and prostate cancer, conclusions are troubling: Overall cancer rates are higher, many more patients are being treated, and the absolute incidence of aggressive or late-stage disease has not been significantly decreased. Screening has had some effect, but it comes at a significant cost, including overdiagnosis, overtreatment and complications of therapy.... Additional gains are unlikely with the current approach and may inadvertently add to the burden of treatment and diagnosis for relatively indolent disease. (Esserman, Shieh, and Thompson, 2009, p. 1688)

It appears then that the rapid adoption of both PSA screening and mammography is a perfect example of the **technological imperative**, which can drive doctors to use all available technology regardless of cost or consequences. This cultural imperative is discussed in more detail in Chapter 13.

false positive:
A test result that indicates that a disease or condition is present when in reality there is no disease.

technological imperative:
The belief that technology is always good, so any existing technological interventions should be used.

Case Study: Intimate Partner Violence as a Health Problem

One health issue in which gender has historically played an especially critical role is domestic violence, also known as intimate partner violence. Although the general public rarely thinks of domestic violence as a health problem, it is a major cause of injury, disability, and death among women worldwide. Depression and post-traumatic stress disorder are also more prevalent among those who have experienced intimate partner violence (Campbell, 2002).

According to victimization surveys that ask respondents about intimate partner violence, approximately 6% of Canadians who had been or were in a spousal relationship reported experiencing spousal violence in the past five years (Brennan, 2011). Although men are as likely as women to be victims of spousal violence, women are more likely than men to experience serious forms of spousal violence, such as having been beaten, choked, or strangled. Crime statistics reveal that three times as many Canadian women as men were killed by a current or former spouse in 2009 (Taylor-Butts and Porter, 2011).

In recent years, the comparable rates of intimate partner violence between men and women have led some to contest the influence of gender. Dutton (2012) argues that because the evidence shows that both men and women commit violent acts against their partners and that violence appears to be the result of psychological problems rather than broader power struggles between men and women, the issue should no longer be framed in terms of women's rights and gender. Others contend that domestic violence is primarily about women's rights and gender because it reflects basic cultural and political forces in our society and, indeed, around the world (Dobash and Dobash, 1998). Through religion, schools, families, the media, and so on, it is argued that women are taught to consider themselves responsible for making sure that their personal relationships run smoothly. When problems occur in relationships, women are taught to blame themselves, even if their husbands respond to those problems with violence. Moreover, once violence occurs, women's typically inferior economic position can leave them trapped in these relationships. Men, meanwhile, often receive the message—from sources ranging from pornographic magazines to religious teachings that give husbands the responsibility to "discipline" their wives—that violence is an acceptable response to stress and that women are acceptable targets for that violence. Although most men resist these messages, enough men absorb them to make intimate partner violence a major social problem. Thus, at a broader and largely unconscious level, intimate partner violence is a form of **social control**: a way that social expectations and power relationships are reinforced. Specifically, intimate partner violence operates as social control by reinforcing men's power over women and women's inferior position within society.

Johnson (2005, 2011) attempts to resolve the issue by distinguishing among three different types of intimate partner violence. **Intimate terrorism** refers to the type of criminal behaviour and efforts to control another human being that most people think of in relation to domestic violence and is the most likely to come to the attention of law enforcement and shelters. Although it is not exclusively male-perpetrated, the majority of offenders of this type of intimate partner violence are men. **Violent resistance** occurs when victims of violence respond in kind, either as an instinctive reaction to protect themselves or as a strategy for preventing further assaults. It also includes cases where a victim kills a partner to escape the cycle of violence. The majority of violent resisters are women. Finally, **situational couple violence**, the most common form of intimate partner violence, occurs when conflict between partners erupts into aggression and violence. This form of intimate partner violence is gender-symmetric, with men and women equally likely to resort to violence. Importantly, Johnson (2011) suggests that this form of intimate partner violence does not revolve around issues relating to the social control of women but rather appears to be situationally provoked.

Data from surveys that ask respondents to indicate whether they have been a victim of intimate partner violence are likely to give us information about the more common instances of situational couple violence, whereas data collected from shelters and crime statistics tell us more about intimate terrorism. To conclude that gender is irrelevant to domestic violence in general is to miss the fact that situational couple violence and intimate terrorism are two different phenomena, where gender is not necessarily an issue in the former but is almost always central to the latter. From the perspective of social workers and health care providers, these differences are also profound. Encouraging men and women to find better ways to express their anger and deal with conflict may be suitable for resolving situational couple violence

social control:
Means used by a social group to ensure that individuals conform to social norms and that the existing balance of power is maintained.

intimate terrorism:
A form of intimate partner violence, committed mainly by men, in which repeated acts of physical aggression and abusive behaviour are used to dominate and control one's partner.

violent resistance:
A form of intimate partner violence, committed mainly by women, who as victims of violence respond in kind, either as an instinctive reaction to protect themselves or as a strategy for preventing further assaults.

situational couple violence:
The most common form of intimate partner violence, occurring when conflict between partners erupts into aggression and violence. This form of intimate partner violence is gender-symmetric, with men and women equally likely to resort to violence.

but inappropriate in dealing with intimate terrorism, where asking spouses to be honest with each other creates greater risk for women who may be beaten or even killed for their efforts (Johnson, 2005). Johnson's classification system, though intriguing, requires more research to be empirically verified. Nonetheless, these debates remind us that gender remains an important and contentious fault line in social life. They also reveal the challenges that social scientists encounter in attempting to link broad social forces (gender ideology) to individual behaviours.

RACE AND ETHNICITY

The concept of "race" is a social construction with almost no biological basis. Yet many people distinguish racial groups by skin colour and other characteristics. Why does this occur if race is not real? According to social scientists, **racialization** refers to the process by which society attributes social significance to groups on superficial physical grounds, by pairing apparent physical characteristics with negative social attributes and creating the perception that there are natural differences between racialized groups. Groups that are dominant have the power to ascribe positive characteristics to themselves and are also able to apply and enforce negative racial stereotypes for those who are different. That we can identify what race we belong to says more about our society than it does about our genetic makeup. The ways our society thinks about and responds to the idea of race mean that race, despite the lack of evidence that it exists on a biological basis, becomes real in its consequences for health.

Critical race theory also contends that race is socially constructed, but further suggests that it is endemic to the very fabric of society. Critical race theory seeks to challenge the thinking of white people who enjoy the privilege of their skin colour but don't perceive its advantages in their lives nor recognize the disadvantages that accrue to those whose skin colour is not white. This awareness can be facilitated by learning about the history of racism in Canada through the stories of those who have been oppressed as a result of their skin colour, particularly when attention is paid to the ways in which they present realities that differ from dominant texts.

Canadians are not used to thinking about themselves as having racist tendencies. More commonly, Canadians look at the struggles over race in the United States and think that they are exempt from such social problems. Yet Canada has a long history of discrimination and racialization. Canada's Aboriginal peoples have historically been racialized through legislation that marked them as inferior to European settlers. For example, the Indian Act of 1876 formally defined the status of Indian and placed Canada's Aboriginal peoples under legislative and administrative control of the state (Li, 2008). By abolishing the right of Aboriginal peoples to govern themselves and their right to determine for themselves who belonged to their communities, this Act was yet another step in the **colonization** of Aboriginal peoples in Canada (Milloy, 2008). Similarly, until a few decades ago, immigration policies in Canada systematically denied entry or deported those who were not light-skinned or from western Europe, conflating dark skin with feeble-mindedness and mental instability (Comeau and Allahar, 2001). For example, the Continuous Journey Ship Act in 1908 specified that immigrants could only gain entry to Canada if their transportation made no stops, effectively ensuring that peoples from India and other parts of Asia would not attempt to come to Canada. We will discuss the characteristics and health of Aboriginal peoples and immigrants in turn.

First Nations Peoples, Inuit, and Métis

As of the 2006 census, there were more than a million people who identified as Aboriginal, accounting for 4% of the Canadian population. Canada's Aboriginal peoples comprise three

racialization:
The process by which society attributes social significance to groups on superficial physical grounds, by pairing apparent physical characteristics with negative social attributes and creating the perception that there are natural differences between racialized groups.

colonization:
The process of subjugating and dispossessing indigenous peoples by foreign peoples who settle and build colonies on the lands of indigenous peoples.

distinct groups: First Nations peoples, Inuit, and Métis. First Nations peoples include status and non-status Indians and, estimated at just under 700,000 people in the 2006 census, represent the largest group. Making up 615 distinct communities, most First Nations peoples (81%) are status Indians, a legal designation that provides entitlements to certain rights and benefits under the law. The Inuit represent the approximately 50,000 Aboriginal people who live in the far northern reaches of Canada, including Labrador, parts of Québec, Nunavut, and the Northwest Territories. "Inuit" means "the people" in the Inuktitut language and has replaced the term *Eskimo* that was originally applied to Inuit by European explorers. One third of all Aboriginal people are Métis, broadly defined as those who are of mixed North American Indian and European ancestry and who self-identify as Métis. It was only in the Constitution Act in 1982 that the Métis were formally recognized by the Canadian government as a founding Aboriginal people.

Aboriginal peoples in Canada vary demographically and socially from the rest of the Canadian population. Canada's Aboriginal peoples are younger on average than Canadians (Table 3.3). Higher levels of fertility and lower life expectancy contribute to the younger age of the Aboriginal population, with differences most marked among Inuit peoples with a **median** age of 22. Because of their location in remote areas in the north, Inuit are also least likely to live in an urban centre. Compared to the Canadian average, approximately twice as many Aboriginal households with children under the age of 14 are headed by a single parent, with First Nations families most likely to be headed by a single parent (37%). Crowded housing, defined as more than one person per room, is comparable between the Métis and the rest of the Canadian population, but there are significantly higher levels of crowding among Inuit (31%) and First Nations peoples (15%). Crowding is regarded as a major health issue because it facilitates the transmission of infectious disease and can increase the risk for injury and violence. The 7% of Canadians who live in a home that requires major repair is also far lower than the rate for Métis (14%) and both Inuit and First Nations, where four times as many live in homes that require major repair.

Aboriginal peoples are also more economically disadvantaged relative to the rest of the Canadian population. In the 2006 Census, approximately half of Aboriginal peoples on-reserve had not finished high school compared to 30% of Aboriginal peoples off-reserve and 15% for the Canadian population. Conversely, few Aboriginal peoples have a university degree (4% for those on-reserve and 9% off-reserve) compared to 23% in the Canadian population. This situation is slowly beginning to change with improvements in funding to keep Aboriginal students in school; the introduction of Aboriginal programs in universities; and the establishment of The First Nations University of Canada, which specializes in indigenous knowledge. Along with education, other indicators of socioeconomic status, including labour

median:

The value or number representing the midpoint of a distribution that is ordered from lowest to highest.

TABLE 3.3
Demographic and Social Characteristics of First Nations, Inuit, Métis, and Canadian Population, 2006

	First Nations	Inuit	Métis	Canada
Median age (in years)	25	22	30	40
% Live in urban centre	76*	17	69	81
% Single-parent households	37	26	31	17
% Crowded housing	15	31	3	3
% Home requires major repair	28	28	14	7

*Refers to First Nations people living off-reserve.
Note: Crowded housing is defined as more than one person per room.

Source: Adapted from: Statistics Canada, *Aboriginal Peoples in Canada: Inuit, Métis, and First Nations, 2006 Census*, Cat. No. 97-558-XIE, Ottawa: Minister of Industry, 2008.

market attachment and income, suggest that there remains a long way to go before the gap between Aboriginal peoples in Canada and the rest of the Canadian population is closed.

Patterns of Death and Illness among Canada's Aboriginal Peoples

Although **life expectancy** for Aboriginal peoples lags that of the rest of the Canadian population, the situation appears less bleak than several decades ago. For example, the gap in life expectancy in 2001 for women was five years, with Aboriginal women living on average 77 years compared to the female Canadian average of 82 years. The comparable gap in life expectancy in 2001 for men was six years, with Aboriginal men living on average 71 years and Canadian men living on average 77 years. In 1980, the gap for both sexes was much larger at 10.9 and 11 years, respectively. This suggests that Aboriginal peoples have been experiencing more rapid improvements in life expectancy than the Canadian average and, at some point in the future, that the health of Aboriginal peoples may be indistinguishable from that of other Canadians. Unfortunately, a more recent analysis suggests that the progress of Aboriginal peoples in terms of improving life expectancy may have stalled. A closer examination of changes in life expectancy between 1991 and 2001 within the Inuit population revealed minimal improvement and even decreases over this period, whereas the Canadian population improved life expectancy by two years during this same period of time (Wilkins et al., 2008).

The pattern appears to be similar for the **infant mortality rate**. In 1979, the infant mortality rate in Canada was 11.0 per 1000, dropping to 5.2 by 2001. For Aboriginal peoples, the infant mortality rate dropped from 27.6 per 1000 in 1979 to 7.2 in 2001. Again, this represents a more rapid decrease in the infant mortality rate among Aboriginal peoples compared to the Canadian average, even though rates for Aboriginal peoples were still 40% higher in 2001 than the Canadian average. As with life expectancy, however, recent research suggests that these improvements may be suspect. In a recent systematic review, Smylie and colleagues (2010) disputed these published figures and concluded that the actual gap in infant mortality rates was more accurately estimated as being between 1.7 and 4 times as high for Aboriginal peoples. The authors noted that the lack of standardized surveillance systems for Aboriginal peoples means that there were greater numbers of missed or late registration of births and infant deaths in this population, and, consequently, previous statistics should be regarded as unreliable. If this is the case, some of the past optimism about the improving health status of Canada's Aboriginal peoples may need to be reconsidered.

Evaluating patterns of morbidity among Canada's Aboriginal peoples is equally challenging, as data are rarely collected in ways that allow for meaningful comparison. Table 3.4 lists the prevalence of some of the main health conditions in the Aboriginal population. Note that the data from First Nations on-reserve estimates are not directly comparable with those

	First Nations On-Reserve	First Nations Off-Reserve	Métis	Inuit	Canadian Average
High blood pressure	20.4	21.8	21.7	20.0	18.2
Diabetes	19.7	11.4	9.5	7.6	6.5
Asthma	10.6	13.3	13.3	9.5	7.4
Heart disease	7.6	9.5	9.8	9.6	5.3

Source: Adapted from: Health Canada, *A Statistical Profile on the Health of First Nations in Canada: Self Rated Health and Selected Conditions, 2002 – 2005*, Ottawa: Minister of Health, 2009; Rochelle Garner, Gisèle Carrière, Claudia Sanmartin and the Longitudinal Health and Administrative Data Research Team, *The Health of First Nations Living Off-Reserve, Inuit, and Métis Adults in Canada: The Impact of Socio-economic Status on Inequalities in Health.* Cat. No. 82-622-X. Ottawa: Minister of Industry, 2010.

TABLE 3.4
Prevalence of Selected Health Conditions, Age-Standardized for First Nations On-Reserve, Aged 18 and Older (2003), and Age-Sex–Standardized for First Nations Off-Reserve, Métis, Inuit, and General Canadian Population, Aged 20 and Older (2006)

from the other four groups, which are comparable with one another, as the estimates from on-reserve First Nations come from an earlier time point, include a slightly younger age range, and are age-adjusted only. Despite these qualifications, it is clear that the four chronic conditions are more prevalent among all Aboriginal groups relative to the rest of Canada.

Nearly fifty years ago, diabetes was virtually absent; today it has reached epidemic proportions in Aboriginal communities. For example, diabetes was non-existent in the Saskatchewan First Nations population in the 1930s, climbed to 10% in 1990, and had jumped to more than 20% by 2006 (Dyck et al., 2010). The rapid rate of increase has been attributed to dramatic changes in the lifestyle and eating habits of Aboriginal peoples, who have increasingly abandoned traditional practices: only 15% of Aboriginal people obtain their meat and fish from hunting and fishing (Young et al., 2000). That diabetes is lower on average in Aboriginal populations located in northern Canada, where traditional practices are more likely to be retained, lends credence to the view that it is traditional practices that are protective against diabetes; however, more research is needed to confirm this association.

Interestingly, rates of diabetes among Aboriginal men and women exhibit a different pattern than in the Canadian population. As noted in our previous discussion of gender differences in diabetes, men are more likely than women to be diagnosed with diabetes in Canada. This relationship does not hold true for the Aboriginal population. As can be seen in Table 3.5, the prevalence of diabetes increased in that province between 1989 and 1998, but in both years, diabetes was higher for First Nations women than for First Nations men in Manitoba (Green et al., 2003). Why First Nations women are more vulnerable remains unknown.

Explanations for the Health Status of Aboriginal Peoples in Canada

Explanations for why Aboriginal peoples in Canada have shorter lifespans and more illness lie in understanding the historical context, rooted in practices of colonization that attempted to assimilate Aboriginal peoples into Canadian society. Viewed as inferior and subordinate, Aboriginal peoples were exploited and their culture reviled. We discuss two aspects of this historical context: environmental dispossession and the residential school system.

Environmental Dispossession

environmental dispossession:

The process through which Aboriginal peoples' access to the resources of their traditional environments is reduced.

Richmond and Ross (2009) discuss **environmental dispossession** as a critical factor in the health of Aboriginal peoples in Canada. Environmental dispossession refers to the process through which Aboriginal peoples' access to the resources of their traditional environments is reduced. Throughout Canadian history, Aboriginal peoples have been systematically deprived of their land. Using its power and privilege, the Canadian government consistently passed legislation that first displaced Aboriginal peoples onto reserves, and then moved them once again when the land was desired by others. For example, Dickason (1992) recounts the

TABLE 3.5
Age-Adjusted Prevalence of Diabetes per 1000 in Manitoba, 1989 and 1998

	1989	1998
First Nations women	181.6	248.7
First Nations men	104.2	170.0
Non-First Nations women	37.1	53.5
Non-First Nations men	41.9	59.6

Source: Adapted from: Chris Green, James F. Blanchard, T. Kue Young, & Jane Griffith, "The Epidemiology of Diabetes in the Manitoba-Registered First Nation Population: Current Patterns and Comparative Trends," *Diabetes Care*, Vol. 26 (7). Pg. 1993-8, 2003.

eviction of First Nations peoples from St. Paul's Reserve near Selkirk, Manitoba, when European settlers wanted to expand in the area. Passed through legislation without First Nations consultation, the St. Paul Reserve Act of 1916 allowed for the forced removal of First Nations peoples from the reserve to a new location upstream that was deemed to be more suitable.

Because land is central to the culture and livelihood of Aboriginal peoples, environmental dispossession has had a devastating and long-lasting impact on their health. Forced to settle in unfamiliar environments that were isolated and often ill-suited for traditional hunting and fishing practices, Aboriginal peoples often struggled to survive. Repeated relocation further eroded ties to the land and diminished cultural identity, creating new dependencies as Aboriginal peoples eventually turned to store-bought foods and abandoned their traditional hunting and fishing practices. In some instances, environmental pollution that contaminated the rivers that ran through reserves made it impossible for Aboriginal peoples to eat fish safely or to make a livelihood from fishing.

Isolation also meant that reserves were located too far from commercial centres for workers to commute, and because the sites of reserves themselves were often chosen because they lacked any investment potential, unemployment in these communities was rampant. Lack of economic activity fuelled boredom, anger, and a sense of powerlessness, causing many to turn to alcohol, drugs, and violence. This resulted in further deterioration of the social environment, with soaring rates of addiction and suicide. High levels of poverty compounded the situation, as reserves were ill-equipped to address the mounting social problems.

Although we are describing the past, similar conditions persist today in many reserves. Out of sight and off the public radar, living conditions on reserves rarely merit scrutiny. The situation of one such community, which for a short time was at the centre of public attention but failed to effect lasting change despite its struggle and greater public awareness of its plight, is detailed in Box 3.3.

The Legacy of the Residential School System

As noted in the opening vignette, the residential school system was undertaken as a joint initiative of the federal government and religious groups and was used to facilitate the assimilation of Aboriginal peoples in Canadian society. Having agreed to take on the function of education in treaties signed with Aboriginal peoples, the federal government attempted to reduce the costs of education by partnering with existing religious organizations instead of the more costly alternative of creating its own infrastructure from the ground up (Dickason, 1992). Thus, the federal government built and maintained schools, and for their part, religious organizations provided teachers and oversaw the day-to-day administration of the school.

It is clear that the schools were a failure on many fronts. First, the schools themselves were not successful in educating the Aboriginal children under their care. As Dickason (1992) notes, only one in ten Aboriginal students made it past grade six compared to one-third in the general population. There also appears to be some resentment from the community that felt government-sponsored training of Aboriginal peoples for industrial trades represented an unfair advantage because it meant that there would be greater competition for jobs. Second, residential schools were detrimental to health as successive epidemics of tuberculosis and other infectious diseases exacted a high toll on life. Between 1894 and 1908, approximately 28% of school residents from Sarcee Boarding School died (Dickason, 1992). Though this is nearly impossible to verify, many Aboriginal peoples believe that a good number of deaths went unreported, which suggests that the death rate could have been even higher.

But the human cost of the residential school system goes well beyond these losses. Punished for speaking their own language and prohibited from engaging in any traditional

BOX 3.3

Kashechewan: A Community at Risk

With a population of nearly 1,700, the Kashechewan First Nation is a Cree First Nation located at the mouth of the Albany River near James Bay in northern Ontario. The federal government first established the reserve in 1912, and in 1957 moved the people of Kashechewan against their will to their current location on a flood plain.

Between 2004 and 2007, the reserve was evacuated three times when severe spring flooding submerged the community. In the fall of 2005, half the community was airlifted to nearby towns for medical treatment after becoming severely ill when *E. coli* bacteria contaminated the water supply. These crises, however, were only a small part of the ongoing problems with water in the community. The residents of Kashechewan had been drinking, cooking with, and bathing in water unfit for human consumption or use for many years with the result that diarrhea, fevers, and skin diseases such as impetigo, scabies, and ulcers were considered **endemic** in the community. The problem was eventually traced to a plugged chlorine injector that had not been detected by water treatment officials because they lacked proper training with the equipment.

Following the tainted water scandal in 2005, the federal government commissioned a report to investigate potential solutions, including the possible relocation of the community. Authored by Alan Pope, a member of parliament, the report described living conditions at the time in Kashechewan. Murdocca (2010) described the findings of the report in this way:

> The reality recounted in the report is stark. At the time, there were no health care providers in the community; there was little access to fresh fruits and vegetables; homes were dilapidated and insufficient and did not meet provincial or federal standards; the dump and waste disposal site was not maintained; there was one police officer on the reserve, and there was no fire protection; the only school was closed due to health, safety, and contamination concerns; employment opportunities were sorely lacking, so economic prospects were bleak; and local operators of the water filtration plant, as previously noted, were not trained or certified. (p. 386)

Soon after the report was published, the Kashechewan First Nation applied to obtain permission from the federal government to relocate and build a new reserve about 30 kilometres upstream on ground that was 100 feet higher than their current location. The request was subsequently denied by Indian Affairs minister Jim Prentice. Stating that the estimated $474 million price tag to move the community to higher ground was prohibitively expensive, Prentice instead offered the community $200 million to redevelop the current location. With few options, the community accepted Prentice's offer.

In 2008, the community was once again evacuated as a result of spring flooding.

Sources: 38th Parliament, 1st Session Standing Committee on Aboriginal Affairs and Northern Development, meeting minutes, Thursday October 27, 2005. Found at: http://www.parl.gc.ca/HousePublications/Publication.aspx?DocId=2067775&Language=E&Mode=1&Parl=38&Ses=1; CBC news: Found at: http://www.cbc.ca/news/canada/north/story/2007/03/16/kashechewan-survey.html (Friday, March 16, 2007); CBC news: Found at: http://www.cbc.ca/news/canada/story/2007/03/30/kashechewan.html (March 30, 2007); Carmela Murdocca, "'There's Something in That Water': Race, Nationalism and Legal Violence." *Law and Social Inquiry*, Vol. 35 (2), Pg. 369–402, 2010.

practices, Aboriginal children were stripped of their cultural identity and actively socialized to despise their heritage. Raised in an institutional setting, where many never saw their parents again, Aboriginal children also failed to learn the necessary parenting skills they would need as adults. Indeed, some of the key adult figures in their lives were verbally and physically abusive to them, and some were sexual predators. As such, many Aboriginal children developed a profound distrust of adults and authority figures. Importantly, when they left the residential school system, many lacked the most basic understanding of how to raise children, launching a subsequent cycle of generational neglect and abuse as they began to have children. These psychological wounds, as we are learning through the Residential Schools Truth and Reconciliation Commission, have left a lasting impression on Canada's Aboriginal peoples, and it may be many years yet before these wounds heal and their harmful effects on Aboriginal culture and communities are no longer observed.

The Health of Immigrants to Canada

On a per capita basis, Canada accepts more immigrants than almost any other country in the world. Every year for nearly two decades, approximately 250,000 immigrants have arrived in Canada to begin a new life. Immigrants are the major reason that the population of Canada continues to grow. Their contributions, as Canada's population ages and fertility rates decline, will help to ensure that Canada continues to remain an economically competitive nation.

Immigrants to Canada are distinguished into four classes: family class immigrants, economic immigrants, refugees, and other immigrants. Family class immigrants are foreign nationals sponsored by close relatives or family members in Canada and include spouses and partners, dependent children, parents, and grandparents. Economic immigrants are applicants who are selected for their skills and abilities to contribute to Canada's economic growth. They include skilled workers who can demonstrate their ability to find work and business owners who invest in approved ventures. Refugees include government-assisted refugees, privately sponsored refugees, refugees landed in Canada, and their dependants. The "other" immigrant category represents a very small number of cases where immigrants who do not fit into one of the other categories are admitted for humanitarian reasons or for public policy reasons.

Accounting for two out of every three immigrants, economic immigrants represent the largest of the four classes. Approximately 20% of Canadian immigrants come from family class, with 9% from refugee class and less than 3% from the "other" immigrant category. Fifty years ago, the majority of immigrants to Canada came from the United Kingdom and northern Europe. In recent years, the majority of immigrants to Canada have come from Asia, including China, India, and the Philippines. Consequently, cultural diversity in Canada has increased over time as different **ethnic** groups have made this country their home.

Using data from the Longitudinal Study of Immigrants to Canada, Zhao and colleagues (2010) compared the health status of different immigrant subgroups who arrived in Canada between 2000 and 2001, tracking these immigrants over a four-year period to evaluate changes in health status as immigrants settled into their new life. Consistent with previous research in Canada and other countries, newly arrived immigrants to Canada tended to be in better health than the rest of the Canadian population. Researchers refer to this phenomenon as the **healthy immigrant effect**. Given that Canadian immigration laws require all potential immigrants to undergo a pre-migration medical examination to ensure that they will not pose a threat to public health or be a burden on the health care system, it is not entirely surprising that they are in better health than other Canadians.

A closer look by immigrant class, however, reveals subtle differences. Economic immigrants were typically in better health upon arrival in Canada than those from the family class or refugees. The health of refugees was lowest of all. Because many refugees come to Canada to escape areas where there is conflict and war, they are more likely to be suffering from the physical shocks of their environment (lack of food or access to health care) as well as the psychological consequences of exposure to traumatic events.

Zhao and colleagues (2010) also found that the healthy immigrant effect does not last. Over time, the health of immigrants declines and comes to resemble the health of the rest of the Canadian population. These patterns have also been observed in other studies, with many suggesting that the converging health status of immigrants is due to **acculturation**, where immigrants increasingly adopt the lifestyles and eating habits of their host country and then acquire the same health risks (De Maio, 2010). Zhao and colleagues (2010) add to this research by showing that declines in health over time were not the same for all immigrants. Immigrants who felt connected to their communities, had larger friendship networks, and experienced fewer barriers in accessing health care were least likely to experience declines in health over time. Other studies have shown that immigrants who encounter racial discrimination report significant increases in depression over time (De Maio, 2010). These findings point to the importance of removing structural barriers that may limit the participation of new immigrants in Canadian society and helping them to feel connected to their new country.

ethnicity:
Cultural affiliation of a group sharing a common culture, language, ancestry, nationality or beliefs.

healthy immigrant effect:
A phenomenon in which new immigrants are in relatively better health than the native-born residents of the country to which they emigrate.

acculturation:
The process by which immigrants increasingly adopt the lifestyles and habits of their host country.

IMPLICATIONS

Far from being purely biological conditions reflecting purely biological factors, health and illness are intimately interwoven with social position. As we have seen in this chapter, death and illness are not randomly distributed in the population: there are systematic variations that are patterned by age, sex and gender, and race/ethnicity. In Canada as elsewhere, those who belong to socially devalued groups are in poorer health than those who are more privileged.

Risk for mortality and morbidity increases with age, yet the assumption that old age is necessarily a time of illness and disability has contributed to exaggerated concerns about the crisis that an aging population will create in our health care system. Sex and gender have complex health consequences: Women enjoy longer lifespans than men do, but the size of the gender gap has fluctuated over the twentieth century, suggesting that social factors play as integral a role as biological factors. Although researchers once believed that women were more likely than men to have a chronic illness, it is now recognized that gender differences in chronic illness depend on the type of condition and the period in the life course. Incorporating a sex- and gender-based analysis also offers the opportunity to understand how health and illness differ not just between men and women, but also among women and among men.

Because social forces as well as biological factors affect health, understanding social trends can help us predict future health trends. For example, as women's social roles have changed in Canada, their rates of tobacco use have approached those of men (contributing to their smaller gains in life expectancy relative to men in recent years), while their ability to protect themselves from the health consequences of male violence has increased. Similarly, to the extent that the lingering effects of the residential school system begin to fade and healing between Aboriginal peoples and non-Aboriginal Canadians occurs, we are likely to see future improvements in the health of Canada's Aboriginal peoples.

SUMMARY

LO-1   1.   Deaths in the first year of life are typically related to congenital anomalies or complications of birth. For those who survive infancy, the risk for mortality is low until approximately age 45; thereafter, mortality rates rise significantly. Reflecting high average life expectancy in Canada, approximately 60% of deaths occur after age 75.

LO-1   2.   The causes of death also vary across the lifespan. Cancer features as a leading cause of death at every age, except in the first year of life. Deaths during the first few decades of life are due mainly to accidents and suicide, but with age, the causes of death increasingly reflect the long-term toll of chronic conditions such as heart disease, chronic respiratory conditions, and stroke.

LO-1   3.   Morbidity also markedly increases with age: the older one is, the more likely one is to have a chronic illness. At the same time, it is a mistake to assume that all older people are in poor health. For example, depression is negatively correlated with age, such that older people are less likely to be depressed than younger adults.

LO-2   4.   The Canadian population is aging steadily. The proportion of Canadians over the age of 65 nearly doubled between 1956 and 2011 from 7.7% to 14.8% of the population. Canada is also experiencing the feminization of aging. That is, each older age cohort has a higher percentage of women than the next younger cohort.

LO-2   5.   There is considerable debate as to whether the aging of the population will throw Canada's health care system into crisis. Proponents suggest that age-related health problems of the growing number of Canadians who are over the age of 65 coupled with declining numbers of younger working-age Canadians will overwhelm the capacity of the health care system; however, opponents point to evidence that suggest the claim is exaggerated.

LO-2　6. According to one's viewpoint, either frailty is a biological condition that can be reliably diagnosed in the senior population or it reflects the ways in which older people are vulnerable to being seen as ill because of the perception that aging is characterized by dependence and decline.

LO-3　7. Men are more likely than women to die at every age, and women generally experience more illness than men; however, this statement often requires qualification. For example, men are more likely than women to have diabetes.

LO-3　8. Gender differences in mortality and morbidity stem from both *sex* (such as hormone levels) and *gender* (such as levels of risk-taking) differences. Sex- and gender-based analysis is an innovative tool for investigating differences in health and illness between and among men and women. Contemporary patterns of heart disease, injuries, and depression in the Canadian population each reflect the complex, intersecting influences of sex and gender.

LO-3　9. Intimate partner violence is a serious source of injury and death. There is ongoing debate as to whether gender remains central to understanding the underlying causes of spousal violence. By distinguishing among different types of intimate partner violence, some suggest that situational violence is gender-symmetric, whereas more serious forms of violence, such as intimate terrorism, remain highly gendered. The latter form continues to exist because it reflects basic cultural and political forces in our society and, indeed, around the world.

LO-4　10. Although there is almost no biological basis for race, the social value that is placed on skin colour and other characteristics believed to signify race is real in its consequences for health. That is, social groups that are dominant often exploit those who are judged subordinate, pairing the superficial physical characteristics of a social group with undesirable social traits in a process called racialization.

LO-5　11. The Indian Act of 1876 took the right of self-determination away from Canada's Aboriginal peoples and set the stage for nearly a century and a half of continued abuse and exploitation. Despite gains in life expectancy and reductions in infant mortality, there is concern among some researchers that progress has stalled and that other conditions such as diabetes are exacting a heavy toll on the health of Aboriginal peoples.

LO-5　12. Explanations for the poor health status today of Canada's Aboriginal peoples lie in the past as well as the present. Environmental dispossession severed the ties that Aboriginal peoples had to the land, compromising their ability to hunt, fish, and engage in other traditional practices and destroying their cultural identity. The residential school system exposed children to suboptimal learning environments and infectious disease, and some were victims of horrific abuses. The effort to "remove the Indian from the child" meant that Aboriginal children were forced to adopt European ways and punished for using their own language and customs. They grew up despising their own culture and never learned what it meant to be a parent, thus perpetuating a new cycle of neglect and abuse when they themselves became parents.

LO-6　13. As a nation, Canada is culturally diverse, with immigrants from around the world flocking to our borders. Immigration policies today do not discriminate against racial and ethnic minorities as they did in the past; nonetheless, barriers to entry that selectively screen out those with health problems mean that new immigrants to Canada are generally healthier than native-born Canadians. Of the four immigrant classes, immigrants from the economic class tend to be in the best health, with the worst health among those from the refugee class.

LO-6 14. The healthy immigrant effect does not persist. Over time, as immigrants become acculturated to their new environment and adopt Canadian eating habits and lifestyles, their health begins to resemble that of the Canadian population. Immigrants who continue to face barriers in participating in Canadian society appear to experience the most rapid declines in health over time, suggesting that efforts to integrate immigrants into Canadian society may have beneficial effects on their health.

REVIEW QUESTIONS

1. What are the health care consequences of an aging population and of the feminization of aging?
2. Why does the statement "men die quicker, but women get sicker" require qualification?
3. Why might sociologists and other observers argue against early detection and treatment of prostate cancer in men and breast cancer in women?
4. How does a feminist perspective increase understanding about the ways in which gender is associated with risk for depression?
5. What are the sources and consequences of intimate partner violence? Why do surveys and crime statistics produce conflicting perspectives?
6. In what ways have Canada's Aboriginal peoples been historically subjected to racialization and colonization?
7. In what ways does the legacy of residential schools continue to affect the health of Aboriginal peoples?
8. What is the healthy immigrant effect and what are the implications of the declining health status of immigrants the longer they live in Canada?

CRITICAL THINKING QUESTIONS

1. How might ambiguity in the definition and diagnosis of frailty contribute to the rising costs of health care?
2. Assume that over the next twenty years both men and women increasingly adopt behaviour patterns now associated with the other gender. What changes would you expect to see in the health of men and women? Explain your answer.
3. Assume that Aboriginal people in Canada gain the right to self-govern in the very near future. Why and in what ways would you expect the health of this population to improve? Why and in what ways would you expect it to remain the same?

KEY TERMS

acculturation (p. 67)
baby boom generation (p. 50)
colonization (p. 61)
environmental dispossession (p. 64)
ethnicity (p. 67)
false positive (p. 59)
feminization of aging (p. 52)
gender (p. 53)
healthy immigrant effect (p. 67)

intimate terrorism (p. 60)
median (p. 62)
phenotype (p. 53)
racialization (p. 61)
sex (p. 53)
situational couple violence (p. 60)
social control (p. 60)
technological imperative (p. 59)
violent resistance (p. 60)

4 Socioeconomic Inequalities in Health

Mario Ruiz/Time Life Pictures/Getty Images

At Home/Chez Soi:
A Research Demonstration Project

Launched in November 2009, At Home/Chez Soi is a national research demonstration project that will run in five Canadian cities until the spring of 2013 (Goering et al., 2011). The purpose of the project is to learn about the best ways to help those dealing with homelessness and mental health issues. Researchers used rigorous research methods to recruit participants from community agencies that provide services to the homeless. Once selected into the study, participants were randomly assigned to one of two groups: those who receive the treatment condition and a control group that is given services normally offered to those who are homeless (called the treatment-as-usual group).

Those assigned to the treatment group receive immediate access to housing without condition. This housing-first approach is radical because most housing programs require homeless people to be stabilized on medication or have substance abuse under control before they are given access to housing. In contrast, a housing-first approach assumes that once a person has a place to live, they can then begin to work on their personal issues. The treatment group also receives recovery-focused services from a dedicated team of professionals that are offered to participants on a voluntary, individualized, and culturally appropriate basis.

As of December 2011, there were 2,234 participants, 1,254 in the housing-first intervention group and 980 in the treatment-as-usual group. The typical participant is a middle-aged male who has been homeless for an average of six years. Approximately 7% of participants had been in a psychiatric hospital in the past five years and more than 90% reported at least one chronic health problem.

At intervals throughout and again at the end of the study, researchers will evaluate whether the housing-first approach produces better outcomes relative to the treatment-as-usual group. Some of the key outcomes are housing stability and social functioning; mental and physical health; quality of life; ability to respond to stress; and use of health care services, including visits to a hospital emergency room.

It is hoped that if a housing-first approach leads to better outcomes for those who are homeless and mentally ill, this will provide needed evidence to change treatment approaches for the estimated 150,000 to 300,000 homeless people in Canada, many of whom have a diagnosable mental illness and serious physical ailments.

In this chapter, students should be able to:

LO-1 **Understand** what it means to say that there is a socioeconomic gradient in health outcomes.

LO-2 **Describe** the patterning of mortality, morbidity, and health behaviours by socioeconomic position in the Canadian population.

LO-3 **Evaluate** explanations for the association between socioeconomic position and health outcomes.

LO-4 **Describe** the principles of a life course approach and **recognize** the contribution of a life course approach to understanding socioeconomic differences in health.

LO-5 **Recognize** the association between income inequality and poor health.

LO-6 **Understand** that differences in socioeconomic position, age, sex and gender, and race/ethnicity intersect in different ways to influence health outcomes.

The link between **socioeconomic position** and ill health is well known. Indeed, as noted in Chapter 2, some sociologists label socioeconomic position a "fundamental cause" of illness (Link and Phelan, 1995) because it is an upstream risk factor that continues to influence health outcomes even when patterns of illness and the intervening mechanisms change. In this chapter, we present evidence for the association between socioeconomic position and health in Canada before exploring the different explanations researchers draw upon to understand why the relationship exists. We then evaluate the income inequality hypothesis, which suggests that it is the amount of inequality in a given society that matters for health. Finally, we discuss how age, sex and gender, and race/ethnicity combine with socioeconomic position to create different risks to health.

SOCIOECONOMIC INEQUALITIES IN HEALTH

Awareness of the association between poverty and health is not new. In the nineteenth century, socially minded reformers, such as Engels in Britain, Virchow in Germany, and Allende in Chile, drew public attention to the uneven concentration of death and disease among the poor. Each argued that the origins of disease and death could be found in the power inequalities of a hierarchically organized society that protected the privileged at the expense of the disadvantaged. Thus, exposed to toxic substances in the workplace, weakened from inadequate nutrition, and crowded into inferior housing, the poor lacked the resources to protect their health and the power to change their living conditions.

In the twentieth century, researchers in the United States systematically documented and drew attention to the relationship between social class and mental illness (e.g., Faris and Dunham, 1939; Hollingshead and Redlich, 1958). It was not until the 1980s, however, that researchers began to give sustained attention to the patterning of mortality and morbidity by social class and other indicators of socioeconomic position. Indeed, the emergence of the current field of socioeconomic inequalities in health owes much to a landmark government report called the Black Report.

The Black Report

In 1977, the Labour government in the United Kingdom commissioned a report to explore differences in health between the social classes and to provide potential explanations for any observed relationships. The committee appointed to undertake the report comprised two medical doctors and two sociologists. In 1980, the committee's work culminated in a document of more than four hundred pages called the Black Report, named after the chair of the committee, Sir Douglas Black. The report made clear that for every condition and

socioeconomic gradient in health:

The graded relationship between socioeconomic position and health in which an improvement in socioeconomic position is associated with a corresponding increase in health (i.e., lower risk for death and disease).

cause of death, there was a **socioeconomic gradient in health**, such that as one progressed down the occupational scale, moving from the professional occupations at the top of the hierarchy to the class of unskilled manual labourers at the bottom, the risk for death and disease increased in a monotonic fashion. Thus, the differences were not just between the wealthiest and the poorest, but rather there was a stepwise improvement in health as one moved one rung up the occupational structure. This gradient association has since been replicated using measures of income and education. In each case, those who have low income or have low levels of education are in worse health than those with a middle-class income and average levels of education, who in turn are in worse health than those with high incomes and high levels of education.

The Black Report might have been relegated to a dusty shelf along with countless other government reports, where policymakers and politicians could safely ignore its findings. Indeed, the Thatcher government that had swept to power a year before the report was released expressed very little interest in pursuing its findings. To minimize its impact, the government released the report in the middle of the summer, on the Friday before a long weekend, a nearly guaranteed tactic that the report would receive little public attention. In addition, they printed a limited number of copies of the report, making it difficult for others to learn about the committee's findings. Finally, the Thatcher government openly discredited the findings of the report and made it clear that the government would not follow any of its recommendations (Gray, 1982).

As sometimes happens when one tries too hard to bury a report, these efforts backfired. The Black Report began to generate enormous interest both in Britain and around the world, as other scholars began to ask whether the same gradient relationship in mortality and morbidity could also be observed in their own countries. A few years later, the Black Report was published as a book, making the findings accessible to an even larger audience. Its wide dissemination did contribute to establishing its place at the forefront of socioeconomic inequalities in health research. But its legacy is also due to the careful work of its authors. The Black Report was so comprehensive, in its attempts both to document social class inequalities in health and to explain these associations, that it had a profound influence on all subsequent research in this area.

In the next section, we present evidence to show that in Canada, as in every other country that has investigated social class differences in health, health is patterned by one's level of income, occupation, and education, as well as other measures that represent one's position in our hierarchically organized societies.

EVIDENCE IN CANADA

The association of socioeconomic position with illness and death is obvious: In Canada as elsewhere, at each age, within each category of race/ethnicity, and for both men and women, those with higher status in a given society have lower rates of mortality and morbidity than those with a lower position in society. The nature of the relationship nearly always conforms to a gradient pattern, such that the risk for mortality and morbidity increases as one's socioeconomic position decreases.

Whereas the Black Report focused only on social class differences that ranked individuals according to the characteristics of their occupation, subsequent research has greatly expanded the ways in which socioeconomic position is measured. We will examine the implications of these different measures when we evaluate explanations for the associations we observe, but for now our review will draw on a range of measures of socioeconomic position. We examine associations with mortality, morbidity, and health behaviours in turn.

Mortality

The relationship between socioeconomic position and mortality begins at birth, with infant mortality significantly lower among the wealthiest (Wilkins, Berthelot, and Ng, 2002). As Figure 4.1 demonstrates, despite overall declines in the infant mortality rate in Canada between 1971 and 1996, rates were consistently lowest for those living in the richest neighbourhoods. Over this period of time, infant mortality rates fell most sharply for those living in the poorest neighbourhoods; however, infant mortality rates in the poorest neighbourhoods were still 61% higher than for those in the wealthiest neighbourhoods by 1996.

As we have previously noted, deaths in childhood are rare events. Even so, children from poor households are more likely to die than children from wealthier households. For example, Birken and her colleagues (2006) found that even though childhood deaths due to unintentional injury decreased dramatically in Canada between 1971 and 1998, there was a consistent gradient in the risk for death by income. That is, more than twice as many poor children died as a result of unintentional injury than children in the highest income group throughout this time period. More recently, Birken has extended her investigation to child homicide, an even rarer occurrence. These findings also show that children who die as a result of intentional injury are significantly more likely to come from poor than from wealthier households (Birken et al., 2009).

Income, education, and occupation also influence mortality risk during adulthood. Veugelers and his colleagues (2001) found that both education and income predicted mortality in the province of Nova Scotia, with risk increasing as levels of education and income decreased. Burrows and her colleagues (2011) found a gradient relationship between education and suicide between 1991 and 2001 for Canadian men, but not women. More specifically, compared to men who had a university degree, the odds of suicide were approximately 57% higher among men who had not completed high school and 36% higher among men who had

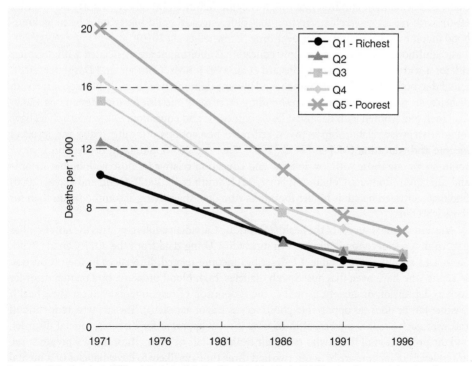

FIGURE 4.1 Infant Mortality Rates, Neighbourhood Income Quintile, Urban Canada, 1971–1996.

Source: Statistics Canada, R. Wilkins, J. Berthelot, & E. Ng, "Trends in Mortality by Neighbourhood Income, Urban Canada, 1971–1996", *Health Reports*, Vol. 13, Pg. 6, Catalogue No: 82-003, 2002.

avoidable deaths:

Deaths that could have
been prevented with
timely access to medical
care.

a high school diploma. Mustard and his colleagues (2010) tracked deaths in Canada between 1991 and 2001, finding that there was an occupational gradient in **avoidable deaths** (i.e., deaths that could have been prevented with timely access to medical care) for both men and women who were in the labour market in 1991. That is, men and women who identified as unskilled workers in 1991 had a significantly greater risk of death in the subsequent eleven years than those in professional occupations.

Researchers have generally found that mortality in later life is associated with educational attainment but not income (Mustard et al., 1997; Strohschein, 2011a). Thus, seniors who have less than high school have a greater risk for death than seniors who have attained any education beyond high school. The lack of association between income and mortality among seniors may reflect that most seniors have retired from the workforce and are no longer earning a wage, and, therefore, income may not be a meaningful measure of material living standards in this stage of life.

Morbidity

As is the case with mortality, the association between socioeconomic position and morbidity in Canada also occurs across the lifespan. Children from poor families are more likely to be disabled (Wilkins and Sherman, 1999) and to have a chronic illness (Cadman et al., 1986; Currie and Stabile, 2003) or mental disorder (Lipman, Offord, and Boyle, 1994). For example, children under the age of 5 living in an economically disadvantaged household (as assessed by parental income, occupation, and education) were significantly more likely to develop asthma relative to children living in a more advantaged household (Midodzi et al., 2010). Behavioural problems were significantly higher in children whose parents lived in rental accommodations than in children whose parents owned their homes (Boyle, 2002). Children from low-income families were four times as likely to be injured in motor vehicle traffic accidents than children from high-income families (Dougherty, Pless, and Wilkins, 1990), with recent research suggesting that differences in child injury rates by neighbourhood income are becoming wider over time (Brownell et al., 2010).

In adulthood, low income and low educational attainment are associated with a greater risk for a wide range of diseases (Mustard et al., 1997). Ross, Gilmour, and Dasgupta (2010) found that both educational attainment and income demonstrated a gradient association with diabetes, such that there was a corresponding increase in the risk for diabetes among Canadian men and women with declining levels of income and education. Other researchers have found a stepwise relationship between self-rated perceptions of health status and levels of income and education (McLeod et al., 2003; Veenstra, 2000). Similarly, depression is more common among those with low income and education relative to those with higher income and education (Romans, Cohen, and Forte, 2011; Smith et al., 2007). Dunn and Hayes (2000) find that self-rated health is higher for adults who own their living accommodation than for those who rent.

A recent national survey of the health of working Canadian adults confirms the now familiar pattern of a socioeconomic gradient in morbidity. Using data from the 2011 Canada Work Stress and Health Survey, Table 4.1 describes income-related differences in the proportion of adults who have been diagnosed with diabetes, high blood pressure, or a mental disorder such as depression or anxiety, as well as the proportion of respondents who say their health is either fair or poor (as opposed to good, very good, or excellent). The stepwise reduction in risk with each $25,000 increment in income is most apparent for diabetes, mental disorder, and the proportion of those who rate their health as fair or poor. Thus, those who are at the lowest levels of income are between two and three times as likely to have diabetes or a mental disorder or to rate their health as fair or poor than those whose income is $150,000 or higher.

Income	Diabetes	High blood pressure	Mental disorder	Poor or fair rated health
Less than $25,000	11.2	26.3	24.4	20.7
$25,000–49,999	9.8	21.7	22.0	18.0
$50,000–74,999	8.0	17.9	18.1	11.4
$75,000–99,999	7.5	17.5	17.0	9.2
$100,000–124,999	7.4	15.8	18.2	8.7
$125,000–149,999	6.1	19.6	14.5	8.3
$150,000 and higher	5.1	19.2	13.5	7.6

TABLE 4.1 Income-Related Differences in Morbidity, 2011 Canada Work Stress and Health Survey

Source: 2011 Canada Work Stress and Health Survey.

The exception to the gradient pattern is high blood pressure. The proportion of respondents with high blood pressure is highest for those whose income is below $25,000; however, the income-related decline reaches its threshold for those whose income falls between $100,000 and $124,999, then climbs for those whose incomes are higher than $125,000. This curvilinear association that finds both the poor and the very wealthy are at greater risk for high blood pressure is interesting and suggests that different factors may be at work. For those who are poor, the financial strain of making ends meet may increase blood pressure, whereas greater stress in the workplace for those in high-paying occupations may account for the upturn in high blood pressure at higher income levels.

Although the evidence is more mixed in later life, a number of studies have found that illness and disease occur more frequently for seniors who are socioeconomically disadvantaged (Mustard et al., 1997). For example, Menec, Lix, and MacWilliam (2010) reported that seniors living in poor neighbourhoods were significantly more likely to have arthritis, diabetes, high blood pressure, heart disease, or stroke than seniors who lived in affluent neighbourhoods. On the other hand, Shields and Chen (1999) found that income and education were unrelated to changes in health status over a four-year period for Canadian seniors. Interestingly, Kaplan and his colleagues (2010) found that high blood pressure was associated with income for seniors living in the United States, but not for seniors living in Canada.

Health Behaviours

As noted in Chapter 2, health behaviours are of interest because they are often predictors of disease and death. For example, it is well known that cigarette smoking is linked to cancer, asthma, and **chronic obstructive pulmonary disease (COPD)**, and that physical activity and a healthy diet reduce risk for diabetes and heart disease; however, fewer people are aware that binge drinking increases the risk for heart attack, violence, and injury (Flegel, MacDonald, and Hébert, 2011). Importantly, health behaviours in the Canadian population, such as cigarette smoking, binge drinking, and physical inactivity, are patterned by socioeconomic position. As is the case with mortality and morbidity, these patterns are observable across the lifespan.

Parental income has been identified as a strong predictor of physical activity in children. Analyzing three waves of data from the Canadian National Longitudinal Survey of Children and Youth, Xu, Gauthier, and Strohschein (2009) found that children from high-income households were nearly four times as likely to participate in an organized sport such as hockey or baseball and more than two and half times as likely to have taken lessons in a physical activity such as dance, archery, or gymnastics than children living in poor households. Their results further showed that neighbourhood income also had an association with participation in an organized sport, even after controlling for household income, with children living in the wealthiest neighbourhoods most likely to participate in organized sport and children in the poorest neighbourhoods least likely to participate. A gradient association between household income and physical activity was also found in a survey of grade five students in Alberta and Nova Scotia (Simen-Kapeu and Veugelers, 2010).

There is also abundant evidence to show that cigarette smoking in adulthood is linked to education, income, and occupation. An Ontario study found that cigarette smoking was highest among low-income households and lowest among high-income households and more common among those working in manufacturing and trades than in those working in management or business (Schwartz et al., 2010). Although fewer Canadians smoke cigarettes today than in past decades, socioeconomic differences have persisted. For example, Reid, Hammond, and Driezen (2010) found that 18% of Canadians in 2006 reported that they currently smoked cigarettes on a daily or occasional basis, a much lower rate than the 24% reported in 1999. Yet as Figure 4.2 shows, throughout this period, approximately twice as many Canadians with less than a high school education were cigarette smokers as those with a university degree.

Similarly, although the proportion of Canadians who engage in sufficient levels of physical activity has been increasing in recent decades, Craig and her colleagues (2004) found that between 1981 and 2000, educational differences in physical activity levels remained constant. In other words, those with a university education were consistently more likely to have sufficient levels of physical activity than those with less than high school education throughout this period, and the gap did not widen or diminish with time. In contrast, the authors found that there were no income differences in physical activity among Canadian adults in 1981, but that these were in evidence by 2000. Thus, the proportion of low-income adults who engaged in sufficient levels of physical activity only increased marginally between 1981 and 2000 (from 21.8% to 33.1%); however, there was a much more substantial increase in the proportion of

FIGURE 4.2 Smoking Prevalence in Canada by Education Level, 1999–2006

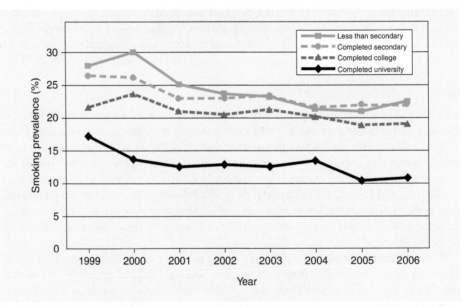

Source: Jessica L. Reid, David Hammond, & Pete Driezen, "Socio-economic status and smoking in Canada, 1999-2006: Has there been any progress on disparities in tobacco use?" *Canadian Journal of Public Health*, 2010, Vol. 101, No. 1, Pg. 74.

Health Behaviour	Men		Women	
	Renter	Homeowner	Renter	Homeowner
Cigarette smoking	46.8	32.1	44.1	25.7
Binge drinking	59.1	53.2	33.2	22.8
Physical inactivity	59.3	57.8	66.2	62.3

Source: 1994 Canadian National Population Health Survey.

TABLE 4.2 Health Behaviours by Housing Tenure, for Men and Women, 1994 Canadian National Population Health Survey

adults with sufficient levels of physical activity in the highest income category (from 25.2% in 1981 to 55.3% in 2000).

Data from the 1994 Canadian National Population Health Survey also reveal that health behaviours among adults are differentiated by whether one rents or owns one's home. Table 4.2 shows the rates of cigarette smoking, binge drinking (i.e., more than five alcoholic drinks at one time), and physical inactivity for men and women, depending on whether they owned or rented their living accommodations. Differences between homeowners and renters are most apparent for cigarette smoking, where rates of smoking among renters (46.8% for men and 44.1% for women) are substantially higher than the rates of smoking among home-owners (32.1% for men and 25.7% for women). Among women, rates of binge drinking are much higher for renters than for owners (33.2% versus 22.8%); however, there appears to be a much smaller difference in the rate of binge drinking between male homeowners and renters. Differences are smaller yet when examining differences in physical inactivity, where female renters appear to be slightly more likely than female homeowners to be physi-cally inactive, with no real differences in physical inactivity between male renters and male homeowners.

Finally, there is evidence to suggest that socioeconomic inequalities in health behaviours also exist in later life. For example, Chad and her colleagues (2005) reported that seniors with higher income and levels of education were more likely to be physically active than seniors with lower income and lower levels of education.

In sum, the evidence is both consistent and compelling: Canadians who experience greater socioeconomic disadvantage, whether it be measured by household income, neighbourhood income, occupation, education, or housing tenure, are more likely to live shorter lives, to become ill, and to engage in unhealthy behaviours than Canadians whose socioeconomic position is more privileged. Moreover, the pattern is replicated across each stage of the life course from infancy into old age. Now that we have reviewed some of the evidence for the association between socioeconomic position and health in Canada, we present and evaluate explanations for this relationship.

EXPLANATIONS FOR SOCIOECONOMIC INEQUALITIES IN HEALTH

Once the authors of the Black Report had presented evidence for social class differences in mortality and morbidity in the British population, they turned their attention to poten-tial explanations for the relationship. They generated a total of four different explanations; however, they dismissed the plausibility of two of these explanations, artefact and social selection, and instead accepted the remaining two explanations, materialist and cultural/behavioural. See Key Concepts 4.1 for an overview. We discuss each of the four explanations in turn.

KEY CONCEPTS 4.1   The Black Report: Potential Explanations for Social Class Differences in Mortality and Morbidity

Artefact	The relationship is artificially created as a result of the methods for evaluating social class and measures of mortality and morbidity.
Social Selection	The relationship exists, but in reverse order: health is a cause of social class.
Materialist	The relationship exists because the material conditions associated with a given social class differentially expose people to health risks.
Cultural/Behavioural	The relationship exists, but social class differences will not disappear by improving the material conditions of the lower social classes alone, but through changing health attitudes and behaviours.

Artefact

The first explanation, artefact, questions the validity of the relationship between social class and health by conjecturing that the relationship may be artificially produced because of the way either social class or health is measured. In noting and then dismissing this explanation, the authors of the Black Report may have anticipated that their work would be criticized for methodological shortcomings. For example, there are a number of weaknesses associated with classifying people according to their occupation, with workers sorted into one of five different social classes ranging from professional to unskilled worker, as was done in the Black Report. First, only those who are employed in the labour market can be assigned to a category, leaving out those who are retired or unemployed. Moreover, occupations can be difficult to categorize, and the categories themselves can change over time as the labour market undergoes change. For example, with economies in many western nations shifting from manufacturing to service-oriented industries, there is some question as to whether these five occupational categories remain valid and whether they can be meaningfully used to compare socioeconomic inequalities in health from a historical perspective.

These weaknesses, coupled with the need to find greater theoretical justification for measures of social stratification, have resulted in changes in how researchers measure socioeconomic position. Once the mainstay of health inequalities research, measures associated with occupational class have receded in importance, while education and income have gained in popularity. In addition, researchers have begun to incorporate more diverse measures, such as those based on consumption, including owning a car, a dishwasher, or one's home. Home-ownership in particular has been used more frequently because, as the largest purchase most individuals make in their lifetimes, a home is an asset whose value generally increases over time and becomes a source of wealth in later life. Renters, in contrast, are not able to rely on their home as a financial asset that can be drawn upon as a resource if needed.

Measures of educational attainment and income have a number of advantages over occupation but also have their own limitations. First, measures of educational attainment are better able to classify those with a weaker attachment to the labour market, including those who are unemployed or retired. Researchers have also theorized more specifically about how educational attainment is relevant for health (Ross and Wu, 1995). Education is thought to operate directly on health by allocating better-paying jobs to those who are more highly educated, thus enabling the acquisition of material resources that maximize health. Indirectly, education may provide opportunities to become more knowledgeable about how to improve health. That measures of parental educational attainment are also highly predictive of child health status suggests that education is an integral family resource that has health benefits for all household members.

Yet, using education as a measure of socioeconomic position also has some disadvantages. First, just as occupations have undergone tremendous change over time, so too has educational attainment. Increasingly, a postsecondary education is seen as a necessary stepping stone to a successful career. Thus, less than 15% of Canadians between the ages of 25 and 39 had a postsecondary degree in 1986; however, by 2009, this had increased to 31% (Turcotte, 2011). Because older generations were much less likely to need or receive postsecondary training, there is much less variation in educational attainment among older cohorts. Moreover, achieving a high school education in past generations meant something different than it does today, making it difficult to compare educational inequalities in health between younger and older people. A second disadvantage of using educational attainment is that it is relatively fixed after early adulthood. This has been said to be a strength because those who evaluate educational differences in health outcomes among adults can show that educational attainment temporally preceded the health outcome. Despite this advantage, however, researchers are not able to show that changes in education are associated with changes in health, a step that is arguably more important for proving causality than demonstrating the temporal sequence of two variables.

Income remains a popular measure for examining socioeconomic inequalities in health. In contrast to the stability of education measures, income changes from year to year and thus researchers are able to capture more effectively the health effects of changes in socioeconomic position. Its drawbacks are that, because the cost of living is not constant across different contexts, income must be adjusted for factors such as family size and geographical region. For example, a family of five whose reported annual income is $50,000 does not enjoy the same economies of scale as a two-person household with the same income (i.e., $10,000 per person versus $25,000 per person). Moreover, survey participants are often reluctant to answer questions about their income, with the consequence that responses are prone to inaccurate reporting and high levels of non-response. In survey research, it is not unusual for anywhere from 10% to 25% of respondents to refuse to answer questions about their income. When this happens, researchers may become worried that their results are biased. That is, when too many people refuse to answer a question, analyses may no longer accurately describe characteristics of the population and observed associations with health may become distorted.

Researchers have also learned to distinguish between income and poverty status, for although income is used to determine poverty status, the two measures are conceptually different. By treating income as a continuous measure that is linearly related to health outcomes, researchers presuppose a graded association with health, such that increases in income are met with corresponding increases in health. As a dichotomous measure, poverty status reflects an arbitrary distinction between those who are considered able to afford the necessities of life and those who are not. Unlike many other countries, Canada does not calculate an official poverty line. Rather, Canada relies on **low-income cutoffs (LICOs)**. LICOs represent the point at which a family must spend a greater proportion of its income on necessities such as food, shelter, and clothing than what an average family would spend, taking into account the size of the family and the size of the community in which the family lives. This means that there are a number of different cutoffs, but in each instance families that are above the threshold, indicating that basic needs consume an overly high proportion of household income, are considered poor.

In recent years, researchers have begun to investigate poverty as a dynamic phenomenon. Until the availability of longitudinal data made it possible to track experiences of poverty for a given individual over time, it was widely assumed that poverty was relatively enduring and irreversible (McDonough and Berglund, 2003). Now, however, researchers recognize that poverty is highly dynamic: most of those who experience poverty in their lifetime tend to be poor only once and for a short spell. In contrast, very few people in western nations, including Canada, remain stuck below the poverty threshold for long periods of time. For example,

low-income cutoffs (LICOs):

An income threshold, varying by family and community size, where a household is considered poor if it spends 20% more of its income on food, shelter, and clothing than the average household, leaving less income available for other expenses, such as health, education, transportation, and recreation.

20% of Canadians were poor in at least one year between 2002 and 2007, but only 2.1% of Canadians were poor throughout this period (Murphy, Zhang, and Dionne, 2012). Theorizing how these variations might influence health, researchers have hypothesized that those who are persistently poor should be at greater risk for unhealthy behaviours, illness, and death than those who are intermittently poor and those who are never poor. To date, these hypotheses have been confirmed in both children (McLeod and Shanahan, 1996) and adults (Mossakowski, 2008; McDonough and Berglund, 2003; McDonough, Sacker, and Wiggins, 2005).

Others contend that the timing of poverty matters. Researchers use the term **biological embedding** to refer to experiences that get under the skin and alter human biological processes (Hertzman and Boyce, 2010). Normal development typically involves sequentially ordered windows of opportunity in which different experiences and exposures can either facilitate or impair the acquisition of new competencies or capacities. The optimal set of experiences enhances development; adversity during a critical moment that prevents the acquisition of skills or capacities may derail the normal developmental trajectory and create permanent deficits.

Biological embedding can happen throughout the life course. For example, achieving a higher level of education as a young adult is associated with a decreased risk for Alzheimer's disease and cognitive impairment in later life. Researchers have hypothesized that this relationship exists because in early adulthood, more effective use of brain networks and cognitive paradigms hard-wires the brain to be protective against future decline. It is poverty early in life, however, that researchers believe may exert the greatest effect on health outcomes. This is because infancy is considered a **critical period** of development in which immature brains and bodies are undergoing rapid development, therefore representing a time in which developing organisms are particularly vulnerable to environmental influences.

That biological embedding occurs in other species is well recognized. Michael Meaney, a renowned Canadian researcher, was the first to discover that rats who were licked by their mothers in the period after birth grew up to be more adventurous and less fearful than rats whose mothers ignored them. When Meaney examined the brains of licked and non-licked rats, he found that the licked rats had a more developed hippocampus and that they excreted less cortisol under duress than the non-licked rats. His work eventually culminated in the discovery that maternal licking released serotonin that turned on the gene that stimulated the development of stress receptors in the developing pup's brain. Remarkably, the simple activity of a mother rat grooming her pups shaped both the pups' brains and their subsequent behaviour.

Applied to humans, researchers believe that poverty and its associated deprivations may deliver a similar biological insult to the developing infant that subsequently compromises their future health status. A disaster known as the Dutch Famine has provided researchers with a unique opportunity to study whether events early in life have a lasting impact on health. During the German occupation of the Netherlands in World War II, food was often in short supply; however, in the winter of 1944–1945, a train strike and an unusually harsh and early winter led to extreme food shortages. In the western portion of the Netherlands, the official daily food rations were limited to between 400 and 800 calories per person, including pregnant women. Despite the immense toll famine took on the population (mortality rates soared), women continued to become pregnant and deliver their babies throughout this time period. After the liberation of the Netherlands in May 1945, the food situation rebounded rapidly.

Decades later, researchers tracked down the Dutch Famine birth cohort and compared their health status to their counterparts born either before the famine or conceived afterward. The results of these comparisons confirmed that children who experienced the famine *in utero,* when their mothers were suffering from extreme malnutrition, were of lower birth weight than their counterparts born before or conceived after the famine. Further, as adults,

biological embedding: Experiences that get under the skin and alter human biological processes.

critical period: A window of opportunity during development in which a particular skill or characteristic is believed to be most readily acquired, and that if missed, will either not be as easily acquired or result in permanent deficit.

they were significantly more likely to have heart disease, diabetes, obesity, and an increased stress response. Given that the war ended shortly after the famine subsided and that the country rapidly returned to its previous level of prosperity, researchers have pointed to the effects of malnutrition on the developing fetus as the sole source of these health problems. The **fetal programming hypothesis**, as it is now known, has considerable attraction for its many proponents but has come under substantial criticism as well. In particular, critics contend that researchers have failed to rule out alternative hypotheses or explanations that might better account for the association between fetal malnutrition and health in adulthood. The lack of information about these individuals between birth and adulthood, however, makes it impossible to test competing explanations and awaits replication with other data.

Despite the lack of irrefutable evidence, there appears to be growing support for the idea that poverty early in life inhibits normal processes of development by disrupting the functions and structures that shape future cognitive, social, emotional, and health outcomes. It remains to be seen whether concrete evidence of the association with human subjects will one day be found to support this position.

As researchers have come to appreciate, designing a measure that reflects how members of a given society are differentially located in the social hierarchy is not an easy task. Yet these methodological challenges give rise to a much deeper theoretical issue. That is, the measures that researchers commonly use to evaluate social location tap into different theoretical understandings of what it means to live in a hierarchically organized society. Thus, terms such as *social class* and *socioeconomic status* should not be treated as if they were interchangeable because each references markedly different ways of thinking about stratification and inequality.

The elaboration of the concepts of social class and socioeconomic status come from Marx and Weber, respectively. For Karl Marx, social class positions were inherently relational and polarizing: those who owned the means of production (bourgeoisie) exploited those who were forced to sell their labour (proletariat) to gain the means to survive. He forecast that this oppressive relation would one day come to an end when the immiserated working classes developed an awareness of their condition and overthrew the capitalist system. Until that time, the interests of the proletariat and the bourgeoisie were in fundamental conflict and permeated all aspects of society.

In contrast, Max Weber recognized that economic relations were an important feature of stratification but viewed them as distributional rather than relational. That is, Weber foresaw the emergence of the middle classes that would fill in the gap between the wealthy, propertied bourgeoisie that Marx vilified and the impoverished working classes that he romanticized. Moreover, Weber envisioned that these classes were not rigid categories, but that there would be a great deal of fluidity as people moved up and down the social ladder. That is, as people acquired skills and education, they could improve their standing in the social order and reap the benefits of better life chances. Thus, if Weber and Marx had conducted analyses on social differences in health, Weber would have gravitated to measures such as education, homeownership, and occupational prestige to evaluate socioeconomic status, whereas Marx would have preferred categorical measures that reflected a simple division of economic groups into those who exploit and those who are exploited.

We have chosen to use the more neutral term *socioeconomic position* over the theoretically laden *social class* and *socioeconomic status* to avoid exclusive identification with either Marxist or Weberian theories. This does not obviate the need for sociologists to investigate and understand the underlying processes that generate inequality in our societies. Rather, we believe that linking theories about the processes of social stratification and inequality in a given society to research on socioeconomic inequalities in health is an important, but as yet unfulfilled, task in sociology.

fetal programming hypothesis:
The supposition that development of the fetus can be shaped by environmental events, such as maternal malnutrition, that will have a permanent impact on the health of the individual, including into adulthood.

Social Selection

The second explanation for socioeconomic inequalities in health centres on the issue of **social selection**. Also known as reverse causation or social drift theory, this explanation posits that rather than socioeconomic position causing poor health, health status determines socioeconomic position. For example, as people become disabled or ill, their abilities to earn a living are hampered, and they fall to a lower social status.

social selection:
A theory holding that health causally influences socioeconomic position such that lower-class persons have higher rates of illness because middle-class persons who become ill drift over time into the lower class.

The authors of the Black Report rejected social selection as an explanatory mechanism in socioeconomic inequalities in health because they interpreted social selection as a Darwinian concept whereby upward mobility is awarded to those endowed with superior health. This blanket dismissal of social selection, however, has since come to be seen as problematic (Macintyre, 1997). In particular, sociologists of health and illness are well acquainted with the social costs associated with having an incapacitating, highly visible mental or physical illness. It is possible that these social sanctions act as gatekeepers that block an ill person's educational and occupational opportunities. The story of Susan Kaysen, recounting her experiences in a mental institution in her book, *Girl Interrupted,* exemplifies the kinds of obstacles those who are labelled mentally ill typically encounter when trying to find a job or a place to live:

> The hospital had an address, 115 Mill Street. This was to provide some cover if one of us were well enough to apply for a job while still incarcerated. It gave about as much protection as 1600 Pennsylvania Avenue would have.

> "Let's see, nineteen years old, living at 1600 Pennsylvania Avenue—Hey! That's the White House!" This was the sort of look we got from prospective employers, except not pleased.

In Massachusetts, 115 Mill Street is a famous address. Applying for a job, leasing an apartment, getting a driver's license: All problematic. The driver's license application even asked, Have you ever been hospitalized for mental illness? Oh, no, I just loved Belmont so much I decided to move to 115 Mill Street.

> "You're living at One Fifteen Mill Street?" asked a small basement-colored person who ran a sewing-notions shop in Harvard Square, where I was trying to get a job.
> "Uhhunh."
> "And how long have you been living there?"
> "Oh, a while." I gestured at the past with one hand.
> "And I guess you haven't been working for a while?" He leaned back, enjoying himself.
> "No," I said. "I've been thinking things over." I didn't get the job.
> As I left the shop my glance met his, and he gave me a look of such terrible intimacy that I cringed. I know what you are, said his look. (Kaysen, 1993: 123–124)*

The empirical research supports two general conclusions about social selection. First, with a few exceptions, social selection does not represent an adequate explanation for the association between socioeconomic position and health. One well-known exception is schizophrenia. Schizophrenia typically strikes at a critical juncture in the life course, that is, as young adults are completing postsecondary education or are launching into careers. In such instances, promising careers are cut short as the illness takes over, and some of these young men and women become homeless. Similarly, some adults who are diagnosed with a severe chronic illness may be forced to leave their jobs, and if they are unable to return, they may deplete their life savings and begin

---

* Susan Kaysen, *Girl, Interrupted*, Turtle Bay Books, Pg. 123–124, 1993.

drifting down into a lower rung of society. Generally, those who were in a higher socioeconomic position prior to the illness are better able to protect themselves from downward mobility, and it is those whose socioeconomic position was precarious to begin with who are least able to prevent a downward slide. For the most part, however, studies that have used longitudinal analyses to determine which comes first have found that social selection explains only a small proportion of the economically disadvantaged ill population (Williams and Collins, 1995). Instead, and far more often, socioeconomic position causes illness (Marmot, 2002, 2004).

The second major conclusion is that there is a role for indirect social selection. Indirect social selection occurs when poor health during childhood makes it difficult to acquire the skills and competencies that will be needed later to achieve a high economic status in adulthood. In the past, researchers assumed that the adaptability of children and the self-limiting nature of most childhood illnesses made such pathways unlikely or inconsequential. An accumulating body of evidence now suggests that there are long-term repercussions associated with poor health in childhood, with health problems consistently interfering with a child's academic progress. For example, McLeod and Kaiser (2004) found that children with behavioural and emotional problems were significantly less likely to finish high school or to enrol in postsecondary education. Others have shown that the lifetime earnings of adults who reported fair or poor health in childhood were significantly lower than that of respondents whose childhood health was assessed as good, very good, or excellent (Haas, Glymour, and Berkman, 2011).

The pathways linking childhood health to socioeconomic position in adulthood are not yet well understood. Some have suggested that progress through the schooling system is the biggest barrier children in poor health face. Chronic health problems in childhood have been linked to higher rates of school absenteeism, often because these children must schedule regular doctor's appointments. Absenteeism in turn is associated with grade failure and early school leaving; correspondingly, those with low levels of educational attainment are likely to have lower earnings than those with higher levels of education. Although these pathways sound plausible, they await empirical verification.

Materialist

In contrast to the previous two explanations, the authors of the Black Report accepted materialist and cultural/behavioural explanations as valid ways of thinking about how socioeconomic position is related to health outcomes. As such, the authors of the Black Report endorsed **social causation**: they believed that socioeconomic position causally influences health status. They remained uncertain, however, as to which of these two explanations was more important.

social causation:
A theory holding that social factors are causally implicated in producing disease and death.

The materialist explanation asserts that economic deprivation prevents individuals from obtaining the resources they need to maintain and promote their own health. Thus, those who have a lower socioeconomic position experience worse health because, compared to persons with a more advantaged position, they have less access to health-preserving resources. These problems play themselves out in many aspects of everyday life. The most important of these are work conditions, environmental conditions, housing, diet, and access to health care.

First, the work available to poorly educated lower-class persons—when they can find it—can cause ill health or death by exposing workers to physical hazards. A coal miner, for example, is considerably more likely than a mine owner to die from accidental injuries or lung disease caused by coal dust. In addition, lower-status workers typically experience both demanding work conditions and low control over those conditions. For example, factory workers must keep pace with the production line but cannot control the speed of the line or even when they take bathroom breaks. Similarly, those working in the service and retail industries often receive little compensation for long hours of work; are generally unable to afford to take time off when they are sick or for holidays; and, increasingly, are on the job as many others enjoy the break of a statutory holiday. In contrast, those employed as professionals receive high levels of compensation for their work, are more likely to feel that their work is personally rewarding and meaningful, have the opportunity and means to take vacation time, and have access to company health benefits that protect them should they become ill.

Second, environmental conditions can increase rates of morbidity and mortality among poorer populations. Chemical, air, and noise pollution all occur more often in poor neighbourhoods than in wealthier neighbourhoods both because the cheap rents in neighbourhoods blighted by pollution attract poor people and because poor people lack the money, votes, and social influence needed to keep polluting industries, waste dumps, and highways out of their neighbourhoods (Bullard, Warren, and Johnson, 2001; Brulle and Pellow, 2006). Such pollution can foster cancer, leukemia, high blood pressure, asthma, and other health problems, as well as emotional stress. Emotional stress in poor neighbourhoods also stems from exposure to social disorder and disorganization. Vandalism, dirty streets, abandoned buildings, and evidence of gang activity make residents feel unsafe and vulnerable, with consequent feelings of powerlessness and alienation increasing the risk for depression and the adoption of risky health behaviours (Ross and Jang, 2000; Ross and Mirowsky, 2009).

Third, inadequate, overcrowded, and unsafe housing increases the risk of injuries, infections, and illnesses, including lead poisoning when children eat peeling paint; gas poisoning when families must rely on ovens for heat; and asthma triggered by cockroach droppings, rodent urine, and mould (Reading, 1997). For example, Dr. Arthur Jones, who runs a clinic in the United States, told author Laura Abraham of his initial response to a patient with severe cat allergies who nonetheless refused to give away her cat:

> "I really got kind of angry," Dr. Jones remembered, "and then she told me that if she got rid of the cat, there was nothing to protect her kids against rats." Another woman brought her 2-year-old to the clinic with frostbite, so Dr. Jones dispatched his nurse ... to visit her home.... The nurse discovered icicles in the woman's apartment because the landlord had stopped providing heat. (Abraham, 1993: 18)

Fourth, the food that the poor eat—or don't eat—increases the risk of physical and mental illness among adults and children (Weinreb et al., 2002). When food is lacking in quantity and quality, the body's natural defences against disease are necessarily weakened. Experiencing either of these conditions indicates that a person lacks food security. **Food security** occurs when "all people, at all times, have physical and economic access to sufficient, safe and nutritious food to meet their dietary needs and food preferences for an active and healthy lifestyle" (Food and Agriculture Organization, 2006: 1).

Turning first to the problem of hunger, in 2008, nearly one million Canadians (7.7% of the population) reported that they ran out of food or money to buy food at least once in the past year. In Canada, as in other countries, those who do not have enough food can turn to a food bank; however, this may not be the best solution. Box 4.1 offers a critical evaluation of food banks as an institutionalized response to the problem of hunger and food insecurity in Canada.

Not surprisingly, hunger is concentrated among the poor and, in particular, among single mothers living on social assistance (McIntyre, Connor, and Warren, 2000). Research has shown that mothers in low-income households often attempt to shield their children from hunger by eating less themselves (McIntyre et al., 2003). Yet, hunger is not limited to the poor, but also exhibits a gradient relationship with socioeconomic position whereby higher levels of income or education increasingly insulate one from experiences of hunger (Power, 2005).

Low income is associated not only with insufficient amounts of food, but also with a lower-quality diet (Veugelers, Fitzgerald, and Johnston, 2005). The fresh fruits and vegetables that are required for a nutritious diet are generally more expensive than energy-dense

food security:
Physical and economic access for all individuals at all times to sufficient, safe, and nutritious food to meet their dietary needs and food preferences for an active and healthy lifestyle.

BOX 4.1
Are Food Banks Good for Your Health?

Governments in Canada and elsewhere rely on food banks as an institutional response to issues of hunger and food insecurity. The first food bank in Canada was established in 1981 in the city of Edmonton to provide relief during the harsh economic recession. Originally intended as a temporary measure, food banks soon thereafter began to sprout across the country. Today, there are more than 800 food banks and approximately 3,000 food programs (Food Banks Canada, 2012). Given their ubiquity, it might be fair to ask whether food banks are an effective solution to the problem of hunger and whether there might be any implications for health for those who regularly use food banks.

Riches (2002) has critiqued the effectiveness of food banks as a solution to hunger on two grounds. First, he points to the growing number of food banks and food bank users in Canada as proof that food banks have not reduced the prevalence of hunger and food insecurity in the population. Second, he notes that food banks ration food by restricting the frequency with which people can access their services. Similarly, not all food programs operate every day of the week, with more than half in the city of Toronto closed on weekends (Tarasuk and Dachner, 2009). Thus, food banks are designed to meet immediate needs but not daily needs and do not resolve the structural problem of hunger.

Moreover, there is growing evidence that the provisions offered by food banks are insufficient to meet daily nutritional needs (Tarasuk and Beaton, 1999). Similar nutritional deficiencies have been found in food programs (Tse and Tarasuk, 2008). Interestingly, Li and her colleagues found that homeless youth in the city of Toronto who used charitable meal programs were as nutritionally vulnerable as youth who did not use these programs (Li, Dachner, and Tarasuk, 2009). These findings raise troubling questions about the long-term effectiveness of these programs for meeting the physical needs of those who are food insecure. Moreover, Riches contends that food banks can be damaging to mental health because they may heighten feelings of dependency and stigmatization for those who are forced to use their services.

Riches charges that food banks **depoliticize** the issue of hunger and that the underlying problem of hunger is due to policy choices that allow governments to abandon responsibility for ensuring the well-being of their citizens. Welfare reforms have repeatedly cut back social assistance benefits that were already at inadequate levels to meet needs, guaranteeing that the poor would be forced to rely on food banks. The erosion of Canada's social safety net and a shift toward market-oriented policies not only contradict Canada's endorsement of international agreements espousing a human right to food but also ensure that the problem of hunger will be a pressing social problem for the foreseeable future.

junk foods, placing them out of reach for those who cannot afford them (Drewnowski and Darmon, 2005). Fast foods and fatty or sweet foods satisfy hunger and provide energy inexpensively yet offer little in the way of nutrients needed for maintaining health. In particular, those who subsist on energy-dense junk foods are at greater risk for obesity and related diseases. It is not surprising, then, that children and youth living in the poorest neighbourhoods of Canada are significantly more likely to be overweight than children and youth living in wealthier neighbourhoods (Oliver and Hayes, 2005). Thus, not only are the poor more likely to go hungry than those who are more economically advantaged, but also they are more likely to be obese.

Finally, poor individuals may be less likely to access needed health care. Access to health care cannot eliminate class differences in mortality and morbidity—differences that exist even in countries where access to care is universal—because it cannot eliminate the other factors that leave poor people more susceptible to illness in the first place (Marmot, 2004; McGrail et al., 2009). For this reason, access to health care plays a smaller role in the relationship between poverty and ill health than do the other factors discussed so far (Feinstein, 1993; Williams and Collins, 1995). Nevertheless, access to health care can protect against some problems, such as debilitating dental disease preventable through routine cleaning and disabling illnesses preventable through immunization. In addition, access to health care can improve quality of life dramatically through such simple interventions as providing eyeglasses, hearing aids, and comfortable crutches or wheelchairs.

Case Study: Health among the Homeless

The impact of material deprivation on health falls heaviest on the homeless. Homelessness is a major problem in Canada. Although accurate estimates are difficult to obtain, anywhere between 150,000 and 300,000 Canadians find themselves without shelter every year (Hwang et al., 2011). In addition, many more Canadians are vulnerably housed, living temporarily with friends (referred to as "couch-surfing"), or making do in hotels or rooming houses.

Not surprisingly, given the physical and emotional strains of life on the streets, homeless persons experience greater risk for mortality and a disproportionate share of chronic and acute illnesses. For example, a recent study found that life expectancy for those living in homeless shelters was on average thirteen years shorter for men and eight years shorter for women than the Canadian average (Hwang et al., 2009). Diseases that are relatively rare in Canada, such as **tuberculosis**, are rampant among homeless people (Frankish, Hwang, and Quantz, 2005). A recent study on Canadians who are homeless or vulnerably housed suggests that more than 85% report a chronic health problem, such as heart disease and diabetes, and more than 50% have a mental health disorder (Hwang et al., 2011).

Among the homeless, children and women are particularly vulnerable. Homeless children and youth account for one out of every three homeless Canadians (Raising the Roof, 2009). With shelters mainly comprising men, homeless women often fear going to a shelter and find ways to remain invisible to protect themselves from rape and violence (Huey and Berndt, 2008).

All the factors explaining high rates of morbidity and mortality among poor persons also apply to homeless persons. However, maintaining health is even more difficult for homeless persons than for other poor persons. For example, because poverty, malnutrition, and cold weaken their bodies, and because they can often find shelter only in crowded dormitories where infections spread easily, homeless persons are more likely than others to develop upper respiratory infections. If they develop an infection, they cannot rest in bed until they recover, because they have no beds to call their own. Similarly, homeless persons often suffer skin problems such as psoriasis, impetigo, scabies, and lice; if left untreated, these conditions can cause deadly infections. Even if homeless persons receive prompt treatment for these skin problems, their living conditions make it impossible for them to keep their linens and clothing clean enough to prevent reinfection. Finally, homeless persons, regardless of age or sex, often can support themselves only through prostitution, which dramatically increases their risks of rape, battering, and sexually transmitted diseases, including **HIV/AIDS**.

Access to health care is also particularly difficult for homeless persons. The struggles necessary to meet basic needs for food, clothing, and shelter can leave individuals with little time, energy, or money for arranging transportation to health care facilities or for purchasing prescription drugs. In addition, both substance abuse and mental illness—which are common among homeless persons and can either cause or result from homelessness—can make it harder for individuals to recognize they need health care, to seek care promptly when they recognize it is needed, to follow the instructions of health care workers, and to return for needed follow-up visits (Cousineau, 1997). In sum, until the underlying conditions causing homelessness are alleviated, health care workers can offer homeless persons only the most temporary of help.

Cultural/Behavioural

The cultural/behavioural explanation targets patterns of socialization that predispose individuals to behave in ways that are damaging to health. For example, the authors of the Black Report seemed to believe that disadvantaged individuals are unlikely to appreciate the effects of smoking, poor diet, and a sedentary lifestyle on their health. Moreover, the authors viewed cultural/behavioural factors as a potential barrier to equality in health. In the event that redistributive policies were enacted to improve the lot of the poor, the authors speculated that beneficial effects might not be realized if disadvantaged individuals could not overcome entrenched patterns of unhealthy behaviour.

As with the previous explanations, researchers have continued to refine this explanation. Greater attention is now being paid to psychosocial pathways, whereby one's sense of placement in the social hierarchy operates over and above the material resources attached to that social location. For example, those who are wealthy not only have the physical means to improve and maintain health but also are aware of their position at the top of the hierarchy and relish the power that this position affords them. The more valued one feels, the more likely it is that one will want to invest in one's health—there are tangible reasons to do so. In contrast, those who are at the bottom of the hierarchy are also acutely aware of their position, frustrated with their lack of power and inability to change their living conditions. This may create feelings of despair and worthlessness, and some research indicates that these emotional responses suppress immune functioning.

Others have suggested that social ties and networks may serve to lessen the effects of material deprivation on health outcomes. Those who are able to forge close relationships with others develop a type of resource known as **social capital**. Social capital refers to those aspects of social ties that both provide and produce resources that can be used by individuals and groups within a social network (Coleman, 1988). Thus, social capital is not something that belongs to an individual but rather inheres in the social relationships in which one is embedded. Tightly knit groups form emotional bonds, sharing resources and information and caring for one another. The closer the bonds, the greater the trust and commitment members in the group have for and to one another and the greater the support that can be mustered where there is a crisis. In contrast, those who are isolated may have no one to turn to at a time of need. The dynamics of social capital come to life in the work of Carol Stack (1975), whose classic book, *All Our Kin,* set out to understand the strategies that poor people use to get by. Her description of the ways in which poor mothers draw on extended "kin" networks to exchange goods and services to meet each other's needs reveals the ways in which the blows of poverty become softened when borne collectively.

social capital:
Those aspects of social ties that both provide and produce resources that can be used by individuals and groups within a social network.

A LIFE COURSE PERSPECTIVE

One of the biggest hurdles facing researchers who study socioeconomic inequalities in health is demonstrating the causal nature of the association. Most of the studies that we have reviewed thus far in this chapter have mainly relied on cross-sectional analyses; that is, socioeconomic position and health outcomes were measured at the same time. A valid criticism of such studies is that the association might be spurious; that is, some other unobserved factor could be producing both socioeconomic position and poor health.

latency:
The amount of time between exposure to a risk factor and the initial signs of illness.

Moreover, because Canada has undergone the **epidemiological transition**, chronic and degenerative diseases are the typical health problems of Canadians rather than infectious disease. Yet chronic and degenerative conditions typically come with a long **latency** period: they take time to develop. Accordingly, to understand the social causes of these conditions, we often need to examine events and conditions far in the past. For example, we might want to know if respondents have ever experienced an episode of poverty, whether they have ever faced eviction or foreclosure or filed for bankruptcy, whether they have ever applied for social assistance, or whether they dropped out of high school because of an unexpected pregnancy. Responses to these questions would provide a better picture of how unfolding events in the life of that individual shaped their life chances, influencing their socioeconomic position and their health over time.

To provide theoretical guidance for understanding how socioeconomic position and health are dynamically interconnected, researchers have turned to a life course perspective to understand how socioeconomic conditions throughout one's life cumulatively shape health outcomes. Our earlier discussions about the influence of early-life poverty on health and socioeconomic position in adulthood touched on ideas that draw inspiration from a life course approach, but we now formally introduce its four founding principles, as first described by Elder (1998).

First, a life course approach asserts that all lives are anchored in a particular time and space that uniquely define the experiences of those located therein. The Dutch Famine exemplifies this anchoring: although life was harsh for all Dutch people during the Nazi occupation and during the Dutch Famine in particular, the long-term effects on health were felt most acutely by those children who were in their mothers' wombs in the western part of the country during the six-month famine. It was these children, circumscribed by time and space, who acquired the risk for heart disease, obesity, and diabetes in adulthood—children born outside this time and space faced no additional risk to health in adulthood. Similarly, Elder (1998) reported that the Great Depression enhanced adolescents' sense of competence and efficacy as they took on greater responsibility in the family and accelerated their transition into adulthood, but for those who were young children, economic crisis resulted in lowered feelings of self-esteem and efficacy and led to poor academic achievement. How the Great Recession might differentially affect the health and well-being of Canadians is an issue that is explored further in Box 4.2.

BOX 4.2

IN THE NEWS

How Is the Great Recession Affecting the Health of Canadians?

The Great Recession, the worst economic downturn since the Great Depression of the 1930s, began first as a housing market crash. From there, it quickly morphed into a banking crisis that nearly brought the entire global economy to a standstill following the collapse of Lehman Brothers in the United States in the fall of 2008. In the aftermath, millions of people in North America and Europe lost their jobs and their homes, and poverty rates began to soar. Although Canada appears to have weathered the Great Recession better than most countries, it is not immune to the effects of a global economic slowdown.

Moreover, even though the U.S. recession officially came to an end in 2009, there are signs that the situation remains precarious and that the entire world economy could face greater dangers ahead. Although it is too early to know how the Great Recession is affecting the health of Canadians, history provides us with some clues to the answer.

In hard economic times, one might anticipate that death rates would rise as people struggled to meet their daily needs. Surprisingly, it appears that mortality rates in the United States actually declined during the Great Depression. Researchers have suggested several reasons for why this unusual pattern occurred. First, the Great Depression occurred after the American population had made the epidemiological transition.

Thus, the health-related consequences of hard times might have been delayed to reflect the longer latency period associated with chronic disease. Second, massive interventions by the state, such as the New Deal, provided the public with a safety net that mitigated the effects of economic hardship and gave them hope for the future. Still others point out that the Great Depression ended with the rise of fascism and the atrocities of World War II, suggesting that hard times may not have affected mortality rates but did encourage extremist views and intolerance.

The health consequences of other recessions in the twentieth century appear to operate as one would expect, with higher mortality rates when the economy sank. Recent findings, however, tell a slightly different story. Suhrcke and Stuckler (2012) reported that although mortality rates did not change appreciably during previous economic crises, there were offsetting differences by cause of death. Thus, the authors noted that increases in the unemployment rate were associated with increases in the homicide and suicide rate but decreases in deaths due to motor vehicle accidents. The authors speculated that reduction in traffic deaths during times of high unemployment was likely due to fewer drivers on the road but lacked the needed data to test whether this is the reason why traffic deaths decline during economic crises.

Economic crises also take a toll on mental health. In particular, there is a wealth of evidence to suggest that those who experience job loss, home foreclosure, and financial strain are significantly more likely to be diagnosed with depression and anxiety than those who do not experience these stressors. Not everyone, however, is equally likely to experience these types of stressors. Those who have secure employment, for example, are unlikely to be faced with job loss or financial strain, even during a recession. In contrast, young adults may be particularly vulnerable. Young people who are just entering the labour market lack seniority in their positions. They are the first to be laid off, and if they can find work, it is likely at a low wage, below their skill level, and short term. The Great Recession appears to have idled the labour market activity of many young people in Canada. Whether or not this will have repercussions for where they eventually establish themselves in the labour market and what delayed transitions might mean for their health are interesting questions for future research.

Second, a life course approach involves the notion of linked lives. Lives are spent forming intimate relationships and developing social bonds, which not only socialize and regulate patterns of social interaction but create ripple effects when events occur to any one individual within a socially bonded group. We have already described how social capital, defined as resources that are formed when people form close social ties, may act to lessen the effects of material hardship on health and well-being. In the next chapter, we will look more closely at how events such as divorce or poor health of a family member can influence the lives of families in ways that have implications for both socioeconomic position and health.

The third element of a life course approach reiterates the relevance of human agency in understanding the impact of broader social structures on individual lives. Individuals knowingly and purposefully undertake action to achieve self-directed goals, and the influence of social structure is continually met with individual response and adaptation. This is an important principle because it serves to counteract the notion that structural forces necessarily force themselves under the skin and alter biological processes and development.

Finally, a life course approach is concerned with the timing of lives. There are normative ideals about how life should unfold, broad expectations for when one should get married, bear and raise children, get a job, retire, and so on. When the scheduling of life events and transitions goes awry or deviates from the anticipated course, there are consequences for the future.

The concept of the timing of lives does not suggest that the life course is inherently unpredictable and unstable. Life transitions may have uncertain moments, but they occur within the context of a long-term pattern or trajectory of prior experiences and circumstances (George, 1993). In discussing the pathways that link childhood experiences to adult outcomes, Rutter (1989) points out that continuities will occur because children carry with them the results of earlier learning and of earlier structural and functional change. This does not necessarily mean that a person's characteristics at one age will predict the degree or type of *change* over a later time period, but it does mean that it is likely to predict later *levels* of functioning, because they will incorporate earlier levels. (p. 26, italics in the original)

A life course approach also helps us to see how differences in social location early in life can create a growing gap in health outcomes between the most and least disadvantaged members of society over time. The principle of cumulative advantage applies to many fields of research, including socioeconomic inequalities in health. Basically, if two people invest their money in a savings account where both have the same interest rate, the person who initially deposits more money will see greater returns on the investment than the person who deposits less. If a higher interest rate kicks in at a certain threshold, then the person who deposited more money initially will also reach that threshold more quickly, with differences between the investments of the two people subsequently becoming exponentially larger. The process by which initial advantages allow for subsequent advantages that systematically widen differences over time between those who enjoyed initial advantages and those who did not is known as the **cumulative advantage hypothesis** (DiPrete and Eirich, 2006).

Although this line of inquiry is relatively new and appropriate longitudinal data are hard to come by, corroborating evidence for the cumulative advantage in health is beginning to trickle in. Analyzing data gathered on American adults between 1984 and 2001, Willson and her colleagues found that declines in self-rated health over adulthood were steeper for those who had less wealth and education initially, and shallower for those who initially had more resources (Willson, Shuey, and Elder, 2007). Similarly, Dupre (2008), analyzing 20 years of data from a different American survey, found an accelerated rate of illness and mortality for respondents with low educational attainment relative to those with high levels of education. Both studies suggest that the relationship between socioeconomic position and health becomes stronger over time, with those who have early advantages increasing their lead over time.

In sum, a life course approach views individual lives as unique personalities that respond, pursue, and give meaning to socially significant events and transitions that, subtly and profoundly influenced by the bond of social relationships, unfold as biographical trajectories delimited by history, space, and time. As researchers begin to apply a life course approach to socioeconomic inequalities in health, they are beginning to generate and test interesting hypotheses about how social conditions get under the skin and influence health for the poor and rich alike, translating social disparities into health inequalities. As such, this is an innovative and rapidly changing area of research that promises to reveal new insights into the relationship between socioeconomic position and health.

INCOME INEQUALITY AS A DETERMINANT OF HEALTH

As we have seen, the evidence linking socioeconomic position to health is extremely strong. However, some sociologists have argued that **income inequality**—the gap in income between a nation's highest and lowest income earners—rather than simply income may best explain why some nations are healthier overall than others (Wilkinson, 1996, 2005). This theory has generated considerable support as well as controversy.

The link between income inequality and health was first systematically explored by Richard Wilkinson, who showed that when a country attained a level of income above a certain threshold, absolute living standards had less impact on health and, instead, the

cumulative advantage hypothesis:
The process by which initial comparative advantages in a certain domain beget subsequent advantages that systematically widen differences over time.

income inequality:
A measurement of the distribution of income that highlights the gap between those making the most income in a population and those making the least.

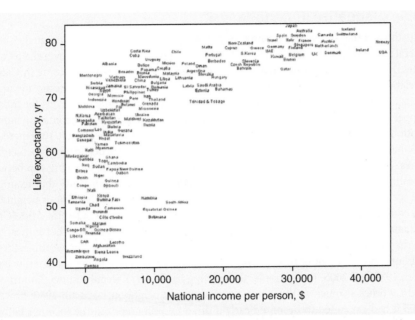

FIGURE 4.3

Relationship
between Life
Expectancy and Gross
Domestic Product
(GDP) per Capita

Source: Richard Wilkinson & Kate E. Pickett, *The Spirit Level: Why More Equal Societies Almost Always Do Better*, London: Penguin, 2009.

relative distribution of income becomes more important for health. As can be seen in Figure 4.3, the effect of a nation's average income on its average life expectancy is not linear. That is, life expectancy increases dramatically when the average income of a nation improves for those countries that are extremely poor. Once average incomes rise to a certain level, increasing average income is no longer associated with an improvement in the average life expectancy of that country. Wilkinson contends that among high-income countries, the influence of absolute income wanes whereas relative income (or how income is distributed) assumes greater importance: the greater the income inequality, the lower the life expectancy. Conversely, countries in which the gap between the richest and poorest is smaller experience longer life expectancies. Thus, the two wealthiest countries in the world, the United States and Norway, are comparable in average income, but Norway enjoys both higher average life expectancy than the United States and a more equitable income distribution.

The **income inequality hypothesis**, also known as the Wilkinson hypothesis, has been controversial from the outset. Importantly, a number of prominent sociologists believe that income in and of itself has a far larger impact on health than does income inequality (Mechanic, 2006). For example, since 1980 income inequality has soared in the United States. If income inequality strongly affected health, life expectancy should have fallen for all Americans. In fact, however, life expectancy fell only for poorer Americans, suggesting that income rather than income inequality is by far the more important factor (Krieger et al., 2008; Ezzati et al., 2008). Others have found that the relationship between income inequality and health disappears once statistical analyses **control** for compositional factors, such as individual-level income. Wilkinson and Pickett (2006) have countered these critiques by suggesting that individual income is not a genuine confounder but is a different aspect of social stratification and therefore should not be controlled. They also maintain that several studies that do include individual-level income as a control variable continue to find that income inequality has an effect on health over and above individual-level income.

income inequality hypothesis:
The supposition that for low-income countries, absolute measures of income are stronger predictors of the health of the population, but among high-income countries, relative income differences are the more important predictors of population health.

Income Inequality in Canada

Despite the fact that there are a number of different ways to assess income inequality, there is general consensus that income inequality in Canada has been increasing over the past few decades. Heisz (2007) reported that the distribution of after-tax family income in Canada was relatively stable during the 1980s, but from the 1990s forward, income inequality increased over time. Growing income inequality occurred when income levels for those at the upper end of the income distribution made rapid gains, while the income for those at the bottom of the distribution stagnated. Thus, the income of the wealthiest 10% increased by 24% between 1989 and 2004, but for those in the lowest income decile (tenth percentile), incomes fell by 8% during this same period. Further evidence of the growing gap between the wealthy and the poor in Canadian society appeared in a recent study that examined difference in after-tax family income for those living in the wealthiest 5% of neighbour-hoods compared to the poorest 5% of neighbourhoods in Canada's eight largest cities (Chen, Myles, and Picot, 2012). Their findings, shown in Table 4.3, demonstrate that in nearly all cities, the ratio between the after-tax family income of those living in the wealthiest 5% of neighbourhoods and that of those living in the poorest 5% of neighbourhoods grew larger between 1980 and 2005. For example, those living in Calgary's wealthiest neighbourhoods earned 1.9 times as much as those in Calgary's poorest neighbourhoods in 1980; however, by 2005 it had expanded to become nearly a three-fold difference in the incomes between the wealthiest and poorest.

If the income inequality hypothesis is true, what evidence exists for the association between income inequality and health in Canada? Findings to date are mixed: an Ontario study reported that self-rated health was lower among communities with high income inequality (Xi et al., 2005), whereas a Québec study found that the association between com-munity level income inequality and mortality was not significant and sometimes displayed the opposite association (Auger, Zang, and Daniel, 2009). As such, this is an ongoing area of inquiry, with little consensus in the literature about the nature of the association. Given that the Great Recession has served to increase income inequality around the world, researchers also anticipate that evaluating the impact of this shift on the health of the population will be an important area of research in the future.

TABLE 4.3 Ratio of After-Tax Family Income for Wealthiest 5% of Neighbourhoods Relative to Poorest 5% of Neighbourhoods in Eight Canadian Cities, 1980 and 2005

	1980	2005
Toronto	2.1	2.9
Montréal	2.0	2.6
Vancouver	1.9	2.1
Ottawa-Gatineau	2.0	2.2
Québec City	1.9	1.9
Calgary	1.9	2.9
Edmonton	1.7	2.2
Winnipeg	1.9	2.5

Source: Adapted from: Wen-Hao Chen, John Myles, & Garnett Picot, "Why have poorer neighbourhoods stagnated economically while the richer have flourished? Neighbourhood income inequality in Canadian cities," *Urban Studies*, Vol. 49: Pg. 877-96. 2012.

INTERSECTING SOCIOECONOMIC POSITION WITH OTHER STATUSES

In the past two chapters, we have reviewed the different ways in which age, sex and gender, race and ethnicity, and socioeconomic position are associated with morbidity, mortality, and unhealthy behaviours. For the most part, we have treated these statuses in isolation, examining how each is uniquely associated with health outcomes. But none of us can be defined or described in just one dimension. We inhabit various social locations simultaneously, and it is at the intersections of these converging social locations that opportunities and constraints for health are fully realized.

Exploring how these various statuses intersect to influence health is a critical task for sociologists of health and illness (Rosenfield, 2012). Researchers pose such questions as: Which statuses are relatively more influential than the others in producing illness and death? That is, does race trump gender, or does socioeconomic position matter more than age? Moreover, are the effects of different statuses on health additive? For example, do poor First Nations women experience a form of triple jeopardy when it comes to their health risks? Or, is it the case that multiple disadvantaged statuses combine to produce paradoxical consequences for health? That is, can the health effects of a devalued status be mitigated when one has high status in another domain?

These are not easy questions to answer, for they require more than a passing familiarity with many different theories and an ability to understand how these theories might interweave. Moving forward, however, requires researchers to delve into the inherent complexities of what it means to occupy different social locations simultaneously. These challenges will undoubtedly stimulate new theories and ideas, just as a life course approach has substantially improved our insight into the dynamic lifelong processes that underlie socioeconomic inequalities in health.

At the same time, we must admit that our understanding of the social determinants of health is still incomplete. We have discussed the influence of different statuses on health outcomes, but we have not yet investigated how individuals both behave and see themselves in their social worlds. Our social locations may visibly and not so visibly shape our life chances, but they are only part of our social makeup. Beyond our different positions in the social structures of our societies, we are known and identified by the functions we perform—the roles that we variously acquire and shed as we move through life. We are daughters, sons, siblings, mothers, fathers, lovers, spouses, housewives, househusbands, grandparents, workers, volunteers—and each of these roles is an important influence on our health. As such, we turn our attention to the ways in which work and family roles affect health and well-being in the next chapter.

IMPLICATIONS

Far from being purely biological conditions reflecting purely biological factors, health and illness are intimately interwoven with social position. In Canada as elsewhere, those who are socioeconomically disadvantaged live shorter lives, are more frequently diagnosed with disease, and acquire more unhealthy habits than those who are wealthier.

Because social forces as well as biological factors affect health, understanding social trends can help us predict future health trends. Global economic instability and growing income inequality are likely to do more than rattle the nerves of millions. Indeed, where one is positioned in our socially structured societies is likely to determine how well one is able to ride out these storms and, in the process, to profoundly influence one's risk for illness and death.

Crises have a way of making the entire population feel anxious and vulnerable. The Great Depression was devastating and unprecedented in its impact; getting past it required new ways of thinking about society. In the current economic crisis, there is a similar opportunity to reflect about the kind of society we want for ourselves and for the next generation. What new ideas will emerge to change how we implement solutions, and what effect these social transformations will have on the health of the population, are yet to be discovered but will surely be known in the years and decades to come.

SUMMARY

LO-1   1.   Knowledge of the association between poverty and health has existed for centuries, occupying the writings of social reformers throughout the ages. The Black Report, published in Britain in 1980, is a watershed report that continues to inform our current understandings of how socioeconomic position is associated with health outcomes.

LO-2   2.   Socioeconomic differences do not vary simply between the wealthy and the poor, but rather there is a gradient pattern such that each corresponding increase in socioeconomic position is associated with a stepwise reduced risk for mortality and morbidity.

LO-2   3.   There is a large body of Canadian research to confirm that the socioeconomic gradient in health can be found regardless of whether health is measured through mortality, cause-specific mortality, morbidity, or health behaviours and has been detected in every region of Canada, at every age group, for both men and women, and across all racial and ethnic groups.

LO-3   4.   The authors of the Black Report proposed four explanations for the association between social class and health, rejecting two and accepting the remaining two explanations. Each of these explanations has produced separate avenues of investigation that have led to new insights in the field in socioeconomic inequalities in health.

LO-3   5.   The first, artefact, suggests that the relationship is artificially produced as a result of the way that either social class or health is measured. Although it has been rejected as a potential explanation by the authors of the Black Report, subsequent researchers have tried to stave off such critiques by developing more systematic measures of socioeconomic position and health and integrating research questions with existing theories of stratification and inequality.

LO-3   6.   Social selection, which hypothesizes that health is a cause, not a consequence, of socioeconomic position, was also initially rejected by the authors of the Black Report; however, there is now growing recognition that this pathway has some validity, even though in the majority of cases, the direction is such that socioeconomic position influences health, not vice versa.

LO-3   7.   The second two explanations suggest that social factors are causally implicated in health, but there is debate on what matters more. The materialist explanation posits that those who have a lower socioeconomic position experience worse health than persons with a more advantaged position because of the differences in their material conditions of living. Thus, better working conditions, fewer environmental hazards, safer housing, more nutritious diets, and generally better access to health care together operate to benefit health for those higher up on the socioeconomic ladder.

LO-3   8.   The cultural/behavioural explanation originally reflected the concerns of the authors of the Black Report, who thought entrenched unhealthy behaviours among the poor would not change even if poverty and economic hardship were eradicated. The updated interpretation suggests that improved health among those who are advantaged stems not only from their material resources but also from the psychosocial boost one gets from occupying a privileged position in the social hierarchy. Moreover, resources can be more than material. Social capital is created when people are able to benefit from their social ties by exchanging goods and information and caring for one another. In some instances, high levels of social capital may offset the lack of material resources.

LO-4   9. A life course perspective has four principles: (a) lives are uniquely shaped by the specific historical times and places one passes through on the journey through life; (b) lives are linked to the lives of others, with shared relationships infusing the experiences of individuals as social groups form and dissolve over the life course; (c) individuals actively construct their own life courses through the choices and actions they take when presented with structural opportunities and constraints; and (d) the timing of events matters to the extent that off-time or unexpected events have the potential to derail and deflect developmental trajectories, whereas on-time and expected events reinforce an orderly developmental trajectory.

LO-4   10. A life course approach to socioeconomic inequalities in health research has led to valuable insights. These include the fetal programming hypothesis, which contends that prenatal exposure to malnutrition biologically imprints on the developing organism and affects health outcomes in adulthood, and the cumulative advantage hypothesis, which posits that compounding returns on early advantages lead to diverging destinies in health over time between those who come from opposite ends of the socioeconomic ladder.

LO-5   11. The income inequality hypothesis suggests that absolute income matters for health only in those places where most people struggle to survive. Once basic needs are meet, relative income differences play a greater role in the health of the population. Consequently, populations where the gap between the wealthiest and poorest is large tend to have worse health outcomes on average than populations where the gap is smaller.

LO-5   12. Existing research on the income inequality hypothesis has been strongly criticized on methodological grounds, yet studies continue to document the association. Given that the Great Recession has generated startlingly high levels of income inequality around the world, further research on the health consequences of income equality and global economic instability is urgently needed.

LO-6   13. Although there are formidable theoretical challenges to conquer, exploring the intersections among age, sex and gender, race and ethnicity, and socioeconomic position in a way that fully captures their complexity may one day answer persisting questions about whether the effects of multiple disadvantage on health outcomes are additive or interactive.

REVIEW QUESTIONS

1. What does it mean to say that there is a gradient relationship between socioeconomic position and health status?
2. Describe how the health of Canadians is patterned by socioeconomic position.
3. Why does socioeconomic position affect the health of Canadians?
4. What are the unique health problems of homeless persons?
5. Why is a life course approach important for understanding how socioeconomic position is related to health status?
6. What is the income inequality hypothesis?
7. How have patterns of income inequality in Canada changed over time?
8. Why is it important to understand how different facets of disadvantage intersect to influence health?

CRITICAL THINKING QUESTIONS

1. Explain why poor persons become ill more often and die younger than wealthier persons.

2. Assume that over the next twenty years the poor increasingly adopt healthier behaviour patterns. What changes would you expect to see in the socioeconomic gradient in health? Explain your answer.

3. In an effort to improve the health of the population, should Canada develop policies to reduce poverty or to reduce income inequality? How are these different and which of the two would you identify as more important? Justify your choice.

KEY TERMS

avoidable deaths (p. 76)

biological embedding (p. 82)

critical period (p. 82)

cumulative advantage hypothesis (p. 92)

fetal programming hypothesis (p. 83)

food security (p. 86)

income inequality (p. 92)

income inequality hypothesis (p. 93)

latency (p. 90)

low-income cutoffs (LICOs) (p. 81)

social capital (p. 89)

social causation (p. 85)

social selection (p. 84)

socioeconomic gradient in health (p. 74)

5

Work and Family Life: The Influence of Social Roles on Health and Illness

Frank Strohschein

The Modern Dad's Dilemma

[My dad's] home life was very structured, and there were expected roles children were supposed to play. He told me a story once about Sundays in Chelsea—Sunday was visiting time, you go to church, and then you walk through the neighborhood, where all the relatives live, and do visits all afternoon. My dad, who was an only child, was expected to be seen and not heard. The adults had adult conversation, and he was usually not included in any of their activities. He determined that when he had children, he wasn't going to be like his dad. My wife's dad was the same way. So both men have made a really big effort to change with their own children. I think that plays a large part in the way my wife and I are raising our daughter.

When I was a kid, if my dad went to work on a Saturday or we weren't in school, we had the option to go with him. We used to love walking through the machine shop and seeing all the guys working on lathes, and we loved walking through the blueprint room. And then there was the diner. I remember when the guys would change shifts and we'd hear them chatting; they'd be using dirty language, and we just loved it. The guys talked to us and let us hang out. We never heard anything like, "You kids don't belong here." …

…[t]he other day at the fire station, I watched Hayden play basketball with some of the guys. They lowered the hoop for her and everything. I thought to myself, Isn't it great that they can include a child like that? My wife and I have surrounded ourselves with people who are willing to do that. For the most part, if we go somewhere, we want to be able to bring our daughter and include her. She's not an accessory that we take somewhere and plop down and say, Okay, stay here, and when we're done, we'll get you. It's not that way. We include Hayden in every area of our life. I also think that playing with my daughter, in her world, helps to build trust and keep our relationship strong. It can be too easy to get caught up in paying bills and worrying about how much oil costs and to lose our sense of imagination and playfulness. We can forget how much fun it is to build a fort, do a puzzle, or splash in a pool….

...[a]s a firefighter, you're there to fix a problem, my job is to show up, do my best to help make things better, and then move on. But I can't come home and do that. I need to be able to come home and invest myself in the relationships with my wife and daughter; I've got to be willing to open up emotionally and deal with everything. We don't deal with emotions much at the fire department. We don't have to deal with Mr. Smith going into the hospital with burn injuries. I'm not saying we don't care, but it's, just a switch you have to turn off.

When I get home from work, early in the morning, I need to restart my day so I can get rid of that portion of it and be an active member of the family. I get out of my uniform, take a shower, get a cup of coffee, read the paper for a few minutes. If I get out of work late, or if something keeps me from getting that full restart, I go into my own little shell or I get very grumpy. To have the patience to listen to Hayden can be very difficult. Fortunately, she likes to tell me when I'm being grumpy. Then I realize I need to take my time and decompress. I'm not necessarily a good listener. I really have to work at it....

Source: Based on the book *The Modern Dad's Dilemma*. Copyright © 2010 by John Badalament. Reprinted with permission of New World Library, Novato, CA. www.newworldlibrary.com.

In this chapter, students should be able to:

LO-1 **Understand** the value of integrating stress process and a life course approach to understand how work and family roles influence health and well-being.

LO-2 **Describe** changes in the patterns of work over the course of the twentieth century and into the present.

LO-3 **Understand** how employment and working conditions are related to physical and mental health.

LO-4 **Describe** changes in marital behaviour and fertility over the course of the twentieth century and into the present.

LO-5 **Understand** how marital status and changes in marital status are related to physical and mental health.

LO-6 **Recognize** what is meant by work-life balance and describe patterns of work-to-family conflict and family-to-work conflict in the Canadian population as well as associations with mental health outcomes.

As the opening vignette illustrates, how individuals perceive and engage in family and work life has undergone profound social change from past generations. Some of these changes have been positive, but other trends have served to reduce the overall security of Canadians. In particular, the ideal image of a stable career and family life has receded into a distant memory as growing numbers of Canadians face the reality of jobs and intimate relationships that no longer last a lifetime.

Our social roles, as workers and family members, have important consequences for well-being because these roles regulate how we interact with others around us and embed us in networks of support and mutual obligation. These roles can be immensely satisfying, but they can also be sources of stress. Using insights from stress process and a life course approach, we outline the ways in which work and family roles can alternately protect us from or increase our risk for disease and death. We also address the issue of whether the dramatic transformations that have occurred in paid employment and family life are producing new vulnerabilities for poor health. Finally, we discuss the emerging issue of work-life balance as a social determinant of health and explore how this issue is being investigated in the Canadian context.

REVISITING STRESS PROCESS AND A LIFE COURSE APPROACH

We reintroduce two conceptual models, stress process and a life course approach, first discussed in Chapters 2 and 4, respectively. To review briefly, stress process is a model that helps us to understand how stressors, occurring as either **stressful life events** or **chronic strains**, undermine health and well-being. In this chapter, we are interested in the health-related consequences of transitions in and out of work and family roles that are experienced as stressful, as well as the health effects of **role strain**, which refers to the problems individuals experience within their major social roles as workers and family members. As we will see, role strain can arise in a variety of different contexts, such as when people occupy unwanted roles or roles that exceed resources and abilities, or when they experience rapidly changing roles or conflicting roles.

A life course approach comprises four principles that help sociologists to understand cohort-specific patterns of age-graded movement in and out of institutional roles and statuses over the lifespan. Two principles in particular are relevant. First, the notion of linked lives posits that people do not exist in a social vacuum but are embedded in a social network of relationships. As such, events do not just affect the lives of individuals. Rather, the ripple effects of the event are experienced collectively by all those within one's social network. Thus, parental divorce does not just result in a changed environment for parents but has implications for the well-being of children, as well as in-laws and the former couple's circle of friends, all of whom will need to renegotiate their relationship with all of the other parties connected to the newly separated couple and each of whom may be affected in different ways by the breakdown of the marriage. A second principle of a life course approach reiterates the importance of the sequencing and timing of life transitions for understanding how biographies unfold. In particular, developing competencies either on- or off-schedule has consequences for the possibility of acquiring future resources and skills that serve to propel some individuals forward and hold others back. This process has been labelled *cumulative advantage.*

What stress process and a life course approach have in common, then, is an interest in understanding how people navigate transitions, albeit for different reasons (Pearlin, 2010b). That is, stress process views transitions in terms of their potential for overwhelming coping and adaptation, whereas a life course approach regards transitions as markers of an individual's movement through the life course (Pearlin, 2010b). Yet, when both are used in tandem, researchers obtain unique insight. For example, when they are viewed from a life course perspective, it is clear that stressors vary across the different stages of life, helping to focus attention on particular moments when individuals may be especially vulnerable. Thus, the transition to adulthood has historically followed a sequence of milestones whereby one finishes schooling, begins a career, leaves the parental home, finds a partner, and starts to raise children. The sheer number of changes in this short period and the ways in which these act as a launch pad, determining subsequent ability to stockpile resources that can be drawn upon in later life, necessarily mean that this is an area that garners substantial sociological interest. In addition, to the extent that recent cohorts of young adults have begun to delay these transitions or follow a different sequence than their parents or grandparents, researchers have begun to investigate the implications of these new trends for the health and well-being of young adults (Furstenberg, 2010).

Moreover, by recognizing that a number of stressors are more likely to occur at specific stages in the life course, researchers can evaluate the consequences of transitions that unfold on- versus off-time. For example, the death of one's spouse may be more troubling in early adulthood than in late life, when it is more likely to be an anticipated event. Similarly, that job loss for a 60-year-old results in unwanted early retirement but is a temporary blip for a 20-year-old, who can more easily move to a place where job prospects are better and still has years to save for retirement, suggests differential effects of stressful life events for individuals of different ages.

These are just a few of the ways in which stress process and a life course approach can enhance understanding of the social determinants of health. As we turn to the task of under-standing how work and family roles influence health and well-being, we will continue to draw on both to further demonstrate the insights obtained through these complementary conceptual models.

WORK AND HEALTH

The Changing World of Work

Paid employment not only provides individuals with the material resources needed to main-tain well-being but is also a source of dignity, self-fulfillment, and identity. One of the first things people do when they are introduced is ask what the other does for a living, signalling just how important work is both as a social value and as a source of identity. Because work is so central to our lives, it has a tremendous influence on our health and well-being.

Yet large-scale structural change in the nature of work itself over the course of the twentieth century has transformed the ways in which Canadians participate in the workforce. Although a complete analysis is beyond the scope of this chapter, we briefly discuss three major shifts: the shift from a manufacturing-based economy to the new knowledge economy, globaliza-tion, and women's participation in the labour market.

At the beginning of the twentieth century, new ideas about economic production began to transform the world of work. Instead of artisanal goods that were created through skilled craftsmanship on a one-off basis, goods came to be mass-produced, which is to say that goods were produced on both a large scale and in a standardized way. Mass-produced goods could be made at a lower cost, thereby increasing their affordability to a larger swath of the popu-lation. Greater consumption of mass-produced goods in turn stimulated further demand. Consequently, the new era of mass-produced goods generated immense wealth, improved living standards dramatically in Western nations, and ushered in a period of relatively stable economic growth through the first three-quarters of the twentieth century.

Underlying the shift to mass production was the philosophy of **scientific management**, which used the methods of science to exert greater control and efficiency over the produc-tion process. Rather than one individual who was involved in every step of transforming raw material into a finished product, scientific management broke down the entire production process into a series of tasks. Using time-and-motion studies that linked each action to its length of time to complete, it was possible to generate a detailed description of how to per-form each task in the most efficient manner. A worker could then be assigned to perform that same task repetitively in an assembly-line process. Once Henry Ford adapted scientific management for the mass production of automobiles by designing an automated assembly line that forced workers to work at a fixed pace set by management, this mode of production came to be known as **Fordism**.

This new mode of production had both benefits and costs for workers. To ensure that workers would be able to purchase mass goods, they were paid higher wages and guaranteed stable employment. This living wage made it possible for families to specialize: men found themselves employed in a lifelong, well-paid job on the shop floor of a manufacturing plant, whereas women were able to stay at home and raise children. But the costs were also enor-mous. The repetitive nature of the work was physically demanding and mindless. Indeed, the

scientific management:
A method of producing goods that emphasized making people work more efficiently by breaking down a large task into its smallest components and assigning each component to a worker who had been instructed on how the work should be done and how long it should take.

Fordism:
A method of producing goods that combines the principles of scientific management with an automated assembly line to achieve even greater efficiency.

goal of scientific management was to remove the thinking capacity of the employee and place it in the hands of managers, who controlled every move of their workers. As such, workers no longer needed to be skilled tradespeople; indeed, their task could be performed by anyone, making them redundant and interchangeable. Finally, by turning them into mindless automatons repeating the same motion over and over again, workers on the assembly line were denied the sense of accomplishment that comes with designing and creating a product from beginning to end. Lack of control over the production process and lack of pride in a finished product inevitably fostered feelings of alienation and low job satisfaction among workers.

Although the principles of scientific management and the Fordist mode of production dominated much of the twentieth century, its influence waned as a new mode of production, called flexible production (or lean production), rose to prominence. Whereas Fordism was based on ownership of the entire supply chain, new competitive advantages came from outsourcing parts to other companies that could produce them more efficiently. The shipment of outsourced parts into the assembly plant began to occur on a just-in-time basis, achieving a new level of cost savings as companies no longer needed to make and store parts in advance. Perhaps even more dramatically, flexible production meant that goods were no longer generically produced for a single mass market, but rather the production of goods became almost entirely consumer driven. That is, companies such as Walmart created a computerized supply chain system to track each item on their shelves and redistribute products based on patterns of consumption. If a certain item is popular in one region of the country but sits on shelves in another part of the country, Walmart is alerted to this trend and will quickly shift its products to be in the right place to maximize sales. Similarly, car manufacturers are able to reorganize their production lines quickly to adapt to market responses. As such, the manufacturing process in the twenty-first century has become flexible, agile, and consumer oriented, rendering nearly obsolete the immense, multilayered factories of the twentieth century.

Instead of viewing the worker as a mindless automaton, flexible production began to recognize the worker as the most knowledgeable about the production process and the most likely to find ways of improving efficiency. Companies now began to need committed and involved workers who had the most up-to-date skills and training and could exercise their authority and knowledge in the workplace. Thus, these new knowledge workers required a workplace that was flattened, or characterized by a less hierarchical production process. The shift from repetitive, low-skilled production work to highly skilled knowledge work seemed to match the predictions of Daniel Bell (1973), who believed that this new postindustrial economy would improve the fortunes of workers.

The shift from Fordism to flexible production was undoubtedly hastened by the forces of **globalization**. As we noted earlier, globalization is the process through which ideas, resources, and persons increasingly operate within a worldwide rather than a local framework. As other countries around the world began to compete in the world economy, emerging economies, such as Brazil, China, and India, were able to produce goods at a fraction of what it cost in Canada or the United States. Lured by the lower costs of production, a wave of factories in North America began to shift their operations overseas. To offset the loss of these key manufacturing industries, Western countries moved toward a knowledge economy, which viewed knowledge as both a product and a tool for creating wealth. That is, the ability to collect vast amounts of information and to act on that information in ways that create wealth is now seen as necessary to compete in a global economy. Aided by a trend in which computer and information systems have become less expensive and more integrated and therefore capable of producing even greater amounts of information, the demand for knowledge workers who can exploit these information systems to generate wealth has grown exponentially.

As with mass production, however, flexible production and globalization have conferred both positive and negative changes on workers' conditions. That is, there has emerged a growing divide in the world of work, whereby jobs are increasingly separated into good versus bad. Good jobs are occupied by knowledge workers, who are highly paid for their work and whose conditions of work are such that they have high levels of independence and derive great satisfaction from engaging in its stimulating challenges. On the other hand, those who lack the needed skills in the new economy find themselves relegated to bad jobs, where they are paid a low wage; have little job security; and continue to perform mindless, repetitive, and unfulfilling work. Thus, Bell's prediction of the new worker in the postindustrial economy has only been partially fulfilled: few have attained the ideal. Importantly, as we learned in the tech bubble of the early 2000s, even the knowledge worker has a precarious grasp on the labour market and can be let go in an instant. Consequently, to be a worker in the new economy is to be under continuous pressure to update and renew one's skill level to maintain a competitive advantage in the workforce.

The loss of the living wage, whereby men no longer enjoyed high-paying stable jobs in a factory setting, also had implications for family life by making obsolete the specialized functions of men and women. Forced to compete with workers in developing countries, workers saw their wages stagnate and even decline as they accepted wage rollbacks just to keep their jobs from moving overseas. Increasingly, the shrinking factory wages of men were not sufficient to meet the needs of the household, destroying the male breadwinner model, whereby men entered the world of work and women remained in the home. That is, the earning capacity of women came to be seen as critical to the economic well-being of the household. Moreover, women themselves were demanding and exercising their right to participate in the labour market on an equal footing with men. Consequently, women's labour force attachment has changed, becoming longer and more continuous than it once was.

Having won their struggle, women soon found themselves with the challenge of the second shift (Hochschild, 1989). The **second shift** refers to the daily chores that still awaited women when they returned home from a full day of paid work. As such, women found it enormously difficult to achieve work-life balance. As men's roles also changed, they too faced the time pressures of meeting the demands of both work and home.

In sum, the world of work has been radically transformed, with mixed benefit for workers. The emergence of the global economy led to the demise of manufacturing industries in North America, paving the way for a new knowledge economy, which ushered in growing inequality as knowledge workers were handsomely rewarded for their work while wages in factory work stagnated or declined. The deterioration of the living wage for male factory workers rendered the work of men more insecure and pulled women into the world of work. While women's paid employment helped to keep the family afloat financially, both men and women increasingly found it difficult to achieve work-life balance. Similarly, the bifurcation of work into good and bad jobs meant that while some enjoyed the rewards of participating in the new knowledge economy, many more continued to labour in inhospitable environments.

It is to the nature of workplace stressors and their influence on health and well-being that we turn next. We first review differences in health between the unemployed and employed, before more critically examining the physical and psychosocial conditions of work that influence the health and well-being of workers.

second shift:
The daily chores that still awaited women when they returned home from a full day of paid work.

Unemployment and Health

Research over the past few decades has shown that the risk for death and disease for those in paid employment is significantly lower on average than it is for those who are unemployed (Garcy and Vågerö, 2012; Jin, Shah, and Svoboda, 1995; Repetti, Matthews, and Waldron, 1989; Wadsworth, Montgomery, and Bartley, 1999; Wanberg, 2012). The relationship also holds true in Canada, with Romans and her colleagues reporting that rates of depression were significantly higher among unemployed Canadians than among those who were employed (Romans, Cohen, and Forte, 2011). American research has shown that men who experienced job loss subsequently experienced nearly a doubling of their mortality risk in the period immediately following the loss relative to those who retained their jobs (Sullivan and von Wachter, 2009). Following on the life course principle of linked lives, Lindo (2011) found that the health effects of job loss also extended to unborn children. That is, children born after a father's job loss weighed significantly less than children born into households where fathers remained employed throughout pregnancy.

Researchers have variously interpreted the association between unemployment and health. The association could reflect the health consequences of socioeconomic shocks that accompany job loss, or, alternatively, it may be that those in poor health are viewed as risky by potential employers and therefore unlikely to find and keep a job. To date, the evidence suggests that both social selection (poor health makes it unlikely one will be employed) and social causation (unemployment causes poor health) are valid pathways.

Applying the conceptual model of stress process to job loss, researchers have begun to identify the possible sequence of subsequent stressors that might further overwhelm an individual's capacity to cope. Indeed, job loss, as is the case with many other stressful events, often unleashes other stressors in a process called **stress proliferation** (Pearlin, Aneshensel, and LeBlanc, 1997). In research on the health consequences of job loss, the event itself is treated as a primary stressor, which does not mean that it is the most important stressor, only that it is the first in the sequence of stressors. If job loss had not happened, none of the other stressors would have happened either. Similarly, secondary stressors are identified by their chronological appearance—they occur after and because of the occurrence of a primary stressor. Sometimes the secondary stressors are even more devastating for health than the primary stressors. Importantly, understanding stress proliferation may help reveal why job loss and unemployment are more stressful for some people than for others, and why the health effects of job loss vary from person to person.

To elaborate on how stress proliferation may help explain variation in the health consequences of job loss, we point out that it is clear that some individuals who experience job loss are able to bounce back relatively quickly. For them, job loss is a temporary setback, and they soon find other employment and carry on with their lives. For others, however, job loss leads to prolonged unemployment and a new set of problems. Unable to find work, an individual may be forced to cut back on expenses to make ends meet, and some may use up their entire life savings. In turn, financial strain may increase tension among family members, who resent living in straitened circumstances and blame the unemployed individual for their failure to get another job. Some marriages even end when chronic unemployment befalls a spouse. In other scenarios, persistent unemployment forces individuals to sell off prized possessions and perhaps even downsize their living accommodations. Each of these dislocations is experienced as stressful. As these stressors pile up and the ripple effects of job loss touch every aspect of an individual's life, it should come as no surprise that the cumulative effects of these stressors wear more heavily on these individuals than for those who experience unemployment for a brief period of time. Thus, although there is wide variation in the type and sequence of secondary stressors following job loss, it is the accumulation of stressors that helps us to understand why some individuals reach their breaking point.

Of course, other factors come into play as well. The intersections of age, sex and gender, race and ethnicity, and socioeconomic position also shape how job loss is experienced and whether there are opportunities for overcoming job loss. Thus, research on the health effects of movement in and out of social roles, including transitions in and out of the labour market, needs to be placed in a context that recognizes these other factors.

stress proliferation:
The process by which an initial stressor gives rise to other stressors.

Workplace Safety

For those who are in paid employment, the workplace can be a dangerous place. Workplace fatalities in Canada are very rare events, yet, as can be seen in Table 5.1, numbers have been steadily creeping upward over the past two decades. Unfortunately, these data, generated by the Association of Workers' Compensation Boards of Canada, actually underestimate the total number of deaths per year because they don't include deaths that occur in workplaces not covered by the Workers' Compensation Board, such as the workplaces of those who are self-employed.

Many more people, of course, do not die but become injured on the job. Some of the most dangerous occupations in Canada are mining, logging, and construction, whereas the jobs with the fewest injuries are those in the financial and insurance industries. Given the loss of manufacturing jobs that involved heavy industrial work in the factory setting and the emergence of less physically demanding computer work in an office, one might presume that office work entails fewer health risks. This appears not to be true. Because many office jobs still require their employees to perform repetitive tasks, such as entering information on a keyboard for prolonged periods of time, soft tissue injuries such as repetitive strain injury have become increasingly common. **Repetitive strain injury (RSI)** is a general term used to label injuries to the tendons or nerves that often result from repetitive movements and that express themselves as pain, numbness, and tingling in the affected body part. In 2000, approximately one in ten Canadian adults reported having experienced an RSI in the past twelve months, and more than half reported that these injuries had occurred in the workplace (Tjepkema, 2003). Importantly, Tjepkema found that those who indicated that their jobs were quite or extremely stressful were significantly more likely to have experienced an RSI than those who indicated that their job was not at all stressful.

In the previous chapter, we noted that socioeconomic position may influence health through the types of jobs people hold, with greater protection afforded to those whose jobs minimize their exposure to physical hazards. In each instance, it is the workers who are at the bottom of the social hierarchy that face the greatest risk. Thus, the low-level office worker who regularly uses the photocopier or printer has greater exposure to the carcinogenic materials found in toner cartridges than the office manager, whose exposure is less frequent. Similarly, agricultural workers may be exposed to pesticides that lead to birth deformities in their offspring, whereas the landowner rarely has any direct exposure to pesticides.

Many of the most hazardous jobs are performed by those who hold little power and occupy marginal positions in our societies. For example, thousands of migrant workers come to Canada every year from Mexico on temporary visas to work in the agricultural industry. Research suggests that too many of these workers are poorly trained, are not given adequate

repetitive strain injury (RSI):
The injuries to tendons or nerves that often result from repetitive movements and that express themselves as pain, numbness, and tingling in the affected body part.

Year	Deaths
1993	758
1997	833
2001	919
2004	928
2007	1,055
2010	1,014

TABLE 5.1 Work-Related Fatalities, Selected Years, Canada, 1993–2010

Source: Adapted from: Association of Workers' Compensation Boards of Canada, 2012, *Number of Fatalities, by Jurisdiction, 1993-2010.* Found at: http://www.awcbc.org/common/assets/nwisptables/fat_summary_jurisdiction.pdf (accessed June, 2012).

protective equipment, toil in conditions where they lack access to basic sanitary facilities, and are generally afraid of losing their jobs if they report illness or injury (Otero and Preibisch, 2009). Wherever one goes in Canada, it isn't hard to find jobs that pose a threat to human health, and more often than not, these jobs are performed by those with little power to change their work situation. Box 5.1 provides one such example by exploring the health risks associated with employment in a nail salon.

Psychosocial Aspects of Work

The psychosocial aspects of work have just as much influence on health as the physical environment of the workplace and have attracted substantial research attention over the past few decades (Väänänen et al., 2012). The demand-control model, as originally outlined by Karasek (1979), is probably the most well-known way that researchers theorize about how the psychosocial aspects of work matter for health. Karasek characterized employment along two

BOX 5.1
Time for a Pedicure?

Going for a pedicure has almost attained the status of a Canadian ritual. Over the summer months in particular, a steady stream of women flock to nail salons, hoping to revitalize tired feet and show off trim, elegant toes in fashionable sandals. At the salon, nail technicians work quickly, dipping their clients' feet in warm water before stripping off old nail polish, shaping nails into squares or ovals, and applying a fresh coat of nail polish.

The booming nail salon industry leaves the impression that customers are very satisfied with the service, and that what is good for the health of the customer is good for all. Indeed, if concerns about health are expressed, they tend to come from customers who worry about the perceived health risks of getting a pedicure. They want to know, for example, that the instruments used are sterile so that fungal infections are not transferred from client to client.

Yet working conditions are far from ideal in the nail salon industry. The work is low paying, involving long work hours and hard work. It also involves exposure to a wide array of hazardous chemicals. Nail polish contains formaldehyde, which can lead to and exacerbate asthma, and both nail polish and nail polish remover contain acetone, which can cause headaches and dizziness. More frighteningly, constant exposure to toxic chemicals such as toluene and dibutyl phthalate has been associated with a number of reproductive problems, including birth deformities in offspring. Workers are not only exposed to these chemicals, as well human nail dust, on a daily basis, but heighten their risk by working in closed, poorly ventilated spaces. Breathing masks, when provided, are helpful for reducing dust exposure but do not protect workers from dangerous fumes.

Reducing workers' health risks is costly and viewed as infeasible in a fiercely competitive industry where profit margins are razor thin. Because statistics on health-related problems in salon work are not collected, the extent of the problem cannot be known with precision. In addition, nail technicians, many of whom are recent immigrants to Canada and have had little experience in the Canadian labour market, may be afraid to complain or unaware that they can complain about their work conditions to the ministry of labour. To the extent that these workers, comprising mainly immigrant women, have become trapped in these job ghettos and are unable to find work that poses fewer risks to health, there are ongoing concerns that these workers are being exploited and unduly exposed to risk.

dimensions: **job demands**, which refer to the extent to which workers feel that they are free from time constraints to perform a task and are not overwhelmed with too many or conflicting tasks, and **job control**, which assesses the degree to which tasks in the workplace are varied and require skill and workers are able to decide for themselves how best to perform tasks.

Karasek then combined these two dimensions to create four job profiles. Active jobs are those where high job demands are matched by high job control. Such jobs are found among those who are professionals or in management positions. Passive jobs are those where both job demands and job control are low. These types of jobs include work as sales clerks or cashiers in a grocery store, parking lot attendants, and janitors. High-strain jobs combine high job demands with low job control. Manufacturing jobs that operate on an assembly line fall in this category, as do jobs as high-pressure sales reps and call centre operators. Finally, low-strain jobs combine low job demands with high job control and include appliance repair technicians, mortgage brokers, insurance salespersons, and the self-employed.

Research by Karasek and others suggests that the job profile that confers the greatest risk to health is the high-strain job. Thus, those who work under conditions where they have little say over how they perform their job and experience high job demands are at greater risk for cardiovascular disease, mental illness, injury, and mortality (de Jonge et al., 2000; Krause et al., 1997; Marmot, Bosma, and Hemingway, 1997; McDonough, 2001). Low-strain jobs appear to be the least damaging to health, with the health effects of active and passive jobs falling somewhere between low-strain and high-strain jobs.

Psychosocial Work Conditions and Health in Contemporary Canadian Society

In Table 5.2, we present data from the 2011 Canada Work Stress and Health survey, which asked a nationally representative sample of working Canadian adults about the level of job control and demands that they experience in paid employment. The majority of Canadian workers indicated that their jobs allow them to develop their skills and abilities (85.9%) and that they had the freedom to decide how to do their jobs (60.0%). Similarly, less than half of Canadian workers indicated that they are frequently given too many tasks to work on at once (40.5%) and that the demands of work frequently exceed the time available to do the job (34.5%). Finally, the proportion of Canadians who hold high-strain jobs (characterized by both high job demands and low job control) is very low (2.6%). These findings suggest that most workers do not experience high levels of job stress in the workplace.

job demands:
The extent to which workers feel that they are free from time constraints to perform a task and are not overwhelmed with too many or conflicting tasks.

job control:
The degree to which tasks in the workplace are varied and require skill and workers are able to decide for themselves how best to perform tasks.

Psychosocial work conditions	Percentage	
	No	**Yes**
Job Control		
My job allows me to develop my skills and abilities.	14.1	85.9
I have the freedom to decide how to do my job.	40.0	60.0
Job Demands		
I frequently have to work on too many tasks at once.	59.5	40.5
The demands of my job exceed the time to do them.	65.5	34.5
High-Strain Job	97.4	2.6

TABLE 5.2 Psychosocial Work Conditions, 2011 Canada Work Stress and Health Survey (N = 5793)

Data source: Authors' calculations of 2011 Canada Work Stress and Health survey.

Next, we examine how work conditions are related to both general feelings of psychological distress and a diagnosed mental disorder. Psychological distress is based on responses to questions about the frequency of feelings of sadness, hopelessness, anger, and frustration in the past month, which are subsequently converted into a scale. The scale ranges from 0 to 28, with higher scores reflecting higher levels of distress. Mental disorder asks respondents whether they have been diagnosed with a mental disorder such as depression or anxiety by their doctor. We report differences for psychological distress as means and use percentages for mental disorder, using the same work stress characteristics reported above.

The results, presented in Table 5.3, reveal statistically significant differences in both psychological distress and mental disorder in each of the work stress conditions. That is, workers who lacked job control (not able to develop skills or lack of freedom to decide how to do one's job) reported higher average levels of psychological distress and were more likely to report having been diagnosed with a mental disorder than workers whose jobs allowed them to develop their skills and the freedom to decide how to do the job. Similarly, workers with high job demands (too many tasks, too little time to complete tasks) had higher levels of psychological distress and were more likely to report having been diagnosed with a mental disorder than workers who did not encounter high job demands in the workplace. These differences were even stronger when comparing those workers in high-strain jobs (both low control and high job demands) to workers in the other three job profiles (active, passive, and low strain). Thus, levels of distress were highest in those with high-strain jobs (mean = 12.16) than in the rest of the working population (mean = 8.16); similarly, 22.4% of workers in a high-strain job had been diagnosed with a mental disorder compared to 16.1% in the rest of the working population.

TABLE 5.3 Psychosocial Work Conditions and Mental Health, 2011 Canada Work Stress and Health Survey (N = 5793)

	Psychological Distress	Mental Disorder
Able to develop my skills and abilities		
Yes	8.02	15.4
No	9.86	21.8
Freedom to decide how to do my job		
Yes	7.73	15.1
No	9.12	18.1
Too many tasks at once		
Yes	9.48	18.8
No	7.47	14.5
Given too little time to complete tasks		
Yes	9.54	18.5
No	7.62	15.1
Have a high strain job		
Yes	12.16	22.4
No	8.16	16.1

Data source: Authors' calculations of 2011 Canada Work Stress and Health survey.

We must remember, of course, that these are cross-sectional data, and, therefore, we are limited in our ability to say that there is a causal relationship between work conditions and health. Longitudinal analysis is needed to determine the extent to which these associations reflect the influence of social selection, social causation, or both. Happily, the Canada Work Stress and Health survey will re-interview the original sample of respondents in 2013, offering the opportunity to disentangle cause and effect and to better understand the dynamic nature of these processes. Clues to what might be learned are found in a recent study that analyzed longitudinal data from the Canadian National Population Health Survey dating back to the early 2000s. That study found that the risk for depression among workers increased if their jobs became more demanding over time; however, their risk for depression did not increase if they experienced a drop in levels of job control (Smith and Bielecky, 2012). Thus, in the future, researchers stand poised to make important inroads in understanding how work conditions and health are related to one another over time within the specific context of Canada.

FAMILIES AND HEALTH

Families in Flux

Families are a foundational institution in society. Connected through blood, formal bonds, and/or emotional commitment, families everywhere are responsible for the reproduction and socialization of the next generation as well as the sharing and transmission of resources and property across generations. Against the backdrop of these functions, however, families themselves have undergone tremendous transformation over the past half-century, prompting question and concern as to the implications of these changes for family life and for the health and well-being of family members.

As we noted earlier, in the latter decades of the twentieth century, women began to participate in the labour market throughout adulthood instead of withdrawing permanently to the private sphere of home life after childbirth. Access to a steady source of income reduced women's economic dependence on men and made it possible for them to leave unsatisfying marriages. In addition, changing ideas about marriage made it easier for couples to dissolve unsatisfactory relationships. A cultural shift toward individualism meant that people sought to free themselves from the constraints of traditional structural arrangements to pursue their own enlightened self-interests. Thus, the traditional bond of duty and obligation that characterized marriages in the past no longer holds relationships together. Instead, couples must work to maintain high levels of trust, intimacy, and emotional communication as these have become the force that binds relationships together. Consequently, contemporary relationships are inherently more unstable than traditional marriages, although their fragility is often measured against the rewards of true marital companionship (Beck, 1992).

Figure 5.1 illustrates the growing numbers of marriages in Canada that ended in divorce between 1928 and 2008. Historical changes to the divorce law in both 1968 and 1986 resulted in subsequent spikes in the divorce rate. In 1968, Parliament passed the first Divorce Act, which established a uniform divorce law across Canada, with divorces permitted on the grounds of adultery, physical or mental cruelty, or desertion or separation for more than three years. In 1986, the Divorce Act was amended to shorten the period of separation to one year before couples could file for divorce. In each instance, once legal barriers to divorce were lifted, divorce rates began to rise as both women and men increasingly exercised their rights to formally end their marriages. In recent years, however, divorce rates have begun to decline. As cohabitation became an acceptable alternative to marriage, fewer couples formalized their relationship in marriage. Thus, divorce rates peaked and began to fall, but as Figure 5.1 shows, this occurred only because marriage rates also began to decline.

FIGURE 5.1 Number of Marriages and Divorces, Canada, 1926–2008

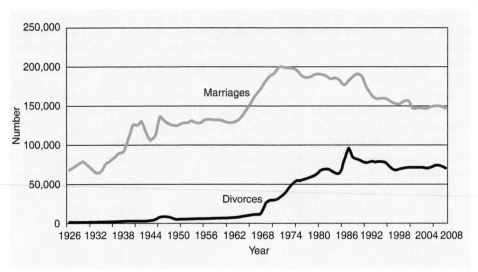

FIGURE 5.1 Number of Marriages and Divorces, Canada, 1926–2008

Source: Mary Bess Kelly, "Divorce cases in civil court, 2010/2011," *Juristat*, Statistics Canada, Catalogue No. 85-002-X, Vol. 5-23. Page 7, Chart 1, March, 2012.

As it pertains to fertility, women's newfound ability to pursue a lifelong rewarding career began to heighten the opportunity costs of having children. Consequently, aided by scientific discoveries that allowed them greater control over their reproductive processes, women chose to delay childbearing, began having fewer children, or avoided having children altogether. Thus, throughout the Western world, fertility rates have plummeted, although there are wide variations in the rates at which fertility rates have declined, and some countries have experienced a small rebound (though still below replacement levels) (Lesthaeghe, 2010). Overall, however, families are substantially smaller than they have been in the past.

Importantly, the links between marriage and childbearing also weakened, rendering obsolete the standard family biography where reproduction takes place after marriage. In the vacuum of a collapsed standard, new family forms have proliferated. Stephanie Coontz (2004) contends that while there is nothing new about today's new family forms when compared to the nearly infinite variation in how people have historically and globally formed intimate relations, what is new is the coexistence of so many different ways of doing family all at once and the greater acceptability of all of these simultaneous expressions of family.

For the first time, population censuses in a number of countries, including Canada, have begun to show that the proportion of adults in the population who are married is below 50%. Although some have taken this to mean that marriage is an institution that is slowly fading away, other studies paint a slightly different picture. When asked about their future plans, most adolescents and young adults express the desire to marry one day and few think that their marriages will not last. Moreover, in North America at least, the majority of the population still takes the position that married-parent households are the best environment in which to raise children.

The health consequences of these upheavals in family life have drawn substantial attention in sociological research. We review what is currently known about the association between marital status and health, before turning to the issue of how a stressful life event such as divorce is associated with health outcomes for both adults and children.

Marital Status and Health

The literature is very clear that those who are married fare better on every measure of health and well-being relative to those who are not married. Thus, those who are married have longer life expectancies, experience fewer illnesses, are less likely to be diagnosed with mental illness, and are less likely to engage in unhealthy behaviours than those who are not married (Kiernan and Pickett, 2006; Liang and Chikritzhs, 2012; Lindström, 2009; Masocco et al., 2008; Murphy, Glaser, and Grundy, 1997; Waite and Gallagher, 2000). With this overwhelming evidence, how do we begin to make sense of this association?

First, we may ask ourselves whether the association reflects social selection rather than social causation. If the association is due to social selection, it may be that people who are healthy are merely better able to find a partner and more likely to keep them. There is some validity to this explanation. Those with serious health conditions often find it difficult to muster the energy to find a partner and worry about whether others will find them attractive, thus avoiding romantic relationships altogether. Similarly, spouses will sometimes leave their partner when the other is diagnosed with a life-threatening or serious illness. Yet, longitudinal research that has sought to capture whether these scenarios actually account for the association have largely found that selection plays a small role and that the direction of the association is such that marriage affects health and well-being (Johnson and Wu, 2002; Joung et al., 1998). In particular, it appears that the reason marriage benefits health is that two adults can live more efficiently than one, particularly if both spouses work, and can use the informational and emotional support that spouses provide one another to provide meaningful ways of staving off illness and staying healthy. For example, researchers have shown that married Canadian men are much less likely to delay seeking help for chest pains than unmarried Canadian men, suggesting that spouses provide an additional source of care and support that encourages married individuals to seek medical attention for a condition more rapidly than unmarried individuals (Atzema et al., 2011). Thus, the better material and social resources of married individuals better protect their health relative to the unmarried.

Efforts to further explore the association between marital status and health have also noted that the quality of the marriage also makes a difference. That is, marriage does not equally improve the health of all who are married, but instead accrues only to those who report a high-quality, emotionally satisfying marriage. In fact, those who report being highly dissatisfied with their marriage are often in worse health than those who are not married. This suggests that running out to get a wedding ring just to improve one's health status may not be the wisest decision!

More importantly, however, researchers have been interested to know whether the health effects of marriage are the same for men and for women. The **sex role hypothesis** suggests that the health effect of enacting a social role such as spouse depends on the sex of the incumbent. Indeed, Jesse Bernard (1972) once famously proclaimed that there were his and her marriages, suggesting that men derived much more benefit from marriage than did women. Such statements seemed to fit with the literature at the time. Research conducted in the 1950s and 1960s confirmed that men were in better health than women in marriage, but that outside of marriage, women were in better health than men.

When attempting to explain the differential effect of marriage on health for men and women, sociologists in the past noted that marriage tended to constrain opportunities for women, because they were largely confined to the home once they got married and began raising children. In contrast, men had more opportunities to find meaning and satisfaction in the world of paid work. Thus, if men were in an unhappy marriage, they had other avenues for fulfilling their needs; however, a married woman had only the marriage as a source of fulfillment, making her more vulnerable than her husband if their relationship was unsatisfactory. With the same logic, single women were on a par with married men because they too had the opportunity to participate in the labour market and to enjoy the health benefits of work. Unmarried men, on the other hand, would be considered vulnerable because as men, they would not have received training on ways to enhance health in the home. Thus, subsistence on a low-quality diet and the acquisition of other unhealthy behaviours were assumed to pose risks to the physical and mental well-being of unmarried men.

sex role hypothesis:
The supposition that the consequences associated with enacting a given social role will depend on the sex of the incumbent.

Having noted earlier that the male breadwinner model, where men enter the world of work and women are relegated to the private sphere, has become largely obsolete and that it is now customary for both men and women to work throughout their adult lives, it is worth asking the question as to whether the sex role hypothesis still holds true today. Results suggest that the "future of marriage" has indeed arrived as the research has consistently found in recent years that men and women derive an equal health benefit from marriage (Strohschein et al., 2005; K. M. Williams, 2003; Uecker, 2012).

As cohabitation has become more common, researchers have investigated whether cohabitation confers as many health benefits as marriage. To date, the research has been mixed. Some studies report no differences in the health status of those who are married versus cohabiting, whereas other studies tend to find that the health status of those who cohabit is not as good as that of married individuals but is better than that of those who are single (Musick and Bumpass, 2012; Soons and Kalmijn, 2009; Wu et al., 2003). Importantly, some of the difference may be because cohabitation remains less accepted in society than marriage and because cohabiting relationships are more fragile than marriages, that is, they are less likely to last. For these reasons, cohabiting relationships may be marked by greater anxiety and tension than marriages, which may help to explain why marriage is sometimes more beneficial to health than cohabitation. If cohabitation one day comes to be fully interchangeable with marriage, with no social sanctions for those who cohabit and an equal chance of relationship stability, it is likely that any current differences in health between those who are married and those who cohabit will disappear entirely.

Finally, there is the issue of same-sex relationships. At the same time that heterosexual couples have increasingly eschewed marriage, same-sex couples have fought hard for the right to marry, and in a growing number of jurisdictions, their requests have been granted. In 2003, Canada began recognizing same-sex marriages. To date, ten countries around the world (Argentina, Belgium, Canada, Iceland, Netherlands, Norway, Portugal, South Africa, Spain, and Sweden) have legalized same-sex marriage. In the United States, several states recognize same-sex marriage, even though the country as a whole does not.

The extension of marriage rights to same-sex couples has made it easier for researchers to study health among same-sex couples. In the past, respondents were often reluctant to disclose their sexual identity for fear of social reprisal; therefore, they were difficult to locate and study. Box 5.2 addresses why sociologists are interested in studying new family forms, including same-sex relationships, despite the fact that this topic generates heated debate and exposes ideological divides. To the extent that same-sex couples are now allowed to marry and can identify themselves as such in the Canadian census, researchers are now equipped with better tools and knowledge to locate and study this family form.

BOX 5.2
Why Study the Health of Same-Sex Couples?

Responding to a study that controversially found that children raised in same-sex parent households fared more poorly on a number of health outcomes than children who grew up in married, two-parent households, Osborne (2012) asked a question that nearly all family demographers must address at one point or another in their careers: why do researchers have an interest in and conduct research on families headed by same-sex couples? According to Osborne, scholarly interest occurs because theory often suggests that a given family structure or dynamic may be associated with indicators of health and well-being, and thus researchers attempt to explore the mechanisms that create these differences. Researchers also tend to get drawn to these research questions because they know that this information can be useful for broader social purposes and that the public has an appetite for understanding the implications of changes in family life for themselves and others.

The problem, however, is that the results of scholarly studies that get disseminated to a larger audience are often cherry-picked by pundits and the general public, who tend to support studies that fit with their preexisting ideas about what families should be like and reject those studies that do not correspond to their preconceptions. This tendency, known as **confirmation bias**, can create barriers to understanding when people refuse to budge from their ideological standpoint. Although researchers must always be on guard that they are not being misled by their own biases, the average consumer rarely questions their own assumptions. Moreover, the average consumer typically lacks the skills needed to critically evaluate the scientific accuracy and merit of a given study. Because the topic is so politicized, Osborne points out that the onus is on scholars to be even more careful in how they present and interpret their research findings. This should not, however, dissuade engagement in this type of research because it has both theoretical and practical importance.

confirmation bias:
The tendency to selectively attend to and favour information that supports one's beliefs and discount information that does not fit in with one's beliefs.

Importantly, prior difficulties in finding same-sex research participants has tempered the findings of past research, which often relied on convenience sampling methods and very small sample sizes. As such, it was hard to generalize findings to the larger population, and, moreover, small sample sizes made it difficult to detect differences where they did exist. Interestingly, researchers have more recently contended that same-sex couples are not a homogeneous category: beyond this label may be important differences that are masked by treating all same-sex couples similarly. These potential nuances suggest that this will be an important area for future research and for theorizing on families and family well-being.

Despite these shortcomings, the literature generally finds that adults in same-sex relationships have health outcomes that are indistinguishable from those in opposite-sex relationships (Wienke and Hill, 2009). Similarly, children living with parents who are in same-sex relationships fare as well, on average, as children living with parents who are in opposite-sex relationships (Biblarz and Stacey, 2010), suggesting that factors other than the sexual orientation of parents matter more for child health and well-being (Strohschein, 2010). As with opposite-sex relationships, the quality of the relationship moderates the association, such that same-sex couples (and their children) fail to reap any health benefits if the relationship is unsatisfying or troubled.

Case Study: The Effects of Divorce on Adults and Children

Research perspectives on the effects of divorce have shifted over time such that divorce, once considered a catastrophic event, is no longer seen as universally detrimental to the health and well-being of adults and children. This statement stands in contrast to early studies that concluded that divorce had a profoundly negative effect on health and well-being.

Once these early research studies began to accumulate, greater scrutiny of the methods used led some to question their findings. Criticism was specifically directed at a series of studies that interviewed children of divorce just after divorce and for as many as twenty-five years afterwards, claiming that parental divorce exerted pervasive and life-long damage on child well-being. A particularly trenchant criticism of these studies was that the researchers selected participants who were known to be struggling with divorce and received counselling in exchange for their participation in the study, effectively excluding from their analyses those for whom divorce was unproblematic (Amato, 2003). These studies also did not include a control group, making it impossible to test whether there were statistically significant differences between those who had experienced parental divorce and those who had not. Most importantly, none of these studies employed a prospective design that allowed researchers to evaluate whether some of the problems detected after divorce could have existed prior to the divorce event.

When researchers used longitudinal data to compare differences in well-being while children were still in intact households, it became clear that children of divorce exhibited mental health problems well in advance of the divorce event (Aseltine, 1996; Block, Block, and Gjerde, 1986; Cherlin, Chase-Lansdale, and McRae, 1998; Strohschein, 2005). For example, Strohschein (2012) found that up to two years prior to parental divorce, children whose parents later divorced showed more symptoms of depression and attention deficit/hyperactivity disorder (ADHD) than children whose parents remained married. Because the divorce had not yet occurred, observed deficits in mental health among children whose parents later divorced could not be attributed to the divorce itself.

These critiques have changed the standard for how researchers investigate the consequences of divorce. Researchers now routinely employ a prospective research design on a sample that is representative of the population, with baseline measures of health and well-being so that they can test whether a change in marital status is associated with a change in health and well-being. Longitudinal analysis reveals that although much of the effect of divorce is apparent prior to divorce, there are also negative effects on health and well-being as a result of the transition. Divorce, then, is both a process and an event. This insight, which draws heavily on stress process, provides new knowledge on the health-related consequences of divorce for adults and children along several fronts.

First, recognizing divorce as a process and as a discrete event has led to the recognition that there are different stressors associated with each stage of the divorce process. These stressors are often connected to the economic resources of the household and the quality of family relationships and, as such, become important influences on health and well-being. Therefore, it is important to evaluate how these factors are interwoven into all stages of the divorce process.

For example, given that households with few economic resources are more likely to be exposed to stressors that erode well-being, it should come as no surprise that poverty and economic hardship also increase the risk for marital breakdown. Additionally, it is typically the case that in the period leading up to divorce, relationships between family members in the household begin to change. These changes signal reduced commitment by one or more adults in the household to the family unit in its present form, affecting how spouses interact both with one another and with their children. Parents may emotionally withdraw from one another or they may become increasingly hostile in their interactions. Such displays of interparental conflict not only move parents one step closer to divorce but also are experienced as emotionally distressing for both parents and their children. Thus, well-being may deteriorate prior to divorce through greater exposure to family conflict and distress.

In contrast, the secondary stressors following divorce reflect changes that happen as newly divorced adults set about reorganizing their own and, if they have children, their children's lives. Importantly, not every adult and child will experience all of these stressors. The role of these secondary stressors in influencing health outcomes needs to be understood because, just as we observed with job loss, they may help to explain why some individuals are more adversely affected by divorce than others. Rather than simply the end of an intimate relationship, it may be the accumulation of stressors following divorce that erodes and eventually overwhelms one's coping resources.

For adults, secondary stressors typically include downward economic mobility and residential relocation. Each of these can produce its own health consequences, with women more vulnerable than men. For example, divorce is associated with a drop in income for women, and, for many, the route out of poverty is through remarriage. Similarly, changing one's residence is a common consequence of divorce, arising out of the need to divide household assets such as the family home as part of a legal separation agreement. To the extent that these changes are seen as disruptive, acting to reduce available resources, including informational and social support from one's family and neighbourhood networks, they may serve to further erode health and well-being.

For children, the secondary stressors associated with divorce include reduced contact with the non-residential parent, downward economic mobility, and residential relocation. Typically, children live with their mothers after divorce, meaning that children of divorced parents are more likely to lose touch with their fathers. It was once thought that contact with the non-residential parent had few effects on child outcomes and that it was the economic contributions of the non-resident parent that mattered most. This perception has been replaced by the recognition that the relationship between children and their non-residential parent is important for child well-being, particularly when contact is not superficial. However, the nature of contact with a non-residential parent and its benefits to children are often determined by the amount of conflict between ex-spouses. Non-residential fathers typically reduce contact with their children when there is ongoing conflict between the former spouses, and children fare poorly when their parents persist in or escalate their hostilities after the divorce. Conversely, children benefit from contact with their non-residential parent when the ex-spouses get along with each other. In short, it is not the amount of contact with a non-residential parent but the degree of cooperation and commitment to shared parenting that determines whether contact helps or hinders a child's psychological adjustment to divorce.

As with adults, children are also vulnerable to the health effects of downward mobility and residential relocation; however, if children are also forced to change schools, residential relocation may be even more detrimental to the health of children than it is for adults. Moreover, research has shown that relocation following divorce is much more likely to involve a move to a less-advantaged neighbourhood than the one the family previously occupied, with the implication that the quality of the ties they form may be lower, and there may be greater difficulty in finding strong and supportive social networks.

Finally, whereas marriage may improve health for adults, the effects of remarriage are less positive for children. If parents remarry, children may find themselves competing with the step-parent for the attention of the biological parent, increasing their sense of isolation and loss. Remarriages are also more likely to fail, and the turbulence associated with yet another change in family structure may further erode a child's ability to adapt. In recent years, researchers have found evidence to support the **family instability hypothesis**, which posits that the repeated movements of parents and their partners and spouses in and out of a child's household may produce a series of short-term crises that cumulatively impair a child's capacity for healthy functioning (Fomby and Cherlin, 2007) and do so in ways that are qualitatively different from a child who experiences only one transition (i.e., divorce alone).

Researchers have not only made progress in specifying how different stressors operating at each point in the divorce process affect the health of children and adults but also recognize that the quality of family life prior to divorce can moderate or change the impact of divorce. Thus, the **stress relief hypothesis** (Wheaton, 1990) posits that what might normally be a stressful life event may in fact be relatively unproblematic and may even improve health and well-being because the stressful life event represents release from chronic strain. For example, a number of studies have shown that there are postdivorce improvements in child mental health when levels of parental conflict are high prior to divorce (Hanson, 1999; Morrison and Coiro, 1999; Strohschein, 2005). For these children, divorce represents escape from a toxic environment.

family instability hypothesis:
The hypothesis that the turbulence associated with multiple changes in family structure cumulatively erodes health and well-being to a greater extent and in a qualitatively different way than a single change in family structure.

stress relief hypothesis:
The supposition that a stressful life event may result in no adverse health effects or a positive effect on health because the stressful event represents escape from the chronic strain of a noxious environment.

Other moderating effects have also been observed. For example, loss of contact with the non-residential parent after divorce lowers well-being when a child was close to that parent but has no effect when the parent-child relationship was already estranged prior to divorce (Videon, 2002).

In sum, this is an exciting time to be a researcher who studies the links between marital status and health or who investigates the effects of changes in family structure on the health and well-being of children and adults. First, these are very active areas of research, with numerous scholars from around the world simultaneously investigating how the dynamics of family life in their own countries are related to health and well-being. These combined efforts are rapidly advancing knowledge in this area. Second, families themselves are continuing to evolve, and researchers are keen not only to document these changes but to generate new theories and ideas about what families might look like in the future and to speculate about what these changes portend for society in general. As such, it is likely that the next few years will yield even more interesting and provocative findings.

WORK-LIFE BALANCE AND HEALTH

Canadians live busy lives. Under pressure to succeed both at work and at home, many find it difficult to achieve work-life balance. **Work-life balance** occurs when people feel that they are able to manage their multiple roles in society and to maintain the boundaries between work and home life so as to achieve satisfactory involvement in both.

There are two ways in which work-life balance can be disrupted. **Work-to-family conflict (WFC)** involves the extent to which work life interferes with responsibilities and expectations at home, both consuming and depleting one's finite amount of time and energy (Grzywacz and Bass, 2003; Schieman and Glavin, 2008). We have already discussed the health implications of performing jobs that involve heavy job demands and little control over what happens during work, as well as jobs that come with low job security or carry the risk of injury or exposure to dangerous chemicals. When the stressors associated with the work role filter down into one's family and personal life, by placing strain on and creating problems in these relationships, a person is experiencing WFC.

WFC does not just arise from workplace stressors, but can occur when workers find themselves performing tasks even after they have left their place of work. Electronic technologies such as the Internet and cell phones now make it possible to contact people anywhere and at any time. Workers who use these technologies in their work and respond to email or text messages in the evenings may feel as though they are never fully off the clock and may come to resent giving up their time with family.

A second way in which work-life balance can be disrupted is when problems at home interfere with job performance. This is called **family-to-work conflict (FWC)**. While all working parents deal with issues of work-life balance, there may be unique challenges for parents who have children with chronic health or school problems. Such parents may struggle to find suitable child or afterschool care, need time off work for school or doctors' appointments, and experience unexpected work disruptions when a crisis occurs. Aging parents may also require additional effort and attention that drain energy and make it difficult to concentrate on work tasks. Finally, tensions in marital relationships or in parent-child relations may consume emotional resources and distract one from completing work-related tasks.

Although research on both WFC and FWC is relatively recent, there is growing evidence that each is associated with worse health. Grzywacz and Bass (2003) were among the first to find that WFC and FWC were both associated with higher levels of depression, anxiety, and problem drinking. Similarly, Moen and her colleagues reported that workers who reported

work-life balance:
The subjective feeling that one is able to manage multiple roles in society and maintain the boundaries between work and home life so as to achieve satisfactory involvement in both.

work-to-family conflict (WFC):
The extent to which work life interferes with responsibilities and expectations at home, both consuming and depleting one's finite amount of time and energy.

family-to-work conflict (FWC):
The extent to which home life interferes with the responsibilities and expectations at one's place of work.

low levels of WFC engaged in more positive health behaviours than those with higher levels of WFC (Moen et al., 2011). Hämmig and his colleagues (2011) found that those reporting high levels of WFC were more likely to have a musculoskeletal disorder than workers with little or no WFC; however, FWC was not associated with the presence of a musculoskeletal disorder (Hämmig et al., 2011).

Research in Canada is at a very preliminary stage. For example, Crompton (2011) found that 27% of working Canadian adults in 2010 characterized their lives as "quite" or "extremely" stressful. Interestingly, working women were more likely to identify family as the source of their stress; whereas working men were more likely to say their stress comes from the workplace.

The 2011 Canada Work Stress and Health survey contains questions on how Canadians perceive WFC and FWC in their own lives, giving us an opportunity to examine how these are distributed in the Canadian population. Table 5.4 presents descriptive information about the proportion of Canadian workers who experience both forms of disruption to work-life balance. The first two items pertain specifically to the subjective feeling of strain that occurs when work life takes over aspects of family life. Findings suggest that approximately one in five experience WFC. The next three items refer to different ways in which work life can seep into family and personal life through communications technologies. It appears that more Canadians respond to text and email messages (28.6%) when they are away from work than answer work-related phone calls (15.7%). Finally, 18% also make work-related phone calls when off work. The remaining items are focused on the ways in which family issues can disrupt work lives. Less than one in five workers reported receiving (17.8%) or making (14.8%) calls to family members during work time. The last two items reflect measures of FWC, whereby individuals feel that family life is taking a toll on job performance. Unlike WFC, FWC is relatively rare, with 6.5% of workers feeling that family troubles make it difficult to concentrate and 4.7% reporting that they feel drained of energy needed to do their work as a result of family or personal troubles.

We next examine how WFC and FWC influence mental health. As can be seen in Table 5.5, for both indicators of WFC, those who feel that work life keeps them from doing a good job at home or from spending time with the important people in their life are significantly more

TABLE 5.4 Measures of Work-Life Balance, 2011 Canada Work Stress And Health Survey (N = 5793)

Psychosocial work conditions	Percentage
Work frequently kept you from doing as good a job at home as you could.	19.8
Work frequently kept you from spending enough time with the important people in your life.	21.0
You were frequently called about work-related matters when you were not at work.	15.7
You frequently read job-related email or text messages when you were not at work.	28.6
You frequently contacted people about work-related matters when you were not at work.	18.0
Family members frequently contacted you during your work hours.	17.8
You frequently contacted family members during your work hours.	14.8
Family or personal life frequently kept you from concentrating on the job.	6.5
Family or personal life frequently drained you of the energy you needed to do your job.	4.7

Data source: Authors' calculations of 2011 Canada Work Stress and Health survey.

TABLE 5.5 Work-Life Balance and Mental Health, 2011 Canada Work Stress and Health Survey (N = 5651)

Work-to-Family Conflict and Family-to-Work Conflict	Response	Mental Disorder
Work-to-Family Conflict		
Work frequently kept you from doing as good a job at home as you could	No Yes	14.2 23.0
Work frequently kept you from spending enough time with the important people in your life	No Yes	13.5 25.3
Family-to-Work Conflict		
Family or personal life frequently kept you from concentrating on the job	No Yes	15.2 28.9
Family or personal life frequently drained you of the energy you needed to do your job	No Yes	15.7 21.4

Data source: Authors' calculations of 2011 Canada Work Stress and Health survey.

likely to have been diagnosed with a mental disorder (23.0% and 25.3%, respectively) than those who don't experience WFC (14.2% and 13.5%, respectively). Similarly, respondents who feel that family life interferes with work by making it difficult to concentrate at work or making them feel too drained to do their work are significantly more likely to have been diagnosed with a mental disorder than those who do not experience FWC.

These findings make it clear that those who feel unable to meet the demands of both work and home, by feeling that work interferes with family life or that family life interferes with work life, are more likely to experience mental health issues. Whether these associations are causal or the result of selection or other unobserved factors awaits longitudinal data that can more satisfactorily disentangle the temporal sequence.

IMPLICATIONS

"Plus ça change, plus c'est la même chose." (The more things change, the more they remain the same.) This saying appears relevant to how sociologists make sense of the health implications of the sweeping social changes that have transformed how Canadians engage in work and family life. That is, as much as structural forces have altered life in the twenty-first century, the underlying factors that influence how social roles are related to health outcomes appear to be the same today as they have always been. Thus, despite the uneven consequences for workers during the transition from a Fordist model of production to a knowledge economy, the conditions under which work poses both benefit and harm to health remain constant: workers who find their work fulfilling, feel they can meet the demands of their job, and can exercise discretion in their work are generally in better health than workers whose work conditions lack these features. Similarly, high divorce rates and the transition from marriage based on tradition and obligation to companionate forms of marriage would appear to have altered the meaning of marriage, yet leave intact the health-related benefits associated with having a committed, intimate relationship.

What may be different is that men and women are increasingly finding themselves squeezed for time as the demands of work and family life compete for time and attention. Whereas researchers from other parts of the world have made inroads into understanding how work-life balance influences the health of men and women, it is only recently that researchers in Canada have begun to address this important topic.

SUMMARY

LO-1   1. There are both commonalities and points of divergence in stress process and a life course approach. Both conceptual models centre around transitions; however, stress process views transitions in terms of their potential for overwhelming coping and adaptation, whereas a life course approach regards transitions as markers of an individual's movement through the life course.

LO-1   2. Nonetheless, when both conceptual models are integrated, unique insights are possible. That is, against the backdrop of normative age-graded transitions, the unique and divergent paths individuals or successive generations adopt for themselves represent opportunities to explore whether and how these differentially shape health outcomes. For example, as more recent cohorts delay marriage and childbearing, sociologists can determine the relative advantages and disadvantages of these choices for health and well-being.

LO-2   3. Large-scale shifts in the world of work include both the rise and fall of mass production as it was succeeded by flexible production, the emerging forces of globalization, and the movement of women into the labour market.

LO-2   4. Characterized by mass-produced generic goods that were affordable and readily available, Fordism was the dominant mode of production throughout much of the twentieth century, generating enormous economic wealth and stability for Western nations. Yet Fordism also produced alienated workers who reaped the benefits of steady work and a living wage but paid the price in terms of mindless, repetitive work on an assembly line. Flexible production, on the other hand, valued the input of the new knowledge worker, whose elite skills and training coupled with greater control over the production process were believed to create further efficiencies. Importantly, the production process also became flatter, leaner, and more agile.

LO-2   5. Globalization allowed countries with cheaper production costs to compete directly with manufacturing plants in North America; over time, plants across Canada and the United States closed their operations and migrated to countries where labour costs were far lower. To retain their jobs, many workers offered wage concessions that eroded their ability to earn a living wage.

LO-2   6. Women, who traditionally withdrew from the labour market permanently once they began having children, not only were needed in the labour market to maintain living standards in the household, following the collapse of the living wage, but were increasingly vocal about their right to enter and stay in the workforce. Ironically, just as men's employment trajectories became less secure, women began to adopt the male pattern of lifelong participation in the labour market.

LO-3   7. The unemployed are generally in worse health than those who are in paid employment, with evidence to support a reciprocal relationship. That is, poor health is a barrier to labour market participation, but it is also a consequence of unemployment.

LO-3   8. Job loss may result in stress proliferation when it begins to unleash stressors in other parts of the unemployed person's life. These variations in the type and sequence of secondary stressors may help to explain why job loss is a relatively harmless event for some individuals but can be catastrophic to health when prolonged unemployment takes its toll on financial well-being, family relationships, and sense of social inclusion.

LO-4   9. The number of workplace fatalities in Canada has been rising throughout the past two decades. Workers also face a range of other health risks, including injury from accidents or from repetitive strain injury and exposure to dangerous chemicals that cause breathing problems, reproductive health issues, and cancer.

LO-5   10.   The job demand–control model suggests that jobs that are demanding (have too many or conflicting demands and are time-pressured) and have low job control (repetitive, low variety, and little say over how the work is done) pose the greatest risk to health, with other combinations of job demands and control posing fewer challenges to health and well-being.

LO-5   11.   Traditional forms of marriage that involve lifelong commitment and have communal value have receded in importance; instead, contemporary marriage is an individual's expression of emotional connection that may be terminated when the feelings dissipate. Thus, freed from committing themselves to a loveless marriage for the sake of their family, individuals are now freed to find their soulmate, with the promise of true love, but also a greater opportunity for disillusionment and marital breakdown when things do not turn out as hoped.

LO-5   12.   Despite these changes in the meaning and stability of marriage, those who are married enjoy better health than those who are not. The association partially reflects the influence of selection, but the majority of the association is causal. The health benefits of marriage disappear entirely in relationships characterized by conflict, high levels of dissatisfaction, and family dysfunction.

LO-5   13.   The sex role hypothesis, that men derive greater health benefit from marriage than do women, may have been true at a time when women were relegated to the private sphere, but now that both men and women participate in the labour market throughout their adult lives, research has consistently shown that the health benefits of marriage extend equally to men and women.

LO-5   14.   Newer family forms such as cohabiting relationships and same-sex relationships have been difficult to study in the past, and differences in health may be attributable to the marginal or incomplete standing such relationships have had in society. As both become more accepted, it is likely that infrequently observed differences in health will disappear.

LO-5   15.   The literature on the effects of divorce for the health and well-being of children and adults has shifted over time, with many now acknowledging that divorce is both a process and an event. From the stress process point of view, researchers can now identify the types of stressors that occur at each stage of the process. Importantly, the stress relief hypothesis reminds researchers of the importance of taking into account the conditions of family life prior to divorce: For those living in highly conflicted and dysfunctional households, divorce actually leads to an improvement in mental health because it acts as a release from a chronic strain.

LO-6   16.   Work-life balance is seen as an important but elusive goal. As Canadian men and women struggle to meet the demands of their multiple roles in society, there are implications for health. Trouble in one sphere has a tendency to spill over into the other sphere, and those who experience WFC or FWC are more likely to report health problems. Understanding the mechanisms that underlie these associations is an important area for future research.

REVIEW QUESTIONS

1.   What are the basic principles of stress process and a life course approach?
2.   How would sociologists using stress process and a life course approach differ in how they view transitions?
3.   What unique insights are obtained by using both stress process and a life course approach to understand how social roles are linked to health outcomes?

4. What are some of the major transformations that have happened in the world of work over the course of the twentieth century?
5. What are the major differences between a Fordist model of production and flexible production?
6. How has globalization affected the status of workers in manufacturing industries in Canada?
7. How has the loss of the living wage and the women's rights movement affected women's participation in the labour market?
8. How is the health of the unemployed different from that of those in the paid labour market? What explanations are used to account for the association?
9. Why are statistics on workplace fatalities underestimated in Canada?
10. What are repetitive strain injuries, and why are office workers susceptible to these injuries?
11. What is the job demand–control model, and which of the four work profiles has been shown to deliver the greatest risk to health?
12. What does it mean to say that families are in flux?
13. Describe what is known about the association between marital status and health.
14. What is the sex role hypothesis? Evaluate the veracity of the sex role hypothesis in contemporary society.
15. How has stress process advanced research on the health effects of divorce on both children and adults?
16. What is work-family balance?

CRITICAL THINKING QUESTIONS

1. Imagine that you are an employer in a small manufacturing company that is in slow decline. What kinds of strategies might you need to use to keep the company viable in the future? What impact might these changes have on the health of your employees?
2. Imagine you are the parent of a child with severe disabilities. What kinds of difficulties in achieving work-life balance might you face, as both a worker and a parent?

KEY TERMS

confirmation bias (p. 115)
family instability hypothesis (p. 117)
family-to-work conflict (FWC) (p. 118)
Fordism (p. 103)
job control (p. 109)
job demands (p. 109)
repetitive strain injury (RSI) (p. 107)

scientific management (p. 103)
second shift (p. 105)
sex role hypothesis (p. 113)
stress proliferation (p. 106)
stress relief hypothesis (p. 117)
work-to-family conflict (WFC) (p. 118)
work-life balance (p. 118)

6

Illness and Death in the Developing World

Courtesy Shining Hope for Communities.

Kibera School for Girls

Kibera School for Girls

To arrive at Kennedy Odede and Jessica Posner's school for girls in Kibera, one must cross a small footbridge. The roughhewn wooden planks traverse an open sewer, which are ubiquitous in this sprawling Nairobi slum, one of the largest in Africa. The massive shanty town is officially considered an illegal squat, so receives no public services. What remains is a seemingly endless labyrinth of muddy, unpaved streets, jam-packed scrap metal huts, burned-out lots, and vendors selling fly-covered dried fish. The HIV rate here has been estimated at twice the national average, and one out of five children do not live to see their fifth birthday.

The footbridge is a small improvement amid a morass of despair, but it has resonance; although it was put in for the school, it helps the whole neighbourhood. The

same goes for the school's toilets, clean water, and health clinic, which are open to the public. In a place with overwhelming illiteracy, where two-thirds of girls have reportedly been forced to trade sex for food, domestic abuse is rampant, women and girls contract HIV at five times the rate of men, and more than 40% of girls do not attend school, these services help give education for girls a newfound prominence....

Odede and Posner's organisation, dubbed Shining Hope for Communities, integrates health, education, and community involvement in an unusually coherent way. They started with the school—the first free school for girls in Kibera—but soon added other projects, including two basic needs frequently neglected by health programmes: toilets and clean water. Currently, they are providing 20 000 litres of clean water a day, which they sell below market rates, and have built a 100 000 litre water tower, that will serve 2000 families a day. They have an eco-logical-toilet facility that recycles methane gas, and are building eight additional toilets, which will be owned and operated by the communities themselves. This, in a community where more than 90% of people lack access to a toilet....

To develop their project, 27-year-old Odede and 25-year-old Posner did not rely on the agendas of big donors or high-priced consultants—instead, they listened to the people they are trying to help. As they put together plans for their health clinic, Odede, who grew up in Kibera, did a series of focus groups with local residents. He found that less than 30% of people in his community had ever attended a government health facility; instead, most rely on unregulated private health clinics or chemist shops, and malpractice and over-prescription of drugs is common, which is especially worrying given the high rates of tuberculosis in the area. When they do go to the doctors, residents complained of 5-hour waiting times, prohibitively high costs, a lack of respect, and frequent misdiagnosis....

In December, 2010, they added the health clinic: a two storey, 16-room building, with both a community health centre and a women's clinic, staffed by a nurse midwife, two nurse practitioners, two lab technologists, a clinic manager, a records staff, pharmacist, and team of community health workers. The clinic sees over 1000 patients per month....

Source: Samuel Loewenberg, "Grassroots project shines hope on Nairobi slum life," *The Lancet*, Vol. 379, Issue 9811, Pg. 108, 2012.

LEARNING OBJECTIVES

In this chapter, students should be able to:

LO-1 **Recognize** the characteristics that distinguish high-income countries from low- and middle-income countries, including the challenges low- and middle-income countries face in maintaining an accurate vital status registry to track deaths and their causes.

LO-2 **Identify** the eight Millennium Development Goals and **understand** why high-income countries have an interest in improving health in low- and middle-income countries.

LO-3 **Identify** the leading causes of death globally and **describe** similarities and differences in the leading causes of death in low-, middle-, and high-income countries at all ages, for those under the age of 5, and for mothers.

LO-4 **Recognize** that deaths due to infectious and non-communicable diseases represent the tip of the iceberg: the many more who survive their illnesses are vulnerable to further health, social, and economic challenges.

LO-5 **Identify** areas of progress and failure in international efforts to reduce the prevalence of major infectious diseases such as HIV/AIDS, tuberculosis, and malaria, as stated in the Millennium Development Goals.

LO-6 **Understand** that the Millennium Development Goals do not address non-communicable diseases, such as heart disease, stroke, cancer, diabetes, lung diseases, and mental illness, which increasingly affect those living in low- and middle-income countries.

LO-7 **Recognize** that injury and disability from road traffic accidents, war, and disaster also take a greater toll on those living in low- and middle-income countries.

LO-8 **Evaluate** explanations for the global distribution of death and disease, which places a greater burden on those living in low- and middle-income countries.

As our opening vignette suggests, the sources and patterns of illness and health care in poorer countries may differ dramatically from those in more affluent countries. We begin this chapter by comparing some of these differences. We then explain the main sources of death and disease, focusing on the role played by social, economic, and political conditions and forces.

In making international comparisons, politicians, social scientists, medical researchers, and others have historically divided the world into two broad groups, the industrialized nations and the developing nations. Essentially, this division reflects the economic status of the various nations. The industrialized nations are primarily defined by their relatively high gross national income (GNI) per capita and diverse economies, whereas the developing nations are generally deeply impoverished and have far simpler economies, in some cases still relying heavily on a few agricultural products, such as rubber or bananas. Yet the rapid economic growth of some of these developing countries has made the binary divide between rich and poor countries obsolete. Middle-income countries represent emerging economies where living standards have risen overall, whereas low-income countries have economies that continue to languish and whose citizens are among the poorest. That is not to say that poverty no longer exists in middle-income countries. China and India, for example, have made the transition from low- to middle-income countries, yet in both countries extreme poverty exists alongside a growing middle class that has increasingly adopted the behaviours and preferences of high-income nations. As such, middle-income countries often have many of the same health problems as low-income countries but have also acquired many of the health problems that characterize high-income countries.

International comparisons of mortality and morbidity can be difficult because many low- and middle-income countries lack the comprehensive information systems and databases that allow illness and death to be accurately recorded. Indeed, it is often the case that countries with the highest mortality and the fewest resources lack quality data. Consequently, estimates from middle- and low-income countries are considered less reliable than estimates from high-income countries.

To overcome glaring gaps in knowledge about the causes of death in resource-poor settings, the World Health Organization (WHO) has developed a method known as the **verbal autopsy**, which interviews family members and caregivers of the deceased using a structured questionnaire to identify signs and symptoms as well as other pertinent information that can be used to assign a cause of death. This method has been used in many countries, including India with the Million Deaths Study (described further in Box 6.1). It is not without its critics; however, the verbal autopsy has vastly improved knowledge about the causes of death globally and remains the only practical method for assessing cause of death in many parts of the world.

verbal autopsy:
A method of determining cause of death in resource-poor settings that involves interviewing family members and caregivers of the deceased with a structured questionnaire to identify signs and symptoms as well as other pertinent information that can be used to assign a cause of death.

BOX 6.1
Million Deaths Study

A vital status registry that records deaths and assigns a cause to each death plays a critical role in population health: It is key to monitoring trends and detecting new epidemics, enhancing knowledge on avoidable causes of death, and evaluating the success of programs to combat disease. Yet, in many low- and middle-income countries, such records do not exist, posing a formidable challenge for these countries to understand and effectively deal with the specific health challenges that occur within their own borders.

India has approximately 9.5 million deaths per year, or about one in six of all deaths worldwide. Only half of deaths in India are registered, and of these registered deaths, few list a cause. As such,

there is insufficient coverage and poor-quality information on deaths and its causes in India. Because most deaths take place at home rather than in a hospital and there are few incentives for households to register deaths, the situation is also not likely to improve in the near future.

The Million Deaths Study, led by Prabhat Jha at the Centre for Global Health Research at the University of Toronto, is developing a cost-effective and reliable source of mortality data that can improve what is known about death and its causes in India. Researchers have been prospectively tracking the vital status of nearly 14 million people in India and will do so until 2014. A verbal autopsy will be used to determine the cause of death for the million people who are expected to die by the end of the study (Jha et al., 2006). Selected households will be visited by two independent surveyors on a monthly and twice-yearly basis, and a trained interviewer will conduct a verbal autopsy when a death has been recorded. These verbal autopsies will be further verified by two physicians working independently. In situations where the two physicians differ on the cause of death, a third physician will be asked to adjudicate.

As the largest study of its kind in the world, the Million Deaths Study not only builds India's capacity for research and for public health action but also has set a compelling example for other countries that lack a vital status registry to develop more comprehensive and reliable measures of mortality and its causes.

This division between low-, middle-, and high-income countries should not keep us from recognizing that social conditions and, hence, health patterns vary from community to community and from social group to social group within each nation. Thus, conditions in Canada's poorest neighbourhoods in some ways resemble those in disadvantaged areas in other parts of the world, whereas conditions in wealthy sections of Bangkok are comparable with those of posh enclaves in North America. Moreover, although the terms *low income, middle income,* and *high income* imply linear progression from one status to the other, this is not necessarily the case. For example, economic and health conditions worsened in Eastern Europe following the collapse of the Soviet Union.

It is also worth noting that *diseases respect no national borders.* Because of **globalization**, diseases and disease-causing conditions spread rapidly from developing to industrialized nations and vice versa. Researchers have proven that air pollution from Asia—caused by deforestation, overgrazing, and the use of toxic chemicals in agriculture and manufacturing—is now affecting air quality in the western regions of North America (Polakovic, 2002). This pollution increases the risk of heart attacks, respiratory failure, and asthma in both continents. Conversely, most used electronics equipment collected in Canada and the United States for recycling is shipped to Asia, where the recycling process poisons water supplies with acids, heavy metals such as lead, and other toxic products (Markoff, 2002). In an age of global travel, infectious diseases can quickly spread from one country to another, as happened in the case of SARS, when a traveller to China brought the disease back to Canada, causing a major outbreak in 2003 that killed forty-four people and sickened many more. As these examples suggest, those who live in the industrialized nations have a vested interest in understanding health and illness in the rest of the world.

At the threshold of the twenty-first century, the recognition that globalization was benefiting the world unequally and in particular contributing to the immiseration of those living in disadvantaged regions of the world motivated a radical proposal by the United Nations to address these disparities. Signed by all 191 member nations in September 2000, the Millennium Development Goals are eight goals with measurable targets that are to be mostly achieved by 2015. These goals are linked to the extent that they target health outcomes as well as the root causes of poor health, such as poverty, **malnutrition**, gender inequality, and rapid urbanization. The Millennium Development Goals are listed in Table 6.1. We will refer to these goals throughout this chapter to evaluate progress on achieving them as we first turn to a general description of patterns of death, illness, and injury in low- and middle-income countries relative to high-income countries and then discuss explanations for these patterns.

malnutrition:
The condition that develops when the body does not get a sufficient amount of food or the right nutrients it needs to function properly.

TABLE 6.1 Millennium Development Goals

Goal 1	Eradicate extreme poverty and hunger.
	Halve, between 1990 and 2015, the proportion of people whose income is less than $1 a day.
	Achieve full and productive employment and decent work for all, including women and young people.
	Halve, between 1990 and 2015, the proportion of people who suffer from hunger.
Goal 2	Achieve universal primary education.
	Ensure that, by 2015, children everywhere, boys and girls alike, will be able to complete a full course of primary schooling.
Goal 3	Promote gender equality and empower women.
	Eliminate gender disparity in primary and secondary education, preferably by 2005, and in all levels of education no later than 2015.
Goal 4	Reduce child mortality.
	Reduce by two-thirds, between 1990 and 2015, the under-5 mortality rate.
Goal 5	Improve maternal health.
	Reduce by three-quarters, between 1990 and 2015, the maternal mortality ratio.
	Achieve, by 2015, universal access to reproductive health.
Goal 6	Combat HIV/AIDS, malaria, and other diseases.
	Have halted by 2015 and begun to reverse the spread of HIV/AIDS.
	Achieve, by 2010, universal access to treatment for HIV/AIDS for all who need it.
	Have halted by 2015 and begun to reverse the incidence of malaria and other major diseases.
Goal 7	Ensure environmental sustainability.
	Integrate the principles of sustainable development into country policies and programs and reverse the loss of environmental resources.
	Reduce biodiversity loss, achieving, by 2010, a significant reduction in the rate of loss.
	Halve, by 2015, the proportion of the population without sustainable access to safe drinking water and basic sanitation.
	By 2020, have achieved a significant improvement in the lives of at least 100 million slum dwellers.
Goal 8	Develop a global partnership for development.
	Address the special needs of the least-developed countries, landlocked countries, and small-island developing states.
	Develop further an open, rule-based, predictable, non-discriminatory trading and financial system.
	Deal comprehensively with developing countries' debt.
	In cooperation with the private sector, make available the benefits of new technologies, especially information and communications.

Source: United Nations, Millennium Development Goals Report, 2011.

DEATH AROUND THE WORLD

In 2004, approximately 58.8 million people died worldwide. Nearly one in five (17.7%) deaths occurred under the age of 5, whereas more than half of all deaths were among those aged 60 and older (WHO, 2008). Yet, the age of death was strikingly different depending on whether it occurred in a high-, middle-, or low-income country. Deaths under the age of 5 were overwhelmingly concentrated in low- and middle-income countries: Only 3% of all deaths under the age of 5 occurred in high-income countries (Mathers, Boerma, and Fat, 2009). Of the 8.1 million deaths that occurred in high-income countries in 2004, 40% were among those aged 80 or older; comparable estimates were 24% and 9% for middle- and low-income countries, respectively (WHO, 2008).

Statistics for the leading causes of death globally and across high-, middle-, and low-income countries in 2004 are shown in Table 6.2. Worldwide, the six leading causes of death were equally split between infectious disease (lower respiratory infections, diarrheal diseases, and HIV/AIDS) and non-communicable diseases (ischemic heart disease, cerebrovascular disease (stroke), and **chronic obstructive pulmonary disease (COPD)**). Together, these six conditions account for four out of every ten deaths globally.

chronic obstructive pulmonary disease (COPD):
A progressive lung disease that makes it difficult to breathe. Chronic bronchitis and emphysema are common examples of COPD.

TABLE 6.2 Leading Causes of Death by Income Group, 2004

	Cause of death	Deaths (millions)	Percentage of total deaths
World			
1.	Ischemic heart disease	7.2	12.2
2.	Cerebrovascular disease (stroke)	5.7	9.7
3.	Lower respiratory infections	4.2	7.1
4.	COPD	3.0	5.1
5.	Diarrheal diseases	2.2	3.7
6.	HIV/AIDS	2.0	3.5
High-income countries		8.1	13.8
1.	Ischemic heart disease	1.3	
2.	Cerebrovascular disease (stroke)	0.8	
3.	Lung, trachea, and bronchus cancers	0.5	
4.	Lower respiratory infections	0.3	
5.	COPD	0.3	
6.	Alzheimer and other dementia	0.3	
Middle-income countries		24.3	41.4
1.	Cerebrovascular disease (stroke)	3.5	
2.	Ischemic heart disease	3.4	
3.	COPD	1.8	

continued

4.	Lower respiratory infections	0.9	
5.	Lung, trachea, and bronchus cancers	0.7	
6.	Road traffic accidents	0.7	
Low-income countries		26.3	44.8
1.	Lower respiratory infections	2.9	
2.	Ischemic heart disease	2.5	
3.	Diarrheal diseases	1.8	
4.	HIV/AIDS	1.5	
5.	Cerebrovascular disease (stroke)	1.5	
6.	COPD	0.9	

Source: World Health Organization, *The Global Burden of Disease 2004 Update*, Geneva, Switzerland, Table 2, Pg. 12, 2008.

A comparison of the leading causes across income categories reveals both similarities and differences. The top four causes of death worldwide, ischemic heart disease (12.2%), cerebrovascular diseases or stroke (9.7%), lower respiratory infections (7.1%), and COPD (7.1%), were found in each of the income categories, although their ordering varied. For example, ischemic heart disease was the leading cause of death in both high- and middle-income countries, accounting for approximately 16% and 14% of deaths in their respective categories, whereas it was the second-leading cause in low-income countries, accounting for less than 10% of deaths. Nonetheless, numerically, more people died from ischemic heart disease in low-income countries than in high-income countries (2.5 million versus 1.3 million). Once considered a disease of affluence, it is clear that heart disease is a major health problem in low- and middle-income countries. For example, of the nearly fifty countries that make up Latin America and the Caribbean, heart disease and stroke together account for 35% of the total mortality burden; however, HIV/AIDS, **tuberculosis**, malaria, and all other infectious diseases combined are responsible for only 10% of that burden (Koehlmoos, Anwar, and Cravioto, 2011).

Differences in the cause of death across the three income categories were also apparent. In each income category there were unique leading causes of death that were not the leading causes in the other income categories. That is, Alzheimer's disease and other dementias were in the top six causes of high-income countries, but not among the top six causes for either middle- or low-income countries. Road traffic accidents as a leading cause of death were unique to middle-income countries, and both HIV/AIDS and diarrheal diseases were in the leading causes of death in low-income countries, but not represented elsewhere.

Deaths Due to HIV/AIDS

The HIV/AIDS epidemic reached its peak globally in the mid 1990s; however, in sub-Saharan Africa, the disease only reached its peak in 2006 (WHO, 2011a). Deaths as a result of HIV/AIDS-related causes declined from a global high of 2.2 million in 2006 to 1.8 million in 2010, with nearly 1.2 million of these deaths occurring in sub-Saharan Africa. These numbers remain unacceptably high given that medical advances have made it possible for people living in high-income countries to treat HIV/AIDS as a chronic disease, whereas lack of access to these drugs necessarily translates into a death sentence for those who become infected with HIV/AIDS in other parts of the world.

As stunning as these numbers might appear, they understate the impact of HIV/AIDS in low- and middle-income countries. Unlike most illnesses, HIV/AIDS most commonly strikes during early and middle adulthood, normally the most economically productive years. In the hardest-hit countries, agricultural production has declined steeply, causing food shortages. The resulting increase in unemployment and poverty has sent ripples of illness and death throughout these countries. In addition, HIV/AIDS typically strikes during the child-rearing years. This situation has produced a rise in child deaths, for whenever mothers die, their children are also more likely to die, especially if they have no surviving relatives to care for them (UNAIDS/WHO, 2007). It has also resulted in a growing number of child-headed households, with Richter and Desmond (2008) documenting a six-fold increase in such households in South Africa since 1995. The hollowing out of the adult population, leaving older adults and children to fend for themselves and the dying, presents daunting challenges in these countries.

Child Mortality

As we noted in Chapter 3, deaths early in life in Canada are mainly preventable; therefore, they are cause for concern. The situation is even more extreme in middle- and low-income countries. Indeed, if low- and middle-income countries had the same death rates for children under the age of 5 that are found in high-income countries, there would be an astounding 23,000 fewer deaths per day in this age group (Shann, 2010).

Many infants are at risk as soon as they are born. Infant mortality occurs most often among babies with low birthweights. In high-income countries, low birthweight typically occurs when babies are born prematurely. In low- and middle-income nations, however, low birthweight typically occurs among babies born at full term to mothers who are underfed, overworked, or suffering from long-lasting, untreated illnesses (World Health Organization, Reproductive Health and Research Department, 2004). Similarly, infant mortality is highest among infants born to very young or very old mothers and to infants born less than eighteen months after a sibling. This situation occurs most commonly in cultures that expect women to marry at young ages and that judge women's worth by the number of sons they produce. In part, these cultural values reflect the economic realities of agricultural life: In agricultural societies, children produce more economic resources than they consume, so a family with many children is more likely to survive than a family with few children.

One of the United Nations Millennium Development Goals (MDG 4) is to reduce deaths globally for children under the age of 5 by two-thirds between 1990 and 2015. The mortality rate in this age group has declined globally from 90 deaths per 1,000 live births in 1990 to 65 per 1,000 live births in 2008, suggesting that progress is being made. At the same time, it is clear that many countries, particularly those in south Asia and sub-Saharan Africa, are unlikely to meet the 2015 target (UNICEF, 2011). Sub-Saharan Africa continues to be the most vulnerable region, where one in seven children does not reach age 5.

Infectious diseases were responsible for nearly two out of every three deaths under the age of 5 in 2008, with the largest percentages due to pneumonia, diarrhea, and malaria (Black et al., 2010). Deaths resulting from HIV/AIDS represented approximately 2.5% of all child deaths in 2004, with more than 90% of these deaths occurring in Africa (WHO, 2008). There are signs of progress in the fight against this disease. Programs aimed at reducing mother-to-child transmission of HIV/AIDS have resulted in significant reductions in new cases of HIV/AIDS, and there has been a steady decline in HIV/AIDS-related deaths among children under the age of 5 (WHO, 2011a). Significant progress has also been made on other infectious diseases, such as tetanus and measles, reinforcing the message that many child deaths are entirely preventable. For example, in 1990, 7% of all deaths under the age of 5 were due to measles; in 2008, less than 1% died from this disease. International efforts, such as the Measles Initiative, have successfully introduced vaccinations for measles throughout the world, achieving 82% global coverage in 2008. Sadly, the Measles Initiative may be a victim of its own success, as funding cutbacks since 2007 have adversely affected ongoing efforts to vaccinate the world's children and make it possible that deaths due to measles may rebound in future years (van den Ent et al., 2011).

Case Study: The Role of Infant Formula Manufacturers

UNICEF (2005) estimates that 13% of all deaths under the age of 5 could be prevented if infants were fed breast milk for their first six months. In low- and middle-income nations, several factors contribute to the especially high rates of death and disease among infants who are not breast-fed. First, in addition to the inherent nutritional limitations of breast milk substitutes, the process of bottle-feeding itself can expose infants to tremendous risks. Infant formula is typically sold as a powder that must be mixed with water and then transferred to a bottle before it can be used. In many places, this water contains dangerous infectious organisms. Those organisms can be killed if the water, bottle, and nipple are boiled. However, families do not necessarily understand how or why they should do so. Moreover, throughout the developing nations, many women and children already spend hours each day getting water and firewood and lack the time and energy to get the extra supplies needed for sterilization.

Second, infant formula is not free. To cut the costs, families often stretch infant formulas by diluting them with water. Babies fed diluted formula in essence starve to death while filling their stomachs.

Finally, by altering the hormonal levels in a woman's body, breast-feeding serves as a moderately effective contraceptive. Breast-feeding thus helps women to space out pregnancies and gives each baby a better chance for survival. For all these reasons, UNICEF (2005) recommends that children throughout the world, in both industrialized and developing nations, receive only breast milk during the first six months of life and a combination of breast milk and other foods until at least age 2.

Given all the benefits of breast-feeding, why don't more women in developing nations breast-feed? Part of the answer lies in traditional cultural beliefs, such as the conviction that children require certain traditional foods for health, or that it is unsafe to have sex with breast-feeding women (Dettwyler, 1995). Part of the answer lies in practical economic and social issues, such as the difficulty of meshing breast-feeding with paid work. And part of the answer lies with multinational food corporations (most of them based in high-income nations) that have convinced women in the developing nations that infant formula is superior to breast milk.

To create a market in the developing nations, corporations provided free or subsidized formula to patients in maternity hospitals (Gerber, 1990). If these women used the formula instead of breast-feeding while in the hospital, they often found it physiologically impossible to switch to breast-feeding later. Corporations also mounted massive advertising campaigns throughout the developing nations to convince women that bottle-feeding produces healthier babies and even lightens babies' skin—a status symbol in many developing nations. One particularly pernicious strategy was to dress saleswomen as nurses and send them to villages and maternity hospitals to encourage women to bottle-feed.

Recognition of bottle-feeding's role in infant mortality led the WHO Assembly in 1981 to adopt an International Code of Marketing of Breast-Milk Substitutes. Among its provisions, the code calls for manufacturers to refrain from advertising infant formula, providing free samples to mothers, promoting infant formula through health care facilities, hiring nurses or women dressed as nurses to promote infant formula, providing gifts or personal samples to health care workers, and providing free or low-cost supplies to hospitals. Officially the code has been accepted by all the major formula producers, but code violations continue to be reported around the world (International Baby Food Action Network, 2007). In addition, years of advertising by formula producers permitted the idea that bottle-feeding is more modern and healthy to take root in the developing nations. Nevertheless, billboards and other advertisements for infant formula have become less common, and health care workers in developing nations now more often actively support women's efforts to breast-feed.

Maternal Mortality

Reducing the **maternal mortality ratio** is also one of the Millennium Development Goals (MDG 5), with the aim to achieve a 75% reduction between 1990 and 2015. Maternal deaths are those that occur to women during pregnancy or childbirth or in the forty-two days following delivery. The maternal mortality ratio expresses the risk of maternal death relative to the number of live births. There were estimated to be 342,900 maternal deaths worldwide in 2008, for a global maternal mortality ratio of 251 per 100,000 live births (Hogan et al., 2010). The annual rate of reduction since 1990, when the maternal mortality ratio was 320 per 100,000 live births, has been approximately 2.3%; however, to achieve MDG 5, the annual rate of decline should be 5.5% (WHO, 2010a). Some countries performed much better than others: The maternal mortality ratio in Egypt dropped from 195 in 1990 to 43 in 2008 and went from 87 to 40 during the same time period in China. Despite the improvements in select countries, ratios in low- and middle-income countries (see Table 6.3) are still well above the ratios for high-income countries (Canada's ratio in 2008 was 7 per 100,000 live births). Indeed, the maternal mortality ratio is the health indicator with the greatest disparity between income groups (van den Broek and Falconer, 2011). Differences are even starker when one observes the gap between the country with the lowest maternal mortality ratio, Italy with 4, and the highest, Afghanistan with 1,575 (Hogan et al., 2010).

Medically, the majority of maternal deaths are due to complications that arise during or following pregnancy or childbirth. These complications include obstetric bleeding, hypertensive disorders such as pre-eclampsia, sepsis or infection, obstructed labour, and abortion. Yet as Patricia Smyke (1991) explains, "looking beneath those immediate causes, one must ask why they occurred or why they were fatal. The answer to that is: lack of prenatal care, lack of trained personnel, equipment, blood or transport at the moment the obstetrical emergency arose, or earlier, when it might have been foreseen and avoided" (p. 61). Because unexpected complications occur for approximately 10–15% of all women, access to skilled obstetrical care is critical for reducing maternal deaths. In 2008, only 65.7% of all women were under the care of a skilled attendant during pregnancy, childbirth, and immediately postpartum (WHO, 2010a). High-income countries had over 99% coverage, while East Africa had the least coverage (33.7%).

maternal mortality ratio:
The number of maternal deaths in the population per 100,000 live births during a given time period.

Income Group	MMR	Lifetime Risk of Maternal Death (1 in)
Low-income countries	580	39
Middle-income countries	200	190
High-income countries	15	3,900
World	260	140

TABLE 6.3 Maternal Mortality Ratio (MMR) by Income Group, 2008

Source: Adapted from: World Health Organization, *Trends in Maternal Mortality, 1990–2008*, Appendix 12, 2010.

Not only does high maternal mortality reflect limited access to health care, but also the low status of women contributes to risk. That is, while it is recognized that women who become mothers at a very young age or who have short intervals between births are more susceptible to pregnancy complications and hence maternal death, gender inequality prevents women from acting on this information. Child marriage is still widely practised, despite the fact that most countries have established the minimum legal age of marriage as 18 for women. The practice persists, particularly in rural and impoverished areas, because it is thought to offer a form of protection for girls. Instead, these girls are made more vulnerable in the long term: With little power or independence in their husband's household, these girls often become pregnant soon after marriage. Becoming pregnant when one's own body is still maturing increases the risk for both maternal and infant death. In addition, if they are married to older, more sexually experienced men, as is often the case, these girls are also exposed to the risk of sexually transmitted diseases. These factors not only increase the risk for maternal death but also have implications for the health of their babies.

Moreover, many women lack access to contraception and are unable to control the timing and spacing of births. Even in jurisdictions where women might have access to contraception, traditional expectations about motherhood may prevent them from delaying or spacing births. There are estimated to be between 42 and 44 million abortions worldwide every year. Although the global abortion rate has been declining, the number of unsafe abortions is rising such that nearly half of these are unsafe (Sedgh et al., 2012). Restricting access to abortion does not decrease the number of women seeking the procedure, but it does increase the risk for maternal mortality (Lester, Benfield, and Fathalla, 2010). Unsafe abortion results in death most commonly because of infections caused by unsterile instruments, hemorrhage when those instruments pierce the uterus, or poisoning when women try to abort themselves by swallowing toxic chemicals (Sedgh et al., 2007).

Many developing nations have restricted or outlawed abortion because of cultural traditions, religious beliefs, a desire by political elites to increase population, or financial and political pressures from the Western world. The United States, for example, has at different times over the past few decades withheld family-planning funding from any international health care agencies that offer abortions. Similarly, Canada's prime minister, Stephen Harper, made a point of excluding contraception and abortion from his administration's plans to advance maternal health in developing countries when Canada hosted the G8 summit in 2010.

ILLNESS AND INJURY AROUND THE WORLD

Many of the same infectious and non-communicable diseases that cause death also take their toll on those who do not succumb to these illnesses. These survivors are more vulnerable to other diseases, may be unable to engage in productive employment, and may be potentially saddled with debts from high health care costs. From this standpoint, deaths due to the leading infectious and non-communicable diseases represent only the tip of the iceberg. In this section, we discuss the prevalence of some of the leading infectious and non-communicable diseases and then turn our attention to the role of motor traffic accidents, war, and disasters in affecting injury and disability around the world.

Infectious and Parasitic Diseases

As in Europe and North America before the twentieth century, the high rates of infectious and parasitic diseases in low- and middle-income nations reflect the dismal circumstances in which many people live. Malnutrition and overcrowding promote the spread of airborne diseases such as tuberculosis, while contamination of the water supply with sewage spreads waterborne diseases such as cholera and intestinal infections. Similarly, poor housing and lack of clean water for bathing result in frequent contact with disease-spreading rats, fleas, and lice. The infectious and parasitic diseases that are most prevalent in middle- and low-income countries are HIV/AIDS, tuberculosis, diarrheal diseases, and malaria. We consider each in turn.

HIV/AIDS

One-third (34%) of all people living with HIV/AIDS reside in ten countries located in southern Africa (Angola, Botswana, Lesotho, Malawi, Mozambique, Namibia, South Africa, Swaziland, Zambia, and Zimbabwe). Although the annual number of people newly infected with HIV/AIDS continues to decline globally (as shown in Table 6.4), there remains wide variation between countries, such that in some regions of the world, such as Eastern Europe, the disease is still on the rise (WHO, 2011a). For example, Russia has experienced one of the fastest growing HIV/AIDS epidemics in the world, doubling over the past decade and now affecting more than 1% of the adult population. The epidemic is concentrated among intravenous drug users, a population that has itself skyrocketed in the past decade and comprises mainly young adults (Niccolai et al., 2010; Wall et al., 2011). These factors, combined with misinformation (e.g., that HIV/AIDS is only found in disadvantaged segments of Russian society) and ineffective policies by the Russian government (e.g., refusing to introduce a needle exchange program and lack of access to treatment), have provoked genuine concern that this health crisis will only worsen in the future.

Table 6.4 also shows that the number of people living with HIV/AIDS globally is increasing, largely as a result of treatments that prolong life but do not cure the person of HIV/AIDS. Treatment involves **antiretroviral drugs (ARVs)** that work to inhibit the HIV virus from multiplying in the human body. A person with HIV/AIDS often takes a combination of ARVs because multiple forms of the drug reduce the chances that the HIV virus will develop resistance to the treatment and, thus, help to increase the effectiveness of ARVs over the long term.

antiretroviral drugs (ARVs):
Treatment with drugs that inhibit the ability of the human immunodeficiency virus (HIV) or other types of retroviruses to multiply in the body.

A lifelong regimen of ARVs has essentially turned HIV/AIDS into a chronic illness to be managed rather than a fatal condition; however, for the most part this is true only in high-income countries, where there is greater opportunity to access these expensive drugs. In other parts of the world, where the cost of ARVs places them out of reach, the disease continues to be a death sentence. Although there has been a rapid escalation in the number of people with HIV/AIDS in low- and middle-income countries receiving antiretroviral therapy over the past decade (as shown in Table 6.4), the Millennium Development Goal (MDG 6) to achieve universal access to treatment for HIV/AIDS for all who need it by 2010 did not meet its target. While explanations for this failure continue to proliferate, it is useful to note that some countries have been much more successful than others. Brazil, for example, has had remarkable success in fighting HIV/AIDS. In 1996, Brazil implemented a controversial policy of free

	2002	2004	2006	2008	2010
Number of people living with HIV/AIDS	29.5	30.7	31.4	32.3	34.0
Number of people newly infected with HIV/AIDS	3.1	2.9	2.8	2.7	2.7
Number of people receiving antiretroviral therapy in low- and middle-income countries	0.3	0.7	2.0	4.0	6.6

TABLE 6.4 Key Indicators of HIV/AIDS Epidemic, 2002–2010

Note: All counts in millions.

Source: World Health Organization, *Global HIV/AIDS response: epidemic update and health sector progress towards universal access: progress report 2011*, WHO, Geneva, Switzerland, Table 1.1, Pg. 1, 2011.

universal access to ARVs that dramatically reduced the size of the epidemic and improved survival rates to the same level as in high-income countries (Marins et al., 2003). As such, Brazil serves to remind the world what is possible when governments become committed to treating HIV/AIDS within their own borders.

Tuberculosis

Each year, tuberculosis infects about nine million people and kills approximately one million (WHO, 2011c). The disease is most common in Asia and Africa. Tuberculosis is particularly devastating because, like HIV/AIDS, it typically hits people during their prime work years and so sharply curtails family incomes. Moreover, nearly 10 million children in 2009 were orphaned as a result of losing at least one parent to tuberculosis, throwing families into turmoil and exacerbating poverty (WHO, 2011c).

As with HIV/AIDS, the incidence of tuberculosis has been declining globally; unlike HIV/AIDS, tuberculosis is decreasing in every region around the world. The sharpest declines have occurred in China, with mortality rates falling by 80% between 1990 and 2010, largely as a result of the implementation of a national program to treat the disease (WHO, 2011c). Nonetheless, the ongoing threat of treatment-resistant forms of tuberculosis, called MDR-TB and XDR-TB for multi-drug resistant and extensively drug resistant tuberculosis, respectively, remains a challenge in several regions of the world, including Russia and China. Of even greater concern is the emergence of TDR-TB, totally drug resistant tuberculosis, which recently cropped up in India and for which there is no treatment.

Diarrheal Diseases

In industrialized nations, diarrhea is generally a source of passing discomfort. In developing nations, diarrheal diseases can be fatal, especially among children under age 2. Diarrhea is a symptom, not a disease, and can result from infection with any of several bacteria, viruses, and parasites. Diarrhea kills by causing dehydration and electrolytic imbalance. It also leads to malnutrition when affected children not only eat less but also absorb fewer nutrients from the foods they do eat. In turn, malnutrition leaves children susceptible to other illnesses. Conversely, other illnesses can leave children susceptible to both diarrheal diseases and malnutrition.

Diarrheal diseases (including dysentery, cholera, and infection with *E. coli*) occur when individuals ingest contaminated water or foods. The likelihood of severe diarrhea is greatest when families lack refrigerators, sufficient fuel to cook foods thoroughly, sanitary toilets, or safe water for cooking and cleaning. The Millennium Development Goal to halve by 2015 the proportion of the population without access to safe drinking water and basic sanitation (MDG 7) is within reach in terms of access to safe drinking water, but much less progress has been made on basic sanitation (United Nations, 2011). Thus, there is nearly 89% coverage of the world's population in regards to access to safe drinking water, with urban areas faring much better than rural areas, but nearly 2.6 billion people do not have access to flush toilets or other forms of sanitation, and, of these, 1.1 billion people continue to practise open defecation.

Malaria

Malaria is caused by protozoan parasites belonging to the genus *Plasmodium*. Malaria is transmitted by certain species of mosquitoes and, consequently, exists only where these mosquitoes live. The disease cycle begins when a mosquito bites an infected individual and ingests the parasite from the individual's blood. The parasite reproduces in the mosquito's stomach and then migrates to the mosquito's salivary glands. The next time the mosquito bites someone, it transmits the parasite to that person.

Each year, about 225 million people (mostly in tropical Africa) become infected with malaria, and approximately seven hundred thousand die from the resulting anemia, general debility, or brain infections (United Nations, 2011). In addition, many of those who survive will experience disabilities from the intermittent chills, fevers, and sweats that malaria brings. In a moderately endemic area, a person may expect to experience anywhere from ten to thirty episodes of malaria during a lifetime (Mendis et al., 2001). Consequently, the cost in terms of treatment and lost productivity can be high. Malaria poses the greatest threat to pregnant women, infants, and young children. Among pregnant women, malaria increases the risks of miscarriage, anemia, and premature labour, each of which increases the risk of potentially fatal hemorrhaging. Infants born to malaria-infected women typically have lower than average birthweights and, hence, higher chances of death or disability. Recurrent bouts of malaria can affect cognitive development in children, making it difficult to complete basic education, leading to diminished economic productivity in adulthood.

Insect repellents, insecticide-treated mosquito netting, and drugs such as chloroquine and mefloquine are commonly used to prevent malaria. Unfortunately, because these drugs can cause debilitating side effects and cost more than many residents of low- and middle-income nations can afford, few use medication. Similarly, insecticide-treated netting is rare. For example, in Uganda, a landlocked country in Africa with high rates of malaria transmission, less than 1% of the population used insecticide-treated netting in 2000. An initiative to provide netting for free led to increased usage; however, in 2009, the proportion of those using insecticide-treated netting had only increased to 32.8% (Okiro et al., 2011). These statistics suggest that efforts to achieve the MDG 6 objective to halt and reduce the incidence of malaria are beginning to have an effect, but that much more is needed to make a difference.

Non-communicable Diseases

Non-communicable diseases are not specifically mentioned in the Millennium Development Goals; however, it is anticipated that these will increase globally, with the most rapid increases projected to occur in Africa (Koehlmoos et al., 2011). The WHO has recently turned its attention to the issue of non-communicable diseases as an emerging health problem that takes a disproportionate toll on social and economic well-being in low- and middle-income countries. The WHO has estimated that low- and middle-income countries bear nearly 80% of the burden from heart disease, stroke, diabetes, cancer, and respiratory diseases (WHO, 2011b). The behavioural risk factors for these diseases are tobacco use, unhealthy diet, inadequate physical activity, and harmful use of alcohol; each is strongly associated with poverty. As such, the poor in these countries are drawn into a reinforcing cycle that differentially exposes them to these risk factors, increases their chances of becoming ill, and further impoverishes them because health care for these conditions is typically extensive and expensive (WHO, 2011b). In addition to poverty, other upstream risk factors include inadequate regulation and control of pollution, lack of population-wide interventions for screening and prevention, and health care systems that neither are designed nor have the capacity to treat non-communicable diseases. For now, we describe the distribution of each of these non-communicable conditions around the world, plus the global burden of mental illness, leaving more thorough explanations for these patterns to the final section of this chapter.

Heart Disease and Stroke

As shown earlier in Table 6.2, together heart disease and stroke account for more than 20% of all deaths globally. Not only do these diseases place a higher burden on low- and middle-income countries that have numerically more deaths from heart disease and stroke than high-income countries, but heart disease and stroke are also associated with substantial long-term morbidity (Kim and Johnston, 2011). Heart disease in low- and middle-income countries starts earlier in life than in high-income countries, with the consequence that the cost in terms of lost economic productivity is much higher. Even though there are proven, inexpensive treatments for heart disease and stroke, their usage around the world is unequally distributed. A recent international study found that rates of preventive drug use among those who had cardiovascular disease were substantially higher in high-income countries than in middle- or low-income countries. Yusuf and his colleagues (2011) reported that overall one in four among those who had heart disease or stroke reported using antiplatelet drugs; however, usage ranged from a high of 62.0% in high-income countries to 22.8% in middle-income countries and 8.8% in low-income countries.

Cancer

In 2008, there were 12.8 million new cases of cancer worldwide. The most common was lung cancer, with 1.6 million cases, followed by breast cancer, with 1.4 million cases (Ferlay et al., 2010). More than two-thirds of all cancer diagnoses now occur in low- and middle-income countries, devastating livelihoods and straining the capacity of health care systems (WHO, 2011b).

For a variety of reasons, delays in seeking treatment for cancer are more common in low- and middle-income countries. For example, approximately 60% of women with breast cancer in Egypt present with late-stage cancer due to cultural taboos, lack of knowledge about the symptoms of breast cancer, and lack of access to care (Mousa et al., 2011). Even when cancer is detected early, the lack of infrastructure in low- and middle-income countries makes effective cancer treatment extremely difficult. Shortages of anticancer drugs and pain treatment such as morphine are common. Similarly, there are too few health care workers trained to treat cancer. For example, Tanzania has a population of 42.5 million people, of whom 21,000 were diagnosed with cancer in 2008; however, the country has only four radiation oncologists and two radiotherapy machines, and only three hospitals are equipped to provide morphine (Hanna and Kangolle, 2010).

Diabetes

Diabetes occurs when the body does not produce any or sufficient amounts of insulin needed to regulate the level of glucose in the blood. Untreated, persistently high levels of glucose in the blood increase the risk for stroke, tuberculosis, lower limb amputation, and blindness. The global prevalence of diabetes in 2008 was approximately 10% among those over the age of 25 (WHO, 2011b). By 2011, 366 million people had been diagnosed with diabetes globally, with diabetes projected to affect 552 million people by 2030 (International Diabetes Foundation, 2011). Approximately 80% of those with diabetes live in low- and middle-income countries.

In all areas of the world, those who are socioeconomically disadvantaged are at greater risk for diabetes than those who are more socioeconomically advantaged (Agardh et al., 2011). The poor are not only more vulnerable but also less likely to have the resources to cope with the disease. People with diabetes consume two to three times the health care resources that people without diabetes use (WHO, 2011b). Such costs are far beyond the reach of many in middle- and low-income countries, with the consequence that few possess medications to manage their diabetes (Smith-Spangler, Bhattacharya, and Goldhaber-Fiebert, 2012). Hence, the complications associated with diabetes are more frequent in low- and middle-income countries than in high-income countries, where blood glucose levels can be monitored and carefully controlled.

Respiratory Diseases

Respiratory diseases, including COPD and asthma, are prevalent in low- and middle-income nations. Because lung function declines with age, COPD is expected to increase globally as people around the world live longer lives (Mannino and Buist, 2007). This can be observed in the increased risk for asthma, which currently affects approximately 300 million people worldwide and whose prevalence has increased by 50% every decade since the 1960s (Braman, 2006).

In addition to the risks associated with aging populations, there are numerous risks in the environment for respiratory disease. Exposure to toxic dusts, chemicals, vapours, and fumes in the workplace is a factor in respiratory disease throughout the world; however, less stringent laws in low- and middle-income countries put workers in these places at greater risk (Mannino and Buist, 2007). For example, asbestos is banned in all high-income countries but permitted throughout the developing world, including China and India.

Environmental exposure is not restricted to the workplace. Long periods spent cooking over open fires in confined spaces expose millions of women to lung-damaging toxins. Meanwhile, those who live in cities like Caracas, Mexico City, or Mumbai risk their health daily because of pollution from automobiles and industries. Unfortunately, in some low- and middle-income nations, government officials lack the political or economic power to control polluting industries and, in other nations, officials profit from and hence promote these industries. Equally important, officials in these countries sometimes believe that pollution and the attendant morbidity and mortality are short-term costs they must pay to industrialize and to improve their nation's health in the long run.

Tobacco also plays a major role in respiratory diseases. There are a billion tobacco smokers in the world, with rates highest in Europe and lowest in Africa (WHO, 2011b). Tobacco smoking is on the rise in low- and middle-income countries, as growing incomes make tobacco products more affordable, but declining in high-income countries (Pampel, 2007). Gender inequality also plays a role in tobacco smoking, whereby the freedoms enjoyed by women in high-income countries are often prohibited for women in low- and middle-income countries. Accordingly, men are most likely to smoke if they live in a middle-income country; women are most likely to smoke if they live in a high-income country.

Not only is tobacco smoking dangerous to the health of the individual, but also health effects are diffused to others. For example, exposure to secondhand smoke increases the risk of asthma in children. Moreover, tobacco serves as a catalyst that increases the risks of other diseases (Nasca and Pastides, 2001). For example, compared with non-smokers, smokers who have parasitic bladder infections are more likely to get bladder cancer, and smokers who work in uranium mines are more likely to develop leukemia. In addition, tobacco use promotes disease by taking a large bite out of small incomes. Smokers spend as much as 15% of family income in Brazil and as much as 10% in India on tobacco; in Egypt, wives name their husbands' smoking as the main reason their children go hungry (Nichter and Cartwright, 1991).

Mental Illness

Finally, mental illness encompasses a broad range of problems, generally characterized by thoughts, emotions, and behaviours or some combination thereof that fall outside the normal range and are distressing to that individual or impair that person's functioning. Examples of mental illness include depression, schizophrenia, mental retardation, and substance-use disorders. Mental disorders are responsible for little more than 1% of deaths but account for almost 11% of the disease burden worldwide (Murray and Lopez, 1996).

The resources to prevent and treat mental illness around the world are woefully inadequate. Almost half of the world's population lives in a country where, on average, there is one psychiatrist or fewer per 200,000 people (WHO, 2011d). Similarly, mental health user/consumer organizations can be found in 83% of high-income countries, but less than half of low-income countries have such organizations. Moreover, the cost of mental illness to society is both high and increasing over time. The global cost of mental health conditions in 2010, in terms of health care costs and lost productivity, was estimated at US$2.5 trillion, with the cost projected to surge to US$6.0 trillion by 2030 (World Economic Forum, 2011).

Motor Vehicle Traffic Accidents

Each year, more than 1.3 million people lose their lives in traffic accidents (WHO, 2012). For each of these deaths, there may be as many as 20–50 people who survive the accident but sustain serious injury and disability. (This range is large given the absence of reporting mechanisms in many countries.) For example, in 2005, traffic accidents in Iran resulted in just over thirty thousand fatalities but more than one million injured people, representing 1.6% of the population (Bhalla et al., 2009).

Road traffic accidents are not randomly distributed in the world but are more heavily concentrated among middle- and low-income countries. We noted earlier that middle-income countries listed deaths due to road traffic accidents among the top six causes of death in 2004. Over 90% of the world's fatalities on the roads occur in low- and middle-income countries, even though these countries have less than half the world's vehicles (WHO, 2009a). Although road traffic accidents are of concern worldwide, they are declining in high-income countries while increasing rapidly in middle- and low-income countries. As a country becomes more economically developed, it experiences an increase in road traffic accidents. Buoyed by new levels of affluence, people begin to purchase motorized vehicles that, coupled with intensive patterns of urbanization, overwhelm the existing infrastructure. Roadways become congested with inexperienced drivers competing for space with cyclists and pedestrians. In some places, such as India, it is not uncommon to find four-legged modes of transportation, including cows, elephants, and camels, on the road. These mixed-use roadways create substantial risks, particularly for cyclists and pedestrians, who have little to protect them in the event of a collision. Because of the growing number of drivers in low- and middle-income countries and the challenges these countries face in developing a safe road traffic system, injury and disability from traffic accidents are predicted to become the third-leading contributor to the global burden of illness by 2020 (WHO, 2004).

Road traffic accidents exert a heavy toll on the health care systems and economies of low- and middle-income countries. The health care costs of treating injuries as a result of road

In many low- and middle-income countries, roads are hazardous, with pedestrians and cyclists sharing space with motorized vehicles.

Frank Strohschein

traffic accidents are enormous. For example, in countries like India, where six new million vehicles are being added to the roadways each year, road traffic accidents account for 15–20% of all hospital emergency visits (Garg and Hyder, 2006). Moreover, road traffic injuries cost low- and middle-income countries between 1 and 2% of their GDP every year—more than what these countries receive in development aid (WHO, 2004). In addition to these costs, there is also a personal toll. Because males between the ages of 15 and 45 are particularly vulnerable to road traffic injury (WHO, 2012), the costs of prolonged medical care as well as the potential incapacity of the family breadwinner and resulting loss of income due to disability can push families into poverty, putting entire households at risk.

War

The most unnatural cause of death and disease in the developing nations is war (Geiger and Cook-Deegan, 1993; Toole and Waldman, 1993). Wars can not only wipe out a generation of soldiers but also take astoundingly high tolls among civilians. For example, the risk of violent death among Iraqi civilians increased fifty-eight-fold after the invasion by U.S.-led coalition forces, with 100,000 civilians, mostly women and children, killed by military forces in the first eighteen months (Roberts et al., 2004). Civilians die not only due to bombs, guns, and machetes but also as a result of forced labour; malnutrition that occurs when crops are burned, farm animals killed, and farmers forced off their lands; and diseases that spread when refugees are forced into overcrowded, unsanitary camps and when water, sewage, and health care facilities are destroyed. During warfare in the Congo during 2005, for example, for every civilian killed directly by warfare, another sixty-two—mostly women and children—died because of turmoil associated with the war (Lacey, 2005).

Survivors, too, pay a huge price, often including both long-lasting disability and the psychological trauma of losing one's family, community, and work. The traumas are particularly high for victims of mass rapes, a common tool of warfare that has been used extensively in recent years in Sudan and the Congo; those who survive can find themselves not only infertile or permanently disabled by their injuries but also stigmatized and sometimes abandoned by families and neighbours. Finally, an estimated 300,000 children as young as age 8 in forty developing nations are serving (usually involuntarily) as soldiers (Crossette, 2001). Mortality rates are very high, as are the health risks experienced by those who survive. These children are exposed to all the horrors and dangers of warfare and to increased risks of malnutrition, disease, landmine injuries, sexual abuse, and substance abuse, while losing opportunities for education and normal family life that might protect their mental and physical health as adults.

Disasters

The devastation wrought by earthquakes, tsunamis, floods, and other natural disasters is impossible to miss: more than 200,000 people dead in 2004 when a tsunami hit Indonesia and other countries along the Indian Ocean, more than 300,000 dead following a 2010 earthquake in Haiti, and so on. Like war, natural disasters typically result in public health disasters, as crops and jobs are lost; sewer, water, and health care facilities are destroyed; and health care workers are scattered or killed.

Although humans can't prevent natural disasters, they can greatly reduce—or increase—their toll (Revkin, 2008). Schools, homes, and other human-made structures can be retrofitted or built to withstand most earthquakes, at costs far less than the cost of replacing or repairing damaged or destroyed structures. Dams, nuclear power plants, and other dangerous structures can be located away from vulnerable flood plains or tectonic faults. And disaster preparedness programs can be developed that will warn people of impending disasters, offer means of escape, and secure public health infrastructures afterwards. Cuba, for example, is regularly struck by major hurricanes but has lost almost no lives to them in the last decade due to its nationwide disaster preparedness program (Oxfam International, 2010). However, for these programs to work, nations need not only technical knowledge but also both appropriate laws and building codes and the commitment to enforce them (Revkin, 2008).

Box 6.2 describes the work of Médecins Sans Frontières/Doctors Without Borders, an organization that offers an inspiring example of doctors and other health care workers who take a truly broad view of the causes and treatment of illness.

EXPLAINING DEATH AND DISEASE IN LOW- AND MIDDLE-INCOME NATIONS

The global burden of disease and death falls more heavily on low- and middle-income countries because these are generally places where the problems of poverty and malnutrition, the low status of women, rapid urbanization, and the globalization of unhealthy lifestyles are most pressing. We discuss these four explanations in turn.

Poverty and Malnutrition

Malnutrition, the condition that results when people do not have sufficient amounts of food or the right nutrients to sustain functioning, is the primary cause of the greater burden of

---

BOX 6.2

CHANGING THE WORLD

Médecins Sans Frontières/Doctors Without Borders

Médecins Sans Frontières/Doctors Without Borders (MSF) is an independent humanitarian organization, founded in 1971, that assists people around the globe whose health has been damaged by disasters, war, or political violence (Bortolotti, 2004).

MSF played an especially important role in two recent disasters. In December 2004, after an enormous tsunami killed more than 200,000 Indonesians, the organization sent doctors, nurses, and other health care workers to treat those who were injured by debris carried by the tsunami, infected by diarrheal diseases spread when sewage systems washed away, or overwhelmed psychologically when loved ones died. Once these "first aid" needs were met, MSF members began working on the broader infrastructure needed to protect the health of the tsunami survivors: organizing vaccination campaigns against tetanus and measles (which had started spreading following the tsunami), food distribution programs (so that malnutrition in the wake of the tsunami would not lead to further mortality), sanitation programs (to prevent disease transmission through unsafe water supplies), and home- and boat-building programs (so families had shelter and incomes).

Similarly, in January 2010, an earthquake centred just outside the capital city of Haiti, Port-au-Prince, killed more than 300,000 people and destroyed thousands of residential and commercial buildings, including landmarks such as the presidential palace. Already providing services in the country, MSF lost twelve of its own members, and two of its hospitals were heavily damaged during the earthquake. MSF provided care during the immediate aftermath, and its efforts continue to this day. More than 3,000 staff provide services in Haiti, and four new hospitals have been built. MSF plays a critical role in treating cholera with oral rehydration therapy and educating the many Haitians who still believe that the disease is punishment for evil rather than the result of unsanitary conditions.

In addition to treating illness and its underlying causes, MSF also works to bear witness to the problems it sees. Because of its impeccable non-partisan reputation, MSF's doctors can speak with great moral authority. On its website (www.msf.ca/), in frequent news articles, in testimony given at the United Nations General Assembly, and the like, MSF speaks out about the social causes of illness, death, and disability. MSF has spoken publicly about how attitudes toward women underlie the use of rape as a military tactic, how international economic dynamics contribute to the short and brutal lives of street children in developing nations, how governments use violence to subdue their own populations, and so on. The doctors and other workers of MSF exemplify a broad-based, sociological understanding of illness and health care.

disease and death in the developing nations. The risk for malnutrition is greatest among those who lack **food security**, defined as access to sufficient, safe, and nutritious food to meet dietary needs and food preferences for an active and healthy lifestyle. Food security in turn occurs when individuals, households, and communities have the purchasing power to obtain food: Purchasing power is lowest among the poor. Therefore, poverty and malnutrition are interconnected causes of illness and death around the world.

Rough estimates suggest that nearly one billion people, one out of every seven people on the planet, are food insecure. Although food insecurity is an issue in high-income countries (as noted in Chapter 4), rates of food insecurity are substantially higher in low- and middle-income countries, as evidenced in the markers of malnutrition. Markers of malnutrition include stunting, wasting, and overweight.

Stunting, when height for age is two standard deviations below the international standard, is the result of chronic, long-term malnutrition. Because the nutritional requirements are high *in utero* and during the first two years of life, children who do not receive sufficient nutrition during this critical period of development are irreversibly harmed. Risks include brain damage caused by iodine deficiency, blindness caused by vitamin A deficiency, and mental retardation caused by anemia. More generally, children who fail to receive adequate or proper nutrition prenatally and in the first two years of life not only fail to reach their full height potential but exhibit reduced cognitive performance; do poorly in school; have compromised immune systems; have a lower work capacity; and, later in life, are at greater risk for non-communicable diseases such as diabetes, obesity, and heart disease (Dewey and Begum, 2011; Vorster, 2010).

The worldwide prevalence of stunting in preschool children declined from 39.7% in 1990 to 26.7% in 2010 (de Onis, Blössner, and Borghi, 2012). This overall decline, however, obscures different rates of change by region. Africa exhibited fairly little change over this period, with rates of stunting in children under the age of 5 stagnant at around 40%. Similarly, rates in high-income countries remained constant at around 6%. In contrast, rates of stunting declined most rapidly in Asia and in certain countries, including Brazil and Mexico.

Whereas stunting is the consequence of exposure to chronic malnutrition, **wasting**, defined as weight for height that is two standard deviations below the international standard, reflects short-term exposure to acute food shortage or to disease. Famines are a common culprit for acute food shortage, placing entire communities at risk when food becomes scarce. Diarrheal diseases, as noted earlier, may result in malnutrition when affected individuals not only eat less but also absorb fewer nutrients from ingested food. Wasting is less prevalent than stunting; nonetheless, it is a critical underlying factor in deaths to children under the age of 5.

It is strange to think that concerns the population might be **overweight**, defined as above-average weight for height, would be an issue in the developing world, given that such places are generally perceived as having a lack of access to food. Rapid changes in the eating habits of the world's population, however, have resulted in what has come to be known as the **double burden of malnutrition**: the growing number of overweight people even as the issue of underweight persists. That is, the overconsumption of energy-dense and high-fat foods worldwide is contributing to a rising obesity epidemic, particularly in middle-income countries. Thus, countries such as Vietnam (Ha et al., 2011) and Mexico (Leatherman and Goodman, 2005) that have made the transition from a low-income country to a middle-income country are struggling to deal with health problems associated with obesity, even as high rates of stunting continue to take their toll on human health. Indeed, the evidence suggests that those who experience stunting during the early years of life are particularly susceptible to becoming overweight in adulthood (Leatherman and Goodman, 2005; Vorster, 2010). We discuss this issue further when we turn to the globalization of unhealthy lifestyles as a cause of the greater burden of disease and death among low- and middle-income nations. We now turn our attention to the role of power in producing malnutrition in low- and middle-income countries.

stunting:
A measure of height for age that is two standard deviations below the international standard and that reflects the consequences of chronic malnutrition.

wasting:
A measure of weight for height that is two standard deviations below international standards and that reflects short-term exposure to acute food shortage or disease.

overweight:
When an individual is above the average weight for height.

double burden of malnutrition:
A situation where high rates of undernutrition, particularly among children, persist even as there is a rapid increase in the rate of people who are overweight.

The Roots of Chronic Malnutrition

Given the link between malnutrition, illness, and death, the importance of investigating the roots of chronic malnutrition is clear. At first thought, we might easily assume that malnutrition in developing nations that have not yet experienced the **epidemiological transition** results naturally from overpopulation combined with insufficient natural and technological resources. Yet, for the last twenty years, food production has surpassed population growth globally, and each year farmers around the world grow enough to feed 1.5 times the world population (Lappé, Collins, and Rosset, 1998; Holt-Giménez and Peabody, 2008).

Nor can malnutrition be blamed on population density (Lappé et al., 1998). The Netherlands, for example, is one of the most densely populated countries in the world, yet chronic malnutrition no longer occurs there. Similarly, malnutrition has largely disappeared from Costa Rica but remains common in nearby Honduras, even though the latter has twice as much cropland per person.

If overpopulation, lack of food, population density, and lack of cropland do not explain chronic malnutrition, what does? The answer lies in the social distribution of food and other resources: *Malnutrition occurs most often in those countries where resources are most concentrated*. In other words, malnutrition occurs not in countries where resources are scarce, but in countries where a few people control many resources while many people have access to very few resources (Dreze and Sen, 1989; Lappé et al., 1998). Similarly, within each country, malnutrition occurs most often among those groups—typically females and the poor—with the least access to resources (Messer, 1997). In essence, then, malnutrition is a disease of powerlessness.

If powerlessness causes malnutrition, then eliminating inequities in power should eliminate malnutrition. Evidence from China and Costa Rica supports this thesis. These two nations—the first essentially communist and the second essentially capitalist—both adopted in past decades socialist strategies for redistributing resources somewhat more equitably. By giving farmland to formerly landless peasants, extending agricultural assistance to owners of small farms, working to raise the status of women, and so on, they made chronic malnutrition almost unknown within their borders. On the other hand, China has not proven immune to acute malnutrition caused by famines. According to Nobel Prize–winning economist Amartya Sen, famines occur only when (1) natural events reduce harvests and (2) non-democratic governments (like China's) can ignore citizen's basic needs because politicians know they cannot be voted out of office (Sen, 1999).

The Role of International Aid

In democratically run developing nations, international aid—both food aid and development projects—has helped improve citizens' standard of living and health status. But in *non-democratic* nations, aid has often had the opposite effect (World Bank, 1998). When a high-income country sends its farm surpluses overseas as food aid, agricultural producers can maintain prices for their goods at home while opening new markets. Once food aid reaches the developing nations, its distribution can unintentionally reinforce inequities in access to resources and thus malnutrition (Lappé et al., 1998). Food aid goes directly to foreign governments to distribute as they choose. In countries run by democratic governments committed to social equality, aid is likely to benefit those who need it most. Unfortunately, many developing nations are run by small, economically powerful elites, who sometimes instead sell the food their governments receive and pocket the profits.

Because the hungriest people cannot afford to buy food aid sold in the marketplace, such food aid does not improve their nutritional status. Rather, food aid *contributes* to the malnutrition of the landless tenants, sharecroppers, and day labourers who form the overwhelming bulk of those suffering from malnutrition (Lappé et al., 1998; Holt-Giménez and Peabody, 2008). When high-income countries sell their surplus agricultural commodities in the developing nations, the prices of those commodities in those nations plummet. As a result, owners of small farms may no longer be able to earn a living and must sell their land to larger landowners who can take advantage of economies of scale. Thus, land ownership and power become more concentrated, as do the inequities that underlie malnutrition and illness.

Like international food aid, internationally sponsored development projects have had mixed impacts on malnutrition and on health in general (World Bank, 1998). According to the politically conservative World Bank, carefully designed projects, sensitive to local conditions and culture and located in countries with democratic governments, open trade, social safety nets, and conservative economic policies can reduce malnutrition and its root causes. In Pakistan, for example, school enrolment of girls soared in 1995 when local communities received development money to open new schools only if they increased girls' enrolment rate (World Bank, 1998). In the long run, this approach should increase the status of women and thus will likely reduce malnutrition, infant mortality, and maternal mortality.

On the other hand, although projects like the Péligre Dam in Haiti, the Akosombo Dam in Ghana, and the Aswan Dam in Egypt have brought electricity to urban elites and industrial sites run by multinational corporations, they have flooded and destroyed agricultural fields and rural villages and brought plagues of waterborne diseases to rural dwellers (Basch, 1999: 280–281; Farmer, 1999). Agricultural development projects have been particularly likely to contribute to malnutrition among women and children (Lappé et al., 1998). These projects often start from the assumption, based on Western ideas about the family and the economy, that raising cash crops will benefit families more than will raising food crops and that men rather than women should be responsible for agricultural efforts. However, cultural traditions in many developing nations hold women responsible for growing food and feeding the family (Lappé et al., 1998). When development projects encourage men to grow cash crops, the men sometimes take over land women had used to grow food. Moreover, because men consider feeding the family a woman's responsibility, men often use their profits to purchase high-status goods such as tobacco or Western clothes for themselves, rather than to purchase food for their families. As a result, malnutrition increases among women and children.

The Role of Women's Status

Gender inequality and gendered norms create vulnerabilities that increase the risk for disease and death among women. Unequal power relations between men and women occur when women are not afforded the same rights and privileges as men. Gendered norms, which vary nationally and culturally, govern what is deemed to be acceptable behaviour for men and women. Thus, in some places in the world, it seems natural that women and girls have restrictions on their physical mobility that prohibit them from appearing in public without the presence of a male. In other places, women are restricted from voting, owning land, operating a motor vehicle, opening a bank account, filing for divorce or pursuing a charge of marital rape (which isn't even a crime in some jurisdictions), or testifying in court. In still other places, girls are only allowed to complete an elementary level of education or may be barred from school altogether. When these restrictions are seen as natural, and political and legal systems condone and reinforce gender inequality, women and girls are powerless to protect themselves from harm and threats to well-being and systematically denied opportunities that would enhance their social position and improve their health.

In Chapter 3, we noted that the gender gap in life expectancy in Canada over the course of the twentieth century and into the current century has consistently favoured women. In fact, in all high-income countries, women live longer lives than men. Yet, in some low- and middle-income countries, the gender gap in life expectancy is much smaller. Moreover, in a number of low-income countries, the gender gap in life expectancy is either entirely eliminated or men live longer lives than women. Table 6.5 illustrates these differences in the gender gap in life expectancy for various high-, middle-, and low-income countries.

How do we make sense of these variations in the gender gap in life expectancy in these different countries? The answer lies in gender inequality. In countries where women enjoy the same privileges as men, women are likely to live longer lives on average than men. In countries where to be female is of little social value, women do not experience substantially longer lives than men, and in some cases, their lives are even shorter on average.

The reverse gender gap in life expectancy has been concentrated mainly in countries that are located in sub-Saharan Africa, where HIV/AIDS has had its most catastrophic effects. Globally, women account for half of those infected with HIV/AIDS, but in many sub-Saharan countries, women constitute 60% of those with HIV/AIDS and 75% of those between the ages of 15 and 24 with the disease (Quinn and Overbaugh, 2005). Women are physiologically more vulnerable to HIV/AIDS than men, with women more likely to contract the disease from men than vice versa. Apart from biological vulnerability, however, women are also socially more vulnerable. Gilbert and Selikow (2011) outline a "lethal cocktail" of political, economic, and cultural forces to account for greater female vulnerability to HIV/AIDS in sub-Saharan Africa. Gendered norms in this region view women as subservient to men and view men as biologically programmed to need multiple sexual partners. In this context, women feel pressured to please men even at their own expense, and men, determined to demonstrate their sexual prowess as a sign of masculinity, demand sex from women without protection (e.g., a

TABLE 6.5 Life Expectancy for Men and Women, Various Countries, 2012

	Men	Women
High-income countries		
Japan	80	86
Switzerland	80	85
Australia	80	84
Canada	79	83
Middle-income countries		
China	73	78
Bolivia	65	69
India	64	67
Ghana	63	65
Low-income countries		
Sierra Leone	47	48
Swaziland	49	48
Lesotho	48	47
Zimbabwe	48	47

Source: Adapted from Population Reference Bureau, *2012 World Population Data Sheet: The World at 7 Billion*, Washington, DC. Pg. 10–13, 2012.

condom) or commitment to the relationship. Moreover, because of these gendered norms, many of these countries are more tolerant of rape. Gilbert and Selikow (2011) note findings from a recent survey that indicated 16.3% of men in South Africa reported that they had raped a non-partner or had participated in gang rape. To the extent that rape is culturally acceptable and there are few sanctions for men who commit these crimes, women will remain vulnerable to HIV/AIDS in these countries.

Son preference represents the cultural, economic, social, and ideological arguments that are marshalled to justify preferential treatment for men and boys as opposed to women and girls (Purewal, 2010). Although it is expressed in many different ways, the preferential treatment of men and boys relative to women and girls starts in the earliest moments of life. Son preference may lead parents to make decisions about whether to terminate a pregnancy based on the gender of the unborn child. Sex-selective abortion is common in countries where more value is placed on the lives of men and boys. Such decisions are often justified for economic reasons. For example, in the absence of any formal provisions for social security, individuals can guarantee their security in old age only by having sons. (Having daughters usually does not help, because daughters in most cultures are expected to take care of their husbands' parents rather than their own.) In countries like India and China, where efforts to curb population growth have resulted in government restrictions on the number of children parents can have, girl babies continue to be killed by families that want only boy babies (Jha et al., 2011; Lawn, Cousens, and Zupan, 2005). (This chapter's ethical debate, in Box 6.3, discusses some of the moral quandaries posed by using abortion for sex selection.)

son preference:
The cultural, economic, social, and ideological arguments that are marshalled to justify preferential treatment for men and boys as opposed to women and girls.

BOX 6.3

ETHICAL DEBATE

The Ethics of Sex Preselection

Zhang Zhiquan and his wife Mei live in a rural village in the People's Republic of China. Growing up in rural China, they learned early that couples needed sons to prosper and to care for them in their old age. They also learned that sons were essential for passing on the family name, that wives who produced no sons deserved mockery and abuse, and that girls were so useless that in the past many rural families did not even bother to name them. When Mei became pregnant, therefore, they had to decide what they would do if the baby were female. In the past, should they have felt unable or unwilling to raise a daughter, their only options would have been to kill the baby or give it up for adoption—choices that some families still make. Now, however, they have one additional option: having a health care worker identify the fetus's sex through ultrasound or amniocentesis and perform an abortion if the fetus is female.

Half a world away, the same issues of sex preselection and selective abortion arise, although in a different form:

Sharon and James Williams live in Mississauga, Ontario, with their two young daughters. Because

they both believe that children need a parent home at the end of the school day, Sharon works only part-time as a secretary, whereas James works two jobs so they can make ends meet. Sharon has just learned she is pregnant again. Although they had only planned on having two children, James always wanted a son with whom he can share his interests in sports and automobiles. Having another child, however, will further strain their finances and make it difficult for Sharon to return to full-time work for several more years. Consequently, continuing the pregnancy does not seem worthwhile unless they know that the fetus is male.

Is sex preselection ethically justified in these cases? Although the circumstances differ enormously, for both families the birth of a daughter would bring substantial economic hardship. For both families, too, a daughter would enter life unwanted and already having failed to meet her parents' expectations. In addition, for the Chinese family and possibly (although to a lesser extent) the Canadian family, the birth of another daughter might lower the wife's status and strain the marriage. Given these circumstances, wouldn't it be best for all concerned if the families use the available medical technology to test their fetuses' sex and to abort them if they are female?

continued

For hundreds of thousands of couples in Asia and a growing number in the West, the answer, resoundingly, is yes. In India, selective abortion, usually after a first-born girl, has increased dramatically over the past few decades, contributing to a widening imbalance in the child sex ratio (Jha et al., 2011). The same forces are at work in the industrialized nations. At the beginning of 2012, the issue of sex-selective abortion in Canada was brought to the forefront in an editorial in the *Canadian Medical Association Journal* that recommended families not be provided with medically irrelevant information, the sex of their unborn child, until after thirty weeks of pregnancy on the basis of evidence showing sex-selective abortion is also occurring in higher-order births in Canada (Kale, 2012).

Those who support prenatal sex selection argue that selective abortion causes little harm, whereas the birth of unwanted girls financially strains families; leaves mothers open to ridicule or even physical abuse; and results in child neglect, abuse, or abandonment. Those who oppose sex preselection argue that it does more harm than good because it reinforces the low status of females. Although in rare circumstances families use medical technologies to ensure that their babies are female (such as families with a history of hemophilia, a disease that affects males but not females), sex preselection almost always means selecting males.

When families select male fetuses over female fetuses, they proclaim male babies preferable. Moreover, when health care workers help families to select male babies, the workers in essence validate this preference. Finally, when health care workers assist in sex preselection—whether helping families to select males or females—they reinforce the idea that males and females are inherently different. After all, if male and female personalities, interests, and aptitudes were more similar than different, why would families need to choose one over the other?

In sum, to assess the ethics of sex preselection, we need to weigh the potential benefits and costs for families and for society as a whole.

SOCIOLOGICAL QUESTIONS

1. What social views and values about medicine, society, and the body are reflected in prenatal sex selection?
2. Which social groups are in conflict over this issue? Whose interests are served by allowing sex preselection? By forbidding it?
3. Which of these groups has more power to enforce its view? What kinds of power do they have?
4. What are the intended consequences of permitting prenatal sex selection? What are the unintended social, economic, political, and health consequences of this policy?

Son preference also occurs through infancy and childhood. Daughters typically receive less food and less health care (including immunizations) than do sons (Messer, 1997). Moreover, girls are often taken out of school earlier than their male siblings in impoverished families, posing challenges for girls to attain economic independence or to gain needed skills and knowledge to protect and enhance their own health. During the years of Taliban rule, girls in Afghanistan were prohibited from attending school; today, girls who are permitted to attend school often face physical harassment and assault from those who still believe females should not be educated. As a result of these gendered norms, illiteracy among women worldwide is estimated at 580 million, nearly twice the estimated number for men (WHO, 2009b). Lack of education among women is a critical factor not only for their health but for the health of their children. Indeed, in all countries, child mortality rates are highest in households where the education of the mother is lowest (WHO, 2009b).

Marriage can also be hazardous to the health of women, particularly when the marriage occurs when women are children or adolescents. Although most countries have established the legal age of marriage as 18 for women, 38% of girls in low- and middle-income countries marry before the age of 18 and 15% marry before the age of 15 (WHO, 2009b). As noted earlier, when young girls marry much older men, they are not only economically dependent but have little say over matters of sex and reproduction. Marriage may also be detrimental to the health of women when they lack the ability to refuse sex or to demand that their partners use protection, increasing their own risk for sexually transmitted diseases, including HIV/AIDS.

Seven-month-old twins Rahul (left), a boy, and Devki, a girl, are held by their paternal grandmother and mother, respectively, at their home in Sesai Khurdi Village in Shivpuri District in Madhya Pradesh State. Both were brought to the therapeutic feeding centre at Managalam Hospital when they were eight days old. At the time, Rahul weighed 2.3 kilograms and currently weighs 5.2 kilograms. Devki, on the other hand, has only progressed from 1.6 to 2.8 kilograms during the same time period. Her more acute malnutrition is a direct result of ongoing discrimination against girls. While Rahul, the boy, gets proper food, hygiene, and care, Devki has been completely neglected.

Women's dependence on men does not dissipate when a spouse dies. Instead, they become more vulnerable. For example, in Kenya, the widow has no claim to her deceased husband's property, which is distributed to and divided among male members of the family. Seen as property herself, she may be remarried to a male relative of her dead husband in a process called **widow inheritance** (Luginaah et al., 2005). In other places, remarriage for widows is frowned upon. If these are older widows, a lifetime of economic dependency may leave them with few alternatives for finding a new livelihood, pushing them into poverty.

In sum, throughout the life course, women are afforded fewer privileges and opportunities than men to act in their own best health interests. Until the structural forces that perpetuate gender inequalities are challenged, women will continue to experience greater risk to their health than men.

Rapid Urbanization

Around the world, people are increasingly migrating to urban settings, many in search of a better future. For example, the industrialization of agricultural production made small-scale farming largely obsolete and pushed farmers off their land; landless, they drifted to major cities to find work. As cities grow larger and the pace of urban migration accelerates, many newcomers find they have nowhere to go and settle in unplanned settlements located near or in cities, often referred to as **slums**. As described in the opening vignette to this chapter, slums can be hazardous places. Danger arises when slum dwellers live in substandard housing and lack access to sanitation and clean water but may also occur when settlements are located in precarious places such as on a floodplain.

MDG 7 aims to improve the lives of at least one hundred million slum dwellers by 2020. Since 2000, the number of slum dwellers has continued to expand, growing from an estimated 767 million in 2000 to 828 million in 2010 (United Nations, 2011). In light of these growing numbers, it is not clear how or whether MDG 7 can be attained.

Rapid urbanization poses health risks not just to slum dwellers but to all urban residents. The pace of growth often outstrips the efforts of cities to anticipate and accommodate incoming waves of migrants, not just creating problems in congested roadways that contribute to high rates of traffic accidents but also increasing the risk for environmental degradation.

widow inheritance:
A type of marriage arrangement whereby a widow is married to a male relative of her deceased husband.

slum:
An informal settlement that is densely populated and characterized by substandard housing and inadequate access to clean water and sanitation.

Unprecedented population growth in urban centres depletes and destroys water resources, overloads sanitation, results in improper waste disposal, contributes to greater air pollution, and contaminates nearby rivers and streams. These are formidable challenges, particularly for cities located in low- and middle-income countries that already feel the strain of poor infrastructure and inadequate resources.

The Globalization of Unhealthy Lifestyles

Globalization offers both opportunities and challenges to the health of the world's population. As markets become increasingly integrated, large multinational corporations have been able to achieve significant cost savings by gaining control of the production and distribution of goods around the world (Hawkes, 2006). One obvious benefit to the consumer is that these goods are more readily available and are relatively inexpensive. Yet, these same processes that make it possible for Canadians to enjoy fresh strawberries in the wintertime also facilitate the worldwide spread of tobacco smoking as transnational tobacco companies promote their products in new markets in developing countries (Huynen, Martens, and Hilderink, 2005). This is also true for manufacturers of alcohol. In essence, globalization not only allows for the movement of goods across the world but facilitates the transmission of culture. When the lifestyles of those in high-income countries are seen as desirable by those in low- and middle-income countries, multinational companies will exploit these desires by promoting products that represent these lifestyles. What results is the globalization of unhealthy lifestyles whereby people around the world increasingly engage in tobacco use and harmful use of alcohol and acquire unhealthy eating habits.

Hawkes (2006) describes how globalization has altered dietary habits in Mexico. In large urban centres, multinational retailers have displaced smaller, family-owned general stores called tiendas. Although consumers benefit from lower prices, large supermarkets have played a role in shifting the diets of the population by offering more processed foods and junk food. Thus, Mexicans have begun to abandon a traditional fibre-rich diet in favour of calorie-dense processed foods. Even in rural areas, where local tiendas have yet to be supplanted by supermarkets, multinational corporations such as Coca-Cola and PepsiCo provide incentives to storeowners to market their brand. These strategies have paid off well for these corporations as nearly 90% of all sales in Mexico of Coca-Cola and PepsiCo products are from rural tiendas. The "coca-colonization" of diets has turned out less well for the health of the Mexican population, which is in the midst of a rising obesity epidemic (Leatherman and Goodman, 2005). The pattern of changing diets is not just happening in Mexico, but is being replicated in countries everywhere, with global implications for health and well-being.

IMPLICATIONS

In this chapter, we have seen how poverty and malnutrition, the low status of women, rapid urbanization, and the globalization of unhealthy lifestyles—rather than overpopulation, tropical environments, lack of natural resources, or other biological factors—underlie the high rates of illness and death found in the developing nations. Consequently, addressing these root causes of poor health in low- and middle-income countries should raise them to the health levels found in high-income nations. Conversely, the situation in Russia demonstrates how an industrialized nation can slide toward health levels lower than those found in some developing nations (Feshbach, 1999; Feshbach and Friendly, 1992).

Following the collapse of the Soviet Union in 1991, political and economic upheaval in Russia led to the spread of poverty across the country and the deterioration of living conditions. Increasingly across this vast territory, people lived in inadequately heated, overcrowded, and ramshackle housing. Moreover, public awareness that the government could no longer guarantee citizens a minimum standard of living demoralized people, encouraging many to find solace in drugs and alcohol. These patterns of substance abuse were particularly true for men, who were more likely than women to be in the labour market and thus felt more acutely the effects of economic displacement.

To these problems were added those caused by environmental degradation. In past decades, the Soviet Union expanded its economic base as rapidly as possible, with little regard for the human or environmental toll. The Soviet government rarely established and almost never enforced regulations designed to protect the environment from industrial pollution. As a result, industries wreaked far greater environmental havoc in the Soviet Union than in other industrialized nations, polluting farmlands and waterways beyond repair and leaving radioactivity, lead, and other dangerous toxins behind. Similarly, the emphasis on increasing agricultural yields as quickly as possible led to overplowing, which has caused perhaps permanent soil erosion, and to overuse of herbicides, chemical fertilizers, and pesticides, which have poisoned the water, the land, and food crops.

Beginning around 2000, median incomes in Russia rose and living conditions improved substantially. Health indicators have begun to improve, but years of environmental damage, social turmoil, and poor living conditions continue to take a toll in human lives. Infant mortality remains twice as high in agricultural areas where pesticides were used heavily than in other regions, and **incidence** rates for numerous infectious diseases have increased. In addition, tuberculosis has spread much more widely than in most of the world (WHO, 2011c). Moreover, the collapse of the social structure and economy during the 1990s contributed to a proliferation of sexually transmitted diseases, with rates of both syphilis and HIV/AIDS skyrocketing. Partly as a result, deaths due to alcohol, suicide, violence, and accidents are far higher in Russia than in Western Europe or North America (World Health Organization Regional Office for Europe, 2006). Because the burden fell more heavily on men than on women, the gender gap in life expectancy is the largest in the world in Russia, with men living on average 63 years compared to 75 years for women (Population Reference Bureau, 2012).

In sum, no natural progression leads countries toward an increasingly healthy citizenry. Rather, as the political and economic fortunes of a country shift, and as the natural environment improves or declines, so too will the health of its population. Only by continued commitment to eliminating poverty and inequality and to protecting the environment can a nation guarantee that it will keep whatever health gains it has achieved.

SUMMARY

LO-1 1. The sharp boundaries that once distinguished industrialized nations with relatively high gross national income per capita and diverse economies from developing nations with relatively low gross national income per capita and relatively simple economies have been blurred to the extent that those countries with emerging economies, rising living standards, and a growing middle class no longer belong in either category. Identified as middle-income countries, these countries are still struggling with the health problems associated with low-income countries, but are increasingly encountering health problems more typically found in high-income countries.

LO-1 2. Many low- and middle-income countries lack a vital status registry that allows them to track deaths and their causes. For this reason, a method known as verbal autopsy is used to improve what is known about the number and causes of death around the world.

LO-2   3.   The Millennium Development Goals, ratified by all 191 nations in the United Nations, has identified eight goals to be mainly achieved by 2015. These goals are intended to ameliorate some of the adverse effects of globalization, by improving health outcomes in the most disadvantaged countries and by addressing the root problems that underlie these health outcomes.

LO-3   4.   Nearly 59 million deaths occurred globally in 2004. Three of the six leading causes of deaths were due to infectious disease (lower respiratory infections, diarrheal diseases, and HIV/AIDS), whereas the remaining three were due to non-communicable diseases (heart disease, stroke, and COPD).

LO-3   5.   There are both similarities and differences in the causes of death in low-, middle- and high-income countries. Four conditions are common to all income categories, although the ordering varies; conversely, each income category has its own unique leading causes that are not among the leading causes in the other two income categories.

LO-3   6.   Although HIV/AIDS-related deaths are decreasing worldwide, HIV/AIDS remains a leading cause of death, particularly in sub-Saharan Africa, where it has decimated the population of working-age adults and created a social and economic crisis for the orphaned children and aging adults who remain.

LO-3   7.   Only 3% of deaths worldwide under the age of 5 occurred in high-income countries. Infectious diseases were responsible for nearly two out of every three deaths under the age of 5 in 2008, with the largest percentages due to pneumonia, diarrhea, and malaria. Targeted efforts to address specific infectious disease early in life have been successful, with far fewer children dying from HIV/AIDS and measles; however, it is uncertain whether the goal of reducing under-5 mortality rates by two-thirds between 1990 and 2015 (MDG 4) will be achieved.

LO-3   8.   Medically, the causes of maternal death are due to complications that arise during or following pregnancy or childbirth. Underlying the excess risk of maternal death in low- and middle-income countries is lack of access to medical care and gender inequality. Because they have little power, girls in low- and middle-income countries may be married off young, bear children before their bodies have matured enough to do so safely, receive too little food to nourish their unborn child or their own bodies, and lack access to birth control or safe abortions.

LO-4   9.   For each person who dies of an infectious or non-communicable disease, many more survive their illness. These survivors are typically made economically, socially, and physically vulnerable as a result of their illness experience.

LO-5   10.   Although there is no cure for HIV/AIDS, medical advances have made it possible for those living in high-income countries to manage HIV/AIDS as a chronic condition; however, the high cost of treatment and lack of health care mean that HIV/AIDS is a fatal condition elsewhere in the world. Efforts to provide ARVs to all who need it by 2010, as stated in MDG 6, fell short of the mark.

LO-5   11.   To date, there has been slow and uneven progress on reducing the prevalence of infectious and parasitic diseases in low- and middle-income countries. Many of these gains are fragile and will not be sustained without continued commitment to achieving the Millennium Development Goals.

LO-6   12.   Heart disease, stroke, cancer, diabetes, lung diseases, and mental illness are non-communicable diseases that are assuming greater importance as the burden of these diseases falls more heavily on middle- and low-income countries that are poorly equipped to prevent or to treat such conditions.

LO-7   13.   The growing number of drivers in low- and middle-income countries coupled with rapid urbanization are overwhelming the existing roadway infrastructure and are predicted to increase rates of injury and disability from traffic accidents in these countries, even as rates are decreasing in high-income countries. Political and economic instability leaves low- and middle-income countries vulnerable to war, which typically kills far more civilians than soldiers. Disasters are more devastating in low- and middle-income countries because such places often lack the necessary economic funds to prepare for disasters in advance of their occurrence and to rebuild quickly in the aftermath of a disaster.

LO-8   14.   Poverty and malnutrition are interconnected causes that account for a major reason why people living in low- and middle-income countries bear a greater burden of disease and death compared to those in high-income countries. Malnutrition occurs most often in undemocratic countries where a few people control most resources. Within countries, malnutrition occurs most often among those groups with the least access to resources—typically poor women and their children. International aid can increase malnutrition when it increases power inequities.

LO-8   15.   Gender inequality and gendered norms perpetuate the idea that women deserve fewer rights and privileges than men, with the consequence that at each stage in the life course, women and girls experience systematic barriers that prevent them from attaining economic independence or acting in ways that may improve their health and well-being.

LO-8   16.   Rapid urbanization and the globalization of unhealthy lifestyles also account for the greater burden of disease and death in low- and middle-income countries. As millions pour into cities and contribute to environmental degradation, the health of entire communities is jeopardized. Similarly, the global marketing of unhealthy lifestyles plays on the desires of those from low- and middle-income countries; in adopting these behaviours, diseases such as lung cancer, diabetes, and heart disease that were nearly non-existent emerge as major threats to health.

REVIEW QUESTIONS

1.   How do social conditions limit the effectiveness of modern medicine in developing nations?
2.   How do social factors contribute to illness in developing nations?
3.   How do international politics and multinational corporations contribute to illness in developing nations?
4.   How are the effects of natural disasters amplified by the political and economic conditions in low- and middle-income countries?
5.   How do the role and status of women contribute to illness in developing nations?
6.   What are the challenges to overcome in improving the health of the world's slum dwellers?

CRITICAL THINKING QUESTIONS

1.   For the last five years, you have worked as a public health worker in a poor, urban neighbourhood in Canada. You have just accepted an exchange agreement to work for three years in Port-au-Prince, the capital of Haiti. What parallels will you expect to see between these two settings in terms of the nature and sources of health problems and the best ways for dealing with health problems?
2.   Identify the three changes you think would contribute most to improving the health of people in the developing nations. Justify your choices.
3.   Identify three selfish reasons why Canadians (individuals, corporations, government, voluntary organizations) should care about illness and death in developing nations.

KEY TERMS

antiretroviral drugs (ARVs) (p. 135)

chronic obstructive pulmonary disease
    (COPD) (p. 129)

double burden of malnutrition (p. 143)

malnutrition (p. 127)

maternal mortality ratio (p. 133)

overweight (p. 143)

slum (p. 149)

son preference (p. 147)

stunting (p. 143)

verbal autopsy (p. 126)

wasting (p. 143)

widow inheritance (p. 149)

Part III

The Meaning and Experience of Illness

Our common sense understandings of the world tell us that illness is a purely biological condition, definable by objectively measured traits. As we will see in Part III, however, what is defined as illness varies considerably over time and space and across social groups. In Chapter 7, we explore the social meanings of illness and examine how ideas about the nature and cause of illness have changed historically. Although it has not always been this way, medicine currently wields considerable power to define what illness is. We describe in greater detail the process of medicalization, describe the role that doctors play in this process, and assess the broader social implications of interpreting conditions or behaviours through the lens of medicine.

In Chapter 8, we examine the lived experience or what it means to be someone who is living with chronic illness or disability. Illness represents failure, and people with chronic illness or disability not only have to struggle with the limitations imposed by their own bodies but also often find themselves resisting the negative view that society has of them. We begin by discussing how society has historically treated those who have chronic illness and disability and then cover more contemporary experiences, including how people with chronic illness and disability come to terms with a changed body and self-image and campaign to change how society views them.

In the last chapter of this part (Chapter 9), we discuss the implications of living in a postmodern world where health is no longer the opposite of illness but a pursuit in its own right. The commodification of health coupled with stunning medical advances suggests that what it means to be healthy in contemporary society is undergoing dramatic change. We highlight some of these trends and discuss the implications of what it means to be healthy in a postmodern, and perhaps posthuman, world.

7

The Social Meanings of Illness

Ezra Shaw/Getty Images

Is Being Short a Disease?

All Marco Oriti has ever wanted, ever imagined, is to be taller. At his fifth birthday party at a McDonald's in Los Angeles, he became sullen and withdrawn because he had not suddenly grown as big as his friends who were already five: in his simple child's calculus, age equaled height, and Marco had awakened that morning still small. In the six years since then, he has grown, but slowly, achingly, unlike other children. "Everybody at school calls me shrimp and stuff like that," he says.

"They think they're so rad. I feel like a loser. I feel like I'm nothing." At age 11, Marco stands 4 feet 1 inch—4 inches below average—and weighs 49 pounds. And he dreams, as all aggrieved kids do, of a sudden, miraculous turnaround: "One day I want to, like, surprise them. Just come in and be taller than them."

Marco, a serious student and standout soccer player, more than imagines redress. Every night but Sunday, after a dinner he seldom has any appetite for, his mother

injects him with a hormone known to stimulate bone growth. The drug, a synthetic form of naturally occurring human growth hormone (HGH) produced by the pituitary, has been credited with adding up to 18 inches to the predicted adult height of children who produce insufficient quantities of the hormone on their own—pituitary dwarfs. But there is no clinical proof that it works for children like Marco, with no such deficiency. Marco's rate of growth has improved since he began taking the drug, but his doctor has no way of knowing if his adult height will be affected. Without HGH, Marco's predicted height was 5 feet 4 inches, about the same as the Nobel Prize–winning economist Milton Friedman and … Masters golf champion, Ian Woosnam, and an inch taller than the basketball guard Muggsy Bogues of the Charlotte Hornets. Marco has been taking the shots for six years, at a cost to his family and their insurance company of more than $15,000 a year.

A Cleveland Browns cap splays Marco Oriti's ears and shadows his sparrowish face. Like many boys his age, Marco imagines himself someday in the NFL. He also says he'd like to be a jockey—making a painful incongruity that mirrors the wild uncertainty over his eventual size. But he is unequivocal about his shots, which his mother rotates nightly between his thighs and upper arms. "I hate them," he says.

He hates being short far more. Concord, the small Northern California city where the Oriti family now lives, is a high-achievement community where competition begins early. So Luisa Oriti and her husband, Anthony, a bank vice president, rationalize the harshness of his treatment. "You want to give your child that edge no matter what," she says, "I think you'd do just about anything."

Source: Barry Werth, "How short is too short? Marketing human growth hormone," *New York Times Magazine*, June 16, Pg. 4, 1991.

LEARNING OBJECTIVES

In this chapter, students should be able to:

LO-1 **Identify** structure-seeking and meaning-seeking as two different approaches that sociologists use to study issues around health and illness.

LO-2 **Understand** that illness is a social construction and **distinguish** the social constructionist perspective from a medical model of illness that portrays illness as objective, amoral, and apolitical.

LO-3 **Describe** what it means to apply a negative social sanction to those who are ill or who endanger the health of others.

LO-4 **Recognize** two ways in which the institution of medicine operates as an instrument of social control: medicalization (the power to define what illness is) and the sick role (the power to control behaviour when one becomes sick).

LO-5 **Recognize** the ways in which medicine may be experiencing erosion in its authority to define what is considered illness and **evaluate** the positive and negative consequences of medicalization.

LO-6 **Identify** the privileges and obligations associated with the sick role and **evaluate** the criticisms that have been raised about Parsons's work on the sick role.

LO-7 **Evaluate** the new health consciousness in terms of how this emerging trend may be weakening the power of medicine as a form of social control, yet comes with its own costs.

Does Marco have an illness? According to his doctors, who have recommended that he take an extremely expensive, essentially experimental, and potentially dangerous drug, it would seem that he does. To most people, however, Marco is simply short.

We start this chapter by describing a shift in perspective that differentiates Part II of this book from Part III. We then evaluate how individuals and social groups make meaning of illness by considering how ideas about the nature and cause of illness have changed historically, from religious explanations that attributed illness to punishment for sin to modern explanations that attribute illness to risky lifestyles. Next, we outline differences between the medical and sociological models of illness from a meaning-making or social constructionist perspective. We then consider how medicine can act as an institution of social control through its power to define what is illness and to control the behaviour of those who become sick, reflecting on the broader consequences of these mechanisms of social control and whether they are weakening. Finally, we evaluate whether the new health consciousness, in shifting attention from illness to health, has begun to weaken the power of medicine in contemporary society and note some of the implications of this shift.

FROM STRUCTURE-SEEKING TO MEANING-SEEKING

As we noted in Chapter 1, sociologists use a variety of perspectives to study issues related to health and illness. Up until this point, however, our attention has been on the social determinants of health and illness, drawing mainly on **conflict theory** to explore how patterns of illness in the population are the consequence of the social organization of our societies. While we have used the terms *social determinants of illness* and *social production of health and illness model,* others, such as Leonard Pearlin (1992), have labelled this type of activity structure-seeking. To uncover how structural arrangements affect health, Pearlin notes that structure-seekers generally use methods that require large-scale studies and quantitative analysis, much like the studies we discussed in previous chapters. For the most part, sociologists who are structure-seekers take measures of mortality, morbidity, and health care utilization as objective assessments of health status.

In contrast, Pearlin describes meaning-seekers as those who explore the meanings of health and illness from people's lived experience of these conditions. Discerning these meanings requires a different set of methods, including qualitative and textual analysis. Though there are far fewer cases for analysis, researchers seek rich and nuanced information that reveals both the dominant ideas about health and illness in our culture and how individuals subjectively interpret and respond to those messages. Provocatively, meaning-seekers would state that disease is not an objective entity that must be discovered through scientific methods but exists because our society has defined it as existing. If you have recognized that we are now drawing on a social constructionist perspective, you won't be surprised to know that some sociologists would also use terms such as *social construction of health and illness model* to refer to meaning-seeking.

Note that this does not mean that we abandon the concept of power. Just as structure-seekers demonstrate how power differentials influence patterns of health and illness in the population, meaning-seekers illuminate how power shapes what is seen and perceived to be illness. Importantly, although there are some inherent differences between structure-seeking and meaning-seeking, including the use of different methodologies, we require both perspectives to gain a fuller understanding of issues relating to health and illness in our society.

EXPLAINING ILLNESS ACROSS HISTORY

Throughout history, people have experienced and feared illness. To relieve their anxiety and make the world seem less capricious and frightening, they have typically sought explanations for why illness occurs and why it strikes some rather than others. Most often, these explanations defined illness as a deserved punishment for sinful or foolish behaviours and blamed individuals for their own illnesses (Brandt and Rozin, 1997; Weitz, 1991). Such explanations provide psychological reassurance by reinforcing people's belief in a "just world" in which punishment falls only on the guilty (Meyerowitz, Williams, and Gessner, 1987).

The history of leprosy illustrates the long-standing belief that moral failure can produce the physical manifestations of disease, although it is important to note that there has been a tendency to exaggerate the extent to which leprosy has always evoked widespread rejection or was even consistently linked to moral failure (Rawcliffe, 2006). In the Old Testament of the Christian scriptures, there are several instances where people are punished with leprosy for sin against God. In contrast, in the New Testament, Jesus frequently denied that disease was punishment for sin, going out of his way to welcome and heal lepers who were treated as social outcasts. Historically, then, responses to leprosy have incorporated both extremes of condemnation and compassion. The persisting belief that leprosy was an outward reflection of spiritual depravity, coupled perhaps with some awareness that leprosy was contagious, may have led Western societies to ostracize affected individuals.

During the late medieval period, a new theory about disease causation began to emerge and grow in popularity, reaching its height in the nineteenth century. The **miasma theory of disease** held that illness occurred when persons came in contact with air corrupted by foul odours and fumes. Thus, disease is transmitted not through contact with humans or human bodily fluids (as per the **germ theory** of disease that would eventually supplant the miasma theory of disease) but by sharing contaminated air. Because illnesses were concentrated among the urban poor of major cities, who endured squalid living conditions, the impoverished came to be seen as synonymous with their filthy, disease-producing environs.

As the history of cholera shows, the miasma theory of disease continued to allow the healthy to blame the ill for their illnesses. Cholera first appeared in the Western world in about 1830, killing its victims suddenly and horrifyingly, through overwhelming dehydration brought on by uncontrollable diarrhea and vomiting. Cholera is caused by waterborne

miasma theory of disease:

A theory of disease causation that posits that disease is caused by foul smells that emanate from soil, water, or air.

bacteria, generally transmitted when human wastes contaminate food or drinking water. It most often strikes poor people because they are the most likely to lack clean water and to be weakened by insufficient food, clothing, or shelter.

To explain why cholera had struck, and why it struck the poor especially hard, early nineteenth-century doctors asserted that cholera could attack only individuals who had weakened their bodies through improper living (Risse, 1988; Rosenberg, 1987). According to this theory, the poor caused their own illnesses, first by lacking the initiative required to escape poverty and then by choosing to eat an unhealthy diet, live in dirty conditions, or drink too much alcohol. Thus, for example, when cholera broke out in Canada for the first time in 1832, the newspaper *The York Colonial Advocate* stated, "Much has been said respecting its contagious or non-contagious nature, but let it be as it may, the thing appears to be demonstrated in the progress of the disease, viz. that intemperance and filthy habits together with filthy habitations have been chief promoters of the disease in this country and as far as we can learn, elsewhere." (Patterson, 1958: 176). Conversely, doctors (and their wealthy patrons) assumed that wealthy persons would become ill only through gluttony, greed, or "innocently" inhaling some particularly noxious air. In sum, instead of believing that immorality directly caused illness, people now believed that immorality left one *susceptible* to illness.

Despite the tremendous growth in medical knowledge about illness during the last century, popular explanations for illness have remained remarkably stable. Theories connecting illness to sin continue to appear, as do theories that conceptualize illness as a direct consequence of poorly chosen and hence irresponsible (although not necessarily sinful) behaviour (Brandt and Rozin, 1997; Zola, 1972). For example, although most Canadians know that viruses cause influenza and the common cold, most continue to warn others to eat warm foods, wear hats and gloves, and cover up against the snow and rain to avoid infection. Similarly, the mass media, public health authorities, and the general public now often blame illness on individual lifestyles (Brandt and Rozin, 1997; Tesh, 1988). Magazines regularly print articles that exhort individuals to protect or restore their health through diet, exercise, stress reduction, and the like. Simultaneously, various provincial governments—even while continuing to subsidize the tobacco and beef industries—spend millions on education campaigns encouraging the public to stop smoking and to eat healthier diets.

Explanations for illness that emphasize individual responsibility make it easy for the media, doctors, policymakers, and the public to ignore how social and environmental factors foster illness (Crawford, 1979; Tesh, 1988; Waitzkin, 1981; Zola, 1972). For example, magazines that emphasize how individuals make themselves ill rarely discuss how factors largely beyond individual control (such as poverty; malnutrition; pollution; and unsafe conditions in our houses, cars, or workplaces) can produce ill health. Nor do these magazines discuss how social factors (including the advertisements for alcohol in some of these same magazines) can pressure individuals to adopt unhealthy lifestyles—how unemployed teenagers with poor job prospects sometimes smoke cigarettes to demonstrate their adulthood, how young mothers who lack assistance with child care probably also lack time for regular aerobic exercise, or how workers sometimes suffer injuries because of unsafe equipment rather than because of personal carelessness. In sum, whether or not they are accurate, theories of illness that focus on individual responsibility reinforce existing social arrangements and help us justify our tendency to reject, mistreat, or simply ignore those who suffer illness.

MODELS OF ILLNESS

But what do we mean when we say something is an illness? As Marco's struggles with shortness suggest, the answer is far from obvious. Most of us are fairly confident that someone who has a cold or cancer is ill. But what about women whose bones have become brittle with age; men who have bald spots or enlarged prostates; or young boys who have trouble learning, drink excessively, or enjoy fighting? Depending on whom you ask, these conditions may be defined as normal human variations, as illnesses, or as evidence of bad character. As these questions suggest, defining what is and is not an illness is far from a simple task. In this section, we explore how these questions are addressed in the medical and sociological worlds.

The Medical and Sociological Models of Illness

In Chapter 1, we discussed some of the differences between the **medical model of illness** and sociological perspectives on illness. We noted that the medical model of illness is the dominant conception of illness in the world and refers to what doctors typically mean when they say something is an illness. Conversely, sociological perspectives reflect sociologists' view of how the world currently operates, not how it should ideally operate. Key Concepts 7.1 compares these two models, using as an example female sexual dysfunction (FSD), a recently developed and still contentious diagnosis.

KEY CONCEPTS 7.1   Medical and Sociological Models of Illness

Medical Model	Sociological Model
Illness is an *objective* label: There is scientific consensus on what is normal and what is illness.	Illness is a *subjective* category: What is normal and what is illness may be highly contested.
Example: Female sexual dysfunction (FSD) is a biological disease characterized by lack of sexual responsiveness.	Example: Female sexual dysfunction (FSD) is a label given to women who are distressed by their lack of sexual responsiveness with their current sexual partner.
Illness is *non-moral*: Conditions and behaviours are labelled *illness* scientifically, without moral considerations or consequences.	Illness is a *moral* category: Conditions and behaviours may be labelled *illness* when they are considered bad (deviant).
Example: Labelling FSD an illness and labelling individuals as having FSD are neutral biological statements that do not reflect moral judgments of the condition or individual.	Example: We label sexual non-responsiveness an illness because we find it repugnant, and we typically look down on those who have FSD.
Illness is an *apolitical* label.	Illness is a *political* label: Some groups have more power than others to decide what is illness and who is ill.
Example: FSD was first identified by doctors through scientific research.	Example: The concept of FSD was promoted by pharmaceutical companies to sell drugs.

There are several major differences between the two models. First, the medical model of illness assumes that illness is an objective label given to anything that deviates from normal biological functioning (Mishler, 1981). Doctors might further explain that, because of scientific progress, all educated doctors can now recognize these problems as illnesses, even though they were not considered as such in earlier eras. Based on the assumption that illness is an objective category, the medical model of health care assumes that each illness has specific features, universally recognizable in all populations by all trained doctors, that differentiate it both from other illnesses and from health (Dubos, 1961; Mishler, 1981). The medical model thus assumes that diagnosis is an objective, scientific process.

In contrast, the sociological model of illness begins with the statement that illness is a *subjective* label, which reflects personal and social ideas about what is normal as much as scientific reasoning (Weitz, 1991). Sociologists point out that ideas about normality differ widely across both individuals and social groups. A height of 4 feet 6 inches would be normal for a Pygmy man but not for a North American man. Drinking three glasses of wine a day is normal for Italian women but could lead to a diagnosis of alcoholism in Canadian women. In defining normality, therefore, we need to look not only at individual bodies but also at the broader social context. Moreover, even within a given group, "normality" is a range and not an absolute. The median height of Canadian men, for example, is 5 feet 8.5 inches (174 cm), but most people would consider someone several inches taller or shorter than that as still normal. Similarly, individual Italians routinely and without social difficulties drink more or less alcohol than the average Italian. Thus, what is normal and what is illness are based not on absolute, objective markers of health and illness but on arbitrary, statistical cutoff points—deciding, for example, that anyone in the fifth percentile for height or the fiftieth percentile for cholesterol level is ill. Culture, too, plays a role: In North America, large breasts are seen as desirable and women may pursue the option of breast implants to treat the disease of micromastia (small-breastedness), whereas in Brazil, large breasts are denigrated as a sign of African heritage and macromastia (large-breastedness) is treated with breast reduction surgery.

Sociologists also perceive diagnosis as a *subjective* process. Patients with the same symptoms may receive different diagnoses depending on various social factors. Women who seek medical care for chronic pain, for example, are more likely to receive psychiatric diagnoses than are men who report the same symptoms. Moreover, different cultures identify a different range of symptoms and categorize those symptoms into different illnesses. For example, doctors in North America assign the label of attention deficit/hyperactivity disorder (ADHD) to children who in Europe would be considered lazy troublemakers. And French doctors often attribute headaches to liver problems, whereas North American doctors seek psychiatric or neurological explanations (Payer, 1996). In practice, the medical model of illness assumes that illnesses manifest themselves in other cultures in the same way as in North American culture and, by extension, that North American doctors can readily transfer their knowledge of illness to the treatment and prevention of illness elsewhere.

Second, because the medical model assumes illness is an objective, scientifically determined category, it also assumes there is no moral element in labelling a condition or behaviour as an illness. Sociologists, on the other hand, argue that illness is inherently a moral category, for deciding what illness is always means deciding what is good or bad. When, for example, doctors label menopause a "hormonal deficiency disease," they label it an undesirable deviation from normal. In contrast, many women consider menopause both normal and desirable and enjoy the freedom from fear of pregnancy that menopause brings (Martin, 1987). In the same manner, when we define cancer, polio, or diabetes as an illness, we judge the bodily changes these conditions produce to be both abnormal and undesirable rather than simply normal variations in functioning, abilities, and life expectancies. (Conversely, when we define a condition as healthy, we judge it normal and desirable.)

Similarly, when we label an individual as ill, we also suggest that there is something undesirable about that person. By definition, an ill person is one whose actions, abilities, or appearance do not meet social **norms,** or expectations within a given culture regarding proper behaviour or appearance. Such a person will typically be considered less whole and less socially worthy than those deemed healthy. Illness, then, like virginity or laziness, is a **moral status**: a social condition that we believe indicates the goodness or badness, worthiness or unworthiness, of a person.

norms:
Social expectations for appropriate behaviour.

moral status:
A status that identifies in society's eyes whether a person is good or bad, worthy or unworthy.

deviance:

Behaviour that violates a particular culture's norms or expectations for proper behaviour and therefore results in negative social sanctions.

negative social sanctions:

Punishments meted out to those considered deviant by society.

positive social sanctions:

Rewards of any sort, from good grades to public esteem.

From a sociological standpoint, illness is not only a moral status but (like crime or sin) a form of **deviance** (Parsons, 1951). To sociologists, labelling something deviant does not necessarily mean that it is immoral. Rather, deviance refers to behaviours or conditions that socially powerful persons within a given culture *perceive,* whether accurately or inaccurately, as immoral or as violating social norms. We can tell whether behaviour violates norms (and, therefore, whether it is deviant) by seeing if it results in **negative social sanctions**. This term refers to any punishment, from ridicule to execution. (Conversely, **positive social sanctions** refer to rewards, ranging from token gifts to knighthood.) These social sanctions can be enforced by parents, police, teachers, and peers, as well as doctors.

Two quick examples demonstrate how ubiquitous it is in our societies to apply negative social sanctions to those who are ill or engage in behaviour that is perceived to be health-endangering. First, scientists continue to sound the alarm that the world is overdue for a major flu pandemic such as the one in 1918–1919 that killed millions of people worldwide. In 2009, concern was amplified as a virulent and potentially deadly strain of H1N1 spread rapidly across the globe. Although fears for this particular virus proved to be unfounded, there was a rapid change in social norms about how to comport oneself in public. Coughing openly became an activity that was guaranteed to result in dirty looks from passersby, sometimes accompanied by denigrating remarks. Although the harshness of these negative social sanctions dissipated as the crisis passed, we recognize that negative social sanctions are powerful ways of inducing people to conform their behaviour. Similarly, people who smoke cigarettes are frequently the target of derisive comments and scorn because they are seen to be putting their own health and the health of others at risk. Portrayals of cigarette smokers as stupid and repulsive are common on the Internet, in television commercials, and on government websites. In Box 7.1, we ask whether these attacks have gone too far and whether efforts to stand up for the rights of smokers are warranted. Later in this chapter, we will look at more ways in which negative social sanctions are imposed against those who are ill.

BOX 7.1

Negative Social Sanctions against Cigarette Smokers: A Step Too Far?

Over the course of the twentieth century, there was a sea change in people's behaviours and attitudes around cigarette smoking. As the public slowly absorbed the increasingly broadcast message that smoking was a cause of cancer and altogether bad for health, it transformed from an activity that was associated with men and the middle and upper classes to one that, over time, became concentrated among those who were female and socioeconomically disadvantaged. Accompanying this shift was the increasingly negative view of smokers. At different times over the past century, smoking was positively portrayed as a way of losing weight or treating a sore throat, and as symbolic of the upper-class life of leisure. For women, smoking came

to represent taking up their "torches of freedom" to express their equality with men and as a way to communicate sexual desire and attraction (Greaves, 2003).

Today, cigarette smoking is viewed very differently. The messages are blatant: people who smoke cigarettes are stupid, repulsive, and disgusting; lack self-control; are socially irresponsible; may be sexually impotent; and have no regard for others. For example, the Ontario government has a website (www.stupid.ca) that encourages teens to take a stand against tobacco. Although the messages on this government website are less derogatory than many others, the use of the word *stupid* in its campaign clearly conveys that people who choose to smoke are making dumb choices. Print ads around the world variously depict smokers with rotting teeth, disfiguring cancers, and lesions on their mouths and faces, or hooked up to an oxygen machine. One television ad tells the story of a young woman picking up a male hitch-hiker in a deserted location. Despite the well-known dangers of stopping for hitchhikers, this young woman is not frightened because when she sees him smoking, she assumes that he must be sexually impotent and, therefore, poses no threat to her safety.

Why are smokers singled out for these extremely negative social sanctions? Comparable ads don't exist for other undesirable behaviours, such as speeding in a car, passing along sexually transmitted diseases, or urinating in a public swimming pool, that are also unhealthy and pose risks to others.

Perhaps the backlash has already begun. Some have argued that these ads are not having the intended effect of scaring or humiliating smokers to quit, but instead produce defensive responses, such that the attachment to smoking becomes even more ingrained. And many countries have smokers' rights groups that speak out against their stigmatization in society and call for greater civility and tolerance (Smith and Malone, 2007). In Canada, the Smokers' Rights Association operates a website (http://smokersrightscanada.org) that appears to have become more independent but also less active since 2009, when it lost funding from its major sponsor, Imperial Tobacco. Nonetheless, the website still offers opportunities for those on both sides to weigh in on the issue of whether smokers deserve fairer treatment.

Finally, for the same reasons that the medical model does not recognize the *moral* aspects of illness labelling, it does not recognize the *political* aspects of that process. Although some doctors at some times are deeply immersed in these political processes—arguing, for example, that female sexual dysfunction is a disorder—they rarely consider the ways that politics underlie the illness-labelling process in general. In contrast, sociologists point out that any time a condition or behaviour is labelled as an illness, some groups will benefit more than others, and some groups will have more power than others to enforce the definitions that benefit them. As a result, there are often open political struggles over illness definitions (a topic we will return to later in this chapter). For example, vermiculite miners and their families who were constantly exposed to asbestos dust and who now have strikingly high rates of cancer have fought with insurance companies and doctors, in clinics, hospitals, and the courts, to have "asbestosis" labelled an illness; meanwhile, the mining companies and the doctors they employed have argued that there is no such disease and that the high rates of health problems in mining communities are merely coincidences (Schneider and McCumber, 2004).

In sum, from a sociological perspective, illness is a **social construction**, something that exists in the world not as an objective condition but *because we have defined it as existing*. This does not mean that the virus causing measles does not exist, or that it does not cause a fever and a rash. It does mean, though, that when we talk about measles as an illness, we have organized our ideas about the virus, fever, and rash in only one of many possible ways. In another place or time, people might conceptualize these same conditions as manifestations of witchcraft, as a healthy response to the presence of microbes, or as some other illness altogether. To sociologists, then, *illness,* like *crime* or *sin,* refers to biological, psychological, or social conditions subjectively defined as undesirable by those within a given culture who have the power to enforce such definitions.

social construction:
Ideas created by a social group, as opposed to something that is objectively or naturally given.

MEDICINE AS SOCIAL CONTROL

In everyday life, we use the word *medicine* to refer to the drugs that doctors prescribe. But we can also use the word *medicine* to refer to the world and culture of doctors. For example, we might say that modern medicine is an exceedingly complex enterprise or that modern medicine primarily focuses on treating disease rather than on looking for environmental causes of illness. Even more broadly, sociologists refer to medicine as an **institution**. Sociologists use the term *institution* to refer to enduring social structures that meet basic human needs, such as the family, religion, and education. When we talk of medicine as an institution, we refer to the world and culture of doctors as well as to the economic, social, and political underpinnings of that world. We might, for example, talk about how the power of medicine *as an institution*—doctors, hospitals, the medical way of thinking about the world, and so on—has grown over the last century.

One of the central concepts in the sociology of health and illness is the idea that medicine is, among other things, an institution of social control. As we first noted in Chapter 3, **social control** refers to the formal and informal methods used by a social group to ensure that individuals conform to social norms and to ensure that the existing balance of power between groups is maintained. When we say that medicine is an institution of social control, we are saying that medicine is a basic structure of our society that, sometimes, serves to "keep people in line" with our society's expectations for them. For example, doctors have the power to decide whether someone is a malingerer who should be shunned or is truly ill and deserves sympathy. In such a situation, doctors act as **social control agents**: individuals or groups that enforce social norms, such as parents, religious leaders, and police. In the next sections, we will see how the institution of medicine serves as social control, and doctors act as agents of social control, when the medical world decides which conditions or behaviours are acceptable and which should be labelled as illness and when it pushes sick people to get well and reintegrate into society.

Creating Illness: Medicalization

The process through which a condition or behaviour becomes defined as a medical problem requiring a medical solution is known as **medicalization** (Conrad and Schneider, 1992; Conrad, 2007). For example, as social conditions have changed, activities formerly considered sins or crimes, such as masturbation, homosexual activity, and heavy drinking, have become defined as illnesses. The same has happened to various natural conditions and processes, such as uncircumcised penises, male balding, aging, and pregnancy (Armstrong, 2000; Rosenfeld and Faircloth, 2005; Conrad, 2007). The term *medicalization* also refers to the process through which the definition of an illness is *broadened*. For example, when doctors expanded the definition of Alzheimer's to include elderly as well as middle-aged patients, the number of persons with this diagnosis exploded (Conrad, 2007).

For medicalization to occur, one or more organized social groups must have both a vested interest in it and sufficient power to convince others (including doctors, the public, the government, and insurance companies) to accept their new definition of the situation. Not surprisingly, doctors often play a major role in medicalization, for medicalization can increase their power, the scope of their practices, and their incomes. For example, during the first half of the twentieth century, improvements in the standard of living coupled with the adoption of numerous public health measures substantially reduced the number of seriously ill children. As a result, the market for pediatricians declined, and their focus shifted from treating serious illnesses to treating minor childhood illnesses and offering well-baby care. Pediatrics thus became less well paid, less interesting, and less prestigious. To increase their market while obtaining more satisfying and prestigious work, some pediatricians have expanded their

institution:
An enduring social structure that meets basic human needs, such as the family, education, religion, or medicine (taken in its entirety).

social control agents:
Those individuals or groups of individuals who have the authority to enforce social norms, including parents, teachers, religious leaders, and doctors.

medicalization:
The process through which a condition or behaviour becomes defined as a medical problem requiring a medical solution, or through which the definition of an illness is broadened to cover a wider population.

practices to include children whose behaviour concerns their parents or teachers and who are now defined as having ADHD (Conrad, 2007). Doctors have played similar roles in medicalizing crooked noses, obesity, drinking during pregnancy, impotence, and numerous other conditions (Armstrong, 1998; Loe, 2004).

In other instances, however, doctors have proven indifferent or even opposed to medicalization. This by definition is the case with any **contested illness**: distressing and painful symptoms that affected individuals believe constitute an illness even though many doctors disagree. For example, the symptoms attributed to fibromyalgia are many and common, including pain, dizziness, insomnia, depression, and headache. But no blood test or X-ray can identify an individual as having fibromyalgia. As a result, many doctors question whether the disease really exists. The same is true for chronic fatigue syndrome, multiple chemical sensitivity, Gulf War Syndrome, and other conditions. In these cases, consumers often press for medicalization to get validation for their experiences, to stimulate research on treatments and cures, and to get health and disability insurance coverage for their problems (Conrad, 2007; Barker, 2005, 2008). The rise of the Internet has made it much easier for such consumers to find each other, to reaffirm each other's sense that they suffer from a real illness, and to become a pro-medicalization lobby.

The pharmaceutical industry has also been a major force behind medicalization (Conrad, 2007). As a large and profitable industry, drug makers have a vested economic interest in medicalization whenever it can provide a drug as treatment. In search of ever greater profits, the pharmaceutical industry has begun to have a profound impact on what is seen as illness in our society.

As noted earlier, fibromyalgia is a contested illness—not all doctors agree that it is an illness. Yet in 2007, one pharmaceutical company received approval in the United States to market a drug by the name of Lyrica for the treatment of fibromyalgia, placing immense pressure on physicians to accept fibromyalgia as an illness. (The drug was approved for the treatment of fibromyalgia in Canada in 2009.) Barker (2011) analyzed how the drug was marketed to the public as well as the reaction of fibromyalgia sufferers. She found that television ads presented fibromyalgia as a legitimate disease, using compelling graphics of disordered neural functioning (even though the biological mechanisms underlying the disorder remain unknown) and touting positive messages about the drug's ability to restore individuals to their former selves.

Barker (2011) labels this as an example of **pharmaceutical determinism**, where diseases come to be recognized not on the basis of pathology that can be objectively identified in the body but by the availability of a medication that claims to treat the condition. Barker notes that fibromyalgia sufferers responded positively to the message that their suffering was real, as evident in the following posting to an online support group run by and for those with fibromyalgia:

> I just HAD to tell you all that in the last week I had 2, yes 2 people ask me about my fibro. They said they did not know it was a real disease until they saw the commercial about Lyrica! Its not enough for US to tell them. Noooooooo they have to see it on TV.... We have been telling the truth to family and friends forever.... I think that Lyrica commercial is going to be one of the best things that ever happened to us... whether the med helps or not. It somehow validates us as human beings that have a debilitating illness not just the hypochondriacs they thought we were! (Barker, 2011, p. 839)

At the same time, many with the condition felt that the ads trivialized their symptoms of fibromyalgia and overstated the efficacy of the drug. Moreover, not all who took the drug saw a reduction of symptoms and some had serious enough side effects to warrant

contested illness:
Any collection of distressing, painful symptoms that occur together and that laypeople assume constitute an illness, even though many doctors disagree.

pharmaceutical determinism:
The existence of prescription medication for a condition is used to argue for the biological existence of that condition.

stopping medication. Despite these reservations, the logic of pharmaceutical determinism had a powerful influence on their experiences, affording them legitimacy if not vindication for their suffering and undoubtedly providing them with needed ammunition in their interactions with physicians. Doctors may not have the evidence they need to verify its existence, but rising sales of the drug appear to suggest that this is an increasingly unimportant detail.

In Box 7.2, we discuss direct-to-consumer advertising, which makes it possible for pharmaceutical companies to sidestep physicians and market their products directly to the public—a phenomenon that proved instrumental in the growing acceptance of Lyrica for the treatment of fibromyalgia but has generated considerable controversy.

BOX 7.2
Direct-to-Consumer Advertising

direct-to-consumer advertising (DTCA): The use of mass media (e.g., television, newspapers, magazines, and the Internet) by the pharmaceutical industry to promote drugs, medical devices, and other products that require a prescription to the general public.

Direct-to-consumer advertising (DTCA) refers to the use of mass media (e.g., television, newspapers, magazines, and the Internet) by the pharmaceutical industry to promote drugs, medical devices, and other products that require a prescription to the general public. The practice is illegal in all countries except for New Zealand and the United States. In 2005 alone, the pharmaceutical industry spent $4.2 billion in DTCA in the United States, and Americans spent an average of sixteen hours watching televised drug advertisements (Mintzes, 2009). Because many Canadian television stations pick up American feeds, Canadians are often exposed to these types of commercials as well.

In Canada, the law permits only two kinds of advertisements. The first type, known as reminder ads, may present the name of the drug but cannot reference the disease it treats. In contrast, help-seeking ads describe the condition that is being treated but cannot name the drug. These restrictions have resulted in some fairly creative ads in Canada. One recent reminder ad shows two older men speaking in elated gobbledygook to another. The ad ends when a blue pill with the word Viagra appears above their heads, leaving the viewer to subsequently infer that the men have been recounting how the drug has enhanced their sexual exploits.

Not surprisingly, Canadian regulators are under constant barrage to change the law to allow DTCA. While drug manufacturers claim that these ads will provide important information for consumers, Mintzes (2009) counters that DTCA fails to provide consumers with critical information, such as how much more efficacious the treatment being advertised is relative to existing drugs that are cheaper and have fewer side effects. Moreover, she argues that these ads rely heavily on emotive and deceptive messages that imply that taking the prescription will lead to happiness and greater control over one's life and is a means of obtaining social approval. Mintzes (2002) has also argued that these ads are increasingly aimed at healthy people, who, when presented with a list of vague symptoms, can be persuaded they have the mentioned illness, which serves to create new and profitable markets for drug manufacturers. For example, one current ad simply asks the viewer whether he or she has a tendency to go to the bathroom too frequently, without ever specifying what number of times in a given period is too many. Without a number, this is purely a subjective assessment. Yet it is possible that in even hearing the question, some will begin to wonder whether they in fact do have such a problem. In this way, DTCA may facilitate medicalization by making viewers feel more vulnerable than they really are to illness and disease.

Case Study: Working Together to Medicalize ADHD

Neither doctors nor consumer groups nor pharmaceutical companies have enough influence to medicalize a condition on their own. Successful medicalization depends on the interwoven interests and activities of these three groups and sometimes others. The history of ADHD illustrates this process.

As originally defined, ADHD (then called *hyperkinesis*) lacked any definitive biological markers and instead referred to children above age 5 who were overactive, impulsive, and easily distracted but who had no brain damage (Diller, 1998; Conrad 2007). Since the late 1930s, doctors have known that amphetamines (including methamphetamine or "speed") can reduce distraction in children and adults, regardless of their mental health or illness. In addition, even though, biologically, amphetamines are stimulants, they cause an intense focus that can make users appear less active. These characteristics made amphetamines a natural choice for treating hyperkinesis. However, because amphetamines are highly addictive and have dangerous side effects, physicians avoided prescribing them.

In the absence of a viable treatment, physicians rarely made the diagnosis of hyperkinesis. This situation changed in the 1960s, when the amphetamine Ritalin (methylphenidate) appeared on the market (Conrad, 2007). Ritalin has fewer short-term side effects than other amphetamines and, in the short term, improves the ability to concentrate, reduces the tendency to act impulsively, and increases willingness to accept discipline. Yet Ritalin is far from a panacea. Chemically, it acts much like cocaine (Vastag, 2001). Its immediate side effects can include addiction, loss of appetite, sleep deprivation, headache, and stomach ache. Its long-term side effects may include cancer (Davis, 2007), and its long-term benefits seem minor at best: The little available research suggests that it does not improve users' chances of graduating high school, holding a job, refraining from illicit drugs, or avoiding trouble with the law (Diller, 1998).

Following the development of Ritalin, pharmaceutical companies embarked on a huge campaign to "sell" hyperkinesis both to the public via the mass media and to doctors. According to Peter Conrad and Joseph Schneider:

> After the middle 1960s it is nearly impossible to read a medical journal... without seeing some elaborate advertising for either Ritalin or Dexedrine [another amphetamine]. These advertisements explain the utility of treating hyperkinesis... and urge the physician to diagnose and treat hyperkinetic children. The advertisements may run from one to six pages. They often advise physicians that "the hyperkinetic syndrome" exists as "a distinct medical entity" and that the "syndrome is readily diagnosed through patient histories and psychometric testing...." These same pharmaceutical firms also supply sophisticated packets of 'diagnostic and treatment' information on hyperkinesis to physicians, pay for professional conferences on the subject, and support research in the identification and treatment of hyperkinesis. (1992: 159–160)

Pediatricians proved a ready audience for this marketing campaign, which promised a way to boost their flagging income and prestige. This market further increased in 1987, when hyperkinesis was redefined into ADHD and expanded to include adults as well as children and to include girls who daydream and boys who "act out" physically (Mayes, Bagwell, and Erkulwater, 2009).

Like pediatricians, many teachers readily adopted the concept of ADHD, if for different reasons (Diller, 1998). Faced with cuts in staffing and larger classes at the same time that school boards began placing an increased emphasis on testing and competition at earlier and earlier ages, teachers can hardly be blamed for looking with favour on drugs that make their students more manageable. In addition, diagnosing a student with ADHD shifts blame for poor student performance from teacher to student. Not surprisingly, the suggestion to place a child on Ritalin now often comes initially from a teacher (Diller, 1998).

Parents, too, are often relieved to find an explanation other than poor parenting for their child's behavioural or educational problems. Ironically, mothers, who, more so than fathers, tend to be held responsible for their child's shortcomings, find that this does not deflect scrutiny of their own parenting practices, as health care professionals, teachers, and educational administrators almost universally operate under the assumption that "there must be problems at home" (Malacrida, 2003). Parents may also hope to remove blame from their children, reduce the chances of legal sanctions against their children, and stimulate research on treatment. They may even hope that having their children diagnosed with a disability—ADHD—will give their children access to special educational services plus protection against suspension or expulsion for any disciplinary problems that could be considered part of their disability (Diller, 1998; Conrad 2007).

Taken together, these factors produced an astounding increase in the number of persons diagnosed with ADHD, such that it is now the most common mental health problem for which children visit a mental health professional. Between 3 and 7% of Canadian children have ADHD, with boys nearly four times as likely as girls to have the disorder. Correspondingly, global use of ADHD medications rose threefold between 1993 and 2003 (Scheffler et al., 2007). In Canada, approximately 1.2% of all children aged 4–13 have a prescription for Ritalin (Brownell, Mayer, and Chateau, 2006).

The Consequences of Medicalization

In some circumstances, medicalization can be a boon, leading to social awareness of a problem, sympathy toward its sufferers, and the development of beneficial therapies. Persons with epilepsy, for example, lead far happier and more productive lives now that their seizures are treated with drugs rather than treated as signs of demonic possession. But defining a condition as an illness does not necessarily improve the social status of those who have that condition. Those who use alcohol excessively, for example, continue to experience social rejection even when alcoholism is labelled a disease. Moreover, medicalization can also lead to new problems, known by sociologists as **unintended negative consequences** (Conrad and Schneider, 1992; Conrad, 2007).

unintended negative consequences:
Unplanned, harmful effects of actions that had been expected to produce only benefits.

First, once a situation becomes medicalized, doctors become the only experts able to diagnose the problem and define appropriate responses to it. As a result, the power of doctors increases, while the power of other social authorities (including judges, the police, religious leaders, legislators, and teachers) diminishes. For example, now that troublesome behaviour by children is increasingly diagnosed as ADHD, parents, teachers, and the children themselves have lost credibility when they disagree with this diagnosis. Similarly, doctors are now given considerable authority to answer questions such as who should receive abortions or organ transplants, how society should respond to drug use, and whether severely disabled infants should receive experimental surgeries, while the authority of the church and family members to answer these questions has diminished.

As this suggests, medicalization significantly expands the range of life experiences under medical control. For example, the natural process of aging is increasingly regarded as a medical condition. Doctors now scrutinize all aspects of the aging body and recommend psychological tests to measure mental decline, hormones to improve virility, cosmetic surgery for wrinkles, and more (Conrad, 2007).

Second, once a condition is medicalized, medical treatment may become the only logical response to it. For example, if woman-battering is considered a medical condition, then doctors need to treat women and the men who batter them. However, if woman-battering is considered a social problem stemming from male power and female subordination, then it makes more sense to arrest the men, assist the women financially and emotionally, and work for broader structural changes that will improve all women's status and options.

Third, when doctors define situations in medical terms, they reduce the chances that these situations will be understood in *political* terms. For example, China, Pakistan, and other countries have removed political dissidents from the public eye by committing them to mental hospitals. By doing so these governments discredited and silenced individuals who might otherwise have offered powerful dissenting voices. In other words, medicalization allowed these governments to **depoliticize** the situation—to define it as a medical rather than a political problem.

Fourth, as the example of China and Pakistan illustrated, medicalization can justify not only voluntary but also involuntary treatment. Yet treatment does not always help and can sometimes harm. For example, **community treatment orders (CTOs)** are a controversial legal provision by which a physician can require a person who has a mental illness to follow a course of treatment (typically medication and regular doctor visits) while living in the community. CTOs exist throughout the world, including in Canada, the United States, the United Kingdom, Australia, and New Zealand. With policies varying by province, it is difficult to know how common these are in Canada, but evidence from Ontario suggests that approximately 2% of people diagnosed with schizophrenia have been placed on a CTO (Hunt et al., 2007). Although proponents would argue that CTOs are less restrictive than hospitalization and that society has an obligation to take care of those who are unable to take care of themselves and who lack insight into their own condition, opponents of CTOs contend that coercion in any context is morally wrong, that using CTOs is a slippery slope that will lead to overuse and abuse, and that it may put the therapeutic relationship between doctor and patient in jeopardy (O'Reilly, 2004). It is important to note that compliance with antipsychotic medication is notoriously difficult, as patients may stop medication because they think they are getting better and fail to notice the signs of relapse, or because they are experiencing some of the many nasty side effects associated with their drug regimens. For example, antipsychotics are known to cause a permanent and irreversible movement disorder known as tardive dyskinesia and increase risk for diabetes. This raises the issue of whose interests are best served when mentally ill persons are legally obliged to take their psychotropic medication despite the accompanying risks to their physical health (Busfield, 2004).

Fifth, to the extent that illness represents deviation from the normal, where normal is determined by one's placement in a given distribution, the criteria for illness become a moving target where illness can never be vanquished. For example, if shortness is a diagnosis for those whose heights fall in the bottom fifth percentile, then there will always be someone who falls in that category, even as treatment makes it possible to shift upward the average height of the population (Triggle, 2005). This raises the profound question of where one marks the slippery boundary between the treatment of disease and the enhancement of human capabilities, a topic that we will revisit in Chapter 9.

The Rise of Demedicalization

The dangers of medicalization have fostered a (much smaller) countermovement of **demedicalization** (Conrad, 2007). A quick look at medical textbooks from the late 1800s reveals many "diseases" that no longer exist. For example, nineteenth-century medical textbooks often included several pages on the health risks of masturbation. One popular textbook from the late nineteenth century asserted that masturbation caused "extreme emaciation, sallow or blotched skin, sunken eyes, … general weakness, dullness, weak back, stupidity, laziness, … wandering and illy defined pains," as well as infertility, impotence, consumption, epilepsy, heart disease, blindness, paralysis, and insanity (Kellogg, 1880: 365). Today, however, medical textbooks describe masturbation as a normal part of human sexuality.

Like medicalization, demedicalization often begins with lobbying by consumer groups. For example, medical ideology now defines childbirth as an inherently dangerous process,

community treatment orders (CTOs): Legal provisions by which a physician can require a person who has a mental illness to follow a course of treatment (typically medication and regular doctor visits) while living in the community.

demedicalization: The process through which a condition or behaviour becomes defined as a natural condition or process rather than an illness.

requiring intensive technological, medical assistance. Since the 1940s, however, growing numbers of women have attempted to redefine childbirth as a generally safe, simple, and natural process and have promoted alternatives ranging from natural childbirth classes, to hospital birthing centres, to home births assisted only by midwives. Similarly, gay and lesbian activists have at least partially succeeded in redefining homosexuality from a pathological condition to a normal human variation.

Social Control and the Sick Role

Until now, we have looked at how medicine functions as an institution of social control through defining individuals either as sick or as biologically defective. Medicine can also work as an institution of social control by pressuring individuals to *abandon* sickness, a process first recognized by Talcott Parsons (1951).

Parsons was one of the first and most influential sociologists to recognize that illness is deviance. From his perspective, when people are ill, they cannot perform the social tasks normally expected of them. Workers stay home, homemakers tell their children to make their own meals, students ask to be excused from exams. Because of this, either consciously or unconsciously, people can use illness to evade their social responsibilities. To Parsons, therefore, illness threatened social stability.

Parsons also recognized, however, that allowing some illness can *increase* social stability. Imagine a world in which no one could ever "call in sick." Over time, production levels would fall as individuals, denied needed recuperation time, succumbed to physical ailments. Morale, too, would fall while resentment would rise among those forced to perform their social duties day after day without relief. Illness, then, acts as a kind of pressure valve for society—something we recognize when we speak of taking time off work for "mental health days."

From Parsons's perspective, then, the important question was how did society control illness so that it would increase rather than decrease social stability? The author's emphasis on social stability reflected his belief in **structural-functionalism**. As we noted in Chapter 1, structural-functionalism views society as a smoothly working, integrated whole, much like the biological concept of the human body as a homeostatic environment. In this model, social order is maintained because individuals learn to accept society's norms and because society's needs and individuals' needs match closely, making rebellion unnecessary. Within this model, deviance—including illness—is usually considered **dysfunctional** because it threatens to undermine social stability.

dysfunctional:
Threatening to undermine social stability.

Defining the Sick Role

Parsons's interest in how society allows illness while minimizing its impact led him to develop the concept of the **sick role**. The sick role refers to social expectations regarding how society should view sick people and how sick people should behave. According to Parsons, the sick role as it currently exists in Western society has four parts, comprising two privileges as well as two obligations. First, the sick person is considered to have a legitimate reason for not fulfilling his or her normal social role. For this reason, we allow people to take time off from work when sick rather than firing them for malingering. Second, sickness is considered beyond individual control, something for which the individual is not held responsible. This is why, according to Parsons, we bring chicken soup to people who have colds rather than jailing them for stupidly exposing themselves to germs. Third, the sick person must recognize that sickness is undesirable and work to get well. So, for example, we sympathize with people who obviously hate being ill and strive to get well and question the motives of those who seem to revel in the attention their illness brings. Finally, the sick person should seek and follow medical advice. Typically, we expect sick people to follow their doctors' recommendations regarding drugs and surgery, and we question the wisdom of those who do not.

Parsons's analysis of the sick role moved the study of illness forward by highlighting the social dimensions of illness, including identifying illness as deviance and doctors as agents of social control. It remains important partly because it was the first truly sociological theory of illness. Parsons's research has also proven important because it stimulated later research on interactions between ill people and others. In turn, however, that research has illuminated the analytical weaknesses of the sick role model.

Critiquing the Sick Role Model

Whereas functionalists envision society as a harmonious whole held together largely by socialization, mutual consent, and mutual interests, those who hold a conflict perspective argue that society is held together largely by power and coercion, as dominant groups impose their will on others. Consequently, whereas functionalists view deviance as a dysfunctional element to be controlled, conflict theorists view deviance as a necessary force for social change and as the conscious or unconscious expression of individuals who refuse to conform to an oppressive society. Conflict theorists, therefore, have stressed the need to study social control agents as well as, if not more than, the need to study deviants.

The conflict perspective has helped sociologists to identify the strengths and weaknesses in each of the four elements of the sick role model (see Key Concepts 7.2). That model declares that sick persons are not held responsible for their illnesses. Yet, as we saw earlier in this chapter, and as Eliot Freidson (1970), the most influential critic of Parsons, noted, society often *does* hold individuals responsible for their illnesses. In addition, ill persons are not necessarily considered to have a legitimate reason for abstaining from their normal social tasks. Certainly no one expects persons with end-stage cancer to continue working, but what about people with arthritis or those labelled malingerers or hypochondriacs because they cannot obtain a diagnosis after months of pain, increasing disability, and visits to doctors (Ziporyn, 1992)? Parsons's model also fails to recognize that the social legitimacy of adopting the sick role depends on the socially perceived seriousness of the illness, which in turn depends not only on biological factors but also on the social setting. A non-unionized factory worker, for example, is less likely than a salaried worker with good health benefits to take time off when sick.

KEY CONCEPTS 7.2 **Strengths and Weaknesses of the Sick Role Model**

Elements of the Sick Role	Model Fits Well	Model Fits Poorly
Legitimate reason for not fulfilling obligations	Appendicitis, cancer	Undiagnosed chronic fatigue
Individual not held responsible	Measles, hemophilia	Herpes, lung cancer
Should strive to get well	Tuberculosis, broken leg	Diabetes, epilepsy
Should seek medical help	Strep throat, syphilis	"24-hour flu," cold

Other aspects of the sick role model are equally problematic. The assumption that individuals will attempt to get well fails to recognize that much illness is chronic and by definition not likely to improve. Similarly, the assumption that sick people will seek and follow medical advice ignores the many people who lack access to medical care. In addition, it ignores the many persons, especially those with chronic rather than acute conditions, who have found mainstream health care of limited benefit and who, therefore, rely mostly on their own experience and knowledge and that of other non-medical people. Finally, the concept of a sick role ignores how gender, ethnicity, age, and social class affect the response to illness and to ill people. For example, women are both *more* likely than men are to seek medical care when they feel ill and *less* likely to have their symptoms taken seriously by doctors (Council on Ethical and Judicial Affairs, American Medical Association, 1991; Steingart, 1991).

In sum, the sick role model is based on a series of assumptions about both the nature of society and the nature of illness. In addition, the sick role model confuses the experience of *patienthood* with the experience of *illness* (Conrad, 1987). The sick role model focuses on the interaction between the ill person and the mainstream health care system. Yet interactions with the medical world form only a small part of the experience of living with illness or disability, as the next chapter will show.

Despite these criticisms, some sociologists have revisited Parsons's ideas, finding that some of his remarks have surprising contemporary relevance. We take up this issue as we turn to our final topic in this chapter, the emergence of a new health consciousness.

THE EMERGENCE OF A NEW HEALTH CONSCIOUSNESS

In reassessing Parsons's contributions to the sociology of health and illness, Frank (1991) notes that Parsons not only spoke about illness but also provided insights into health. By suggesting that health is something that is achieved socially, that is, health only acquires value when it is used by an individual to mobilize and acquire resources, Parsons presciently identified the emergence of a new health consciousness. This new health consciousness may help us to understand some of the challenges we raised earlier in this chapter regarding the diminishing power of medicine as a mechanism of social control and reveal how our society's views on health and illness continue to change.

Several features of this new health consciousness stand out. First, there is a shift away from illness toward a preoccupation with health. We no longer merely wish to avoid illness, but we want to become ever healthier. Consequently, there is both greater demand and wider expansion of knowledge about how to improve health. We can see this clearly in our own society: We are constantly bombarded with information about how to be and stay healthy by news media that have entire segments devoted to health and reporters who exclusively report on the latest scientific discoveries. As health comes to stand for the essence of what is good in life, we respond to these media messages by changing our own behaviour. For example, we stop or reduce our intake of a certain food as evidence emerges that it is bad for health. This highlights another feature of the new health consciousness: There is a moral imperative to take personal responsibility for one's health (Petersen and Lupton, 1996). Those who ignore or fail to change behaviour in response to these health messages invite negative social sanctions. In Parsons's sick role, the sick were morally obliged to want to get well and seek treatment. In the health role, individuals are morally obliged to recognize threats to health and to manage that risk (Crawford, 2006; Ballard and Elston, 2005). Fulfilling these moral obligations means that the new health consciousness expands far beyond the realm of medicine; instead, every facet of life is judged according to its health-enhancing or health-endangering properties. For example, physical activity is no longer undertaken for the purpose of leisure or pleasure but increasingly performed as a means to be healthy. Yet, the irony of being the perfect citizen who abandons old behaviours and adopts new ones in the pursuit of health is that it requires the recognition that health is in continuous jeopardy. This is the final element of the new health consciousness: The more important health becomes, the more insecure we feel about our own health. Hence, not only do we demand more information from the science community about how to achieve health, but as these messages become more ambiguous or confusing (is chocolate good for us or not?), we become more cynical toward the experts who dispense health knowledge and less certain about whether or not we are healthy.

IMPLICATIONS

The language of illness and disease permeates our everyday lives. We routinely talk about living in a "sick" society or about the "disease" of violence infecting our world, offhandedly labelling anyone who behaves in a way we don't understand or don't condone as "sick."

This metaphoric use of language reveals the true nature of illness: behaviours, conditions, or situations that powerful groups find disturbing and believe stem from internal biological or psychological roots. In other times or places, the same behaviours, conditions, or situations might have been ignored, condemned as sin, or labelled crime. In other words, illness is both a social construction and a moral status.

In many instances, using the language of medicine and placing control in the hands of doctors offers a more humanistic option than the alternatives. Yet, as this chapter has demonstrated, medical social control also carries a price. For example, the same treatments that have positively changed the lives of some who have mental illness are now becoming morally and legally imperative for all who have mental illness. In the same way, then, that automobiles have increased our personal mobility in exchange for higher rates of accidental death and disability, adopting the language of illness and increasing medical social control bring both benefits and costs. Still, nothing stays the same forever. The new health consciousness may be seen to be weakening how medicine wields social control over illness; however, allowing the moral imperative of health to pervade all aspects of our lives carries other costs, notably cynicism toward the scientific enterprise and rising uncertainty as to whether or not we are healthy.

SUMMARY

LO-1 1. Pearlin has divided the work of sociologists of health and illness into two camps. He conceptualizes structure-seeking as research activities that reveal the influence of structural arrangements on the social distribution of illness, whereas meaning-seeking involves discerning how people subjectively interpret, recognize, and respond to ideas about health and illness.

LO-1 2. Although power can be central to both structure-seekers and meaning-seekers, the former relies on large-scale studies and quantitative methods and typically views measures of mortality and morbidity as objective indicators of health status. Meaning-seekers, on the other hand, prefer the richness that comes from in-depth, small-scale studies and qualitative methods and fundamentally question illness as an objective condition.

LO-2 3. To say that illness is a social construction is to reject the idea that it simply exists in the world as an objective condition discovered through scientific methods. Rather, illness exists *because we have defined it as existing.* The term *illness* refers to biological, psychological, or social conditions that are subjectively defined as undesirable by those who have the power to enforce their definitions.

LO-2 4. The medical model of illness assumes that illness is an objective label, applied scientifically, non-morally, and without any political bias. That model also assumes that illness is a concrete, unchanging reality, specific and universal, and caused by unique biological forces.

LO-2 5. According to social constructionists, a sociological perspective of illness regards illness as a social construction, a moral category, and a political label and emphasizes that what is labelled illness changes over time and space.

LO-3 6. Because illness is undesirable, those who are ill or who visibly pose a threat to the health and well-being of others are often exposed to negative social sanctions. Even so, not all illnesses are perceived in the same way, nor are these perceptions stable over time. For example, cigarette smokers appear to draw more condemnation than those who partake in other health-endangering activities and are increasingly depicted as repulsive, stupid, and irresponsible. Their treatment in the public sphere has similarities to the treatment of lepers in previous centuries—both conditions appear to justify their social exclusion and rejection from mainstream society.

LO-4 7. The institution of medicine serves as a form of social control in all issues related to health and illness. Thus, medicine has been afforded the social power to decide what is considered illness. Over the course of history, medicine has increased the number of conditions that fall under the jurisdiction of medicine and has also broadened the definition of what it means to be ill, a process called medicalization. Three groups that currently play prominent roles in medicalization are doctors, lay interest groups, and the pharmaceutical industry.

LO-5 8. With an eye focused on profits, the pharmaceutical industry has increasingly challenged the authority of medicine to decide what is considered illness. Not only have drug companies sought to obtain government approval to treat conditions that are not yet recognized as disease by medicine (e.g., fibromyalgia), but increasingly they have directly marketed their wares to the public through television, web, and print advertisements. In doing so, they have successfully sidestepped physicians as the accepted conduit for putting medications in the hands of consumers and made it possible for patients to exert greater control in the medical encounter.

LO-5 9. Medicalization can reduce stigma, increase social awareness, and encourage medical research. It can also worsen the social status of affected individuals, increase the power of doctors at the expense of other social groups, depoliticize dissent, and justify medical—and only medical—treatment.

LO-6 10. The institution of medicine acts as social control when it pressures individuals to seek health care and strive to get well (both aspects of the sick role). The sick role has four parts: (a) sickness is considered beyond individual control, (b) sick persons are considered to have legitimate reasons for not fulfilling their normal social roles, (c) sick persons must recognize that sickness is undesirable and work to get well, and (d) sick persons should seek and follow medical advice. The first two parts represent privileges of the sick role; the latter two denote obligations.

LO-6 11. Critics of the sick role model note that the model best fits acute rather than chronic illness and suggest that the model confuses the experience of being a *patient* with the much broader experience of *illness*.

LO-7 12. In the new health consciousness, health assumes greater social importance than illness, displacing doctors as the all-knowing centre of medical discourse. Constantly presented with media messages on ways to improve health, we are compelled by the moral imperative of health to change our lifestyles accordingly. The net effect of these changes is that as health increases in social value, paradoxically, we become less certain of whether we actually are healthy.

REVIEW QUESTIONS

1. What does it mean to say that illness is a social construction and a moral status?
2. How have explanations for illness changed over time, and how have explanations for illness blamed or held people responsible for their illnesses?
3. What is the medical model of illness, and what are some of the problems that a sociologist from a social construction of health and illness model would identify?
4. What are some examples of negative social sanctions in television, print, and Internet ads applied to people who are ill or who are perceived to create health risks to others?
5. What is medicalization, and what social groups have played a role in medicalizing the human condition?
6. What is the sick role model, and what are some of the problems with that model?
7. How does the new health consciousness change our relationship to medicine?

CRITICAL THINKING QUESTIONS

1. Imagine you work for a city public health department and have been asked to contribute your ideas about how the department should proceed in developing a thirty-second television or social media public health advertisement that warns young people about the dangers of sexually transmitted infections (STIs). What methods do you think should be used to keep the attention of your target audience? Do you want to provoke disgust for those who act promiscuously and are careless about protection or do you think affirmation and encouragement are a better strategy? Will your ad suggest that individuals shoulder full responsibility for avoiding disease or should other structural factors be identified as important for prevention?
2. Psychiatrists apply the diagnosis of premenstrual dysphoric distress syndrome (PMDD) to women who each month suffer from depression and anger prior to menstruating. How might women benefit from psychiatry's decision to label this condition a disease? How might women be harmed by it?
3. Do the four characteristics of the "sick role" apply to persons who have high cholesterol but no known evidence of heart disease? Do they apply to persons who learn that they have a gene that carries with it a high chance of developing breast cancer? Explain your answers.

KEY TERMS

community treatment orders (CTOs) (p. 169)
contested illness (p. 165)
demedicalization (p. 169)
deviance (p. 162)
direct-to-consumer advertising (DTCA) (p. 166)
dysfunctional (p. 170)
institution (p. 164)
medicalization (p. 164)

miasma theory of disease (p. 158)
moral status (p. 161)
negative social sanctions (p. 162)
norms (p. 161)
pharmaceutical determinism (p. 165)
positive social sanctions (p. 162)
social construction (p. 163)
social control agents (p. 164)
unintended negative consequences (p. 168)

8

The Experience of Disability, Chronic Pain, and Chronic Illness

fotosmith

Nancy Mairs

Nancy Mairs

Nancy Mairs is a writer, teacher, social activist, mother, and wife who has multiple sclerosis (MS). She writes:

> I am a cripple. I choose this word to name me.... People—crippled or not—wince at the word "crippled," as they do not at "handicapped" or "disabled." Perhaps I want them to wince. I want them to see me as a tough customer, one to whom the fates/gods/viruses have not been kind, but who can face the brutal truth of her existence squarely. As a cripple, I swagger....
>
> I haven't always been crippled.... When I was 28 I started to trip and drop things. What at first seemed my natural clumsiness soon became too pronounced to shrug off. I consulted a neurologist, who told me that I had a brain tumor. A battery of tests, increasingly disagreeable, revealed no tumor. About a year and a half later I developed a blurred spot in one eye. I had, at last, the [symptoms] ... requisite for a

diagnosis: multiple sclerosis. I have never been sorry for the doctor's initial misdiagnosis, however. For almost a week, until the negative results of the tests were in, I thought that I was going to die right away. Every day for the past nearly ten years, then, has been a kind of gift. I accept all gifts.

Multiple sclerosis is a chronic degenerative disease of the central nervous system.... During its course, which is unpredictable and uncontrollable, one may lose vision, hearing, speech, the ability to walk, control of bladder and/or bowels, strength in any or all extremities, sensitivity to touch, vibration, and/or pain, potency, coordination of movements—the list of possibilities is lengthy and, yes, horrifying. One may also lose one's sense of humor. That's the easiest to lose and the hardest to survive without....

I don't like having MS. I hate it. My life holds realities—harsh ones, some of them—that no right-minded human being ought to accept without grumbling. One of them is fatigue. I know of no one with MS who does not complain of bone-weariness.... As a result, I spend a lot of time in extremis and, impatient with limitation, I tend to ignore my fatigue until my body breaks down in some way and forces rest. Then I miss picnics, dinner parties, poetry readings, the brief visits of old friends from out of town.... My life often seems a series of small failures to do as I ought....

[Over time], I [have] learned that one never finishes adjusting to MS. I don't know now why I thought one would. One does not, after all, finish adjusting to life, and MS is simply a fact of my life—not my favorite fact, of course—but as ordinary as my nose and my tropical fish and my yellow Mazda station wagon. It may at any time get worse, but no amount of worry or anticipation can prepare me for a new loss. My life is a lesson in losses. I learn one at a time. (1986: 9–12, 19)

From *Plaintext* by Nancy Mairs. © 1986 The Arizona Board of Regents. Reprinted by permission of the University of Arizona Press.

In this chapter, students should be able to:

LO-1 **Understand** the differences between a medical model approach and a social model of disability approach in terms of how each model views the relationship between impairment and disability.

LO-2 **Recognize** that the experiences of persons with disabilities are in many ways comparable to those of a minority group.

LO-3 **Identify** the shortcomings of a social model of disability and **understand** how a postmodern perspective and a sociology of the body approach overcome some of these limitations.

LO-4 **Recognize** the challenges associated with the diagnosis and treatment of chronic pain in Canada.

LO-5 **Describe** the social processes through which individuals recognize that they are not well and **understand** how the diagnosis of serious or life-threatening illness or disability can trigger biographical disruption.

LO-6 **Recognize** that the ripple effects of disability, pain, and chronic illness also radically affect social interactions with family, friends, colleagues, and the general public.

LO-7 **Describe** strategies for managing stigma and **recognize** the limitations of the current definition of stigma.

Nancy Mairs's story illustrates some of the central tasks faced by those who live with **chronic illness,** chronic pain, or disability—searching for an accurate diagnosis, coming to terms with a body that does not meet social expectations for behaviour or appearance, nurturing social relationships despite a contrary body, and constructing a viable and life-sustaining sense of self. In this chapter, we look at these and other issues in the lives of people who have chronic illnesses, chronic pain, or disabilities. We also consider the social context in which these individuals live and see how that context can affect individuals' lives at least as much as the bodily changes Mairs describes.

This chapter begins with an exploration of the meaning and history of disability. After that, we look at chronic pain, which falls on the border between disability and illness, and then consider the experience of living with these conditions.

UNDERSTANDING DISABILITY

Defining Disability

As explained in Chapter 7, the meaning of the term *illness* is far from obvious. The same is true for the term **disability**. Competing definitions of *disability* reflect differing stances in an essentially political struggle. The World Health Organization (WHO) definition is probably the most widely used. WHO defines *disability* as "a restriction or inability to perform an activity in the manner or within the range considered normal for a human being, mostly resulting from impairment," and defines **impairment** as "any temporary or permanent loss or abnormality of a body structure or function, whether physiological or psychological" (Barbotte et al., 2001). By this definition, disability includes some but not all persons who have chronic illnesses (the majority of those with disabilities), as well as, for example, persons who are born deaf, become paralyzed in an auto accident, or experience chronic pain that limits their ability to function.

As many disability activists and social scientists have noted, this definition reflects a **medical model of disability**, which locates impairments—and thus disabilities—solely within the individual mind or body. At first glance, such a definition seems perfectly reasonable. After all, isn't a disability something that an individual has, a defect in his or her body? According to many people with disabilities, the answer is no. Instead, they argue, their disabilities primarily

disability:
A restriction or inability to perform an activity in the manner or within the range considered normal for a human being, mostly resulting from impairment (WHO definition).

impairment:
Any temporary or permanent loss or abnormality of a body structure or function, whether physiological or psychological (WHO definition).

medical model of disability:
A model of disability that assumes disability stems solely from forces within the individual mind or body, rather than from constraints built into the environment or into social attitudes.

stem not from their physical differences but from the way others respond to those differences and from the choices others have made in constructing the social and physical environment. For example, a man whose energy waxes and wanes unpredictably during the day might be able to work forty hours per week on a flexible schedule but not within a rigid nine-to-five schedule. Similarly, a woman who uses a wheelchair might find it impossible to work in an office where furniture can fit only persons who walk and are of average height, but she might have no problems in an office with more adaptable furniture. Disability activists argue that making an office accessible to wheelchair users does not mean providing special benefits for the disabled, but rather compensating for the unacknowledged benefits that existing arrangements offer those who walk, such as chairs to sit in, stools for reaching high shelves, and carpeted floors that make walking easier but wheeling more difficult.

social model of disability:
A model of disability that assumes that disability stems solely from constraints built into the environment or into social attitudes, rather than from the physical, intellectual, or sensory impairments of an individual.

This approach reflects a **social model of disability** in its emphasis on social forces and public issues rather than on individual physical variations and troubles. Whereas the medical model approach identifies disability through impairment, the social model of disability suggests that there is no necessary relationship between the two. Instead, a social model of disability contends that it is society that disables those with impairments, highlighting that it is the problematic response of society that constitutes disability. Accordingly, a social model of disability directs attention to the oppressive social relationships that exist between people who have impairment and those who are marked as normal (Thomas and Corker, 2002).

Not surprisingly, the medical model of disability and the social model of disability have strikingly different implications. As Paul Higgins (1992: 31) notes, "To individualize disability [as the medical model does] is to preserve our present practices and policies that produce disability. If disability is an internal flaw to be borne by those 'afflicted,' then we do not question much the world we make for ourselves. Our actions that produce disability go unchallenged because they are not even noticed." Individualizing disability conveys the message that disability is a problem of the individual and that the onus falls on a disabled person to adapt in order to participate in society. In contrast, a social model of disability challenges us to look at the problem of disability from a very different perspective. If we conclude that the problem resides primarily in social attitudes and in the social and built environment, then we can solve the problem most efficiently by changing attitudes and environments, rather than by "rehabilitating" people with disabilities. Box 8.1 describes the struggle of Pistorius, a double-amputee, to compete in the Olympics, illustrating some of the challenges involved in changing social attitudes toward those with a disability.

BOX 8.1

IN THE NEWS

South Africa's Blade Runner

South African Oscar Pistorius was born with a major and irreplaceable bone—the fibula—missing from each leg. Just before his first birthday, in 1987, doctors amputated both his legs halfway between his knees and his ankles. Six months later he began to walk on his first prosthetic legs.

Despite this disability, Pistorius excelled in sports from an early age and by 2007 held track records in both disabled (Paralympic) and able-bodied competitions. In January 2008, however, the International Association of Athletics Federations declared Pistorius ineligible to try out for the 2008 Olympics because the carbon-fibre prosthetic blades he uses (shaped more or less like skis bent into upside-down question marks) seemed to give him an unfair advantage. Yet, no one has argued

that athletes who receive laser eye surgery to improve their vision or pitchers who get elbow surgery to prolong—and perhaps improve—their athletic careers have an unfair advantage. Ironically, if Pistorius used prosthetics that more closely mimicked human legs in order to better meet social expectations for how bodies should look and function, he would have been theoretically eligible to compete but far too slow to do so. Instead, he chose to use prosthetics designed by a fellow amputee to facilitate running.

Pistorius appealed the IAAF decision, arguing that although his prosthetics offered some potential advantages, they also held him back in other ways, making him no different from any other runner who had to deal with the inherent advantages and disadvantages of his or her particular body. Although he won his appeal, he did not in the end win a spot on the 2008 South African Olympics team—perhaps because of the time and energy he had lost in fighting his legal battle.

Pistorius finally had his chance at the 2012 Olympics held in London, England. He competed in the men's 400-metre race, propelling himself into history with each clink of his prosthetic legs on the track. As the first double-amputee Olympian, his performance was impressive. His time of 45.44 seconds (thirteenth in a field of forty-nine runners) advanced him to the semifinals, where he was subsequently eliminated. Despite this, his Olympic performance, along with the many accolades and awards he has received for his determination, passion, and skills, proves that he is a true athlete.

People with Disabilities as a Minority Group

Once we start thinking of disability as primarily based on social attitudes and built environments rather than on individual deficiencies, strong parallels emerge between people with disabilities and members of **minority groups** (Hahn, 1985). A minority group is defined as any group that, because of its cultural or physical characteristics, is considered inferior and subjected to differential and unequal treatment and that therefore develops a sense of itself as the object of collective discrimination (Wirth, 1985). Few would argue with the assertion that we differentiate disabled persons from others on the basis of physical characteristics. But can we also argue, as the definition of a minority group requires, that people with disabilities are considered inferior and subject to differential and unequal treatment?

Unfortunately, the answer is yes. Even a cursory look at the lives of people with disabilities reveals widespread prejudice and discrimination. **Prejudice** refers to unwarranted suspicion, dislike of, or disdain toward individuals because they belong to a particular group, whether defined by ethnicity, religion, or some other characteristic. Prejudice toward disabled persons is obvious in the fact that, throughout history, most societies have defined those who are disabled as somehow physically or even morally inferior and have considered disabilities a sign that either the individual or his or her parents behaved sinfully or foolishly (Albrecht, 1992).

Prejudice typically expresses itself through **stereotypes**, or oversimplistic ideas about members of a given group. Non-disabled people typically stereotype those who are disabled either as menacing and untrustworthy or as childlike—asexual, dependent, mentally incompetent, the passive "victims" of their fate, and suitable objects for pity (Zola, 1985). These attitudes permeate the health care world as well as the general public. In one study, for example, researchers divided a large sample of health care students and practitioners into two groups and showed each group a videotape of a job interview. Both videotapes used the same actors and scripts, but in one the actor playing the job applicant walked, and in the other he used a wheelchair. Those who saw the videotape with the "disabled" applicant rated the applicant significantly more cruel, selfish, incompetent, weak, dependent, and mentally unstable than did those who saw the same actor portraying a non-disabled applicant (Gething, 1992).

Stereotypes about people with disabilities are reflected and perhaps reinforced in the popular media, which often portray disabled individuals as pitiful, maladjusted, or evil (Higgins, 1992: 80–97; Safran, 1998). In book and film characters from Captain Hook in *Peter Pan* to Freddie Krueger in *Nightmare on Elm Street* and the Penguin in *Batman* comics and films, the media have equated physical deformity with moral deformity. Moreover, when the media do not portray persons with disabilities as horrifying, they often portray them as pitiful—whether depicting Tiny Tim in Charles Dickens's classic novel *A Christmas Carol* or Maggie Fitzgerald in *Million Dollar Baby,* for whom death was preferable to life. Although contemporary media sometimes do present more positive images, such as stories about people who have "heroically" compensated for their disabilities, who have chosen to live

minority group:
A group that, because of its cultural or physical characteristics, is considered inferior and subjected to differential and unequal treatment.

prejudice:
The unwarranted suspicion, dislike of, or disdain toward individuals because they belong to a particular group, whether defined by ethnicity, religion, or some other characteristic.

stereotypes:
Oversimplistic assumptions regarding the nature of group members, such as assuming that people who are obese are lazy and that people with mental illness are dangerous and unpredictable.

"saintly" lives, or whose innocence can help the rest of us learn to live better lives (*Riding the Bus with My Sister* and *Forrest Gump,* for instance), these stories, too, typically ignore the social nature of disabilities and instead offer simplistic stories about individual character. Exceptions to these rules—films such as *The Station Agent, Murderball,* and *Children of a Lesser God*—remain rare, although they have become far more common in the last 20 years.

discrimination:
Differential and unequal treatment grounded in prejudice.

All too often, these prejudices against persons with disabilities result in **discrimination**, or unequal treatment grounded in prejudice. During the 1930s and 1940s, doctors working for the government of Nazi Germany murdered about 100,000 disabled children and adults as *Lebensunwertes Leben*—"life unworthy of life" (Lifton, 1986). Though these practices are now considered horrific, the underlying sentiment that the disabled do not deserve the same rights as those who are able-bodied served as justification for practices that persisted long after the atrocities of the Nazi era. For example, in both Canada and the United States, the sterilization and institutionalization of those with disabilities were common up until the 1970s. (We discuss the history of the sterilization of the feeble-minded in Canada in greater detail in Chapter 14.)

People with disabilities continue to face discrimination in Canada. Disabled people are more likely to be poor and less likely to be employed (Galarneau and Radulescu, 2009). Moreover, even when employed, disabled people are more likely to have part-time or temporary jobs. As we noted in Chapter 5, precarious forms of employment can be associated with risk for morbidity in their own right. Government employment assistance programs may unwittingly reinforce a pattern of temporary work for disabled people because some employers tend to lay off the disabled employee once subsidies run out, and then hire a new employee who is disabled to requalify for the subsidy (Chouinard, 2010). Disabled people may also face greater barriers to advancement within their place of employment as only 6% are in management positions, compared to 11% of workers in the general population (Williams, 2006).

To fit the definition of a minority group, a group must not only experience prejudice and discrimination but also consider themselves objects of collective discrimination. This is the weakest link in defining disabled people as a minority group (Higgins, 1992: 39–44). Unlike members of other minority groups, disabled individuals are rarely born to disabled parents. As a result, they might have little contact with, let alone sense of connection to, other people with disabilities. Moreover, most disabilities are acquired rather than present at birth. Therefore, most establish their sense of individual and group identity before they become disabled, and not all will change their sense of identity following disability. In addition, those who develop a sense of community with others who share their disability do not necessarily feel a connection to persons with other disabilities; deaf people, for example, might identify with others who are deaf, but not with those who have arthritis.

Critiquing the Social Model

In the 1990s, scholars began to question some of the ideas underlying a social model of disability. These scholars acknowledged that the disability movement had experienced success in drawing attention to the ways in which society had created barriers to participation for people with disabilities and had made gains in terms of removing some of those barriers. For example, there were improvements in accessibility with the introduction of angled curbs on sidewalks and ramps into buildings for people in wheelchairs. A growing number of elevators had Braille markings and electronic voices to guide those who were blind. Here in Canada, the 1982 Canadian Charter of Rights and Freedoms for the first time guaranteed that people with disabilities could not be discriminated against on the grounds of their disability. Progress had been made, though far more slowly and unevenly than was needed or called for by people with disabilities. (Box 8.2 describes the life of Rick Hansen and his ongoing work as an advocate for people with disabilities in Canada.)

BOX 8.2

CHANGING THE WORLD

Rick Hansen and the Man in Motion World Tour

Born in 1957 in Port Alberni, British Columbia, Rick Hansen grew up wanting to be part of a great adventure. A few months before his sixteenth birthday, Rick was thrown from the back of a truck on his way home from a fishing trip, sustaining a spinal cord injury that left him paralyzed from the waist down. Undaunted by his injury, Rick became the first person with a physical disability to graduate with a degree in physical education from the University of British Columbia. He went on to enjoy a stellar career as an athlete by competing in wheelchair marathons, winning the world title four times.

Supported by a close-knit family and inspired by mentors and friends, including Terry Fox, Rick began to plan his big adventure. On March 21, 1985, Rick and his team launched the Man In Motion World Tour (MIMWT), wheeling a distance of 40,598 kilometres in thirty-four countries over a period of twenty-six months. Their goals were to raise money for spinal cord injury research, rehabilitation, and sport and to bring attention to the marginalization of people with disabilities.

Since that time, Rick has continued to be a powerful advocate for the disabled. In 2000, he established the Rick Hansen Awards program to help schools motivate and recognize students who are socially conscious, have outstanding qualities, and are making a difference in the lives of others. In 2009, The Rick Hansen Institute was founded in Vancouver to bring together researchers from around the world to facilitate the translation of the latest advances in knowledge on spinal cord injuries into practical interventions that measurably improve the lives of people with spinal cord injury. In 2010, Rick had an inspirational role as one of the four final torchbearers who carried the Olympic Flame into BC Place at the Opening Ceremony for the Olympic Winter Games in Vancouver.

To commemorate the twenty-fifth anniversary of the MIMWT in Canada, a cross-Canada relay that followed the same path Rick originally took began in mid-2011 at Cape Spear (the easternmost point of Canada) and ended in the spring of 2012 in Vancouver. Approximately 7,000 people took part in the relay, travelling through more than 600 communities. The goals of the race remained as before: to raise money to improve the lives of people with disabilities and to make the world a more inclusive and accessible place.

Despite these advances, dissatisfaction with a social model of disability centred on concern that an exclusive focus on overcoming the social barriers encountered by disabled people prevented greater attention to the experiential aspects of disability, which were often ignored or downplayed (Barnes and Mercer, 2003). In other words, it was felt that there was a need to integrate impairment into a social model of disability and to develop theory that explained how impairment might be linked to disability.

The problems with a lack of attention to impairment in a social model of disability are now well recognized. First, silence about their experiences with their bodies put people with disabilities in an unusual position: they were liberated to acknowledge their social suffering but prevented from sharing with one another their corporeal experiences. As Morris notes:

> …there is a tendency within the social model of disability to deny the experience of our bodies, insisting that our physical differences and restrictions are *entirely* socially constructed. While environmental barriers and social attitudes are a crucial part of our experience with disability—and do indeed disable us—to suggest that this is all there is to it is to deny the personal experience of physical and intellectual restrictions, of illness, of the fear of dying. (Morris, 1991, p. 10; italics in original)

The reluctance to acknowledge bodily and personal suffering was certainly understandable for early proponents of the social model, who sought to combat the simplistic stereotypes that perceived disabled people only in the context of their failed bodies. Having made the point that disability was grounded in the social environment, many now felt the time had come to bring the body back in.

A second implication of neglecting impairment is that the social model fails to challenge the medical model. By focusing on disability and neglecting impairment, the social model simply concedes the body to medicine (Hughes and Paterson, 1997). Because impairment is still framed in biological terms, the bodies of disabled people can only be understood through the discourses of medicine, and the authority and the knowledge of doctors remain privileged. Persuaded to politicize their social lives, disabled people still receive the message that their bodies are dependent on medicine (Hughes and Paterson, 1997). Stated differently, it appears that both the social model and the medical model accept the premise of Cartesian dualism. That is, each assumes that the body is a biological object that is completely separate from the self and that changes in one will have no effect on the other.

Finally, when researchers fail to consider impairment in a social model of disability, they are unable to see that impairment influences people's experiences of disablement. Although disabled people encounter many of the same barriers (e.g., discrimination in employment and greater vulnerability to poverty), not all experience disablement in exactly the same way. Indeed, Thomas and Corker (2002) contend that social responses are tied to the type of impairment that one has, such that those who are blind will evoke different social responses than those who are in wheelchairs or those who are learning disabled or are mentally ill. This helps us to understand why not everyone who has an impairment sees themselves as disabled (e.g., because of their shared language, deaf people prefer to identify as a cultural group) and why people with mental illness, who sometimes refer to themselves as psychiatric system survivors, often feel excluded from and misunderstood by disability discourses (Beresford, 2000).

In attempting to integrate impairment into a social model of disability and rethink the relationship between impairment and disability, sociologists have turned to a postmodern perspective and a sociology of the body approach. The postmodern perspective suggests that impairment and disability should not be understood as dichotomous (placement into either yes or no categories) but rather as different places on a continuum, with meanings that are not fixed (Thomas, 2004). These shifting meanings imply that there are a plurality of ways in which disabled people see, understand, and represent themselves that cannot be reduced to one overarching narrative. In other words, the experiential aspects of impairment and disability come to be seen as more important than the totalizing aspects of either the medical model (which individualizes the problem) or the social model of disability (which politicizes the problem).

Those working from a sociology of the body approach contend that impairment is essential to theorizing about disability. Importantly, the body represents more than a passive surface upon which a socially constructed label is applied (Kelly and Field, 1996). The body is both the way one experiences one's self and how one is able to have a social presence in the world. Because impairment affects how the body looks and/or how it acts, the body provides salient clues that shape how one sees oneself and how others see one's body. As bodies change through time, the relationship between impairment and disability also changes dynamically. For example, in the early stages of multiple sclerosis, sporadic symptoms may place restrictions on the body that temporarily alter how one manages one's body and interacts socially with others, and may successfully delay others' awareness of their condition. In the latter stages of MS, the physical reality of being in a wheelchair requires greater attention to bodily processes and discomforts, and has consequences for how one is able to use one's body socially and manage the perceptions of others. We return to some of these ideas later on in the chapter.

Although the postmodern and sociology of the body perspectives have begun to theorize the relationship between impairment and disability in new ways, there is concern among disability activists that theorists will lose sight of the emancipatory goals of the social model of disability and engage in arcane discussions that are incomprehensible to all but a few. A counterargument is that all emancipatory projects require greater theorizing to mature and to contribute more broadly to the development of inclusive societies. Needless to say, disability activists and sociologists of health and illness still struggle with these ideas. The difficulty of finding an appropriate language to capture these ideas emerges even at the most fundamental level of identification. A social model of disability once rejected the term *disabled people* in favour of *people with disabilities* because the latter term emphasized personhood and helped others to see that disabled people were people first (Zola, 1993). In recent years, using the term *people with disabilities* has also come to be seen as problematic to the extent that it implies disability is an add-on or an appendage that is separate from one's sense of self. There is no consensus as to which might be more appropriate, nor have new terms been proffered, and in the interim, *disabled people* and *people with disabilities* have become common expressions and tend to be used interchangeably, as we have done.

We also propose a different definition of *disability*, which refers to restrictions or lack of ability to perform activities resulting from the interplay between physical, intellectual, or sensory limitations; social responses to these limitations; and the built or social environment. Although this definition does not satisfy all disability activists and theorists, it is a more acceptable definition than the medically oriented definition used by the WHO and the overly socialized definition used in a social model of disability.

disability:
Restrictions or lack of ability to perform activities resulting from the interplay between physical, intellectual, and sensory limitations; social responses to these limitations; and the built or social environment.

UNDERSTANDING CHRONIC PAIN

Defined as pain that lasts for more than three months, chronic pain affects one in six Canadians. The prevalence of chronic pain increases with age, affecting approximately 10% of Canadians between the ages of 15 and 24 and rising to 35% for those over the age of 75 (Millar, 1996). At each age, women are more likely than men to report chronic pain.

Chronic pain can be difficult to diagnose because it is a symptom as well as an illness. As a symptom, chronic pain may be the result of an injury or an ongoing illness, such as arthritis or cancer. Chronic pain may also be attributed to **contested illnesses** or to illnesses that are difficult to diagnose, such as irritable bowel syndrome, fibromyalgia, and chronic fatigue syndrome. In some cases no specific cause for chronic pain can be identified. For example, doctors often lack explanations for chronic headaches or back pain, the two most common types of chronic pain. Because there is no formal diagnostic test for chronic pain, diagnosing chronic pain often means ruling out other conditions and illnesses, which can be a lengthy and frustrating process. Contributing to the difficulty in diagnosing chronic pain is the fact that few doctors receive specific training in chronic pain and many remain reluctant to prescribe opioid medication to treat chronic pain (Dobkin and Boothroyd, 2008).

Although the causes of chronic pain are often unclear and the diagnosis difficult to obtain, its consequences are obvious. In addition to its physical toll (which includes sleep deprivation and exhaustion), chronic pain damages social relationships and increases depression, anxiety, and the risk of suicide (Ramage-Morin and Gilmour, 2010; Tang and Crane, 2006). It is estimated that the direct health care costs to treat chronic pain in the Canadian population are more than $6 billion per year, and productivity costs related to job loss and sick days are as high as $37 billion per year (Lynch, 2011).

Knowledge of how to treat chronic pain has advanced considerably over the past couple of decades. Although Canadians with chronic pain take medication such as analgesics, narcotics, tranquilizers, sleeping pills, and antidepressants at far higher rates than the general population (Millar, 1996), the most effective treatment combines medication with other strategies, including cognitive behavioural therapy and physiotherapy. Canadians are increasingly able to rely on clinics that specialize in the treatment of chronic pain using a multidisciplinary approach; however, the **median** wait time for a first appointment to these facilities is approximately six months, suggesting that Canadians with chronic pain are underserved (Peng et al., 2007).

LIVING WITH DISABILITY OR CHRONIC ILLNESS

Living with disability or chronic illness, whether or not it results in chronic pain, is a long-term process that includes responding to initial symptoms, injuries, or diagnoses; making sense of one's situation; and continually reconceptualizing one's future. In this section, we examine this process and explore how illness, pain, and disability affect individuals' lives, relationships with others, and sense of self.

Initial Symptoms and Diagnosis

Becoming a chronically ill or disabled person begins with recognizing that something about the body is troubling. This recognition does not always come easily. Health problems often build gradually, allowing individuals and their families slowly and almost unconsciously to adapt to them and to minimize their importance (Charmaz, 1991: 24–28; Schneider and Conrad, 1983). In addition, the signs of illness and disability often do not differ greatly from normal bodily variations. A child who doesn't walk by twelve months might have a disability or might simply be a slow developer. Similarly, children with epilepsy, for example, can for many years experience "strange feelings," "headaches," "spaciness," "blackouts," and "dizzy spells" before they or their families recognize these as signs of epilepsy. As one man recalled:

> I'd always had the tendency to roll my eyes back in my head … to kind of fade out for a while. But I thought that was nothing, but … I guess they call them petit mal [epileptic seizures]? I'd lose consciousness for a while. I wasn't really conscious of it and [the only] time anybody would notice it was when the family was all together at the dinner table and I, I'd be like daydreaming for a while and then I'd roll my eyes back and they'd go, "Stop that!" and I'd go "Stop what?," y'know, I didn't know what I was doin'. (Schneider and Conrad, 1983: 57–58)

illness behaviour:
The process of defining, interpreting, and otherwise responding to symptoms and deciding what actions to take.

illness behaviour model:
A model that predicts the circumstances in which individuals are most likely to seek medical care.

Social scientists refer to this process of defining, interpreting, and otherwise responding to symptoms and deciding what actions to take as **illness behaviour** (Mechanic, 1995). Individuals typically begin by medicating themselves or those under their care with non-prescription medications recommended by friends, families, store clerks, or pharmacists or, more rarely, with prescription medicines left over from previous illnesses.

When and whether individuals seek formal diagnosis for acute or chronic medical problems depends on a variety of factors. According to the **illness behaviour model**, developed by David Mechanic (1995) and summarized in Key Concepts 8.1, individuals are most likely to seek medical care if their symptoms are frequent or persistent, visible, and severe enough to interfere with daily activities *and* if they lack alternative explanations for the symptoms. At the same time, how individuals interpret these factors depends on the social context; symptoms that seem serious to a middle-class professional who generally enjoys good health might seem quite minor to a homeless or elderly person who expects a certain amount of bodily discomfort. Friends and relatives also play a large role in determining how individuals will interpret and respond to symptoms when they reinforce either a medical or a non-medical interpretation of the problem (Pescosolido, 1992). Finally, access to care and attitude toward health care providers also affect how quickly individuals seek care. Those who live in remote regions or whose experience of clinics has taught them to expect long waits and rude treatment often put off seeking care for some time.

KEY CONCEPTS 8.1   Some Factors Predicting Illness Behaviour

Individuals Are Likely to Define Themselves as Ill and Seek Medical Care When	Individuals Are Unlikely to Define Themselves as Ill and Seek Medical Care When
Symptoms appear frequently or persistently (e.g., coughing blood once per day for a week).	Symptoms appear infrequently (e.g., coughing blood every few months).
Symptoms are very visible (e.g., rash on face).	Symptoms are not very visible (e.g., rash on lower back).
Symptoms are severe enough to disrupt normal activities (e.g., epileptic convulsions).	Symptoms are mild (e.g., annoying but tolerable headaches).
Illness is the only likely explanation for physical problems.	Alternative explanations are available (e.g., recent stresses may explain headaches).
They have ready access to health care (e.g., clinic is in one's neighbourhood).	They have poor access to health care (e.g., live in a remote community).
They have a positive attitude to health care providers (e.g., trust doctors' abilities and motives).	They have a negative attitude to health care providers (e.g., distrust doctors' abilities and motives).

Eventually, however, if symptoms persist—and especially if they progress—individuals and their families are likely to reach a point where they cannot avoid recognizing that something is seriously wrong. As their previous interpretations of their symptoms crumble, individuals find themselves in an intolerable situation, torn by uncertainty regarding the changes in their bodies and their lives. At this point, any diagnosis can become preferable to uncertainty and so the incentive to seek diagnosis increases (Pierret, 2003).

Seeking a diagnosis, however, does not necessarily mean receiving one. Although some problems are relatively easy to diagnose—a 45-year-old white man who complains to his doctor of pains in the left side of his chest will probably quickly find himself getting tested for a heart attack—others are far less obvious. Persons with fibromyalgia, for example, often find that doctors initially dismiss their symptoms as psychosomatic or trivial (Barker, 2005). In addition, the same symptoms may more rapidly produce a diagnosis for some than for others. For example, doctors have historically displayed a tendency to dismiss women's complaints as merely emotional problems but to accept men's complaints at face value (Ehrenreich and English, 2005a).

Initially, both women and men can find these alternative diagnoses comforting and welcome—after all, it is far easier to hear that you are suffering from stress than that you have a serious illness. When symptoms persist, however, individuals find themselves torn by ambiguity and uncertainty, suffering anxiety about their failing health but often receiving little sympathy or help from relatives and colleagues (Schneider and Conrad, 1983; Barker, 2005). As a result, most people eventually seek more accurate diagnoses. Some go from doctor to doctor, seeking a more believable diagnosis; others research their symptoms, diagnose themselves, and then press their doctors to confirm their self-diagnoses through testing. In the end, even those diagnosed with life-threatening conditions typically conclude that this certainty is preferable to continued uncertainty.

Responding to Illness or Injury

Once newly diagnosed or newly disabled individuals learn the nature of their conditions, responses vary widely. Some individuals with **HIV/AIDS**, for example, find it easiest to cope by immediately considering their diagnosis a "death sentence," thus eliminating any uncertainty from their minds (Weitz, 1991). Others initially assume they can "beat" their illness, refusing to take seriously any dire predictions about their future. Still others cope by accepting their diagnoses intellectually but denying them emotionally. For example, one young man told how, two months after learning he had HIV/AIDS, he thought that he had picked up someone else's medical file when he noticed that his file read, "Caution: Patient has AIDS" (Weitz, 1991). Similarly, following traumatic injuries, some individuals refuse to participate in rehabilitation because they consider their situation hopeless; others refuse because they consider their injuries temporary.

Although learning the nature of one's condition answers some questions, it raises new questions about why the condition has happened at all (Pierret, 2003). This search for explanations is often a painful one, set as it is in the context of a culture that continues, at least partially, to believe that individuals deserve their illnesses and disabilities. Nevertheless, some individuals do manage to avoid allocating blame to themselves. For example, one gay man with HIV/AIDS stated in an interview: "Nobody deserves it [HIV/AIDS]. I have friends that say 'Well, hey, if we weren't gay, we wouldn't get this disease.' That's bullshit. I mean, I don't want to hear that from anybody. Because no germ has mercy on anybody, no matter who they are—gay, straight, babies, adults" (Weitz, 1991: 68).

Other individuals, however, readily conclude—whether accurately or not—that they caused their own health problems by acting in ways that either contravened "divine laws" or put them at risk (such as smoking tobacco, having multiple sexual partners, or driving fast). As another man with HIV/AIDS stated, "I should have helped people more, or not have yelled at somebody, or been better to my dad even though we have never gotten along.... Maybe if I had tried to get along better with him, maybe this wouldn't be happening" (Weitz, 1991: 68).

When people who are disabled or seriously ill began to ask the question "why," they are engaging in a process that Michael Bury (1982) calls **biographical disruption**. Biographical disruption occurs when, confronted with a serious or life-threatening condition, an individual becomes aware of the ways in which the body asserts itself in daily life, questions taken-for-granted explanatory frameworks for what life means and what one hopes to achieve in life, and begins to respond and mobilize resources that are sensitive to their altered situation. We discuss each of these three aspects of biographical disruption in turn.

The Body and the Self

One aspect of biographical disruption due to illness and disability occurs when the body begins to assert itself in daily life. In health, the body is treated as if it is the same as the self. The body disappears to the extent that one is not conscious of its actions, which is to say that one is not always mindful of how the self directs the body to perform. Illness fundamentally disrupts the unquestioned relationship between body and self. In illness, the body is no longer responsive to the instructions it is given; consequently, the self is forced to pay greater

biographical disruption:
The process that occurs when, confronted with a serious or life-threatening condition, an individual (1) becomes aware of the ways in which the body asserts itself in daily life, (2) questions taken-for-granted explanatory frameworks for what life means and what one hopes to achieve in life, and (3) begins to respond and mobilize resources that are sensitive to their altered situation.

attention to bodily states, recognizing that the body has become a source of uncertainty and betrayal.

According to sociologist Kathy Charmaz, who interviewed more than one hundred chronically ill people, illness can be experienced as an interruption, an intrusion, or something in which an individual is immersed (Charmaz, 1991). Although Charmaz's research addressed only chronic illness, similar patterns undoubtedly apply to at least some individuals with disabilities, especially those that worsen over time.

When illness or disability is an **interruption**, it remains only a small and temporary part of a person's life (Charmaz, 1991: 11–40). Viewing it as an interruption means regarding it as essentially an acute problem—something to be dealt with at the moment, but not something that will have a significant long-term impact. This strategy can work as long as episodes of illness are minor or rare, or the disability is a mild one. For example, because of unexpected physical problems, someone in the early stages of multiple sclerosis may need to change plans for a given day but not necessarily for the next week.

If the illness or disability progresses, however, it can become an **intrusion**, demanding time, accommodation, and attention and requiring that a person "live day to day" (Charmaz, 1991: 41–72). And if it progresses still further, people can find themselves immersed in their bodily problems (Charmaz, 1991: 73–104). Upon reaching this stage of **immersion**, they must structure their lives around the demands of their bodies rather than structuring the demands of their bodies around their lives. Social relationships often wither, and people often withdraw into themselves. Dealing with the body and illness can take most of a person's day and require the assistance of others. One woman, for example, told Charmaz that her kidney dialysis

> just about takes up the day.… I'm supposed to be on at 12:30, but sometimes don't get on until 1:00, then I'm dialyzed for four and a half hours and then it takes approximately half an hour to be taken off the machine and to have it clot. So quite often it's 6:00 or 6:30 before I ever leave there. So the day is shot. (1991: 83)

There is an uneasy tension in managing the separation between body and self. On one hand, to cope with these threats to the self, individuals may attempt intellectually to separate their essential selves from their recalcitrant bodies. They might mention how their leg is acting up today, as if they were talking about a neighbour rather than a part of their body, or talk about their lives and their selves with no mention of their bodies at all. This strategy succeeds best when symptoms follow a predictable course and the problem affects only one part of the body. Distancing oneself from one's body also makes it possible to see oneself as a victim of external forces rather than as responsible for the condition, providing a level of comfort and reassurance for a troubled self (Bury, 1982).

On the other hand, coping with illness and disability often means finding a way to integrate the self and the body so that the relationship between the two once again operates seamlessly. This is accomplished when the nature of the chronic illness and its bodily consequences are permanently incorporated into one's sense of self (Kelly and Field, 1996). For a person who is diabetic, attending to the demands of the body by engaging in routine blood sugar tests and insulin injections offers the opportunity to minimize the centrality of the body. Not all will find the task feasible, necessitating the exploration of other strategies.

Other strategies may include learning to place a lower value on physical appearances, derive a sense of self from other sources, and focus on the present rather than on an intangible future (Weitz, 1991: 136–140). Individuals may learn to set priorities in their lives so that, often to a greater extent than before, they accomplish their most important goals rather than wasting precious energy on trivial concerns (Charmaz, 1991: 134–166).

interruption:
A situation in which illness is experienced as only a small and temporary part of one's life.

intrusion:
A situation in which illness demands time, accommodation, and attention and forces one to live from day to day.

immersion:
A situation in which illness becomes so demanding that a person must structure his or her life around it.

Finally, they may come to define their condition simply as part of who they are, with good points and bad points, and to recognize that much of their personalities and accomplishments exist not *despite* their physical condition, but *because* of it (Higgins, 1992: 141). Individuals with illness and disability who take this stance not only find a way to dissolve the divide that illness creates between the body and self but also are attempting to address the crisis that illness introduces to one's taken-for-granted assumptions about the world.

Questioning Taken-for-Granted Assumptions

Having a serious or life-threatening illness is often seen as a distant probability or as something that happens to others, but when it happens, recognizing it is a moment where one confronts the foreseeable end of one's existence. Plans for the future must be adjusted in light of the uncertainty of what lies ahead. Important life goals, such as finishing one's education, finding a life partner, having children, occupational ambition, and retirement, become items in a balance sheet where achievements that have occurred are measured against aspirations that may no longer be possible. Emanating from these calculations are the questions: Why me? Why now?

To answer these questions, one must sort through the wreckage of one's disrupted explanatory frameworks and create new destinations and a renewed sense of purpose. In his book *The Wounded Storyteller,* Arthur Frank (1995) notes the importance of **narrative reconstruction**, not just to repairing the narrative of the storyteller but for the audience to develop empathic bonds to the storyteller, bonds that expand outward as the story is subsequently retold to others. These narratives of illness come in essentially three forms, drawn from cultural understandings of what it means to be ill in today's society. Thus, individuals draw on these narratives to create their own stories and then feed these stories, interwoven with their own specific experiences, back to others who will absorb and respond to them in ways that reflect their shared meaning.

The first narrative is a **restitution story**, which recounts a timeline of how one was healthy, became ill, and then was restored back to health. This is a culturally preferred narrative because in achieving a cure, the restitution story reinforces the idea that medicine is capable of solving health problems, that medical interventions are successful. The story follows the person's journey through the medical system but recounts experiences in a way that renders illness a distant memory. Thus, the storyteller may aspire to become a hero as much as the physician who achieved the cure because they have been able to leave illness successfully in their past.

In contrast, the plot of a **chaos story** is full of anxiety and dread because it imagines a life that never gets better. To tell the chaos story is to lose the pretence of control and thus it is frightening for both the teller and the listener. Those who have been diagnosed with inoperable cancer and given a few short weeks to live are likely to tell a chaos story. Because it is about the unmaking of one's world, however, Frank argues that a true chaos story cannot be told. Yet, he suggests it is important that elements of the chaos story be recognized because to deny it would be to make its horror worse.

Finally, the **quest story** is about the journey of illness that becomes a voyage of discovery about the self and one's ability to find meaning in suffering. The insight that has been gained through illness, whether one has any chance of recovery or not, becomes the guiding motivation for sharing one's story. Such stories are inspiring because they show what is possible in woundedness.

A quest story, in the writings of Barbara Rosenblum, a sociologist and artist who died of breast cancer at age 44, is excerpted below:

---

narrative reconstruction:
Stories that one tells about one's experiences of illness that not only act as a form of self-repair but, because stories draw on cultural understandings of illness, make it possible to create bonds and shared meanings with others about illness.

restitution story:
One of Frank's three types of narrative reconstruction, which celebrates triumph over illness, as achieved through both medical intervention and the personal perseverance of the person who has been healed.

chaos story:
One of Frank's three types of narrative reconstruction, which is about suffering that makes an individual unable to imagine a life that gets better.

quest story:
One of Frank's three types of narrative reconstruction, which seeks to find meaning in illness, whether or not recovery is attainable.

I am a very different person now: more open, much more honest, and more self-knowing.… I turned it [cancer] into a possibility of opening up to myself, for discovering, and for exploring new areas.

I've realized that I want to list the ways in which cancer can do that. You can get courage to take larger risks than you ever have before. I mean, you're already sick, so what can happen to you? You can have much more courage in saying things and in living than you ever had before.…

And you can do things you've always wanted to do. Cancer, by giving you the sense of your own mortality, can entice you into doing those things you have been postponing.…

You have this sense of urgency. And you can turn this urgency—you can harness this energy that propels you—so that you go ahead and do these things and discover new parts of yourself. All the things you ever wanted to do, all the dreams you had. And the dreams that you couldn't even dream, because you didn't allow yourself.…

Cancer has put me in touch with that. And then also, it has taught me to enjoy the tenderness and the preciousness of every moment. Moments are very important because there may not be any after that—or you may throw up. Cancer exquisitely places you in the moment.

I have become very human to myself in a way that I would never have imagined. I've become a bigger person, a fuller person. This to me is one of the greatest lessons: just being human. Having cancer doesn't mean that you lose yourself at all. For me it meant that I discovered myself. (Butler and Rosenblum, 1991: 160–161)*

Responding and Mobilizing Resources

Responding and mobilizing resources to help one cope with an altered situation is the third aspect of how chronic illness and disability create biographical disruption. Strategies include how one interacts with conventional health care providers and service agencies, experiments with alternative therapies, seeks out information from the Internet, and engages in collective efforts to raise awareness about the condition. Moreover, beyond the medical aspects of one's condition, mobilizing resources also means adjusting to changes in social and intimate relationships as well as devising strategies for how one presents oneself to the general public.

Using Conventional Health Care

Living with chronic illness or disability often means living a life bound by health care regimens. However, in the same manner that, following injury or diagnosis with a chronic illness, some individuals seek and some avoid knowledge, some will strictly follow prescribed regimens of diet, exercise, or medication and others will not. Researchers have traditionally framed this issue as a matter of compliance—whether individuals do as instructed by health care workers.

The most commonly used framework for studying compliance is the **health belief model** (first introduced in Chapter 2). This model was developed to explain why healthy individuals adopt preventive health behaviours and to understand why people who have acute or chronic health problems comply with medical advice regarding treatment (see Key Concepts 8.2). The model suggests that individuals will be most likely to comply if they believe they are susceptible to a health problem that could have serious consequences, believe compliance will help, and perceive no significant barriers to compliance. For example, people who have diabetes

---

* Sandra Butler & Barbara Rosenblum, *Cancer in Two Voices*, San Francisco: Spinsters Ink, 1991.

will be most likely to comply with their prescribed diet if they believe that they face substantial risks of blindness due to diabetes-induced glaucoma, that blindness would substantially decrease their quality of life, that the prescribed diet would substantially reduce their risk of blindness, and that the diet is neither too costly nor too inconvenient.

KEY CONCEPTS 8.2   The Health Belief Model and Medical Compliance

People Are Most Likely to Comply with Medical Advice When They	Example: Compliance Likely	Example: Compliance Unlikely
Believe they are susceptible.	Fifty-year-old man with hypertension who believes he is at risk for a heart attack.	Fifteen-year-old boy diagnosed with epilepsy who has had only minor problems. Does not believe he is at risk for convulsions.
Believe the risk is serious.	Believes that a heart attack could be fatal.	Believes that convulsions would not be physically dangerous.
Believe compliance will reduce the risk.	Believes he can reduce his risk by taking medication regularly.	Believes he doesn't really have a problem, so doesn't see how medication could help.
Have no significant barriers to compliance.	Medication is affordable and has no serious or highly unpleasant side effects.	Medication makes the boy feel drowsy, dull, and set apart from his peers.

The health belief model is a useful but limited one for understanding compliance with medical treatment because it largely reflects the medical model of illness and disability. First, the health belief model assumes that non-compliance with medical recommendations stems primarily from psychological processes internal to the patient. Although this is sometimes true, in other cases patients do not comply because health care workers did not sufficiently explain either the mechanics of the treatment regimen or the benefits of following it (Conrad, 1985). Patients also might not comply because they lack the money, time, or other resources needed to do so.

Second, the health belief model implicitly assumes that compliance is always good (i.e., that health care workers always know better than patients what patients should do). Yet, although health care workers can often help their patients considerably, this is not always the case. Bodies rarely respond precisely as medical textbooks predict. Nor can those textbooks determine whether an individual will consider a given treatment worth the impact it has on his or her quality of life. For example, persons with bipolar disorder (manic depression) often resist taking medications because the medications leave them feeling sedated and deprive them of the sometimes pleasurable highs of mania. Moreover, for numerous chronic conditions, the only available treatments are disruptive to normal routines, experimental, only marginally effective, unpleasant, or potentially dangerous. For example, tardive dyskinesia, a condition characterized by involuntary and repetitive movement of the tongue, lips, face, and trunk, occurs in those who have been long-time users of neuroleptic drugs for schizophrenia. As a result, many people who at first diligently follow prescribed regimens eventually abandon them and lose some of their faith in mainstream health care (Conrad, 1985). Meanwhile, health care providers who do not understand why their patients did not respond to treatment as expected will often blame the problem on patient non-compliance, further eroding relationships between patients and providers and leading to future non-compliance.

Dealing with Service Agencies

For those who experience disabilities, whether or not they are chronically ill, dealing with social service agencies can become a major part of life. Unfortunately, and despite the best intentions of many social service providers, the philosophies and structures of these agencies create systems that sometimes harm more than help those they serve (Albrecht, 1992; Higgins, 1992: 151–187).

Typically, social service agencies adopt a medical model of disability, focusing on how individuals can compensate for their individual deficiencies rather than on how social arrangements handicap them (Phillips, 1985). This approach has several **unintended negative consequences.** First, to accept someone as a client, agencies must define him or her as disabled. As a result, workers spend much of their time certifying individuals as disabled—identifying internal individual problems rather than looking for individual strengths. Through this process, individuals learn to think of themselves as disabled. According to Paul Higgins (1992: 132), "When service agencies evaluate, place, categorize, transfer, educate, rehabilitate, and so much more, the agencies are informing people who they are and who they are becoming." At the same time, because agencies receive funding based on how many clients they serve, agencies sometimes unintentionally encourage individuals to remain dependent on their services.

Second, because agencies use a medical model that defines people with disabilities as inherently flawed, agencies typically define "progress" as making those with disabilities as much like the non-disabled as possible (Albrecht, 1992; Higgins, 1992). Therefore, rehabilitation workers might, for example, encourage someone to use a prosthetic leg even though the individual could move more quickly and less painfully on crutches or in a wheelchair.

Third, the medical model encourages agencies to adopt a hierarchical pattern of care. This pattern of care is based on the premise that social service providers understand clients' needs, desires, problems, and strengths better than the clients themselves do and that social service providers are thus better equipped than clients to make decisions regarding clients' lives. Like other health care professionals, those who work in service agencies "evaluate, plan, treat, monitor, revise, discharge, and in other ways manage people. Disabled people (and their families) are expected to do what they are told" (Albrecht, 1992: 178). Thus, unwittingly, agencies encourage dependency.

As people's faith in mainstream medicine and other agencies declines, some begin experimenting with their treatment regimens, learning through trial and error what works best for them not only physically but also socially, psychologically, and economically (Conrad, 1985). Others begin using **complementary and alternative medicine,** which refers to diverse systems of diagnosis, treatment, and prevention based on philosophies and techniques other than those used in conventional Western medicine.

Using Alternative Therapies

Interest in alternative therapies (CAM) has grown rapidly in North America, both among healthy persons interested in avoiding illness and among those with chronic or acute illnesses. Most who use alternative therapies do so because conventional treatments have not helped them. Alternative therapies often complement rather than replace mainstream medicine; however, more than 60% of those who use alternative therapies do not tell their doctors that they have done so (Tindle et al., 2005). Moreover, many choose their herbs without advice from a practitioner of any sort.

complementary and alternative medicine (CAM):
Diverse systems of diagnosis, treatment, and prevention based on philosophies and techniques other than those used in conventional Western medicine.

The popularity of CAM rests on belief—or at least hope—in the efficacy of these treatments. These beliefs are supported both by personal experience and by recommendations from friends and acquaintances who believe alternative therapies have helped them. In some of these cases the therapies no doubt did help, either because of the biological effects of the therapies or because consumers' belief in the therapy helped the body to heal itself, as happens in about 30% of all persons treated with **placebos** (drugs known to have no biological effect). In other cases, individuals attribute cures to alternative therapies when actually the problem went away on its own, as happens with 70–80% of health problems (Lundberg, 2001: 123). Finally, people sometimes convince themselves that the therapies helped them even though their health did not actually improve.

Use of alternative therapies also rests on the belief that "natural" treatments are unlikely to do harm. This can be a dangerous assumption. For example, the Chinese herb *ma huang* helps dieters but can cause heart attacks and strokes. Kava kava tea may reduce anxiety but can also cause liver damage, and gingko biloba both stimulates circulation and increases bleeding during surgery (McNeil, 2002). Since 2004, Health Canada has regulated natural health products such as herbal remedies, vitamins, homeopathic medicines, and traditional Chinese medicine as a subset of drugs under the Food and Drugs Act. Although kava kava has not been approved for sale in Canada, there have been instances where Canadian consumers have been able to purchase the product in Canada, suggesting that efforts to limit use of harmful drugs have not been completely effective.

A fascinating study by Matthew Schneirov and Jonathan David Geczik (1996) suggests that alternative healing appeals to individuals as a **new social movement,** a term first coined by German sociologist Jürgen Habermas (1981). Habermas argued that whereas older social movements arose out of discontent with material social conditions such as poverty, the new social movements stem from discontent with modern society's emphasis on science and rationality and its devaluing of the **lifeworld** of everyday human interaction, identity, and needs. Because new social movements focus on the lifeworld, they are less concerned with political strategies for social change and more concerned with creating ways of living that reflect their values. Thus, new social movements depend less on formal organizations and more on "submerged networks" (Melucci, 1995) in which like-minded individuals can trade resources and obtain social support for adopting non-normative ways of life. Although more recent writers tend to argue that movements cannot be neatly dichotomized into "new" versus "old," Habermas's insight regarding the importance of the lifeworld to social movement growth is nonetheless an important one.

Using Habermas's model, Schneirov and Geczik argue that the rise of alternative healing reflects dissatisfaction with the lack of match between doctors' concerns and patients' concerns: Whereas doctors are typically concerned with solving the puzzle of diagnosis and identifying a specific body part that requires treatment, patients are primarily concerned with the impact of illness on their lives (Mechanic, 1995). This mismatch can leave patients feeling like depersonalized objects and deeply dissatisfied with the care they receive, even if it is technically competent. In contrast, Schneirov and Geczik argue, CAM offers patients the opportunity to work as collaborators with health care providers and the promise to look holistically at the sources of their health problems and the consequences of any treatments. To the extent that CAM practitioners value the experiential knowledge of their clients and treat them as equals, alternative medicine could also be said to reflect a postmodern approach to health care.

In this chapter's ethical debate (Box 8.3), on the international trade in human organs, we discuss one of the extreme solutions some individuals adopt when encountering catastrophic illness.

placebo:
Anything offered as a cure that has no known biological effect.

new social movements:
Groups of individuals who reject modern society's emphasis on science and rationality, value human interaction, and hope to create a more humane society primarily by living their lives in ways that reflect their ideals rather than through organized political activity.

lifeworld:
The everyday needs of people and ways in which they interact and live their lives.

BOX 8.3

The Ethics of the Sale of Human Organs

One of the most extreme situations an ill individual can face is the failure of a major organ, be it heart, lung, kidney, or liver. Such situations are death sentences unless the organ can be replaced either with a mechanical substitute or with a donated human organ. But mechanical replacements are often poor substitutes for bodily organs. In addition, some mechanical replacements severely restrict individuals' lives by tethering them to machines. Human organs, on the other hand, can be difficult or even impossible to obtain legally. As a result, a multimillion-dollar international market in human organs has emerged (Rohter, 2004).

Most commonly, the organs sold through this market are kidneys, although livers, lungs, corneas, and other organs also are sold. Because (almost) every human is born with two kidneys, and only one is needed to live, an individual can sell one kidney and still hope to live a normal and healthy life.

Selling an organ carries great risks but can seem worth it if an individual is poor enough. In Brazil, for example, a person can earn $80 per month working at minimum wage—if work is available—or can sell his or her kidney for $3,000. Such sales are illegal in many countries, but these laws are rarely enforced.

To some observers, the trade in human organs is a natural and reasonable market response, in which supply (organs for sale) develops to fill an obvious need (organs wanted). These observers see no difference between selling organs and selling any other valued commodity, be it drugs, cars, or food. Similarly, they argue, people should have at least as much right to buy an organ that will save their life as they have to buy a television or a facelift, and as much right to risk their health by selling an organ as they have to risk their life by selling their labour in dangerous occupations (Cherry, 2005).

Other observers, however, compare the trade in human *organs* to the trade in *humans* and consider selling organs no more ethical than selling slaves. They argue that no one truly sells their bodily organs freely but rather does so because they are coerced by poverty. They also argue that whenever a highly profitable commodity is for sale unregulated by laws, unscrupulous individuals will find ways to profit from the sale and vulnerable individuals will be exploited—whether they are buyers or sellers. Individuals who purchase black market organs have no guarantee that the donor was healthy or that the organ is a good match for them, and those who sell organs have no guarantee that the surgery will be conducted safely, that it will not harm their health, and that they will receive needed health care afterward. A study conducted in the Indian state of Tamil Nadu found that virtually all who (illegally) sell their kidneys do so to pay crippling debts. Yet because most (86%) were in worse health in the years following surgery, their average family incomes declined by one-third, even while average incomes in the state increased (Goyal et al., 2002). Despite these problems, though, the trade in organs is likely to continue so long as demand continues to outstrip supply.

SOCIOLOGICAL QUESTIONS

1. What social views and values about medicine, society, and the body are reflected in policies that allow or forbid the selling of human organs? Whose views are these?
2. Which social groups are in conflict over this issue? Whose interests are served by laws forbidding the sale of human organs? By laws permitting it?
3. Which of these groups has more power to enforce its view? What kinds of power do they have?
4. What are the intended consequences of permitting the sale of human organs? What are the unintended social, economic, political, and health consequences of this policy?

Seeking Information on the Internet

Whether individuals rely primarily on mainstream or alternative therapies, many seek information about their conditions on their own, rather than relying solely on information provided by health care professionals. In the last few years, public access to information has exploded due to the exponential growth of Internet use. In the United States, a 2010 national survey called the Pew Internet and American Life Project found that 80% of Internet users went online to find health-related information. Most frequently, online users were looking for information on a specific health condition or problem, but more than half also used the Internet to find out about medical procedures as well as to find information on doctors and other health care professionals (Fox, 2011). No comparable survey exists in Canada, but it would not be unreasonable to assume that such practices are equally common in Canada. Unfortunately, there are no controls in either country on the quality of materials posted on the Internet, and its vast size makes it impossible to police for fraudulent information, such as claims that herbs can cure cancer or HIV/AIDS. Moreover, more often than not, popular websites, such as google.com, Yahoo.com, and MSN.com, take readers seeking health-related information to websites run by individuals or corporations that have vested economic interests in selling certain drugs or treatments (Green, Kazanjian, and Helmer, 2004).

Despite limitations in most people's ability to effectively search the Internet or evaluate the information they find there, the Internet has proven enormously beneficial to those living with chronic health problems. The Internet has allowed individuals to find information far beyond what they could otherwise access (Barker, 2008) and to find others who share their troubles. When individuals go online to find others who have similar health concerns, they are engaging in what has been called **peer-to-peer health care.** Again, there are no Canadian data on this topic, but results from the 2010 Pew Internet and American Life Project reveal that one in five Americans engage in peer-to-peer health care. Armed with the information they have gathered from Internet searches and from their online exchanges with others who have the same diagnosis, many feel empowered when they negotiate with health care providers regarding appropriate treatment and navigate the daily difficulties of living with illness or disability.

peer-to-peer health care:
Going online to find others who have similar health concerns.

Health Social Movements

Those who live with or are at risk of illness or disability have increasingly turned to collective political action to address their grievances. Like other social movements, **health social movements** are collective (rather than individual) efforts to change something about the world that movement members believe is wrong (Brown et al., 2004).

Health social movements have a variety of goals. Many are primarily concerned with meeting the needs (including access to health care) of a particular group. For example, the Schizophrenia Society of Canada states on its website that it exists to improve the quality of life for those affected by schizophrenia and psychosis through education, support programs, public policy, and research. In addition, a growing number of health social movements have as their goal gaining medical acknowledgment for contested illnesses.

health social movements:
Informal networks of individuals who band together to collectively challenge health policy, politics, beliefs, or practices.

The rise of health social movements reflects a variety of factors (Brown et al., 2004). The civil rights, women's rights, and gay rights movements set the stage for a broader discussion of rights and a broader acceptance of political action. Health social movements are partly a product of this changed cultural climate. In addition, the same cultural forces that increased use of CAM and the same technological changes that increased Internet usage have fostered health social movements by reinforcing the idea that individuals have the right and the obligation to challenge medical authority. Individuals are probably most likely to participate in health social movements when they come to believe that medical authorities have failed to protect them from diseases, to identify their diseases, to treat their diseases appropriately, or to validate their experiential knowledge. For example, the environmental breast cancer movement was organized primarily by women diagnosed with breast cancer who questioned why medical research has focused almost exclusively on early diagnosis and treatment of breast cancer rather than on its prevention. Similarly, the Chronic Pain Association of Canada came into being to provide greater support to people with chronic pain, provide greater awareness of the condition, and change how doctors perceive and treat persons with chronic pain. As these examples suggest, people who live with chronic illness, chronic pain, and disability are not simply victims of their fate but may actively work to better their situation and those of others like them.

Illness and Subsequent Changes in Existing Social Relationships

For better or worse, chronic illness and disability alter relationships with friends, relatives, and colleagues. Illness and disability can strengthen social relationships, as families pull together to face health problems, old wounds are healed or put aside, and individuals realize how much they mean to each other. Illness and disability, however, can also strain relationships. Friends and family might help each other willingly during acute illnesses or the first few months of a chronic illness or traumatic injury, but they might become more loath to do so over time. This is especially true for male friends and family, who less often than women are socialized to be caregivers (Cancian and Oliker, 2000; Fine and Asch, 1988). Moreover, the growing burden of gratitude can make those who have chronic illnesses or disabilities reluctant to ask for needed help. Problems are especially acute among elderly persons who have outlived their close relatives and friends and thus must rely on more distant social connections. For all these reasons, relationships may flounder and fade.

Relationships also suffer if individuals can no longer participate in previous activities. How do you maintain a relationship with a tennis partner once you can no longer hold a racket? How do you maintain a relationship with a friend when architectural and transportation barriers keep you from going to movies or restaurants? And how do you maintain a relationship with a spouse or lover when your sexual abilities and interests have changed dramatically—or when your partner no longer finds you sexually attractive?

The sexual changes accompanying disability and illness can affect women and men differently. Social norms for persons with and without disabilities expect men to be sexually active but regard women's sexual desires with suspicion. When men lose the ability to perform sexually as they had in the past, they can lose esteem in both their own eyes and those of their partners. And when disability leaves women unable to meet social norms for sexual attractiveness, they often find that others assume they have no sexual feelings at all (Lonsdale, 1990).

Declines in financial standing also strain relationships. An individual might, for example, have the physical ability to go to a movie with a friend but lack the price of admission. Women and minorities are especially hard hit because they typically earned lower wages and had more erratic work histories before becoming ill or disabled, and so qualify for lower benefits from the federal government, if any. At the same time, the stress caused by financial pressures can damage relationships with children, lovers, and spouses.

Managing Stigma

Illness and disability affect not only relationships with friends and family but also less intimate relationships. Most basically—and despite the predictions of the **sick role** model— living with illness or disability means living with **stigma**. Goffman originally defined stigma as the social disgrace of having a deeply discrediting attribute, whether a criminal record, a gay lifestyle, or a socially unacceptable illness. Stigma may be further classified into those that are discredited, referring to an attribute that visibly makes one different, and discreditable, referring to an attribute that is hidden from view, but would result in social rejection if it became known. Examples of the former include being in a wheelchair or having late stage Parkinson's disease, whereas clinical depression, early stage cancer, and epilepsy are examples associated with the latter.

Some illnesses, especially acute illnesses, such as influenza and streptococcal infections, produce relatively little stigma, but others, such as leprosy, obesity, and HIV/AIDS, are so stigmatized that they can affect even relationships with health care providers. Individuals whose illnesses carry a heavy burden of stigma can manage that stigma in various ways. First, individuals can attempt to **pass**, or to hide their illnesses or disabilities from others (Charmaz, 1991: 68–70, 110–119; Goffman, 1963: 73–91; Schneider and Conrad, 1983; Weitz,

stigma:
The social disgrace of having a deeply discrediting attribute, whether a criminal record, a gay lifestyle, or a socially unacceptable illness.

pass:
To hide one's deviance (such as illnesses or disabilities) from others.

1991: 128–132). For example, an elderly man who bumps into furniture because of failing eyesight might try to convince others that he is merely clumsy, and one who sometimes does not respond to questions because of hearing problems might try to convince others that he is merely absentminded. Similarly, those who have chronic illnesses can choose to go out only on days when their symptoms are least noticeable.

Although passing offers some protection against rejection, it carries a high price. Fear of disclosure means constant anxiety. Relationships with friends and families suffer when disabled or ill individuals lie about their conditions. In addition, those individuals forfeit the emotional or practical support they might receive if others understood their situation. Individuals also risk losing jobs or flunking courses when they cannot explain their reduced productivity and increased absences.

covering:

Attempting to deflect attention from deviance, including illnesses or disabilities.

Those who cannot tolerate the stresses of passing can instead adopt a strategy of **covering**— no longer hiding their condition but instead trying to deflect attention from it (Goffman, 1963: 102–104). A woman with a visible leg brace can wear eye-catching jewellery, and persons with mobility limitations can arrive early to social gatherings to accustom themselves to the setting, identify potential physical hazards, and find accessible seats. Similarly, elderly persons who no longer see well enough to drive at night can schedule their social activities during daylight hours.

disclosing:

Making one's deviance more widely known by telling others about it or making it more visible.

Conversely, those who have discreditable disabilities sometimes find advantages in **disclosing** their disability to elicit sympathy or aid (Charmaz, 1991: 119–133). For example, a woman might choose to wear a leg brace or tell co-workers about her arthritis in order to avoid being labelled lazy when she cannot do certain tasks.

deviance disavowal:

The process through which individuals attempt to prove that, despite their apparent deviance, they are no different from other people.

Other people deal with the potential for stigma through a process of **deviance disavowal**, that is, convincing others that they are the same as "normal" people (Davis, 1961). These individuals do not try to pass or cover their deviance but instead try to prove that their illnesses or disabilities make them no different from others. Such "supercrips"—in the slang of disabled activists—often appear in the pages of popular magazines: the quadriplegic who paints holding a brush between her teeth, the blind man who is a champion skier, the participants in Special Olympics and Paralympics, and so on.

Each of these strategies can ease ill or disabled people's lives in an intolerant society. None, however, challenge the basis of that intolerance. Those who pass or cover in no way threaten the prejudices of those who would reject them. Even those who attempt to disavow their deviance do not challenge social prejudices regarding disabilities as much as proclaim they are not like others who have disabilities.

challenging:

Rejecting the social norms that attach stigma to a behaviour or condition, including illness or disability.

In contrast, other people take the more radical step of rejecting their rejecters and **challenging** the stigma of illness and disability. These individuals reject the social norms that denigrate them and refuse to adopt the accommodative strategies of passing, covering, or disavowing deviance. Instead, they argue that their deviations from bodily norms should not limit their civil rights or social status. Rather than accepting the stigma of illness and disability, these individuals attempt instead to label those who discriminate against them as foolish or immoral (Weitz, 1991: 132–133). They disclose their illness or disability not to elicit sympathy or aid but to affirm their dignity and pride in the lives they have made for themselves despite—or perhaps because of—the ways their bodies differ from social expectations. For example, a woman born without a hand who, after a year of wearing a hot, uncomfortable, and functionally useless artificial hand, decided to switch to a metal hook told an interviewer about her habit of looking at herself when passing store windows:

> I never failed to get a reaction from people, so I always looked too. What the hell are they looking at? I looked and I saw a woman with a surprisingly short arm! But when I got the [cosmetic] hand, I looked and I thought, oh my God, that's

what I would have looked like [if I had been born with a hand]! And I saw this
person that I would have been. But maybe I would have been an asshole just like
all the rest of them [the non-disabled].... And [now] when I see the hook, I say,
boy, what a bad broad. And that's the look I like the best. (Phillips, 1990: 855)

This quote illustrates how individuals can construct an alternative view of both themselves
and "normals"—in this case, redefining the self as feisty, independent, and rebellious and
defining "normals" as voyeuristic "assholes."

As we did with disability, we now take a moment to reevaluate our earlier definition of
stigma. By implying that stigma is an attribute of the individual, Goffman's definition has
many similarities to a medical model approach. That is, this definition may reinforce the
belief that stigma is a problem that those with disability or chronic illness must solve by
altering how they present their bodies in public. Moreover, it reinforces the notion that
focusing on the attributes that mark a person as disabled or ill is a meaningful way of
understanding that person, something that we have seen would be strongly repudiated.
In following the logic of our revised definition of disability, we would propose a more
satisfactory definition of stigma that focuses on the systematic social exclusion and discrimination that happens to people with illness and disability and that acknowledges the
interplay between their specific impairment, their own experiential knowledge, and the
social response.

IMPLICATIONS

Given the progressive aging of the Canadian population and the increasing ability of medical technology to keep alive ill and disabled individuals, many more of us can expect to
eventually live with illness, chronic pain, and disability—whether our own, our parents', or
our children's. Consequently, understanding what it means to live with these conditions has
never been more important.

As both social constructions and social statuses, illness and disability affect all aspects
of life. Most obviously, they force individuals to interact with health care providers and to
manage health care regimens. But illness and disability also affect family relationships; friendships; work prospects; educational performance and opportunities; and, perhaps most important, sense of self and relationship with one's own body. Living with illness and disability also
requires people to come to terms—or to refuse to come to terms—with uncomfortable questions and harsh realities regarding their past, present, and future.

Illness and disability can confer social disadvantages similar to those experienced by
members of traditionally recognized minority groups. Yet, the impact of illness and disability is not always negative, for illness and disability at times can provide individuals with
the basis for increased self-esteem and enjoyment of life. Moreover, like other minorities,
those who live with illness and disability have in recent years moved from pleas for tolerance
to demands for rights. Those demands have produced significant changes in Canadian architecture, education, transportation, and so on and have laid the groundwork for the changes
still needed.

Researchers who incorporate a sociology of the body approach to chronic illness, chronic
pain, and disability remind us of the theoretical importance of the body, which has too often
faded into the background in sociological analysis. The body remains salient to our understanding of health and illness because it is how we experience our selves and how we have a
social presence in this world. By valuing experiential and corporeal knowledge, we can change
how we think about disability and illness and potentially transform medical care, as evidenced
by the increasing popularity of alternative therapies.

SUMMARY

LO-1 1. The World Health Organization (WHO) defines impairment as any temporary or permanent loss or abnormality of a body structure or function, whether physiological or psychological, and defines disability as a restriction or inability to perform an activity in the manner or within the range considered normal for a human being, mostly resulting from impairment. In accepting the WHO definition, a medical model treats disability as something located solely within the individual mind and body. A social model of disability, on the other hand, defines disability as the outcome of social barriers that restrict the activities of people with impairments.

LO-2 2. Like members of minority groups, persons with disabilities experience prejudice and discrimination; however, unlike members of minority groups, not all collectively identify with the label or even see themselves as disabled.

LO-3 3. Criticized for placing too much emphasis on disability and overlooking the issue of impairment, the social model of disability may need revision. By neglecting impairment, people with disabilities (a) are encouraged to think solely about the ways they are socially oppressed, but prevented from sharing their corporeal experiences; (b) remain dependent on the medical profession, whose authority and privilege over the body is not contested; and (c) are assumed to experience disablement in exactly the same way.

LO-3 4. A postmodern perspective and a sociology of the body approach may help overcome some of the limitations of a social model of disability. A postmodern perspective rejects the notion that there is a grand narrative that captures all experiences of disability and instead attends to difference. A sociology of the body approach assumes that the body is central to disability because the body is how one experiences the self and how one has a social presence in the world. Thus, self and body are always engaging with and shaping one another.

LO-4 5. Chronic pain affects one of every six Canadians, with women and older persons at greater risk. Although it is difficult to diagnose, there are a growing range of treatment options for people who have chronic pain.

LO-5 6. Becoming a chronically ill or disabled person begins with recognizing that something about the body is troubling, a process that may develop slowly. The process of responding to symptoms and deciding whether to seek diagnosis and treatment is known as illness behaviour.

LO-5 7. Coming to terms with serious or life-threatening illness and disability involves biographical disruption. One aspect of this is that the body and self are experienced as separate entities, with greater attention drawn to bodily states. Individuals may experience illness or disability as an interruption, an intrusion, or an immersion.

LO-5 8. Questioning taken-for-granted assumptions about the expected trajectory of one's life is a second aspect of biographical disruption, involving seeking explanations for why this has happened and repairing one's narrative through storytelling. Western culture has typically devised stories that fall into one of three categories: restitution, chaos, and quest stories.

LO-5 9. Finally, biographical disruption involves ways of responding and mobilizing resources to adjust to the changed circumstances that accompany illness and disability. Responses include how one engages with the medical system. The health belief model predicts the conditions under which individuals are most likely to comply with medical advice, but critical sociologists have noted that individuals may have rational reasons for medical "non-compliance."

LO-5 10. Social service agencies that adopt a medical model of disability, focusing on how individuals can compensate for their individual deficiencies rather than on how social arrangements handicap them, may also create dissatisfaction among those who seek out their services.

LO-5 11. Alternative therapies (CAM) are typically used in addition to mainstream medicine by individuals who find that conventional treatments have not helped them. The use of alternative therapies can be viewed as a new social movement, that is, a social movement that stems from discontent with modern society's emphasis on science and rationality. From this perspective, the use of CAM reflects the mismatch between doctors' concerns and patients' concerns.

LO-5 12. Similarly, discontent with medical advice may prompt individuals who struggle with illness or disability to go on the Internet to find out more information about their condition or to connect with others who have the same health problem. People who find others with the same experiences as themselves may collectively organize themselves in order to bring greater attention to their condition and to change how they are treated by the medical establishment.

LO-6 13. Responses and mobilization of resources are not restricted to managing encounters associated with medical care but affect social relationships as well. Illness and disability can initially strengthen but eventually exhaust social and intimate relationships and have implications for how one presents oneself to others.

LO-7 14. Individuals who experience illness or disability must learn to manage stigma by passing, covering, disclosing, deviance disavowal, or challenging the norms that stigmatize them.

LO-7 15. Although Goffman's definition of stigma is widely accepted, some have suggested that it focuses attention on the individual and implies that it is the individual who must adapt. Alternative definitions situate the problem and solution to stigma in the social processes through which people with devalued attributes are treated with discrimination.

REVIEW QUESTIONS

1. How do the medical and social models of disability differ?
2. Are disabled people a minority group? Explain.
3. What are some of the limitations that result from neglecting impairment in a social model of disability?
4. How common is chronic pain, and why is it difficult to diagnose?
5. What difficulties do individuals face in responding to initial symptoms of illness or disability, obtaining diagnoses, and coming to terms with their diagnoses?
6. What is illness behaviour?
7. What does it mean to experience biographical disruption?
8. How can illness serve as an interruption, an intrusion, or an immersion?
9. Why do individuals sometimes ignore medical advice and turn to alternative health care, go online to learn more about their condition, or reach out to others with the same health condition?
10. How can illness or disability affect social relationships?
11. How do individuals manage the stigma of illness or disability?
12. How does Goffman's definition of stigma reinforce the idea that it is a problem of the individual, and how do alternative definitions of stigma serve to politicize the issue?

CRITICAL THINKING QUESTIONS

1. Think of a recent experience you, a close friend, or a relative had with a chronic or acute illness. Explain which concepts from the sociological literature on the experience of illness applied to your experience. If *few* concepts applied, explain why these concepts generally did *not* apply.

2. To protect or improve their health, many individuals take actions that lack scientific proof of effectiveness, such as taking vitamin C to cure colds. Think of something that you, your friends, or your relatives do that falls into this category; ask around if you can't think of anything. Why did you/they decide to adopt this measure? Why have you/they continued? What beliefs or principles underlie these decisions? Why doesn't the lack of scientific proof affect these decisions?

3. What are some of the reasons why individuals seek *alternative* health care? What does the growing use of alternative health care tell us about modern *medical* care?

KEY TERMS

biographical disruption (p. 186)
challenging (p. 196)
chaos story (p. 188)
complementary and alternative medicine
  (CAM) (p. 191)
covering (p. 196)
deviance disavowal (p. 196)
disability (p. 177)
disclosing (p. 196)
discrimination (p. 180)
health social movements (p. 194)
illness behaviour (p. 184)
illness behaviour model (p. 184)
immersion (p. 187)
impairment (p. 177)
interruption (p. 187)

intrusion (p. 187)
lifeworld (p. 192)
medical model of disability (p. 177)
minority group (p. 179)
narrative reconstruction (p. 188)
new social movements (p. 192)
pass (p. 195)
peer-to-peer health care (p. 194)
placebo (p. 192)
prejudice (p. 179)
quest story (p. 188)
restitution story (p. 188)
social model of disability (p. 178)
stereotypes (p. 179)
stigma (p. 195)

The Body and the Pursuit of Health

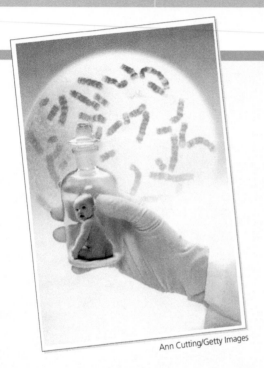

Ann Cutting/Getty Images

Measuring Life: Choosing Walker

In the early years of my son's existence, before I understood how far outside the norm his disabilities took us, I was always astonished to hear a parent say, "I wouldn't change my disabled child for anything." My wife, Johanna—an exceptionally compassionate person and a terrific mother—never made such statements. Lying on our backs in bed, talking in the night, which we did on the rare occasions Walker fell asleep, Johanna once admitted,... "I would trade Walker, if I could just push a button, for the most average child in the world, who got C's in school. I would trade him in an instant. I wouldn't trade him for my sake, for our sake. But I would trade him for his sake. I think Walker has a very, very hard life."

Trading him still isn't possible, but choosing him is getting closer. A new raft of ultra-accurate, at-home fetal-DNA tests are flying off North American and Internet shelves these days, and a massive debate is close behind.

The DNA-testing industry ... has no sooner offered us the opportunity to select the number and gender of the babies we can have—to say nothing of the chance to guarantee they are free of some debilitating syndrome—than doctors and bioethicists are up in arms, accusing medical researchers of promoting genetic cleansing....

The more science lets us interfere in the beginnings of life, to engineer what kind of babies we can make, the more we seem to need to debate who we want to be as human beings....

In my house, such debates always bring on an identity crisis. Walker suffers from CFC, an impossibly rare affliction (150 known cases, globally) caused by a completely random genetic mutation. He's 15 now, looks 10 and has the mind of a two-year old. He always will.

He is often a charming and fantastic companion, but he can't speak, or live on his own (or even with us, any more), or manage the toilet, or eat without a tube, or go for long without smashing his ears flat and ugly with his fists.

We raised him on our own for 10 years, and the experience almost shattered everything I valued—my family, my marriage, my healthy daughter's life, my finances, my friendships, life as I wanted to live it.

There was no genetic test for his syndrome when he was born (there still isn't). For a long time, not a day went by when

I didn't wish there'd been one. Today, I'm glad no test existed then—that I never had to decide, based on a piece of paper ... whether my strange and lonely boy ought to exist.

Still, wouldn't he have been better off, thanks to a simple genetic test, not living his shadowy, pain-filled, so-called life? I understand the question. I understand the appeal of the DNA test, its trouble-free promise. But the answer is complicated....

I have no objection to genetic testing. If you can avoid it, I don't want your child to face the daunting, aimless future Walker may have, especially after his mother and I are gone.

But I have an objection if the results of those tests are the only measure you accept of what constitutes a valuable life. I object if you say that my son is a mistake, that we don't want more of him, and deny what he is: an exotic, living form of freedom, a way of being liberated from the grind of the survival of the fittest; free of all the orthodoxies by which we normals measure a "successful" life—the Harvard acceptance, the hot partner, the good job, the fit body, the size of one's bank account....

It's the very lack of so-called normal expectations, the absence of the possibility that Walker and I can ever "achieve" much or even disappoint each other, that frees us from the status quo, to be who we actually are with each other, rather than what society says we are supposed to be. A rare and often impossible form of love lives in that hollow....

It doesn't matter that Walker will never pass his genetic test. What matters is that I pass his test, that I had a chance to be a human being, a friend, a chatting buddy, a decent if doltish dad, and that I seized it....

I regret many things in my life. But I never regret the strange, lifting afternoons I spend with the test-failing boy and our pointless but utterly unpredictable strolls together. They're just one more way of measuring what we might be.

Ian Brown, "I'm glad I never had to decide whether my strange, lonely boy ought to exist," *The Globe and Mail*, Aug. 27, 2011.

LEARNING OBJECTIVES

In this chapter, students should be able to:

LO-1 **Understand** the relevance of postmodern perspectives to changing ideas on health and the emergence of body projects.

LO-2 **Recognize** how medicalization, commodification, and new medical technologies have altered what it means to be healthy in contemporary society.

LO-3 **Understand** the different visions of the future as expressed by transhumanists and bioconservatists.

LO-4 **Describe** the ways in which medicine is able to transform all aspects of the human body, from its surface appearance and internal processes down to its genetic and molecular structure.

LO-5 **Understand** what is meant by the pharmaceutical self and **recognize** how expanding the number of psychiatric diagnoses and blurring the boundary between normalcy and mental illness offers the opportunity for people to be better than well.

LO-6 **Understand** the ethical implications of these new medical technologies.

In the previous two chapters, we explored the social meanings of illness, noting first that health is seen as socially desirable whereas illness may elicit social rejection and second that the boundaries between health and illness can be and often are socially contested. In this chapter, we join these two ideas together to evaluate how two processes, medicalization and the commodification of health, in conjunction with new medical technologies to improve the human condition, have profoundly altered the meanings of and the means by which people achieve health in the twenty-first century. Drawing on postmodern theory and a sociology of the body perspective, we show why the transformation of our bodies in the pursuit of health represents a new frontier in human history, the implications of which are only just beginning to be grasped.

HEALTH AS MORE THAN THE ABSENCE OF DISEASE: A POSTMODERN VIEW

Dramatic changes in social life over the course of the twentieth century and into the present era signal to some that we have entered a new social order. Whereas modernism implies progress, rationality, and continuity, a postmodern social order values subjectivity over objectivity and shifts power from established bases toward new social movements organized around identity and lifestyle. Similarly, societies shift away from being centrally organized around the production of goods and services toward operating under the logic of consumption. As these postmodern impulses are diffused throughout society, they transform how we view and pursue health.

The transition to a postmodern society begins when the project of enlightenment, whose goal is to improve the human condition through the acquisition and application of knowledge, comes to be seen as problematic. Increasingly, there is the rejection of a positivist stance that maintains that facts exist independently in the world and can be verified through observation and experimentation. Instead, postmodernists contend that there are multiple realities that are open-ended and constructed. In modernity, rationality is applied to solve empirical problems; in postmodernity, life is chaotic and fragmented and its understanding is contingent and partial. As such, postmodernism is an exercise in **deconstruction**: established categories are broken down so that multiple, even contradictory, understandings can proliferate.

The postmodern tendency to deconstruct categories also severs the links between illness and health: they are no longer opposites of one another. This new approach to health is exemplified in the discourses of **health promotion**. As we noted in Chapter 2, health promotion involves encouraging individuals to accept greater responsibility for their health and to make positive lifestyle choices. In outlining the tenets of health promotion, the Ottawa Charter also redefined health:

> Health is, therefore, seen as a resource for everyday life, not the objective of living. Health is a positive concept emphasizing social and personal resources, as well as physical capacities. (World Health Organization (WHO), 1986)

This definition makes clear that health is not the absence of disease: it has become diffused beyond a singular entity that can be known and studied and instead is subjectively defined and discursively constructed. Importantly, health becomes fused with lifestyle, identity, and all that is deemed good in life. This allows health to be seen as an aesthetic project where one can experiment with different ways of being, at both the individual and the societal level.

Postmodernism is also ushered in by a dawning recognition that science and technology create at least as many problems as they solve. For example, industrialization has generated enormous wealth and improved living standards, but it has also produced pollution, environmental degradation, and climate change, which pose a threat to human health and to life itself (Beck, 1992). As these risks proliferate alongside scientific progress, they begin to overshadow past accomplishments and create growing uncertainty about the future, paving the way for a society that is increasingly organized around managing risk.

The management of risk permeates all aspects of living, including our preoccupation with health. No longer viewed as the absence of disease, health is increasingly measured in terms of how we detect and manage risks. Risk management requires individuals to maintain constant vigilance and to make corresponding changes in lifestyle and behaviour. For example, we hear on the news that eating eggs increases the risk for heart disease, and we subsequently reduce our intake of eggs as a means of staying healthy (avoiding risk). Yet engaging in these practices has implications for how we see ourselves. Because health cannot be revealed in objective tests administered by a physician (a test can only indicate the presence or absence

deconstruction:
A postmodern approach that dismisses singular understandings of the world, embracing interpretations that are fluid and multiple, including those that have an inherent contradiction.

of a specific disease), it must be subjectively and discursively constructed. Who we think we are or imagine ourselves to be is constantly changing as we absorb new messages about what it means to be healthy and apply them to our lives.

As a result of these postmodern tendencies, Rose (2007) contends that we have begun to create a somatic sense of self, that is, we see ourselves "as beings whose individuality is, in part at least, grounded within our fleshly, corporeal existence, and who experience, articulate, judge and act upon ourselves in part in the language of biomedicine" (p. 13). For example, the notion that "we are what we eat" expresses a direct link between the foods we ingest and how we construct our identity, with the implication that modifying our diet can help us become who we want to be. Not surprisingly, given the high social value that is placed on health, people define both themselves and others by how well they succeed or fail in adopting healthy practices (Crawford, 2006).

Accordingly, the body is no longer a biological given, with fixed and immutable characteristics. Instead, in a postmodern era, the body is seen as malleable and unfinished, requiring constant monitoring, maintenance, and modification. As such, pursuing health means to engage in a **body project** whereby bodies become the means by which individuals display compliance to cultural norms of health and express their identities (Shilling, 2003).

body project:
The shaping of one's body to express identity and to meet cultural norms of beauty and health.

The conflation of health with identity, lifestyle, and bodily appearance has interesting implications. Subjective interpretations of what it means to pursue health may lead down divergent paths. For example, some may undergo cosmetic surgery, fulfilling their own vision of what it means to be healthy, while others, concerned about the health consequences of needless surgery, refrain from it. Similarly, male bodybuilders construct narratives to justify using steroids to achieve the appearance of health, while downplaying the risks. In his interviews with male bodybuilders who use steroids, Monaghan (2002) records one of these narratives:

> With our drugs, the end justifies the means. Whereas if you're using recreational drugs like coke or H [heroin] or something like that, there's no end to it is there? The end is probably, you know, death perhaps…. With steroids it tends to be— it's not a negative drug as such, it's a plus drug. You're trying to do something constructive. You're trying to build a body—whether you call it art or sport— you're trying to build something and there is an end product. (p. 699)

By constructing their motives as directed toward self-fulfillment and the achievement of their body projects, bodybuilders attempted to legitimize their steroid use by emphasizing its positive effects. Moreover, drawing on their experiences within the bodybuilder subculture, they claimed expert knowledge about how to minimize the risk of side effects and addiction that subverted accepted medical knowledge about the risks of steroid use.

These discourses also articulate ideas found in the sociology of the body. A sociology of the body perspective recognizes that the body has symbolic value (through the messages it culturally transmits) but is also centrally interested in exploring how bodybuilders negotiate meaning as they act upon their bodies to achieve their own ends. Thus, there is an ongoing dialogue between the meanings that are generated and the body that is being produced. Whereas postmodernism tends to view bodies as infinitely malleable, a sociology of the body perspective recognizes that ideas about bodybuilding derive from the lived experiences of those who participate in the bodybuilding subculture. In short, bodybuilding is taken up by embodied social actors who rely on ideas expressed in bodybuilding subculture to create their own version of the perfect body (Monaghan, 1999).

Body projects do not accomplish the work of health in postmodern societies by themselves. They are facilitated by two other processes: medicalization and commodification. Although we have already discussed medicalization in a previous chapter, we now make the argument that medicalization itself has undergone change, first by its efforts to transform rather than merely cure bodies, and second by decentring the medical doctor as an instrument of social control. Commodification turns health into a commercial enterprise, whereby consumers realize health by purchasing goods and services that symbolize healthy lifestyles and "living the good life." We discuss each of these in greater detail in the following sections.

Medicalization

In Chapter 7, we first introduced the concept of **medicalization**, which suggests that medicine acts as a form of social control by reframing various aspects of life as medical conditions that fall under its jurisdiction. Sociologists continue to view medicalization as a major force in our societies but have also begun to make the case that medicalization in the twenty-first century no longer works in the same way as it did in the past. Scholars have identified the following shifts in medicalization.

First, Clarke and her colleagues (2003) suggest that medicine no longer acts simply to exert control over particular conditions but rather is increasingly deployed to achieve the transformation of bodies and lives. As such, medicine has utility for both curing disease and achieving health, although as we will note shortly, the influence of medical doctors in the latter sphere is much more limited. Indeed, the task of making people better than well and helping them to produce aesthetically pleasing bodies is now served by an astonishing array of medical interventions.

Rapid advances in medical technology have increased the scope of medical intervention, but these body-altering and life-changing interventions also profoundly alter established ideas about health and illness and life and death. Rose (2007) uses the example of organ transplantation to demonstrate the radical implications of an intervention that joins the bodies of different individuals together in space and time and has the power to disrupt one's sense of ownership of the body and established ways of thinking about life and death. Similarly, new screening technologies are no longer used solely to detect disease but to reveal the risk for disease. In effect, these technologies deconstruct the category of patient and medicalize future health. For example, Griffiths and Green (2003) discuss the implications of new bone density measurement technologies that assess the amount of mineral matter in the bone of middle-aged adults to predict risk for osteoporosis and bone fracture in the future. The diagnosis is accompanied by treatment that aims to prevent osteoporosis from ever occurring, so that a person becomes a patient, receives treatment, and adjusts their own behaviour—all without actually having a disease. Thus, patienthood is possible in both sickness and health. And in a different way, medicine transforms lives as much as bodies through infertility treatment, whereby medical advances now allow those who otherwise would not be able to conceive to become parents.

Second, although medicalization remains a potent form of social control, it is no longer doctors who are at the centre of that process. To accomplish health in a postmodern world, an army of diverse experts is required. Fitness trainers, dietitians, beauticians, massage therapists, manicurists, psychotherapists, life coaches, vacation planners, and even health researchers are summoned to provide the latest advice to consumers who want to make healthy choices. Amidst the clamour, the physician is but one voice. Moreover, as we have noted earlier, individuals no longer respond in the medical encounter as passive patients who depend on the expertise of medical doctors, but rather they act as empowered consumers, who now weigh the physician's advice against their experiential knowledge and the counsel of other experts. In an age where cynicism and the distrust of experts are rampant, however, empowerment seems to be exercised only inasmuch as consumers are able to choose which voices to heed in the relentless call to pursue better health.

Commodification of Health

That patients have become consumers should trigger awareness that health itself has been commodified. **Commodification** refers to the process of turning things, particularly things that are unlikely to be seen this way, into products that are bought and sold in the market. That health is both amorphous and subjectively defined makes it ripe for market exploitation. Consumer culture offers a dizzying array of options for achieving health through the purchase of goods and services that are promoted for their health-enhancing effects.

Because health does not have a clear referent, the only way to demonstrate adherence to health in contemporary society is to adorn one's body with the symbols of health. Without any reality behind the representation, these accoutrements are nothing more than circulating symbols that acquire temporary significance as their value is recognized by other consumers. For example, lululemon athletica apparel is meant to be worn not just in the gym but in everyday life and, as such, becomes a fashion statement proclaiming one's commitment to the pursuit of health (Ayo, 2012). In the same way, all companies advertise their products as having health-promoting advantages, without the need to prove their claim. For example, fast food corporations readily sponsor Olympic athletes, implicitly and sometimes even explicitly suggesting that their products are not just winning products but health-enhancing products.

commodification:
The process of turning things or people into products that can be bought or sold.

The Proliferation of Medical Technology

Finally, the shifting engines of medicalization and the commodification of health are accompanied by the proliferation of medical technologies whose advances far outstrip our ability to appreciate their implications. As the pace of medical discovery has accelerated, there are growing questions about the benefits of these new medical technologies for individuals and for society as a whole. These questions typically emerge after the technology has already been introduced into the public realm, providing few opportunities to anticipate the possible consequences in advance of its implementation. Thus, it is when people begin to make use of these new technologies for their own purposes, rather than the uses for which the technology was intended, that the social consequences become evident. Genetic testing that is now used in India, China, and even Canada to abort female fetuses, as discussed in Chapter 6, is but one example of how a new technology is used in ways that are unanticipated and that can have harmful social consequences. See Box 9.1 for a discussion of the unanticipated social implications of the off-label use of oral contraceptive pills.

off-label use:
Taking prescription medication for purposes other than the condition it has been approved to treat.

menstrual suppression:
The off-label use of oral contraceptive pills in which, rather than following a twenty-one-day phase of active pills followed by seven days of placebo pills, active pills are continuously taken so as to reduce the frequency of menstruation or eliminate bleeding altogether.

BOX 9.1

Off-label Use of Oral Contraceptive Pills

First introduced in the 1960s, oral contraceptive pills ("the pill") revolutionized women's reproductive choices by allowing them for the first time in history to exert nearly complete control over pregnancy. Nearly a decade later, the first reports of **off-label use** of the pill to avoid menstruation began to emerge. The movement to suppress or eliminate periods altogether, however, did not commence until the late 1990s and has only gained attention as pharmaceutical companies have begun to offer such products to women. As such, the public controversy over the off-label use of oral contraceptives for **menstrual suppression** has been relatively recent.

In their book *Is Menstruation Obsolete?*, Coutinho and Segal (1999) make the case that menstrual suppression is health enhancing and can be used to provide relief from specific ailments such as

continued

anemia, endometriosis, and PMS. Lauding menstrual suppression as an idea whose time has come, they encourage women to reject the idea that menstruation is a normal part of life. Indeed, they suggest that because menarche begins at an earlier age and women now give birth to fewer children, contemporary women have far more periods than previous generations of women. Stating that the only purpose of the menstrual cycle is to facilitate conception, the authors also suggest that suppressing menstruation will have no effect on the rest of the body.

Subsequent research has found that large numbers of women would prefer to menstruate less frequently, suggesting that menstrual suppression is both popular and desirable. Indeed, advocates of menstrual suppression point to the benefits for women in unique and demanding workplaces, such as being on active military duty in hostile or remote settings (Powell-Dunford et al., 2011). It appears then that menstrual suppression is meeting the needs of a new generation of women.

Others, however, note that there may be **unintended negative consequences** of this practice. Hitchcock (2008) notes that although women may wish to practise menstrual suppression because it is convenient, that does not mean that they are willing to trade off what is essentially a lifestyle choice for unknown risks to health. She points to the fact that there are no empirical studies that evaluate the health consequences of long-term menstrual suppression; therefore, it is premature to assume that there is no risk. Moreover, there is no evidence to support the idea that menstrual suppression aids in any of the health conditions it has been claimed to treat. Finally, she notes that menstruation is only the visible part of an endocrine reproductive cycle that likely produces many other benefits for women's bodies. Indeed, there is growing evidence that the menstruation cycle is linked to other processes in the body; tampering with menstruation might alter these other functions. As such, she urges caution against claims for harms or benefits until they are verified in research.

But, Hitchcock more forcefully argues that there are also social implications embedded in the practice of menstrual suppression. Historically, women's bodies have been constructed as deficient relative to men's bodies, and menstruation in particular is seen as an inherent weakness of the female body. Girls are taught from an early age that bleeding is dirty and shameful, that evidence of menstruation should be hidden, and that it is their responsibility to contain and control their leaky bodies. These negative perceptions infiltrate how women feel about menstruation. If it were more highly valued, Hitchcock argues it is unlikely that women would choose to be free of it.

Not surprisingly, then, the media has depicted menstruation as problematic and portrayed menstrual suppression in a favourable light. In their analysis of Canadian and American newspapers, magazines, and online articles dealing with the topic, Johnston-Robledo and her colleagues found that the media exaggerated the benefits of menstrual suppression and failed to mention the lack of evidence for safe long-term use of oral contraceptives for menstrual suppression (Johnston-Robledo, Warnack, and Wares, 2006). Moreover, menstruation itself was treated as bothersome, incapacitating, unnecessary, and a hindrance to attaining success and health in life.

The rush to commercialize products for menstrual suppression appears to be in full swing. Sensing an untapped market, pharmaceutical companies have already received approval in Canada and the United States to sell women medications that will suppress their periods for three months at a time. For example, Seasonale allows women to have four periods a year, and it is anticipated that newer products will soon allow women in Canada to suppress menstruation indefinitely. Meanwhile, the critical issue about what menstrual suppression tells women about their bodies seems to have faded away, or at least failed to register as a concern for the growing numbers of young women who use these products.

But, beyond the different ways in which people take up these new technologies and use them for their own purposes, there is a deeper and more fundamental issue at stake. That issue has to do with the type of future these new medical technologies are ushering in. Responses to this question run the gamut, but positions at the extreme ends of the debate as to whether these technologies are beneficial or harmful to humankind are respectively labelled **transhumanism** and **bioconservatism**. Transhumanists believe that new medical technologies should be used in ways that advance the human species, and they welcome the opportunity to create a posthuman world. For example, transhumanists believe that science and technology should attempt to extend the normal human lifespan indefinitely; enhance existing abilities, such as giving humans photographic memory and greater control over their emotions; and enable humans to acquire new sensory capabilities, such as X-ray vision or moving at superhuman velocity from one place to another. One of its major spokespersons is Ray Kurzweil, a futurist who has predicted that indefinite lifespans will soon be a reality and whose most recent book, *The Singularity Is Near: When Humans Transcend Biology*, actively promotes the union of human and machine (Kurzweil, 2005).

In contrast, bioconvervatism expresses concern about the implications of technologies that are designed to catapult human capacities far beyond their current levels. In his book *The Case against Perfection*, Michael Sandel (2007) argues that the decision to use technology to alter the human condition poses moral quandaries about what humans are and what they are becoming. In particular, there is concern that future manipulations of the human body will be so extensive as to destroy any appreciation for what it means to be human. He contends that life is a gift because we cannot choose what we are—our talents derive from the genetic lottery—we may improve upon these talents through discipline and practice, but we do not choose them. If, in the future, parents do have the ability to choose their child's talents, they stand to lose an opportunity to delight in the unexpected, to wonder what kind of child they will have. Not only does this represent an immeasurable loss in what it means to be a parent, but also it speaks to the immense hubris associated with parents' attempts to select children's abilities for them. Moreover, if a child's talents are selected in advance, he suggests any admiration for that child's talents must surely go to the parents and not the child. Finally, Sandel wonders about the kind of world we will live in when we are all programmed with our talents and abilities. He suggests several unexpected implications: first, that the option to choose who we will be means that we will be held even more responsible in the future for who we are, and second, that as a result, we will lose our sense of solidarity because those who don't succeed in life can be rightly blamed for their failures. As he puts it, the coach who today criticizes the athlete for being out of position may tomorrow criticize the athlete for being too short.

Thus, as science and technology continue to be applied to the betterment of human life, an impending "crisis of meaning" is unfolding (Shilling, 2003). That is, as the nature and boundaries of our bodies become more fluid and changeable, we are becoming increasingly uncertain about what our bodies are and what they are becoming. As Simon Williams (2003) suggests, science and technology have turned humans into **cyborgs** (short for cybernetic organisms). The definition of this futuristic term, coined in the 1960s, which originally referred to beings that have both biological and artificial parts, has been broadened by Donna Haraway to refer to any creature that transgresses established binary divisions, including what is considered dead versus alive, machine versus human, and unnatural versus natural. To the extent that new medical technologies pervade every aspect of the human body, from its surface to its internal workings and even farther down to its genetic and molecular composition, we must ask ourselves how prevalent cyborgs have become in our society and whether we have already entered a posthuman era.

In the remainder of this chapter, we describe some of the myriad ways in which medical technology has transgressed these established boundaries and created a new world of cyborgs, concluding with a discussion of the ethical implications of these changes.

transhumanism:
The philosophy that science and technology should be used to enhance and expand human mental and physical characteristics and capacities.

bioconservatism:
The belief that the use of science and technology to enhance and expand the capacities of humans may be morally problematic and may fundamentally erode what it means to be human.

cyborg:
A hybrid entity that breaches established boundaries, such as those between life and death, or human and machine.

THE PURSUIT OF HEALTH IN CONTEMPORARY SOCIETY

It is difficult to capture the breadth and complexity of the immense changes that science and technology have been able to accomplish in just a few short decades or stay abreast of the countless innovations that occur on a daily basis. As such, the following discussion barely scratches the surface, yet serves to illustrate how dramatically our world is shifting. We first discuss changes that affect the body, using the concepts of plastic bodies, interchangeable bodies, and genetically engineered bodies as formulated by Simon Williams (2003) to show that science has become insinuated with the alteration of bodies at every level, from its surface and interior processes down to its genetic and molecular composition. We then turn to the issue of altering human traits and characteristics through psychopharmaceuticals, discussing some of the personality and cognitive performance enhancements that are currently available to consumers.

Plastic Bodies

Plastic bodies refer to the application of medical technologies to alter the surface characteristics of the human body. The moulding of the human body occurs through both reconstructive surgery and cosmetic surgery. **Reconstructive surgery** restores function or normal appearance as a result of catastrophic injury or birth defect. For example, between one and two children per 1,000 are born with a cleft palate, an abnormal opening in the roof of the mouth that results from incomplete prenatal development. Repairing these abnormalities as well as other birth defects through surgery is a relatively straightforward procedure. Similarly, breast reconstruction following mastectomy and skin grafts following burns or trauma have become routine procedures.

Yet advances in medicine have begun to produce astonishing, futuristic results in reconstructive surgery. In 2002, an article in the *Lancet* by Hettiaratchy and Butler (2002) discussed the technical difficulties that stood in the way of reconstructing a catastrophically damaged facial injury through facial transplantation but predicted that this science fiction procedure would be achieved in the next ten years. The authors were off the mark only in that they misjudged the rapidity with which technology successfully resolved the outstanding issues. In 2005, a woman in France, whose lower facial features were obliterated in a dog attack, was the first to receive a partial face transplant from a cadaver. Then, in 2010, the first full facial transplant was performed in Spain on a young man injured in a shooting accident, and since then, a few other successful full facial transplants have been conducted.

Facial transplants have been a controversial issue in medicine for some time. Because the face is so closely identified with the self, there have been concerns that families of a potential donor will not consent to removing that person's face and having it transplanted onto someone else, that the risks of surgery are too high given that facial disfigurement is not a life-threatening condition, and that those receiving a new face might encounter psychological difficulties in reconciling their identity and coming to terms with "wearing" another person's face. While the few who have received a facial transplant have been reported to be coping well with their new appearance, it remains unknown whether future recipients will experience problems and how such situations will be treated.

In contrast, **cosmetic surgery**, or aesthetic surgery as it is also known, consists of procedures that alter the surface or shape of the body for the purposes of enhancement. Popular procedures include liposuction (suctioning unwanted deposits of fat from under the skin), facelifts (removal of excess facial skin to present a more youthful appearance), rhinoplasty (reshaping the nose), and breast augmentation (insertion of implants to increase breast size). There are many more but less well known types of cosmetic surgery, such as handlifts, which

reconstructive surgery: Surgical intervention to restore or repair function or normal appearance as a result of catastrophic injury or birth defect.

cosmetic surgery: Procedures that alter the surface or shape of the body for the purposes of enhancement.

use injections of fat to reduce the bony appearance of aging hands, and calf reshaping, which can enhance the muscular appearance of the leg.

Although information on cosmetic surgery is not collected in Canada, estimates from the United States indicate that nearly 1.6 million cosmetic surgery procedures were performed in 2011 (American Society of Plastic Surgeons, 2012). This estimate represents a 2% increase over the previous year but is below estimates for the years preceding the Great Recession. Yet, as common as cosmetic surgery appears to have become, these surgical procedures are but a drop in a new tidal wave of efforts to reshape the human body and to improve upon it in the name of health.

Among the proliferation of non-surgical procedures, the most popular is Botox, the brand name for a neurotoxin that is injected under the skin to remove facial wrinkles for a period of about four months. Botox has even been used to prevent excessive sweating. Another non-surgical facelift procedure, known as Thermage, uses radio frequencies to heat the deep layers of facial skin, while cooling the surface to stimulate new skin growth and reduce wrinkles.

Not all enhancements require medical intervention. Indeed, countless beauty products that line store shelves are promoted for their appearance-altering and health-enhancing properties. A relatively new choice that consumers can purchase for their own use is teeth-whitening products. As is the case with other visible signs of aging (wrinkles, sagging midlines), teeth that naturally darken with age are increasingly viewed as undesirable. Although whitening teeth has been part of standard dental practice for many years, it is only in the past decade that teeth-whitening products have become widely available for purchase over the counter. Consumers have the option of a toothpaste or gum containing abrasives that remove stains from the surface of the tooth or the more potent option of bleaching agents that actually alter the colour of the tooth.

Cosmetic Surgery: A Feminist Issue?

Scholars have generally argued that cosmetic surgery is a feminist issue, such that it is women's bodies in particular that are constructed as deficient and in need of enhancement. While men do seem increasingly vulnerable to the beauty myth—the proportion of men who are choosing to enhance their physical appearance through cosmetic surgery is on the rise, from about 5% in the early 1990s to 15% in the first decade of the twenty-first century—many are doubtful that gender equality in cosmetic surgery will be achieved (Davis, 2002). That is, Davis contends that the pressure to conform to cultural ideals of beauty is stronger for women than for men because women are generally expected to alter their bodies to achieve beauty as a performance of gender. For men, cosmetic surgery violates the expectation that men use their bodies for instrumental rather than aesthetic purposes.

In her book *Unbearable Weight*, Susan Bordo (2003) notes that, for women, the bar for perfection is consistently being lifted higher. Women, she states, increasingly compare themselves not to other women but to the images that they are bombarded with in the media. As such, the comparisons women make are not to real bodies but to images that are digitally enhanced to perfection. And although women are increasingly cynical about the veracity of these images, they generally feel powerless to resist the message that they too must conform to the ideal.

Nonetheless, research with Canadian men on the topic of cosmetic surgery is insightful. In their interviews with men assessing their attitudes toward cosmetic surgery, Ricciardelli and Clow (2009) found that men were generally open to the idea but typically talked about it in terms of a hypothetical other. This stance, the authors suggest, allows men to remain ambivalent even as they recognize pressure to achieve masculine cultural ideals. Atkinson (2008), in his interviews with men who had had cosmetic surgery, found that men chose surgery to resolve long-standing insecurity and discomfort with their bodies but framed the surgery as a masculine endeavour in which they stoically withstood the pain. Kevin, a 39-year-old man living in southern Ontario, describes his experience with cosmetic surgery in the following way:

> When the doctor stripped away the layers of fat from around my waist, he removed 30 years of anguish from my soul. I'd always been the fat outsider, the little boy who never quite made the cut for anything. Being inside a body that is a gelatinous prison kills a tiny piece of you every moment of your life…. When I woke up after the surgery and looked down, I felt strong and confident as a man should. I could, never ever in my life, speak to anyone about how much being heavy hurt me emotionally, and now I don't have to…. Surgery is the best psychotherapy offered on the market. You have to go through hell and the pain [of surgery] to come out on top. Being beaten up through surgery is temporary, but being beaten up socially can last a lifetime. (p. 78)

Thus, both studies reveal that men may increasingly feel compelled to use cosmetic surgery to accomplish their own body projects. They also make clear, however, that those who contemplate or undergo cosmetic surgery necessarily struggle with framing their experiences within the context of a gender order that continues to see cosmetic surgery as more appropriate for women than for men.

Case Study: Body Modification

What people who undergo cosmetic procedures share is a desire to reshape the surface of the body in ways that convey to the rest of the world that one is healthy, happy, and living the good life. These goals are also expressed by those involved in the practice of body modification; however, as a countercultural movement, reshaping the body takes on a whole new meaning. Adherents of body modification reject conventional norms of beauty, instead experimenting with radical ways of altering the body. These practices include full-body tattooing; piercings in different parts of the body; tongue-splitting; and the insertion of plastic or silicone implants such as ridges, beads, or horns under the skin. Even more radical procedures are branding (burning a forged metal design into the skin) and scarification (cutting a pattern into the skin with a sharp object). As such, by pushing the boundaries of what bodies might look like, body modification is a body project taken to an extreme level.

As an art form and an act of cultural defiance, body modification is intended to evoke responses of revulsion from the general public: Exhibiting their bodies communicates to the rest of the world that they are indeed different. In their interviews of Canadians in Calgary and Toronto who engaged in body modification practices, Atkinson and Young (2001) show how these practices also allow a collective identity to emerge, as the following quote illustrates:

> No matter how much disdain people show me for my tattoos and brandings, I find solace in the fact that I know so many others who share my perspectives on life; we cling to one another in times [of] doubt and pain. There's a great sense of community that emanates out of this studio. (p. 129)

Body modification, then, must be understood as an activity that is purposely undertaken by individuals whose subjective perceptions of beauty and health are uniquely expressed through their body project. At the same time, because of their identification with the body modification movement, the body project becomes a political statement for collectively rejecting the norms of beauty and health held in mainstream society and a desire to create new ways of living and being. These groups, then, are one example of the **new social movements** discussed in the previous chapter.

Interchangeable Bodies

Simon Williams (2003) characterizes interchangeable bodies as transformations of the human body that take place below the surface of the skin and alter its interior. As with technologies that alter the exterior surfaces of the human body, the ease with which technology has been able to renovate the interior of the body heralds the arrival of the future. We discuss in turn the insertion of inanimate objects, organ transplantation, and practices of xenotransplantation, ending with an emerging innovation called brain-technology interface.

Before we do so, however, we note that each of these procedures is made possible by accepting the premises of two of the four operating assumptions of a medical model approach. First, Cartesian dualism allows the self to be perceived as separable from the body. Thus, when parts are removed from the body and replaced with other parts, whether they are inanimate, organs from a donor or an animal, or the latest computer technology, the assumption is that the self remains intact. In other words, personhood does not reside in the body part and cannot be harmed when the original parts are taken out and exchanged for different parts. The second operating assumption, that the body is comparable to a machine with unique functioning parts that can be fixed when broken, allows medical doctors to treat bodies as comprising almost entirely interchangeable parts.

Yet, these operating assumptions have broader implications. For example, when the body is separable from the self, body parts themselves are susceptible to commodification. Nancy Scheper-Hughes (2001) suggests that when body parts are seen as having economic value, selling a kidney or a liver may be an organ of opportunity for the buyer but an organ of last resort for the seller. It is no surprise, then, she says, that a thriving black market for organs involves a flow of capital similar to other goods, whereby the body parts of the disenfranchised poor are transferred into the bodies of the wealthy.

Another implication is that when a body part is removed from a deceased donor who has agreed in advance to donate their organs, it becomes imperative that the distinction between what is living and what is dead is precisely defined so that individuals who are incapacitated do not lose their rights as human beings. Importantly, although science may have determined that death occurs when the brain is dead, this viewpoint is in contradiction with many religions. For example, some orthodox Jews believe that death occurs when the heart stops beating, and Tibetan Buddhists believe that the spirit occupies the body for several days following death. These beliefs complicate efforts to discern when it is morally acceptable to harvest organs from a donor.

Our exploration of bodies that are interchangeable begins with the wide array of foreign objects that are now routinely inserted into the human body. These include titanium hips and knees, polymer blood vessels, cardiac pacemakers, and cochlear implants, to name a few. In many instances, the new materials introduced into the body are far superior and more durable than the body part that is being replaced. For example, after the age of 50, it is common for people to develop cataracts, which involves deteriorating eyesight as a result of a gradual clouding of the lens. Advances in medicine have made it a relatively straightforward procedure to remove the clouded lens and replace it with an artificial lens. The artificial lens is designed not only to restore clear vision but sometimes also to correct for other problems with eyesight, such as astigmatism. Thus, seniors who have the surgery often find that they no longer need glasses or other corrective devices. Moreover, the artificial lens does not break down in the same way that the human lens does, and an artificial lens that results in 20-20 vision can be expected to last the remainder of that individual's life. Not surprisingly, such surgeries are becoming increasingly popular and are beginning to be offered more widely as an enhancement technology rather than simply as a cure for cataracts.

An **organ transplant** is a surgical operation in which a failing or damaged organ in the human body is removed and replaced with a functioning organ. The body part may come from a deceased donor, whereas living-donor donation is possible for certain organs, such as kidney (where the donor retains one of two kidneys) and liver and lung transplants (where only a portion of the organ is taken from a living donor). Living-donor transplants require that donor and recipient have the same blood type and are matched on other characteristics, depending on the organ.

Regardless of whether the donor is deceased or living, organ transplant recipients must take a powerful cocktail of immunosuppressant drugs for the rest of their lives to ensure that their body will not reject the transplanted organ. These drugs come with their own substantial health risks, including an increased risk for diabetes, kidney disease, and cancer. Ongoing medical advances, however, have begun to make significant inroads in immunosuppressive medication, with some kidney recipients able to stave off rejection through one pill taken daily. Such advances make organ transplantation more attractive, which implies that in the future, organ transplantation will be used not just to save lives but to improve the quality of life. If so, this would heighten demand for organs, even as supply remains scarce.

Although organ transplantation from human cadaver donors may transgress the divide between living and dead, **xenotransplantation** involves the transgression of a different boundary, whereby non-human animal parts are transplanted into human bodies. Because of increased demand and ongoing organ shortages, researchers have turned to xenotransplantation as a potential solution. Xenotransplantation has been used since the seventeenth century, when physicians in France experimented with transfusing the blood of various animals into humans; however, no animal organ has ever been successfully transplanted into the human body, with patients surviving more than a few months. Notable attempts include Keith Reetsma's unsuccessful attempts to transplant dozens of chimpanzee kidneys in the 1960s; James Hardy's attempt in 1964 to transplant a chimpanzee heart into a patient who died hours later; and the transplant of a baboon heart by Leonard Bailey into an infant girl named Baby Fae, in 1983, who died twenty days later (Cooper, 2012).

That is not to say that xenotransplantation does not occur on a regular basis: the heart valves of pigs are routinely used in heart surgery on humans, and before they were replaced by synthetic materials, cow vessels were also routinely inserted into the human body. Future attempts at transplanting animal organs into humans will almost certainly rely on pigs. Pigs are considered suitable candidates because their organs are of comparable size and they are easier to breed than other animals (such as chimpanzees).

To make xenotransplantation a reality, however, scientists must resolve two outstanding problems. The first problem to overcome is rejection of the transplanted porcine organ. Transplantation of porcine organs invariably triggers an immediate and vigorous human immune response. Although no solutions currently exist, researchers are working on finding a way to genetically engineer porcine tissue so that it provokes a weaker immune response once transplanted into the human body. The second problem is the concern that diseases yet to be experienced by humans would be transferred from the porcine population into the human population. Evidence suggests that such transmission is possible, raising concerns that the human population may be exposed to new and unknown diseases should the first problem be overcome.

Finally, a promising technology to help those with spinal cord injuries is a **brain-technology interface device**, which is implanted in the brain and delivers messages directly from the brain to the muscles, bypassing the spinal cord. The device detects the activity of the specific neurons in the brain responsible for different hand movements and responds by wirelessly transmitting information to microelectric stimulators in the hand to produce the desired movement. To date, this research has been carried out with primates, but the hope is that one day, people who are paralyzed as a result of spinal cord injury will be able to regain some of their lost mobility through these devices.

The social implications associated with all aspects of organ transplantation are enormous. As Ciara Kierans (2011) notes:

> Organ transplantation is controversial, therefore, partly because it tests many different boundaries at once: between the bodies of selves and others; between the immune system and the environment; between humans and machines; between giving and receiving; between buying and selling; between countries, cultures and communities; and between the rich and the poor. Organ transplantation calls into question our personhood and humanity, and how the line is drawn between living and dying. It draws our attention to the interconnectedness between the social and the biological, the local and global: "sites" where transplantation practices connect and reconnect through the processes of organ exchange. This is what commends transplantation as an object of study. (p. 1469)

It is clear that as these technologies progress, allowing bodies to become even more interchangeable, understanding these broader implications will take on greater urgency.

Genetically Engineered Bodies

Whereas plastic bodies refer to alterations to the surface of the body and interchangeable bodies refer to changes to the interior of the body, genetically engineered bodies are modifications that occur at its most basic level. As astounding as the advances in medicine to achieve plastic bodies and interchangeable bodies are, they may pale in comparison to the feat of genetically engineered bodies. That is, inasmuch as the other technologies represent different ways in which medicine has been able to control the processes of the human body, genetically engineered bodies transcend these boundaries by making it possible to select or choose bodies and, as such, may make advances in these other two categories redundant (S. Williams, 2003). For example, synthetic organ transplants already make it possible to reproduce some organs, such as a trachea, using stem cells grown from the person's own body in a laboratory. Known as 3-D bioprinters, these new technologies may one day be able to reproduce more complex organs, such as kidneys and livers, obviating the need for other forms of organ transplantation. In the following pages, we elaborate on the advances and implications of stem cell research in more detail as well as those associated with reproductive technology.

Stem Cell Research

One way of producing genetically engineered bodies is through the use of **stem cells** and the associated technique of cloning (Dunn, 2002), one aspect of what is increasingly called regenerative medicine. Stem cells are naturally occurring human cells that have the ability to grow into numerous types of cells. Although no successful treatments have yet been developed from stem cells, researchers hope some day to use them to replace defective cells in individuals with diseases such as diabetes and Parkinson's disease.

stem cells:
Cells that have the ability to differentiate into various other kinds of cells.

There are two ways to grow stem cells. First, scientists can grow stem cells in the laboratory after harvesting them from adults or from fetal blood left in a woman's blood system after giving birth. No ethical issues have been raised about this use of stem cells, which now accounts for about half of all research in this area (Kolata, 2004). Second, scientists can grow stem cells from embryos. To do so, researchers fertilize human eggs with sperm in a laboratory to turn them into embryos. They then leave the embryos for a week or so, until each has grown into a few hundred cells, and then extract their stem cells (thus destroying the embryos).

Alternatively, researchers can replace the nucleus from an unfertilized human egg with a cell nucleus taken from a donor's skin or muscle, artificially stimulate this egg (instead of fertilizing it) so it develops into an embryo, and then extract its stem cells. This second process is a form of cloning, because the embryo will be genetically identical to the donor.

To many opponents of stem cell research, the destruction of human embryos to harvest stem cells is the same as killing humans. Other critics argue that producing human cells to treat other humans is too close to selling human beings and human body parts. This is particularly worrisome because heavy political opposition to stem cell research has shifted much of this research to the for-profit sector, where it escapes most regulation. Others object specifically to the use of cloning to produce stem cells, on the grounds that it is only a matter of time before some doctors begin using cloned embryos to create cloned babies. They wonder whether in the future babies will be "farmed" and "harvested" to match parents' images of the perfect baby.

Supporters of human stem cell research argue that its potential benefits outweigh its potential problems. Most of the support for this research has come from persons who hope stem cells will provide a cure to the diseases that afflict them or their loved ones. Supporters also argue that destroying an artificially created embryo that has no potential to grow into a human being unless it is somehow implanted in a woman's uterus is not morally equivalent to destroying a human being. Finally, with regard to cloning, supporters argue that many women who want babies are already having donor eggs implanted in their uteruses and that few would choose to use cloned eggs because the chances of success are so low. (So far, no researcher has been able to keep a cloned egg alive for more than a few days, much less for a nine-month pregnancy.) For all these reasons, supporters of stem cell research argue that instead of trying to eliminate this research, we should adopt regulations to ensure that it is conducted ethically.

Reproductive Technology

reproductive technology:
Medical developments that allow doctors to control the process of human conception and fetal development.

in vitro fertilization:
A specialized technique by which an ovum (egg) is fertilized by sperm outside the body, with the resulting embryo later implanted in the uterus for gestation.

Since the late 1970s, debate has raged over the use of **reproductive technology**, or medical developments that allow doctors to control the process of human conception and prenatal development. Reproductive technology first came to the public's attention in 1978, with the birth of Louise Brown, the world's first "test-tube baby." Louise's mother was unable to conceive a baby because her fallopian tubes, through which eggs must descend to reach sperm and be fertilized, were blocked. Using a technique known as **in vitro fertilization**, her doctors removed an egg from her body, fertilized it with her husband's sperm in a test tube, and then implanted it in her uterus to develop. Nine months later, Louise Brown was born.

Louise Brown's birth raised questions about how far doctors should go in interfering in the normal human processes of reproduction. Subsequent cases raised even trickier questions. For example, courts have had to decide whether embryos should be placed for adoption when the biological parents have died and whether custody of embryos following divorce should go to the parent who wants the embryos implanted or the one who wants them destroyed. In addition, doctors and others have debated whether couples should be allowed to hire women to carry their fetuses to term for them and whether postmenopausal women should be allowed to have a baby using another woman's egg.

In Canada, in vitro fertilization and other assisted reproductive technologies are increasingly popular, growing in each year since record-keeping began in 2001. As of 2007, there were twenty-six assisted reproductive technology centres (ART centres) distributed across Canada, with in vitro fertilization as the most common procedure performed (Gunby et al., 2011). Although assisted reproductive technologies continue to improve, less than a third

(28.6%) of all procedures result in a live birth (Gunby et al., 2011). A widening definition of infertility also means that more women are eligible for assisted reproductive technologies. Bushnik and her colleagues recently estimated the prevalence of infertility in the Canadian population to be 15.7%, which is substantially higher than estimated rates of 5.4% and 8.5% reported in 1984 and 1993, respectively (Bushnik et al., 2012).

With the advent of genetic testing, assisted reproductive technologies can further help parents choose the kind of child they want. For example, for parents who have used in vitro fertilization, **preimplantation genetic diagnosis (PGD)** makes it possible to identify embryos that might harbour genetic abnormalities and to implant only those embryos that are free of defect. As alluded to in the opening vignette of this chapter, prenatal genetic testing is also widely available to pregnant women, although testing is currently limited to a small number of conditions. As technology advances, there is growing concern that as it becomes possible to determine child characteristics and potential defects well in advance of birth, parents will have greater ability to decide what kind of child they want.

Yet, in one sense, these controversies are not new. For decades, women have been encouraged by their doctors to undergo blood tests that screen for conditions such as Down syndrome, trisomy 18, and open neural tube defects. Because the tests produce a high rate of **false positives**, women with a positive blood test are then encouraged to undergo more invasive procedures to determine more accurately whether or not the condition exists. What is less clear is how women should proceed once they have been informed that they are likely to have a baby with one of these conditions. Typically, websites and pamphlets indicate that women will be given further options, although the words *abortion* and *pregnancy termination* are not used. Rather, the language is framed as a woman's choice, giving her responsibility for what happens next. Consequently, critics charge that prenatal testing actually constrains women's choices because there is a cultural imperative to do anything possible to avoid having a child with a disability (Ratcliff, 2002). To the extent that consumers will soon be able to conduct prenatal genetic testing in their own homes, the implications of these new technologies appear to be even more profound than the choices women currently make in the context of routine prenatal genetic testing.

The greater use of assisted reproductive technologies has raised basic questions regarding the morality of intervening so directly and invasively in the process of human reproduction, including whether individuals are harmed or helped by having access to such technologies. Those who favour using reproductive technology argue that the technologies give couples greater control over their destinies. Moreover, others suggest that such technologies should not be withheld from parents because society does not require that parents work to ensure the continued existence of people with disabilities nor are the motives of parents generally questioned, making it difficult to argue that their motives should be questioned when it comes to what they do about the potential disabilities of their unborn child (Murphy, 2011).

Those who oppose reproductive technology, on the other hand, argue that couples may be seduced into spending enormous amounts of time and money in a usually futile effort to have children or to have disease-free children, rather than finding other ways to make meaningful lives for themselves. Opponents also question whether these technologies encourage the idea that children are purchasable commodities that, as consumer objects, can be subjected to the processes of quality control (Lippman, 1991). Moreover, prenatal testing may undermine the normalcy of reproductive processes whereby pregnancy increasingly becomes perceived as tentative and fraught with risk. Finally, these technologies do not in and of themselves tell us how we should use the information they provide. As Box 9.2 makes clear, there is even the issue of whether the knowledge generated from genetics can be used in a proprietary way that limits how others can use that information.

preimplantation genetic diagnosis: An assisted reproductive technology that allows an embryo created through in vitro fertilization to be tested for genetic abnormalities.

BOX 9.2

Patenting the Breast Cancer Gene

In the mid-1990s, an American biotechnology company named Myriad Genetics filed patent applications on two genes known as BRCA1 and BRCA2. Myriad was the first to identify that mutations in these genes were linked to hereditary breast and ovarian cancer. A **patent** is a legal monopoly that the state grants to an inventor, preventing others from using, making, or selling an invention for a set period of time. Having beaten the competition in the race to identify these genes, Myriad wanted to use these patents to market a diagnostic test to be used by doctors to test patients with a family history of the disease for the gene mutation. After securing the necessary patents in the United States, Myriad subsequently applied for and obtained similar patents in other countries, including Canada.

Shortly thereafter, Myriad began sending cease and desist letters to laboratories that were conducting BRCA testing in countries where the genes had been patented by Myriad. This provoked a major backlash from the international research community, who feared that Myriad was willing to put profit ahead of scientific progress on breast cancer research. Although Myriad vehemently denied these charges, its aggressive stance soon led to trouble. In Canada, Myriad encountered stiff opposition from the Ontario government, which already had in place a genetic test for breast cancer that was far cheaper and did not require samples to be sent to the United States for testing. Thinking that it had the upper hand with patent protection, Myriad sent cease and desist letters to four provinces, including Ontario, in 2001, demanding it instruct laboratories under its jurisdiction to halt genetic-testing services covered by the patents (Gold and Carbone, 2010). When the Ontario government failed to act immediately, Myriad enjoined the American government to threaten Ontario with trade sanctions for failing to comply. This move only further annoyed officials in Ontario, who convinced the Canadian federal government to strike a task force to study the issue more closely. Ultimately, the task force failed to influence patent law in Canada. By then, however, Myriad had decided to back out of the Canadian market. To its detriment, Myriad made similar missteps in Europe and eventually withdrew from those markets as well.

Although the test is useful only for women who are at risk because of a family history of the disease, Myriad decided to market the test more broadly to American consumers with television and radio ads. Moreover, despite falling costs of conducting the test with improving technology (from approximately $1 per test to a tenth of a cent), fees charged by Myriad more than doubled from $1,600 to $3,340 during the same period (Matloff and Brierly, 2010). These actions did nothing to allay the overly negative impression that Myriad was an irresponsible and greedy corporation.

In May 2009, a lawsuit was filed against Myriad by the Association for Molecular Pathology and others, who contended that patenting a gene sequence was unconstitutional. A year later, a judge ruled that the patents held by Myriad for BRCA1 and BRCA2 were invalid, stating that natural processes were not patentable. In July 2011, the U.S. federal court of appeals overturned this decision; however, in March 2012, the U.S. Supreme Court sent the case back to the federal court of appeals, advising them to reconsider their decision in light of more stringent rules recently imposed by the Supreme Court for patenting genes.

As such, the issue of patenting genes currently remains unresolved, in both Canada and the United States. Medical doctors and researchers generally argue that elements of the human genome are part of our humanity and should not be owned by private companies. On the other hand, lawyers representing the pharmaceutical and biotechnology industries argued that genetic research is expensive and difficult, and that their discoveries should be protected so that they can continue to generate new knowledge. Which of these opposing viewpoints will ultimately win out and the implications of these decisions remains unknown.

patent:
A legal monopoly that the state grants to an inventor, preventing others from using, making, or selling an invention for a set period of time.

Typically, we think of genetic testing as an individual decision: Should someone whose mother died of breast cancer, or whose sister has Down syndrome, get a genetic test to ascertain their own risks of having or passing on these diseases? But genetic testing also has implications for communities. Genetic tests can lead to the stigmatization of an entire community, can challenge ideas about who belongs to a community (when genetic differences are found within a population), and can challenge community ideas of their origins (as, for example, when First Nations stories regarding tribal origins clash with genetic findings). For these reasons, researchers have begun involving communities in discussions of research priorities, research design, and the dissemination of research findings. This leaves open, however, the very large question of who constitutes, and who should represent, a community.

Enhancing Human Traits

Reshaping Personality

We noted earlier that body projects are based on the linking of self with body, in a trend that Nikolas Rose refers to as somatic selves. Elsewhere, Rose (2003) has suggested that we also see ourselves as neurochemical selves whereby the "modification of thought, mood and conduct by pharmacological means has become more or less routine" (p. 46). That is, as individuals come to recognize that undesirable feelings or emotions can be eliminated through a pill, they will increasingly choose to use medication to deal with their problems over other solutions.

Over the past few decades, rates of mental illness have soared. It is difficult to argue that the increased prevalence of mental disorder in the population is due to changes in human biology or that psychiatrists have just become better able to diagnose disorder. Psychiatrists diagnose mental disorder by using the **Diagnostic and Statistical Manual (DSM)** to match symptoms in their patients to symptom checklists indicative of various disorders. To be labelled mentally ill, one must have a diagnosis that is found within the DSM. Over the years, however, as ideas about mental illness have changed, the DSM has been revised accordingly. Notably, earlier versions tended to have fewer diagnostic categories. Thus, DSM-I and DSM-II, published in 1952 and 1968, respectively, each had fewer than thirty diagnoses. In contrast, DSM-IV has 357 diagnoses, and DSM-5, which is due to be published in the spring of 2013, is anticipated to have even more diagnostic categories. The expansion of the number of ways in which one can be considered mentally ill makes it nearly inevitable that more and more people will find themselves defined as such.

But beyond the expansion of the number of categories or ways in which one can be diagnosed as mentally ill, many have suggested that there has also been a general blurring of the differences between what is considered normal and what is considered mental illness. That is, the DSM has increasingly reframed what were once considered normal aspects of life into mental disorder. **Post-traumatic stress disorder (PTSD)** is one example of the successive changes to a diagnosis with different editions of DSM. PTSD is an anxiety disorder that is associated with three symptom clusters: intrusions (where past events intrude into the present through either flashbacks or nightmares); avoidance (where the person tries to avoid situations that bring on intrusions or uses emotional numbing); and hyperarousal (evidenced by increased startle response, paranoia, and inability to relax or sleep). PTSD is different from other mental disorders because it is the only disorder that has an external cause: exposure to an unusually stressful event. It first emerged as a diagnostic category in 1980 with the publication of DSM-III. The criteria for PTSD were that the symptoms had to have been in evidence for longer than six months and that the event that the person had experienced must be outside the range of normal experience. Thus, war, acts of terrorism, and natural disasters were considered events that fell far outside the range of day-to-day experiences.

With the publication of DSM-IV in 1994, the criteria for PTSD changed significantly. First, the duration of symptoms was reduced from six months to one month, and, second, the types of events that could trigger PTSD became much more mundane. Thus, no longer was exposure to an extreme event a necessary condition for developing the disorder; rather the event must simply be experienced by that person as distressing. As such, individuals who were informed of a terminal illness, who witnessed a crime but were not otherwise harmed, or who were in an automobile accident may all be at risk for PTSD. Rather than any change in medical knowledge, Summerfield (2001) suggests that the construction of PTSD as a diagnosis reflects how our society has come to convert human misery into technical problems that can be treated by experts.

Diagnostic and Statistical Manual (DSM):

A manual published by the American Psychiatric Association and used by mental health workers to assign diagnoses to clients.

post-traumatic stress disorder (PTSD):

An anxiety disorder that develops following exposure to a stressful event and is generally characterized by intrusions, avoidance, and hyperarousal.

The blurring of the boundaries between what is considered illness and what is considered normal has also occurred for depression. Horwitz and Wakefield (2005) examine the history of depression as a diagnosis and argue that it has increased without any plausible genetic or psychological explanation. Instead, they claim that the increase in depression is due to changes in the way it is diagnosed. According to Horwitz and Wakefield, traditional definitions of depression recognized normal sadness as being "with cause" and abnormal sadness as being "without cause." Horwitz and Wakefield point out that the "with cause" and "without cause" distinction remained prominent in the psychiatric definition of clinical depression until the release of the DSM-III in 1980. Internal and external challenges to psychiatry in the 1970s meant that when DSM-III was published, it had shifted its focus to rely on descriptive rather than etiologic factors to diagnose disorder. The net result was that the diagnosis of depression eliminated the consideration of context, rendering invisible the difference between normal sadness and depression. Thus, feelings of intense sadness are necessarily defined as disordered by the clinician who uses the diagnostic criteria of the DSM even if sadness is a normal response to a particular event.

Horwitz and Wakefield argue that this change in the criteria for depression represents a logical error because an individual who exhibits normal responses to distressing events should not be diagnosed as depressed. Although changing the criteria for depression has produced some advantages, the authors suggest there are negative consequences for blurring the distinction between depression and normal sadness. For example, the growing number of people who meet the criteria for depression may give pharmaceutical companies a legitimate means of exploiting the diagnosis for their own profit and risks creating inefficiencies in a health care system that treats the problems of living rather than mental illness. Importantly, the authors worry about the cultural consequences of people reframing their own experiences of sadness as a mental disorder to be fixed with a prescription.

The explosive popularity of drugs such as Prozac and Zoloft to treat depression attests to the widening demand for pharmaceuticals that can produce moods and emotions that are socially desirable. The growing demand for these medications does not represent new understandings of depression as a clinical entity but rather reflects the ways in which sadness is seen as an undesirable mood that can be eliminated. As Rose (2003) notes:

> …the new generation of psychiatric drugs treat conditions whose borders are fuzzy, whose coherence and very existence are matters of dispute, and which are not so much intended to "cure"—to produce a specific transformation from a pathological to a normal state—as to modify the ways in which the vicissitudes in the life of the recipient are experienced, lived and understood. (p. 58)

As such, psychiatric drugs are, as with other enhancement technologies, increasingly viewed as opportunities to pursue and realize health, rather than to treat illness.

Cognitive Enhancement

Cognitive enhancing drugs, also known as smart drugs, neuro-enhancers, and nootropics, not only represent important pharmacotherapies for neurocognitive disorders such as dementia and ADHD but are increasingly used off-label by millions in an effort to better the minds of the healthy. For example, modafinil is a drug used to treat narcolepsy, which is a type of sleep disorder, but because it enhances working memory and wakefulness without the jittery side effects that come with too much coffee, it is flying off store shelves. Indeed, a recent study found that nearly 90% of prescriptions filled for modafinil were for off-label use (Kesselheim et al., 2012). Similarly, growing numbers of university students take Ritalin, a drug that is used to treat ADHD, to enhance their concentration while studying.

As with the modification of mood, using psychopharmaceuticals to produce a desired self, where enhanced cognitive abilities allow people to perform better than well, has profound social and ethical implications for the type of society we are becoming and the type of beings we aspire to be in the future. It is to these ethical implications that we now turn.

WEIGHING THE ETHICAL IMPLICATIONS OF ENHANCEMENT TECHNOLOGIES

As we have reviewed the various medical technologies that have the capacity to reshape what it means to be human, we have touched on some of the ethical issues that are associated with their uptake. As should be clear from our discussion, the importance of addressing the ethical questions regarding enhancements has increased as their use has proliferated (Whitehouse et al., 1997). In this final section, we systematically outline the ethical implications of using medical technologies to enhance human capabilities. De Jongh and his colleagues (2008) identify six ethical concerns about the use of psychopharmaceuticals. We broaden their discussion to encompass the ethical issues associated with all forms of enhancement technologies, including cosmetic surgery, organ transplantation, and genetic testing. We elaborate on each of these six ethical concerns in turn, following the summary below in Key Concepts 9.1.

KEY CONCEPTS 9.1   Ethical Concerns Associated with Enhancement Technologies

Safety	Many enhancement therapies are relatively recent, and their long-term effects are not yet known. Are the safety issues of enhancement therapies equivalent to the safety issues of therapeutic interventions?
Societal pressure	Will the broad use of enhancement technologies compel greater usage among those who would not otherwise choose them? That is, would the fear of being left behind motivate choices to use enhancement technologies?
Fairness and equality	Do enhancement technologies represent a form of cheating that would otherwise be banned? If access to such technologies is based on ability to afford them, could this lead to greater social inequalities over time?
Enhancement versus therapy	Which enhancement technologies fall under medical jurisdiction (doctors decide if treatment is appropriate) and which should be left to the discretion of the consumer? What is the goal when using an enhancement technology?
Authenticity and personal identity	If enhancement technologies are capable of altering mood, behaviour, and personality, what is the "real me"?
Happiness and human flourishing	Can enhancement technologies alter what it means to be human?

Safety

First, De Jongh and his colleagues (2008) suggest that scientists know too little about the long-term effects of new enhancement technologies, even as more and more of the population begins to use them. For example, little is known about the long-term effects of neuro-enhancers, and researchers have rarely evaluated the possible side effects of using a medication on a healthy population. For example, Mohamed and Sahakian (2012) note that modafinil has been shown to adversely affect dopamine functioning in healthy brains, increasing the risk for addictive behaviour. As growing numbers of people use modafinil for off-label purposes, will the risks to health outweigh the supposed benefits? Worryingly, the public is too frequently given misleading information on new enhancement technologies. In their analysis of all newspaper articles on neuro-enhancers published between 2008 and 2010, Partridge and his colleagues (2011) found that the articles overwhelmingly conveyed the impression that usage was common and on the rise, but whereas 95% of the articles stated the benefits of neuro-enhancers, only half mentioned possible risks.

Moreover, there is also an unresolved issue as to whether the standard for safety should be the same for enhancement technologies as it is for therapeutic interventions. Some side effects might be acceptable in therapeutic interventions because they are outweighed by the potential benefits, but interventions that are intended for enhancement should have minimal risks. For example, because a ruptured appendix is a fatal condition unless it is surgically removed, patients are typically willing to accept the subsequent risk for an obstruction in the bowel or for wound infection. In contrast, it may be that any risk is unacceptable when the medical intervention does not remedy an illness. Less is known about how to decide when side effects and risks outweigh the potential improvement offered by an enhancement technology. In the case of breast implants, how does one weight the potential benefits of breast implants (for the purpose of improving one's physical appearance) against the increased risks for breast pain, numbness of the breast or nipple, breakage or leakage, and necrosis?

Societal Pressure

A second ethical concern about enhancement technologies is that the societal pressure to use these technologies may overwhelm an individual's better judgment to refrain from them. The pressure may be particularly intense when the costs of not using the technology are high. For example, if neuro-enhancers allow students to excel academically, and growing numbers of students partake in these technologies, students who choose not to use them may find that their marks and academic standing decline relative to those of their peers (Cakic, 2009). Similarly, employees may find it difficult to resist pressure from their employers, who sense a competitive advantage with enhancement technologies. For example, women on combat duty in the military may find themselves pressured to practise menstrual suppression, and both men and women in the military may be encouraged to take neuro-enhancers to improve wakefulness on the front lines.

Fairness and Equality

A third ethical concern, according to De Jongh and his colleagues, involves issues of fairness and equality. Currently, professional sports organizations forbid their athletes from taking substances that would enhance their performance, on the grounds that it constitutes cheating. Athletes who have been caught using performance-enhancing substances have been stripped of their accomplishments and awards and banned from further participation in the sport. The lack of tolerance for performance enhancement technologies in professional sports organizations and the public's repudiation of sports legends who are caught cheating suggest that these activities are universally viewed as morally repugnant. As such, it is difficult to see how using enhancement technologies to gain a competitive edge in other facets of life is morally acceptable when it remains explicitly prohibited in athletic performance. That is, if Olympic athletes are forbidden from taking drugs to improve their performance, why are waitresses allowed to get breast implants to generate more tips and businesspeople allowed to take Ritalin to improve their concentration?

A related concern is the issue of equality. One consequence of living in a society where people can purchase enhancement technologies that give them a competitive advantage in life is that there may be a growing gap between those who can afford to purchase them and those who cannot. Should we create a society where posthuman endeavours result in markedly different outcomes depending on one's wealth? And is it ethical to provide potentially harmful medical care for the sake of enhancing some individuals while others still lack basic services? Conversely, is it ethical to restrain the options of those who would provide or purchase such services?

Enhancement versus Therapy

Fourth, De Jongh and his colleagues note that enhancement technologies blur the boundary between what is therapy and what is enhancement. As medical technologies are increasingly used to achieve non-medical means, health care professions and institutions are being asked to separate that which is medically necessary (treating a medical condition) and that which is enhancement (not medically necessary).

The dilemma has important practical considerations. Health care systems have limited budgets. Confronted with what may be an inexhaustible demand for enhancement, health care systems limit coverage to services that are medically necessary—meaning that they treat disease. When medical technologies are used to attain non-medical purposes, at issue is whether these merit coverage. But these decisions are not easily made because health is subjectively defined. Should health insurance plans cover drugs such as Viagra, which helps men achieve erections, on the grounds that it can improve quality of life? Should health insurance plans cover depression medication for the worried well, that is, those who don't meet the criteria for clinical depression, but insist on Prozac to improve their moods? Should cognitive enhancers be used to stave off diseases such as dementia or prescribed to those who want a competitive edge in the workplace?

Moreover, the ambiguity between therapy and enhancement offers opportunities for disease-mongering companies who stand to make hefty profits if they can convince the public and the medical profession of their claims. Vague symptoms that characterize many of the new diseases may encourage people to feel that they are experiencing the signs of illness and to turn to medication as a solution. For example, **restless leg syndrome**, a sleeping disorder characterized by twitchiness in the legs on lying down, is so vaguely defined that such sensations, even if experienced once, may be enough to trigger uncertainty as to whether one has the condition. Similarly, ads that ask women if they urinate too often do not specify what constitutes too often. Ambiguous ads that offer treatment may encourage women to think this may be a problem for them and to ask their doctors for a prescription. Making the distinction between what is therapy and what is enhancement, therefore, may serve to protect the public from those who would exploit the fears and anxieties of a population striving to be healthy.

Finally, blurring the differences between therapy and enhancement prevents us as a society from clarifying what the goals of enhancement might be. That is, therapy is considered successful when it cures the person of disease. How then should we determine the measure of success for those who undergo enhancement?

Authenticity and Personal Identity

The fifth ethical implication of enhancement technologies, according to De Jongh and his colleagues, is the consequence for authenticity and personal identity. As the desire to

restless leg syndrome:
A sleeping disorder characterized by twitchiness in the legs when one lies down.

reshape and transform the body as a means of expressing identity and fulfilling one's body project intensifies in a postmodern world, Hogle (2005) notes the irony of an emerging debate over authenticity. Authenticity means that one's presentation and performance match and are consistent with the self that one believes one is. By seeking to make the body consonant with self, one must always be in a position to judge whether one has accomplished the goal of authenticity. Importantly, the repetitive act of making these comparisons inevitably creates uncertainty as to what is authentic. To the extent that regular monitoring and modification are required in the elusive pursuit of health, authenticity is necessarily open to contestation too.

The idea that personality itself can be changed through medication also throws into question what aspects of our personality are truly our own. Peter Kramer, a psychiatrist who speculated about the implications of Prozac for shaping personhood in his book, *Listening to Prozac,* expressed discomfort with the ways in which his patients were transformed rather than cured of depression when they took Prozac, and how they subsequently saw their true selves as their transformed selves rather than the person they had been previously (1993). Unlike other medications he had prescribed to patients, Prozac had a remarkable ability to reshape personality and to do so almost instantaneously. If human personality was so malleable that it could be altered with a single pill, he argued that it begged the larger question of whether personhood is an illusion—the self is nothing more than one's biology. As such, the emergence of psychopharmaceuticals appears to reduce personhood to its biochemical brain processes, contradicting the generally held view that personhood is shaped by the sum total of one's subjective reflections of and responses to life experiences.

Happiness and Human Flourishing

Finally, De Jongh and his colleagues identify issues surrounding the future of the human race and how enhancement technologies may redefine what it means to be human. Picking up on the concerns of bioconservatists addressed earlier in this chapter, they ask whether the pursuit of enhancement can make us forget what it means to be human. For example, does extending lifespans indefinitely erode a fundamental aspect of what humans are? Is the cost of engaging in enhancement technologies the loss of our humanity? Will humankind flourish in the wake of enhancement technologies or be destroyed by it?

IMPLICATIONS

Postmodernism allows us to deconstruct what it means to be healthy in our society, leading to the conclusion that health is no longer the absence of disease, but rather signifies a subjective awareness of oneself. As such, there are no limits to the possible meanings of health that can be generated, and the pursuit of health becomes synonymous with and indistinguishable from all that is desirable in life. The body necessarily becomes an ongoing project on which to fashion new realizations of health and well-being. The possibilities do not end with the surface or the internal workings of the body but pervade into all aspects of being, including personality traits and cognitive abilities, which become targets for enhancement, and the possibility of choosing or designing one's offspring.

Ultimately, however, a postmodern perspective fails to offer a way forward. In particular, postmodernism resists offering an alternative methodology for understanding ongoing changes in how health and illness are defined and experienced. Indeed, postmodernism goes out of its way to avoid such pursuits. Lacking a method, postmodernism collapses under its own weight: It cannot assess its own arguments (Bury, 1998). Similarly, the postmodern conception of an infinitely flexible body reduces the body into an ephemeral space for projection.

That is, the attempt to experiment with the appearance of the human body assumes that the body has no biological limits and that there are no harmful consequences to its manipulation.

In contrast, a sociology of the body perspective salvages some of the deficiencies of a post-modern approach because it recognizes the materiality of the body and acknowledges that it is the "thing" that is acted upon when individuals engage in their body projects. As such, the ethical implications of new medical technologies find their significance: Bodies do suffer and feel pain. Therefore, the application of enhancement technologies does not refer to some imaginary surface or illusory trait but to selves who inhabit those bodies and can recount their lived experiences of those bodies as they encounter new medical technologies (Schicktanz, 2007).

What remains unknown is what the future holds as these new medical technologies prolif-erate. Are we hurtling toward a posthuman world, and, if so, what are the implications of this new world for how individuals and societies envision and pursue health?

SUMMARY

LO-1 1. Postmodernism represents a shift away from the belief that reality can be objectively known; instead, postmodernism deconstructs what are taken to be objective categories and offers in its place fragmented, chaotic, and competing realities. As such, postmodernism breaks the links between illness and health so that they are not opposites but rather each is subjectively defined. Indeed, both may exist simultaneously in the same body.

LO-1 2. Similarly, in postmodernism, the body is no longer a biological given, with fixed and immutable characteristics. Rather, the body is seen as malleable and unfinished, requiring constant monitoring, maintenance, and modification. Body projects represent efforts to shape one's body as an individualistic expression of one's identity and as a way of meeting cultural norms and expectations for how bodies should look.

LO-2 3. In the twenty-first century, medicalization no longer operates as it did in the past. Although medicine continues to claim jurisdiction over what is defined as illness, it increasingly seeks to exert control over health as well, by seeking to transform bodies rather than merely heal them. At the same time, medical doctors are no longer at the centre of that process, as a new army of experts claim territorial knowledge about how to achieve health.

LO-2 4. Health has also become commodified, which is to say that it is seen as something that can be bought and sold. As such, body projects typically involve the purchase of materials (such as lululemon athletica sportswear) that are thought to signify health and that demonstrate to others one's commitment to healthy lifestyle choices. In the same way, all companies advertise their products as having health-promoting advantages, regardless of their actual qualities.

LO-2 5. The proliferation of new medical technologies makes it possible for consumers to purchase and pursue the elusive goal of health in ways that increasingly transform bodies, minds, and life chances.

LO-3 6. Advances in new medical technologies occur more rapidly than the ability of society to absorb or anticipate their consequences. Those who wonder whether these technologies are a harbinger for the future find themselves in a debate as to whether technology should be used in ways that propel the human species far beyond its present capabilities and into a posthuman future (transhumanism) or whether implementing such technologies without careful contemplation of their consequences might irrevocably destroy what it means to be human (bioconservatism).

LO-3   7.   Ray Kurzweil, a futurist and transhumanist, has predicted that humans will soon enjoy indefinite lifespans and actively promotes the integration of humans and machines to enhance human capabilities. In contrast, Michael Sandel cautions against seeking perfection, suggesting that there are unintended negative consequences when humankind exerts too much influence on what we can become. These include growing inequalities, reduced solidarity, and increased responsibility for what one is.

LO-4   8.   Cyborgs represent entities that breach established boundaries by embodying elements that are simultaneously living and dead, human and machine, natural and unnatural, or animal and human. New medical technologies transgress each of these boundaries as they produce plastic bodies, interchangeable bodies, and genetically engineered bodies

LO-4   9.   Plastic bodies refer to both reconstructive surgery, which aims to restore or repair bodily surfaces, and cosmetic surgery, which aims to create aesthetically pleasing body surfaces. Both reconstructive surgery and cosmetic surgery have accomplished futuristic results that are truly mind-boggling and that have been achieved far more quickly than scientists had anticipated. Nonetheless, cultural expectations for how bodies should look not only persist but according to some are experienced differently by men and women (reinforcing the gender order). Although women are more likely than men to feel compelled to change their bodies to meet cultural beauty norms, men too can experience such pressures but often frame them in masculine terms. In contrast, those who identify with the body modification movement explicitly reject normative standards of beauty, marking their bodies in ways that express their own radical views of what bodies might become.

LO-4   10.   Interchangeable bodies refer to changes to the interior processes of the human body by transplanting foreign materials into the human body. These include deceased- and living-donor organ transplantation, the former of which transgresses the boundaries between living and dead. Xenotransplantation involves cross-species organ transplantation, which transgresses the boundaries between non-human animal and human. There are few difficulties with transferring pig and cow blood vessels into the human body; however, science has yet to overcome challenges with transplanting animal organs, such as hearts and livers, into humans. Finally, the insertion of inanimate objects such as titanium hips, cardiac pacemakers, and more recent innovations such as the brain-technology interface breaches the boundary between natural and unnatural. Although the technologies associated with interchangeable bodies were often invented to save lives, they are increasingly being used to enhance the quality of life, creating a growing demand for body parts that far exceeds the existing supply.

LO-4   11.   Genetically engineered bodies promise to reshape bodies at their most basic level: their cellular and genetic composition. As such, advances in this field may one day obviate the need for the medical technologies involved in producing plastic bodies and interchangeable bodies. These include stem cells, which may in the future be used to generate new body organs using 3-D bioprinters, and reproductive technologies, which increasingly allow parents to choose what kind of child they will have.

LO-5   12.   Alongside the emergence of somatic selves are pharmaceutical selves, in which the modification of mood, thought, and behaviour through medication becomes common. As psychiatry expands the range of diagnosable mental illnesses and blurs the boundaries between what is normal and what is abnormal, people increasingly come to redefine themselves as disordered and seek medical intervention. In this way, normal sadness, even when triggered by an unwelcome experience or loss, comes to be interpreted as mental illness and thus amenable to psychiatric treatment through pharmaceuticals. Because we live in a society where negative emotions are seen as undesirable, pills such as Prozac that can alter both mood and personality have become enormously popular.

LO-5   13.   Similarly, neuro-enhancers, originally designed to treat cognitive problems associated with aging and rare sleep disorders, are increasingly used off-label by those seeking a competitive advantage at school or at work, representing a new way of making people better than well.

LO-6   14.   The chapter ends with a comprehensive discussion of the six ethical implications of new medical technologies whose purpose is to enhance rather than heal. The first three include issues around safety (where long-term effects are unknown, and where the acceptable threshold for risk might be lower for enhancement than for healing); societal pressure (where the fear of being left behind might place undue pressure to use enhancement technologies on those who would otherwise not choose them); and issues of fairness and equality (where advantages produced by enhancement technologies might be perceived as unfair and lead to an even more unequal world).

LO-6   15.   The fourth ethical implication of new enhancement technologies is the need to resolve the boundaries between therapy and enhancement to prevent needless exploitation and to set goals for what enhancement technologies might accomplish. The fifth implication is that enhancement technologies can complicate efforts to establish an authentic self, raising questions about personhood when personality is so easily altered with a pill. Finally, ethical issues around happiness and human flourishing reprise our earlier discussion about whether enhancement technologies may usher in a posthuman future and the extent to which such a future is either welcomed or feared.

REVIEW QUESTIONS

1.   Describe what it means to live in a postmodern world. What does it means to deconstruct health? What is a body project?

2.   Describe how medicalization has changed. What does it mean to say that health has become commodified?

3.   Explain the differences between how a transhumanist and a bioconservatist view the potential of new medical technologies to enhance human capacities far beyond their current levels.

4.   What is a cyborg? What is meant by plastic bodies, and how do plastic bodies introduce cyborgs into the population?

5.   Do men and women experience similar pressures to use cosmetic surgery? Why or why not?

6.   How is the body modification movement an example of the new social movements?

7.   How do interchangeable bodies produce cyborgs in the population? What challenges prevent scientists from transferring animal organs such as hearts and lungs to humans?

8.   Why might the new medical technologies associated with genetically engineered bodies one day supplant medical technologies associated with plastic bodies and interchangeable bodies?

9.   What are stem cells and why is their use controversial?

10. What is in vitro fertilization? What is the difference between prenatal testing and preimplantation genetic diagnosis (PGD)?

11. Why do some contend that prenatal testing actually constrains women's choices?

12. What is the pharmaceutical self? How have the criteria for PTSD and depression changed in successive editions of DSM? What are neuro-enhancers?

13. List the six ethical implications of using medical technologies to enhance and transform rather than to heal and restore.

CRITICAL THINKING QUESTIONS

1. Researchers have identified a gene that, if present, indicates that a person has a significant risk of developing Alzheimer's disease at a young age. Alzheimer's disease causes people to gradually lose their memory and mental abilities. Imagine that you are a physician. Explain to a concerned patient your arguments both for and against getting tested for the gene.

2. If health is more than the absence of disease, how would you define health? How would this definition shape your own efforts to achieve health?

3. In the future, do you think that men and women will achieve gender equality in cosmetic surgery, with men and women equally likely to undergo a cosmetic procedure? Justify your answer.

KEY TERMS

bioconservatism (p. 209)
body project (p. 205)
brain-technology interface device (p. 214)
commodification (p. 207)
cosmetic surgery (p. 210)
cyborg (p. 209)
deconstruction (p. 204)
Diagnostic and Statistical Manual (DSM)
    (p. 219)
in vitro fertilization (p. 216)
menstrual suppression (p. 207)
off-label use (p. 207)

organ transplant (p. 214)
patent (p. 218)
post-traumatic stress disorder (PTSD)
    (p. 219)
preimplantation genetic diagnosis (p. 217)
reconstructive surgery (p. 210)
reproductive technology (p. 216)
restless leg syndrome (p. 223)
stem cells (p. 215)
transhumanism (p. 209)
xenotransplantation (p. 214)

Part IV

Health Care Systems, Professions, Settings, and Technologies

In Part III, we looked at social meanings of health and illness and the lived experiences of illness primarily from the perspective of the ill individual. Moving to a macrosociological level, in Part IV we address the social organization of health care. In Chapter 10, we describe the history of Canada's health care system up to the present day and evaluate the extent to which Canada's health care system is in crisis. Using some basic measures for evaluating health care systems, in Chapter 11 we compare Canada's health care system to those in other high-income countries and provide a brief analysis of the health care systems of the United States, the United Kingdom, Germany, and China. In Chapter 12, we discuss the hierarchical organization of the health care professions. Although allopathic physicians typically hold the most power and influence, we shall see that threats to their authority come from many sources. Other health care professions must also continually struggle for authority and privilege in the health care field. We document some of the territorial struggles between different professions in Canada, including those who have gained ground (pharmacists) and those who are losing ground (chiropractors), as well as the ways in which boundaries between formal health care and complementary and alternative medicine (CAM) are becoming blurred. Finally, in Chapter 13 we examine several health care settings, including hospitals, mental hospitals, long-term care facilities, assisted living facilities, home care, and hospices, for the purpose of providing an overview of these different settings in the Canadian context as well as a social analysis of the technologies used in those settings.

10

A History of Health Care in Canada

Todd Bigelow/Aurora Photos

Health Care in Crisis

In 2007, Shona Holmes filed a lawsuit against the Ontario government, claiming that she had been denied medically necessary surgery to remove a potentially deadly brain tumour. As a young, married mother of two, Shona went to her doctor when she first started experiencing vision loss and painful headaches. Not satisfied to wait months to see a specialist, Shona decided to fly to Arizona to obtain further tests. After a week of tests, the doctors at the Mayo Clinic in Arizona confirmed the presence of a tumour in her brain and informed her that she risked blindness and death if she did not receive immediate medical attention. Shona flew back to Canada with the results of her tests, only to be told that she had to wait to undergo more tests and appointments. Again unwilling

to wait, Holmes travelled back to the Mayo Clinic in the United States to have the $100,000 surgery performed at her own expense.

Shona's story became widely known when the American media presented her story as a cautionary tale for Americans who were in the midst of debating health care reform. She was interviewed on Fox and CNN and invited to present testimony to Congress. She received even greater attention when she was featured in a television ad sponsored by Patients United Now, a right-wing group opposed to Barack Obama's plan to introduce Canadian-style universal health care insurance. In the ad, Shona proclaimed, "I survived a brain tumour, but if I'd relied on my government for health care, I'd be dead."

The intense media attention inevitably brought closer scrutiny of Shona's story. Further investigation revealed that Holmes did not have a cancerous tumour but rather a Rathke's cleft cyst, which is considered benign and not life-threatening. Shona countered these claims by suggesting that she had other medical complications but refused to release her medical records, citing her ongoing litigation as limiting any further disclosure. The lawsuit, filed on her behalf by the Canadian Constitution Foundation, continues to wend its way through the court system. The intent of the lawsuit is not to pursue compensation for the expenses she incurred by having the surgery performed in another country but rather to challenge Ontario law, which prohibits the sale of private health care and private health insurance for essential health services. The Canadian Constitution Foundation is also funding a similar challenge in British Columbia against the ban on health care in that province.

LEARNING OBJECTIVES

In this chapter, students should be able to:

LO-1 **Distinguish** between the different types of health care practitioners that Canadians relied on two centuries ago.

LO-2 **Describe** the apprenticeship system and understand how the Flexner Report changed medical education in both Canada and the United States.

LO-3 **Recognize** the critical turning points in the history of Canada's health care system that led to its

eventual implementation and describe the principles that guide the operation of the health care system.

LO-4 **Understand** that factors associated with its development contributed to the perceived crisis in health care.

LO-5 **Describe** past and current attempts to reform Canada's health care system.

Canadians are generally proud of their health care system, which is popularly but unofficially referred to as medicare (not to be confused with the American Medicare program for seniors). Many Canadians identify their health care as a source of national pride and as something that makes them different from Americans. Yet ongoing criticism that Canada's health care system is too costly or that it is unresponsive to health care needs in the population has created uncertainty that Canada has the "best health care system in the world." Is our health care system in crisis, as some have suggested? Does health care in Canada need to be reformed, and, if so, how should it be changed? In the next chapter, we will compare Canada's health care system with health care systems in other parts of the world, using criteria that are commonly used to evaluate the performance of a health care system. First, however, we must discover how Canada's health care system came to be, for to assess whether it is indeed in crisis we must understand how the system developed and what aspects of its formation laid the foundations for the problems that exist in our current system. This is the task we turn to in this chapter.

MEDICINE IN THE NINETEENTH CENTURY

An Assortment of Health Care Providers

To begin, we must consider what life would have been like two centuries ago when Canadians fell ill. Today, when confronted by illness, most Canadians seek care from a doctor of medicine. Back then, however, that would not have been the case. Instead, Canadians received most of their health care from family members. If they required more complicated treatment, they could choose from an array of poorly paid and typically poorly respected health care practitioners (Starr, 1982: 31–59). These included **regular doctors**, who were the forerunners of contemporary doctors. They also included such **irregular practitioners** as patent medicine makers and apothecaries, who sold drugs they concocted from a wide variety of ingredients; homeopaths; eclectics; barber-surgeons; bonesetters, who fixed dislocated joints and fractured bones; and midwives.

Regular doctors were also known as **allopathic doctors**, or allopaths (from the Greek for "cure by opposites"), because they typically treated illnesses with drugs selected to produce symptoms *opposite* to those caused by the illnesses. For example, allopaths would treat patients suffering the fevers of malaria with quinine, a drug known to reduce fevers, and treat patients with failing hearts with digitalis, a drug that stimulates the heartbeat.

Their main competitors were **homeopathic doctors**, or homeopaths (from the Greek for "cure by similars"). Homeopathy had its origins in the work of a seventeenth-century German physician and chemist named Samuel Hahnemann, who discovered that Cinchona

regular doctors:
Nineteenth-century forerunners of contemporary medical doctors.

irregular practitioners:
Nineteenth-century health care practitioners other than allopathic doctors, such as homeopaths, midwives, eclectics, barber-surgeons, bonesetters, and patent medicine makers.

allopathic doctors:
Early forerunners of contemporary medical doctors. Also known as regular doctors.

homeopathic doctors:
Early health practitioners who treated illnesses with extremely dilute solutions of drugs that, at full strength, produced similar symptoms to a given illness.

bark, used to treat fever, actually caused fever if administered in minute doses. The field of homeopathy was born as Hahnemann theorized that treating illnesses with minute amounts of drugs that produced symptoms *similar* to those caused by the illnesses would stimulate the body's natural healing properties. Though this may appear to be an unusual philosophy, inoculation against certain diseases has depended on similar logic. For example, people who were inoculated with a small quantity of cowpox cells, and who developed a mild form of cowpox, subsequently developed immunity to the related but far more serious smallpox.

eclectics:
Those who practised a form of botanical medicine in North America for nearly two hundred years, involving the complex combination of concentrated plant extracts to treat illness.

Allopathic doctors also competed with the **eclectics**, who practised a form of botanical medicine and relied on complex combinations of concentrated plant extracts to treat illness. Eclecticism was popular for nearly two hundred years in North America. Nonetheless, beyond their extant published works containing the accumulated knowledge of herbal remedies for various ailments, there is little evidence of their existence today.

That Canadians before the twentieth century placed no greater trust in allopathic doctors than in any others who claimed knowledge of healing should not be a surprise. Although by the nineteenth century, science—the careful testing of hypotheses in controlled experiments—had infiltrated the curricula of European medical schools, where many of the wealthiest or most dedicated Canadians trained, it had gained barely a foothold in North American medical schools. Indeed, most doctors in Canada trained through apprenticeships.

Apprenticeships involved indenture to a practitioner for a period of anywhere from three to seven years. The apprentice accompanied the physician as an assistant, acquiring the practical skills of the trade, such as learning how to draw teeth, bleed, dress minor wounds, and pulverize bark and roots to make ointments and treatments, but also performing menial tasks such as grooming horses and tending to the daily affairs of the physician (MacDermot, 1952). Once apprentices had acquired the knowledge and skills of the preceptor physician, they would launch their own practices.

In 1823, Canada opened its first medical school in Montréal, with a second medical school established at King's College in Toronto in 1842. Both schools were first opened privately but subsequently became affiliated with universities when they could not obtain charters from the provincial government allowing them to confer degrees on graduates. The difficulties medical schools originally encountered in obtaining charters in Canada resulted in a markedly different scenario from what was happening south of the Canadian border. Because there were no such barriers to granting degrees in the United States, a multitude of uncertified medical schools sprouted in the United States, almost all of which were private, for-profit institutions, unaffiliated with colleges or universities and lacking any entrance requirements beyond the ability to pay tuition (Ludmerer, 1985).

That is not to say that standards for training were any better at university-based medical schools. For example, in 1871, Henry Jacob Bigelow, a Harvard University professor of surgery, protested against a proposal to require written graduation examinations on the grounds that more than half of Harvard's medical students were illiterate (Ludmerer, 1985: 12). Training was minimal and depended almost entirely on lectures, so that almost no students ever examined a patient, conducted an experiment, or dissected a cadaver. Any student who regularly attended the lectures received a diploma. Similarly, training standards at medical schools in Canada would not be considered rigorous by today's standards. For example, when Charles Edward Doherty took over as medical superintendent of the British Columbia Hospital for the Insane in 1905, his formal training would have been limited to one or two courses in psychiatry taken as a medical student at the medical school at Trinity College in Toronto (Kelm, 1994).

Lacking knowledge or access to scientific research, allopathic doctors developed their ideas about health and illness either from their clinical experiences with patients or by extrapolating from abstract, untested theories. The most popular theory of illness, from the classical Greek era until the mid-1800s, traced illness to an imbalance of bodily "humours," or fluids. Doctors had learned through experience that ill persons often recovered following episodes of fever, vomiting, or diarrhea. From this, doctors deduced—in part correctly—that fever, vomiting, and diarrhea helped the body restore itself to health. Unfortunately, lacking methods for testing their theories, doctors carried these ideas too far, often inducing life-threatening fever, vomiting, purging, and bloodletting. Consider, for example, the following description of how Boston doctors in 1833 used what was known as **heroic medicine** to treat a pregnant woman who began having convulsions a month before her delivery date:

> The doctors bled her of 8 ounces and gave her a purgative. The next day she again had convulsions, and they took 22 ounces of blood. After 90 minutes she had a headache, and the doctors took 18 more ounces of blood, gave emetics to cause vomiting, and put ice on her head and mustard plasters on her feet. Nearly four hours later she had another convulsion, and they took 12 ounces, and soon after, 6 more. By then she had lapsed into a deep coma, so the doctors doused her with cold water but could not revive her. Soon her cervix began to dilate, so the doctors gave ergot to induce labor. Shortly before delivery she convulsed again, and they applied ice and mustard plasters again and also gave a vomiting agent and calomel to purge her bowels. In six hours she delivered a stillborn child. After two days she regained consciousness and recovered. The doctors considered this a conservative treatment, even though they had removed two fifths of her blood in a two-day period, for they had not artificially dilated her womb or used instruments to expedite delivery. (Wertz and Wertz, 1989: 69)*

heroic medicine:
An aggressive system of treatment used by allopathic doctors during the nineteenth century that emphasized curing illnesses by purging the body through bloodletting, causing extreme vomiting, or using repeated laxatives and diuretics.

As this example suggests, because of the body's amazing ability to heal itself, even when doctors used heroic medicine, many of their patients survived. Thus, doctors could convince themselves they had cured their patients when in reality they either had made no difference or had endangered their patients' lives.

By the second half of the nineteenth century, most doctors, responding to the public's support for irregular practitioners and fear of heroic medicine, had abandoned their most dangerous techniques. Yet medical treatment remained risky. Allopathic doctors' major advantage over their competitors was their ability to conduct surgery in life-threatening situations. Unfortunately, until the development of anaesthesia in the 1860s, many patients died from the inherent physical trauma of surgery. In addition, many died unnecessarily from postsurgical infections. Dr. Ignaz Semmelweis had demonstrated in the 1850s that because midwives (whose tasks included washing floors and linens) had relatively clean hands, whereas doctors routinely went without washing their hands from autopsies to obstetrical examinations and from patient to patient, more childbearing women died on medical wards than on midwifery wards. Yet, it took another thirty years before hand-washing became standard medical practice.

Until well into the twentieth century, then, doctors could offer their patients little beyond morphine for pain relief; quinine for malarial and other fevers; digitalis for heart problems; and, after 1910, salvarsan for syphilis—each of which presented dangers as well as benefits. According to the 1975 edition of *Cecil's* Textbook of Medicine, one of the most widely used medical textbooks, only 3% of the treatments described in the 1927 edition of this textbook were fully effective, whereas 60% were harmful, were of doubtful value, or offered only symptomatic relief (Beeson, 1980). Doctors' effective pharmacopoeia did not grow significantly until the development of antibiotics in the 1940s.

---

* R. Wertz & D. Wertz, Pg. 69, 1989.

BEGINNINGS OF MEDICAL DOMINANCE

Despite the few benefits and many dangers inherent in allopathic medical care and the lack of public confidence in their methods, allopathic doctors have historically worked to restrain the practices of other health care occupations. In this section, we discuss the outcome of these power struggles.

Competition between allopathic doctors and homeopathic doctors and eclectics intensified at the beginning of the nineteenth century. Indeed, allopathic doctors in Canada made their first unsuccessful attempts to organize and control admittance to the practice of medicine as early as 1795. It was the homeopaths, however, who were the first profession in 1859 to be legalized and to create a board that would license and regulate homeopathy. They were followed by the eclectics, who attained professional status in 1861. It was not until 1869 that allopathic physicians were successful in passing self-regulatory legislation. Known as the Ontario Medical Act, the legislation created the College of Physicians and Surgeons of Ontario, which began to regulate the practice of medicine and control entry to the profession. Frustratingly for the allopaths, the College also included homeopaths and eclectics. Although eclectics were excluded from the College in 1874, it took until 1960 for allopathic doctors to deny homeopathic doctors representation in the College (Torrance, 1998).

One of the reasons for the delay allopathic doctors experienced in achieving professional status lay in its diverse and divided composition. Allopaths were drawn from the elite classes, where medical men received formal training in universities and medical colleges, but also consisted of those who had received their training through apprenticeship and whose class background was less privileged. The lack of shared interests—with medically trained doctors seeking to limit the admittance of those trained through apprenticeships—impeded allopaths from presenting a united front. It was only as they began to quash internal divisions that they were able to mobilize effectively.

The Flexner Report and Its Consequences

Differences between allopathic doctors and other health care practitioners increased during the early years of the twentieth century. Since the 1890s, the better medical schools in the United States and Canada had begun tightening entrance requirements, stressing higher academic standards, emphasizing research and science, and offering clinical experience. Moreover, public pressure to enhance the quality of training increased following publication in 1910 of the **Flexner Report** on the state of American and Canadian medical education (Ludmerer, 1985: 166–190). The report, which was written by a high school teacher named Abraham Flexner and commissioned by the non-profit Carnegie Foundation, shocked both nations with its descriptions of the lax requirements and poor facilities at many medical schools.

Having thoroughly condemned the existing methods of training physicians, the Flexner Report made several key recommendations to improve standards. Among them, the Flexner Report recommended abolishing the apprenticeship system entirely so that all medical doctors would instead receive formal training through the medical school system. Further, the Flexner Report recommended that medical schools themselves should be affiliated with universities rather than being allowed to operate independently. Training should involve lectures as well as a minimum of two years of clinical experience. Moreover, training should be grounded in the scientific method, as a way of understanding the causes of disease and discovering how to cure disease. The Flexner Report also recommended that medical schools and hospitals be formally linked to one another. Hospitals were no longer to be warehouses where the poor and the sick languished, but instead refashioned into centres

Flexner Report:
The report on the state of American and Canadian medical education produced in 1910 by Abraham Flexner for the Carnegie Foundation. This report identified serious deficiencies in medical education and helped to produce substantial improvements in that system.

of learning where medical students honed their skills and applied the latest technologies to treat disease.

In the United States, the recommendations of the Flexner Report led to dramatic changes as more stringent licensing laws for medical schools were subsequently implemented (Ludmerer, 1985: 234–249). These laws hastened the closure of all proprietary and most non-profit schools, many of which were already suffering financially from the costs of trying to meet students' growing demand for scientific training. As a result, the number of medical schools in the United States fell from 162 in 1906 to 81 in 1922 (Starr, 1982: 118, 121).

The impact in Canada was also substantial, even though with fewer schools and long-standing affiliation with universities, many of the problems found in the medical schools of the United States did not apply to Canada. Nonetheless, in 1912, following the recommendations of the Flexner Report, legislators passed the Canada Medical Act, which introduced standardized licensing procedures for medical doctors throughout Canada. In eliminating the apprenticeship system and ensuring that medical students would be required to receive their training through university-affiliated medical schools and to pass exams before becoming certified as doctors, allopathic medicine had achieved **medical dominance**. That is, medical doctors had attained for themselves freedom from control by others in that they alone were able to decide who could call themselves a medical doctor, and, similarly, they had acquired the ability to control other health care occupations, in that the work of a medical doctor was protected and could not be performed by others.

medical dominance:
The freedom of allopathic physicians from control by other occupations or groups and the ability to control other occupations working in the sphere of health care.

THE BEGINNINGS OF CANADIAN HEALTH CARE

Around the time that allopathic physicians had achieved medical dominance in Canada, some countries had already implemented or begun to consider developing a health care system to be offered universally to their citizenry. These discussions took place in Canada as early as 1919, but while other western European countries, including Britain, and more far-flung countries, such as New Zealand, implemented health care systems within their own jurisdictions, Canada did little more than debate the issue for several decades (Torrance, 1998).

From the outset, medical doctors were opposed to the idea of a universal health care system as they perceived it as a threat to their newly established power base. Indeed, as we will see, the medical profession never wavered from its opposition to government health insurance, except for a very brief period during the Great Depression of the 1930s, when pervasive economic hardship led to a temporary softening of their position. Entrenched in the elite power structures of Canadian society and buoyed by their successes in attaining medical dominance, allopathic physicians were confident they could use their power to prevail. They also believed that larger forces were on their side. A free-market philosophy, rejecting government intervention, permeated Canadian attitudes, and the British North America Act enshrined health as a provincial responsibility, making it seem unlikely that a national health insurance plan would ever see the light of day (Torrance, 1998). For many years, physicians' instincts served them well and they were successful in their efforts to resist the implementation of a national health care plan.

A promising moment for health care occurred at the end of World War II, when the provinces and federal government came together to discuss plans for rebuilding the country. Popular support for a health insurance program had been gaining momentum, and, sensing the time was right, the federal government under William Lyon Mackenzie King began to more vigorously pursue a plan to implement national health insurance. A carefully devised proposal to be jointly financed by both levels of government was presented during the Dominion-Provincial Conference on Reconstruction; however, the meetings concluded without an agreement that was amenable to all provinces. Frustrated with the lack of progress, the newly elected premier of Saskatchewan, Tommy Douglas, made the bold decision to forge ahead. In 1947, he successfully introduced the Hospital Insurance Plan, which relied on municipal databases to enrol residents in the province of Saskatchewan into the plan. For an annual fee of $5 per person to a maximum of $30 per household, citizens were able to obtain hospital-based services without cost. Within the first year of the program, a majority of the population was covered by hospital insurance, constituting a remarkable feat given the many detractors who suggested it could not be accomplished so rapidly.

Saskatchewan's hospital insurance plan proved inspirational to other provinces as they subsequently began to offer hospital insurance in their own jurisdictions, albeit in different ways. Some of these attempts proved disastrous, as occurred in British Columbia, where an ineffective and poorly administered system led to public outrage and eventual reform once the Social Credit party swept to power in 1952. As hospital insurance slowly rolled out across the country, the federal government once again initiated discussion with the provinces to implement a nationwide hospital insurance plan. As part of this process, public hearings were held across the country to gauge support for such a plan. Not surprisingly, private insurance companies who stood to lose profit were fierce opponents of the plan, as were the provincial and federal medical associations. In contrast, the public was overwhelmingly supportive.

On March 25, 1957, Paul Martin (Senior), federal minister of Health and Welfare, introduced the Hospital Insurance and Diagnostic Services Act (HIDSA). The bill proposed a joint funding arrangement shared equally by the federal government and the provinces. In exchange, provincial governments would agree to provide hospital-based services to all its citizens without condition; submit to an annual audit of hospital expenses; and work with the federal government to develop and maintain standards for hospital care, including the licensing and inspecting of hospitals (Ostry, 2009). Funding for mental hospitals was not included in the legislation, as these were still considered a provincial responsibility. HIDSA was passed into law on April 12, 1957, and over the next few years, the provinces agreed to these conditions and began receiving federal funding. Even so, the provinces were not entirely happy with this arrangement, resenting the intrusion that annual audits by the federal government represented to their autonomy.

From Hospital Insurance to Doctor Insurance

With shared funding from the federal government for hospital-based care, Tommy Douglas now had the necessary finances to turn his attention to health care services offered outside the hospital system. The push to bring medical insurance to Saskatchewan was launched in 1959 with a proposal that had five underlying principles. First, the plan must be offered to all citizens without concern for cost, age, or physical disability, as was typically the case in privately offered health insurance plans. Second, funding for the program would be offered through the prepayment of annual fees, as had been implemented in hospital insurance. Third, similar to the hospital insurance program, the program would be publicly administered. Fourth, the government committed itself to high-quality medical care, promising to make the necessary investments in infrastructure to improve and apply consistent standards for health care throughout the province. Finally, the government vowed that it would not proceed unless it had the backing of health care providers and the general public.

Although there had been muted resistance to hospital-based insurance a decade earlier, medical doctors in Saskatchewan were now bitterly opposed to the expansion of coverage for all medical services through government-sponsored insurance, preferring instead private for-profit insurance. This issue became central to the provincial election of 1960. In an effort to sway public opinion, the College of Physicians and Surgeons of Saskatchewan (CPSS) outspent all of the political parties by launching its own advertising campaign (Blakeney, 2009). Critical of the medical insurance plan proposed by Tommy Douglas and his party, the Cooperative Commonwealth Federation (CCF), the CPSS sought to convince the public that its implementation would erode the quality of care in that province. Such efforts proved futile, as the CCF handily won the election, but further strained relations between medical doctors and the province.

When the Saskatchewan Medical Care Insurance Act was introduced in the legislature in October 1961, the conflict between the government and physicians moved into the open, as it became apparent that the government had proceeded without obtaining their approval. Indeed, staunch in their opposition, the CPSS had refused to participate in the process at all. The bill itself retained many of the same features as has been laid out in Douglas's earlier proposal. That is, the bill aimed to establish a provincially funded, universal, prepaid insurance system whereby doctors would be paid for their work on a **fee-for-service compensation** basis. Moreover, the system would be publicly administered and would operate under the oversight of a commission composed of laypersons and medical doctors.

fee-for-service compensation:
The practice of paying doctors for each health care service they provide, rather than paying them a salary.

As the date for implementing medical insurance in the province of Saskatchewan drew nearer, medical doctors threatened to go on strike. The government continued to negotiate with the medical doctors to avert any job action but quietly began hiring doctors from Great Britain and elsewhere. On July 1, 1962, Saskatchewan doctors followed through on their threat and shut down their practices. Reaction to the doctors' strike was swift and decisive, attracting international media attention at this unprecedented event. While newspaper headlines around the world roundly condemned the strike, local communities added further pressure by rallying behind the government. Twenty-three days later, the doctors ended their strike, winning some concessions in their negotiations with the government (including guaranteed autonomy over medical decision-making) but losing the larger battle. Ironically, when the Liberals swept to power two years later, medical insurance in Saskatchewan proved to be so popular with the public and doctors (who were now enjoying the benefits of being paid on a more consistent basis for their work) that no effort was made to dismantle the program.

At the same time, the Canadian Medical Association had begun to lobby the federal Liberal government, hoping that the government would side with its position for private coverage and pre-empt any shift at the national level toward government-sponsored insurance. Lacking clear direction and hoping to buy some time, Prime Minister John Diefenbaker put together a royal commission to investigate the issue. The Royal Commission on Health Services was tasked in 1961 with evaluating existing and future needs for health services and recommending appropriate measures to ensure the best possible health care for all Canadians. Led by Supreme Court Justice Emmett Hall, the commission comprised seven members drawn from medicine, nursing, and dentistry, as well as from academia and the business community. The commission visited countries such as Great Britain and Australia to learn about their health care systems, sponsored external research on the topic, and held public hearings throughout Canada. Their final report, issued in two separate volumes in 1964 and 1965, respectively, made the recommendation that the Saskatchewan model be adopted across all of Canada, stating that it was the best way to ensure the highest health standards for all Canadians. The report, however, went much farther than what had been introduced in Saskatchewan. That is, it recommended that prescription medications, prosthetics, and home care be included as an insured benefit for all, and that dental and optometry services be provided for children and welfare recipients. The report also advised the federal government to use funding as a leverage to entice provinces but to give the provinces latitude in determining the timing and order of implementation.

In the interim, the federal election of 1963 had left the Liberal party with a minority government under Lester B. Pearson. When Pearson met with the provincial premiers in the summer of 1965 to discuss national health insurance, two provinces, Québec and Alberta, strongly objected to the idea. Both provinces were increasingly critical of federal intervention into provincial affairs, due to rising nationalism in Québec; in the case of Alberta, resistance stemmed from the fact that it had already established a private insurance health care system (dubbed Manningcare after its premier, Ernest Manning). Nonetheless, the proposal that was submitted in the Medical Care Act on July 12, 1966, was in large measure similar to the proposal presented a summer earlier to the provinces. Its chief nod to the provinces was a system that minimized oversight by the federal government and allowed the provinces great discretion outside its four guiding principles. For example, provincial governments had the ability to negotiate physician fees without ceilings imposed by the federal government. In order to receive federal funding, however, provinces would be required to implement an insurance plan that (a) provided universal access, (b) was publicly administered, (c) offered comprehensive coverage of medically necessary services, and (d) was portable for people who moved to another province. See Key Concepts 10.1 for an overview of the four principles of the Medical Care Act.

KEY CONCEPTS 10.1   Four Principles of the Medical Care Act, 1966

Principle	Description
Universal	The province must entitle all eligible residents of the province to insured health services on uniform terms and conditions.
Publicly administered	The health insurance plan of a province must be administered and operated on a non-profit basis by a public authority accountable to the provincial government.
Comprehensive	The plan must insure all medically necessary services provided in hospital and by physicians.
Portable	Residents are entitled to coverage when they move to another province.

The bill sharply divided parliament. Political parties on the right bitterly criticized federal interference in provincial affairs and further argued that it was financially infeasible. Those on the left were opposed because the Medical Care Act only included care from medical doctors and had ignored the recommendations of the Hall Commission's Report for extending coverage to other services, such as dental care, pharmaceuticals, and home care. As in the past, private insurance companies and medical associations launched media campaigns to influence public opinion and lobbied members of parliament to sway their vote. Despite concerted opposition from these lobby groups and the uncertainty of a minority government, the bill passed into law in December of that same year.

Although the schedule for implementation had been set for 1968, only two provinces, Saskatchewan and British Columbia, had successfully introduced their health care insurance systems by that timeline. Not until 1972 were all provinces operating their health care systems and receiving federal funding. It was at this moment that Canada had finally achieved a national health care system, although there was one last scene to be played out in this historical drama. The final turning point, occurring with the Canada Health Act of 1984, revealed yet again the difficulties of achieving consensus on the hotly contested issue of health care.

The Canada Health Act

The Canada Health Act, introduced in 1984 by the federal government, was intended to serve two purposes. First, it replaced the Medical Care Act of 1966 and the Hospital and Diagnostic Services Act of 1957 by harmonizing both into a single piece of legislation. Its second purpose was to address a problem that had emerged almost immediately after the provinces introduced their health care systems. Seeking to circumvent restrictions that health insurance imposed on their incomes, physicians had begun to charge additional fees to their patients for their health care services. The practice of **extra-billing**, as it was called, soon became widespread. Similarly, hospitals in some provinces had also introduced **user fees** that levied a fixed charge for those who made use of hospital care. For example, Ontario hospitals charged patients $9.80 per day after the sixty-first day as an inpatient. Because there were no provisions in the Canada Medical Act to deal with the possibility of extra-billing and user fees, there was no mechanism in place to stop this practice. Over time, concern began to mount that a two-tiered health care system was emerging, where those who could afford to pay the extra costs would get better care than those who would be shut out or receive inferior care because of their inability to pay.

To study these problems, the minority Conservative government under Joe Clark appointed Justice Emmett Hall in 1979 to head another commission to evaluate the health care needs of Canadians and to determine whether the original principles of the Medical Care Act were serving their intended objectives. Hall's report, issued nearly a year later, when a Liberal majority government had assumed power under Pierre Trudeau, affirmed the four existing principles but recommended that a fifth principle be added. The principle of accessibility would ensure that income would not become a barrier to receiving health care for Canadians and explicitly prohibited doctors from charging fees in excess of what had been negotiated with the provinces.

As a means of ensuring compliance, the Canada Health Act also laid out a penalty for provinces that did not enforce the principle of accessibility. Essentially, the federal government would reduce its transfer payments to the provinces on a dollar-for-dollar basis for those provinces that did not eliminate the practice of extra-billing and user fees. In effect on July 1, 1984, the new legislation had to be implemented by the provinces within a three-year window. Unwilling to concede defeat on the issue of extra-billing, medical doctors once again responded to these provincial directives with job action. For example, in Ontario, there was a twenty-five-day strike by medical doctors in 1986. As had been the case in Saskatchewan, doctors failed to win public sentiment and were forced to capitulate under mounting public pressure.

In sum, the road to national health care for Canada was long and winding, with a number of critical turning points. As a result of this history, Canada's current health care system can be described as follows. It is a first dollar coverage, publicly funded, privately provided, provincially administered, national health care system. **First dollar coverage** means that a third-party payer (in this case, the provincial government) assumes liability for covered services as soon as the first dollar of expense for such services is incurred. It is publicly funded because costs are covered through revenues generated through taxes. As the system

extra-billing:
Billing patients for the difference between the amount provincial governments have agreed to pay for a given procedure and the amount the doctor desires to charge for that procedure.

user fee:
A fixed amount charged at the time of use to an individual who receives a health care service or product.

first dollar coverage:
An insurance plan under which the third-party payer assumes liability for covered services as soon as the first dollar of expense for such services is incurred.

**financially
progressive:**
Describes any system in
which poorer persons pay
a smaller proportion of
their income for a given
good or service than do
wealthier persons.

single-payer system:
A health care system in
which the medical costs
of the entire popula-
tion are financed by
one source, usually the
government.

is based primarily on graduated income taxes, it is also considered **financially progressive**: wealthier persons pay a higher proportion of their income in taxes and therefore pay more toward health care than those who are poor. It is privately provided in that physicians independently own and operate their own practices; they are not employees of the state. It is provincially administered in that the provinces assume responsibility for operating a health care system within their own jurisdiction. As an exception, health care coverage for First Nations, RCMP, armed forces, veterans, and inmates of federal institutions is a federal responsibility. Because each of the provinces assumes sole responsibility for costs and issues payment for all services covered under the provincial health plans, it is also a **single-payer system**. It is a national health care system in that all provinces and territories must adhere to the principles of the Canada Health Act in order to receive their federal share of funding. As such, commercial insurers are banned from offering health care services that are covered by provincial health care plans.

Having described how Canada's health care came into being, we can now evaluate how and why problems began to emerge and the solutions that were implemented to fix these problems. We address these issues in the next section.

HEALTH CARE IN CRISIS?

Once medical insurance had been passed into law, how long did it take for the system to be seen as in crisis? For some, the answer would be in the 1990s, a period in which most Canadians can remember the visible efforts of both federal and provincial governments to control the spiralling costs of health care. As it turns out, the correct answer points to a much earlier time period.

First, however, we must review three notable factors in the history of Canada's health care system that contributed to the perception of an emerging crisis (Burke and Stevenson, 1998). Each in its own way has left an indelible mark that shaped how health care came to be in this country, sowing the seeds for the problems that were soon to follow.

The first factor was that medical dominance was entrenched long before the debate on a national health care system got under way. Once allopathic physicians had achieved power, any plan to implement health insurance necessarily required the input of physicians, who were consulted at every step. Though they ultimately lost the battle, doctors won many key concessions along the way. Importantly, doctors managed to retain medical dominance, allowing them to exert complete control over all aspects of medical decision-making and to ensure that their interests were given precedence over those of other health care profes-sions, even as the health care system took shape around them.

A second factor was that because provinces such as Saskatchewan chose to go it alone rather than wait for a federal-provincial agreement on health care, the federal government generally followed rather than led the process. Consequently, offers made by the federal government revolved around the promise of shared funding, with relatively little input on how the system would be managed to make sure it ran effectively and efficiently. That is, the federal government simply agreed to share the costs with the provinces in return for a small amount of oversight in specific areas. Similarly, the provinces entered into agree-ments with their doctors that promised to compensate them for their work but otherwise imposed few controls. In short, doctors sent their bills to the provincial government, who reimbursed their expenses, who then in turn submitted half of their expenses to the federal government. Thus, the costs of health care were driven solely by the doctor, with few levers available to either the provincial or the federal government to contain costs should they rise too rapidly (Swartz, 1998).

The final influence on Canada's health care system was that hospital insurance preceded medical insurance by a full decade. Consequently, the focus of health care from the start emphasized the curative functions of medicine rather than the prevention of illness and disease. Hospitals were situated as the centrepiece of the health care system, with substantial resources invested by both federal and provincial governments to ensure that hospitals were equipped with the latest life-saving technologies. As noted in Chapter 2, however, Canada had already experienced the **epidemiological transition**, with chronic diseases replacing infectious and parasitic disease as the leading causes of death. Meeting these new health challenges required a preventative approach. Yet the principles of **health promotion** were at odds with the hospital-based care of Canada's health care system, which best served patients whose health problems called for heroic intervention.

Together, these three influential factors reinforced a power structure in which doctors' interests were consistently protected and perpetuated an unwieldy system in which governments, at both the federal and the provincial level, were constrained in their ability to respond to emerging challenges. Not surprisingly, as new issues arose, these almost inevitably resulted in further skirmishes between the federal government and the provinces as each insisted on their right to control health care. Indeed, the example of Insite (see Box 10.1) perfectly illustrates the types of legal and ethical challenges that were emerging as well as the battles such issues provoked between the federal and provincial governments, where the final decision as to who has jurisdiction over a certain aspect of health care has at times required the deliberations of the Supreme Court of Canada.

harm reduction:
Public health programs, policies, and practices designed to reduce the harmful consequences associated with illicit drug use and other high-risk activities for people who are unable or unwilling to stop.

BOX 10.1

ETHICAL DEBATE

Insite and the Ethics of a Safe Injection Site

Since its inception in 2003, Insite has been controversial. Although similar facilities can be found in Europe and Australia, Insite is the only safe injection site in North America. Located in Vancouver's notorious Downtown Eastside, the facility offers a safe haven for intravenous drug users (IDUs), who are allowed to inject themselves with pre-obtained illicit drugs under medical supervision. Funded by the British Columbia Ministry of Health, the facility also provides sterile injection equipment, addiction counselling, and health care for a segment of society that rarely seeks out medical care.

A safe injection facility is rooted in the principle of harm reduction. **Harm reduction** refers to public health programs, policies, and practices designed to reduce the harmful consequences associated with illicit drug use and other high-risk activities for people who are unable or unwilling to stop. As such, harm reduction aims to meet people where they are, focusing on their needs and respecting them as humans with rights that do not disappear simply because they are drug users. Importantly, harm reduction is situated as a medicalized response to the problem of substance abuse and as an alternative to failed policies and practices that criminalize people who use illicit drugs and force them to operate in risky drug environments.

Insite came into being when it was granted a legal exemption by the federal Liberal government on the condition that its effects be rigorously evaluated. When the Conservatives won the next federal election in 2006, it revoked the exemption and attempted to close the facility. The British Columbia government fought back, claiming that Insite was providing health care services and thus decisions about its operation fell under its authority. Because the Canadian constitution gives the federal government authority over criminal law but allocates responsibility for health care to provinces, both levels of government claimed the right to decide whether Insite remained open. The fate of the facility was ultimately decided in 2011 when the Supreme Court of Canada upheld the earlier decision of the British Columbia Supreme Court, allowing Insite to remain open.

Although the future of the facility has been resolved, there are broader questions about whether a medically supervised facility for IDUs is an appropriate response to the problem of substance abuse. Some argue that such facilities encourage illicit drug use by sanitizing and

continued

legitimizing the practice. Others see the introduction of a safe injection site as a step toward decriminalizing illicit drug use. Still others decry any practice that suggests that there may be a safe way to use illicit drugs.

In contrast, those who support a safe injection site for IDUs argue that there are both health and social benefits. More than a dozen studies show that these facilities effectively operate as a gateway to medical and social services. At a practical level, the provision of sterilized needles halts the transmission of blood-borne diseases such as hepatitis C and HIV/AIDS within the community, saving lives and health care costs that would be used to treat these conditions. Moreover, offering counselling and other social services on site increases subsequent enrolment in treatment programs, suggesting that harm reduction does not reinforce illicit drug use but provides an intermediate step out of addiction. The community benefits too by having to deal with fewer publicly discarded syringes and fewer people injecting on the

streets. Studies also suggest that safe injection sites do not increase drug use or crime in the communities in which they are located.

SOCIOLOGICAL QUESTIONS

1. What social views and values about medicine, society, and the body are reflected in the debate over a safe injection site for drug users? Whose views are these?
2. Which social groups are in conflict over this issue? Whose interests are served by a safe injection site? Whose interests are harmed?
3. Which of these groups has more power to enforce its view? What kinds of power do they have?
4. What are the intended consequences of offering a safe injection site to IDUs? What are the unintended social, economic, political, and health consequences?

So, how long did it take before Canada's health care system was perceived to be in jeopardy? That moment arrived in 1977, when the federal government, concerned that the system was unsustainable and lacking in accountability, moved to change the funding agreement for health care. In a bill titled the Established Programs Financing Act (EPF), the costs for health care were no longer to be shared equally by the federal government and the provinces; rather, the federal government would rely on block funding. Block funding meant that the federal government would annually transfer a fixed amount of money to the provinces, who would then allocate these funds as they saw fit, provided of course that they adhered to the four basic principles of the Medical Care Act (the Canada Health Act did not yet exist). In addition, the federal government allowed for the transfer of tax points to provincial governments so that provinces had the ability to set their own tax rate. In other words, provinces gained the capacity to raise or lower provincial taxes depending on their own priorities. Such measures were immensely attractive because they gave the provinces the autonomy they had been clamouring for. The downside was that future increases to block funding would depend on economic growth. If the economy faltered, increases in federal funding would be lower than in more prosperous times. Consequently, it would be up to the provinces to cover any shortfall between what was spent on health care and the amount received from the federal government. To ensure that this arrangement did not unfairly benefit the more prosperous provinces, the block-funding arrangement also had a redistributive function, attempting to equalize the burden so that transfer amounts also depended on the size and growth of the population. Thus, poor provinces received greater benefit under EPF than wealthier provinces.

The net result of EPF was that the federal government found a way to reduce its share of the costs of health care and to download responsibility for controlling costs to the provinces. In subsequent years, the share of costs for health care borne by the federal government decreased from 50% to approximately 25%. Struggling to meet the challenges of assuming a greater burden of the costs of health care, the provinces took up their long-standing complaint that the federal government was underfunding health care. The federal government in turn would fire back that controlling costs was a provincial responsibility.

The period leading up to and subsequent to EPF, from 1975 to 1991, represents the first of three stages in the evolution of spending on health care in Canada. A second stage, during the mid-1990s, was a time of retrenchment where overall health spending declined. The third stage, lasting from the end of the 1990s to the present, has been characterized by continuing growth. Figure 10.1 depicts the pattern of total expenditure on health care as a proportion of economic growth (GDP) between 1975 and 2011 (note that the final two years are projections). We describe each of these three stages and their implications for health care in Canada in turn.

In 1975, health care costs for Canada as a whole were 7.0% of GDP. In the early years of EPF, increases in health care spending moved in tandem with the pattern of steady economic growth; however, an economic recession in the early 1980s led to a sharp divergence. As the economy contracted, health care costs continued to rise, resulting in health care accounting for a larger proportion of GDP. It was not until 1984 that health care costs once again moved in tandem with economic growth. Throughout this period, however, the federal government unilaterally changed the conditions of EPF, at first reducing the guaranteed annual increase and finally freezing increases altogether, beginning in 1990. With the federal share of health care costs diminishing over time, the provinces found themselves carrying a larger and larger burden of health care costs.

Once the federal government froze annual increases in transfers, the provinces found themselves in crisis mode: their ability to absorb an even greater share of health care costs was seen to have reached a threshold. This led to an unprecedented period of retrenchment that unfolded over much of the 1990s. As can be seen in Figure 10.1, health care costs as a proportion of GDP actually declined during this period, falling from their highest point up to that time (10.0% in 1992) to 8.9% in 1997. This dramatic decline was only accomplished through extreme measures enacted by the provinces.

The provinces relied on a number of strategies to rein in out-of-control health care costs in the different provinces. First, provinces made substantial cuts to their health care budgets. Provinces variously laid off health care workers, rolled back wages, and imposed hiring

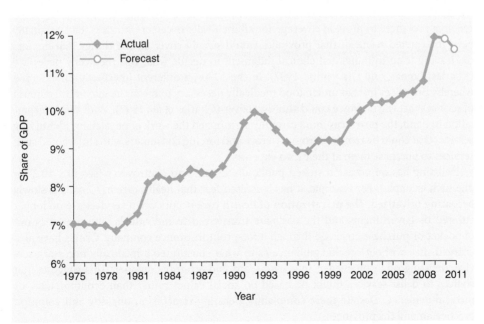

FIGURE 10.1 Total Health Expenditure as a Percentage of GDP, Canada, 1975 to 2011

Source: CIHI, *National Health Expenditure Trends, 1975 to 2011*, Fig. 13, Pg. 18, 2011.

bans and wage freezes in contract negotiations with health care workers. Sensing the difficult straits that the provinces found themselves in, most unions chose not to contest these efforts. For example, in 1994, Alberta nurses held many protests, but eventually conceded to a 5% rollback of their wages. Doctors, however, appeared to fare somewhat better during this time. In 1995, Premier Mike Harris of Ontario made sweeping changes to existing collective agreements between the government and all health care workers. As a result, doctors faced a clawback of their income above a certain threshold, elimination of government subsidies for malpractice insurance premiums, and penalties for establishing medical practices in "over-doctored" areas. When doctors protested and refused to accept new patients, the government rescinded many of these measures and instead increased physician income (Williams et al., 2001). Similar concessions to other health care professions in the province were never made.

As the single largest item in provincial health care budgets, hospitals were also targeted for cuts. The closure of hospital beds and hospitals occurred across the country but was particularly dramatic in Québec, Ontario, and Alberta. For example, in Ontario, nearly 10,000 hospital beds were closed and 40 of 139 hospitals in the province were ordered to close or merge (Naylor, 1999). Hospital closures also affected smaller provinces, such as Saskatchewan, in which fifty-two small rural hospitals (averaging fewer than ten beds each) were permanently shuttered or converted to community health centres (CIHI, 2000).

Other provincial health care reforms included the practice of delisting services. **Delisting** refers to the practice of removing a given medical procedure or health care service from the list of services covered under a provincial health care plan. On one hand, this may be viewed as a positive mechanism for allowing the coverage of services to evolve as medicine advances. Medical procedures that are no longer useful should lose coverage; correspondingly, new interventions that improve disease outcomes should be added to the list of covered procedures.

Under enormous pressure to reduce costs, on the other hand, provinces found that delisting was an attractive way to shift some of the costs for health care onto the consumer. It was facilitated by a new approach to the principle of comprehensiveness as laid out in the Medical Care Act of 1996 and the Canada Health Act of 1984. The principle, which requires provinces to provide coverage for all medically necessary services, had originally been interpreted to mean that provinces would simply cover all the things that doctors do, leaving it up to individual clinical judgment to decide what was medically necessary (Charles, Lomas, and Giacomini, 1997). In the 1990s, a different interpretation emerged whereby provinces instead understood medically necessary to mean the maximum amount of services that the province could afford to cover (Charles et al., 1997). With this interpretation in hand, the provinces more carefully scrutinized the work of physicians, identifying services that could be removed from coverage and forcing consumers who still wanted such services to purchase them at their own expense.

Delisting has on occasion stoked public discontent and controversy (see Box 10.2 for one such example). For example, it has increased fear that health care in Canada is slowly becoming privatized. The **privatization of health care** occurs when services are no longer covered by governments and the costs are transferred to individuals who must pay out of pocket or purchase coverage through a for-profit insurance company. Critics have also charged that, without specific guidance as to what constituted a medically necessary service, delisting often proceeded in a haphazard and arbitrary manner. This suggests that choices to delist services might be based on social values rather than economic cost or medical evidence. Despite these complaints, delisting remains an ongoing and common practice among the provinces.

delisting:
The removal of a specific medical procedure or health care service from the list of services covered under a provincial health care plan.

privatization of health care:
The shift toward encouraging the private purchase of health care; the private, for-profit practice of medicine; and, in general, the operation of market forces in health care.

BOX 10.2

Delisting Sex Reassignment Surgery

Struggling to contain the costs of health care, provinces have seized on the vague wording of the principle of comprehensiveness in the Canada Health Act to justify delisting services. With a narrower interpretation of what constitutes a medically necessary procedure, provinces have removed a number of procedures from their list of covered services, shifting the costs for these onto the consumer. The delisting of one medical procedure, known as sex reassignment surgery (SRS), has been particularly controversial.

Internationally recognized as a medical condition, gender identity disorder (GID) involves a deep-seated and long-standing desire to become a member of the opposite sex, with significant emotional distress arising out of the incongruence between one's assigned gender and one's perceived gender. GID is an extremely rare condition, with rough estimates suggesting that anywhere from 1 in 3,000 to 1 in 40,000 individuals meet the criteria for diagnosis (Sohn and Bosinski, 2007). Of those diagnosed, only a few seek medical intervention. The medically recommended treatment, SRS, encompasses hormonal therapy and a range of medical surgeries that transform the sex characteristics of the physical body to fit the opposite-sex body. Research suggests that patient satisfaction with SRS is generally high, and advances in medicine have resulted in fewer complications and better outcomes. Although those who undergo the surgery remain at increased risk for suicide and psychiatric morbidity (Dhejne et al., 2011), research suggests there are both psychological and social benefits for those who undergo the surgery (Mate-Kole, Freschi, and Robin, 1990).

In Canada, fewer than 200 people seek to undergo SRS each year, with costs ranging from $20,000 to $70,000. Expertise in GID is concentrated in a few areas of Canada. The Gender Identity Clinic at the Centre for Addiction and Mental Health (CAMH), affiliated with the University of Toronto, has counselled and provided services since 1969. More recently, the Vancouver Coastal Authority created the Transgender Health Program, which provides information and counselling to transgender people and service providers in that province.

The issue of whether SRS is medically necessary was determined by the Canadian Human Rights Tribunal, which, in 2001, ruled that it is an essential medical treatment. Speaking to this issue, Giordano (2012) contends, "Whether or not medical treatment should be offered and paid for depends not on the type of condition one has, but on whether the condition (whether associated with gender, ethnic belonging or others) is severe enough to impinge significantly upon the quality of life of the sufferer, to markedly jeopardize his/her psycho-social functioning, and whether available medical treatment is likely to ameliorate his/her condition" (p. 37). Thus, she contends, when the risk-benefit ratio is balanced in favour of medical intervention, the service should be provided and society has an obligation to provide support for that service (Giordano, 2012).

Despite these sentiments, neither the federal government nor the provinces have been deterred from delisting SRS. Currently SRS is covered under the provincial health care plans of Newfoundland and Labrador, Québec, Ontario, Manitoba, Saskatchewan, Alberta, and British Columbia. Several of these provinces require that patients be recommended for the surgery by the CAMH Gender Identity Clinic, and some provinces that lack the proper facilities require that SRS be performed in a clinic in Québec. Several provinces have never officially provided coverage for SRS, although some have covered costs on a case-by-case basis (New Brunswick, Prince Edward Island, and Nova Scotia).

In the past, a number of provinces have delisted SRS only to reverse the decision under pressure from legal challenges.

continued

Thus, British Columbia was the first province, in 1988, to delist SRS from health care coverage, but it was reinstated in 1993. In 1998, the Ontario government delisted SRS, but reinstated it in 2008. In April 2009, the Alberta government announced that it would delist SRS, labelling it a cosmetic procedure rather than a medically necessary procedure. At the time, the cost to the health care system was estimated to be approximately $700,000 out of its $12.9 billion annual budget. Subsequently, numerous complaints were lodged with the Alberta Human Rights and Citizenship Commission, and in June 2012, the government announced it was reinstating coverage, providing up to $1 million per year for SRS.

Not all decisions have been revoked. In 2008, the federal government instructed the Correctional Service of Canada to stop performing SRS for federal inmates. Vic Toews, public safety minister, stated the federal government's position that the procedure was not considered medically necessary and that Canadian taxpayers should not have to foot the bill for criminals who seek SRS. It remains to be seen whether the federal government will follow the path of British Columbia, Ontario and Alberta in reinstating coverage for SRS.

regionalization:
The organization of all health care institutions and agencies in a given geographical area under a single administrative board.

To exert greater control over the costs of health care, the provinces also pursued regionalization. **Regionalization** involves organizing all health care institutions and agencies in a given geographical area under a single administrative board. This process usurps the power of a local hospital to make decisions on its own behalf and instead delegates authority to an administrative body, which oversees the entire system. The purpose of regionalization was to avoid duplication of services and achieve efficiency in the system through integrating and coordinating services. Consequently, instead of an approach where hospitals and other health care bodies tried to be all things to all people, decisions about their functions were decided in a way that was meant to maximize their utility. For example, rather than having highly specialized surgeries such as organ transplantation be performed in each hospital, substantial cost savings could be achieved by concentrating such services in certain hospitals. These hospitals both housed the necessary equipment and doctors with the prerequisite skills and allowed these doctors to maintain their skill level by doing such procedures on a regular basis.

Not surprisingly, the provinces pursued different methods to create regional health authorities and have continued to make adjustments. For example, Saskatchewan created thirty regional health authorities in 1992, stipulating that two-thirds of the members of the board in each region be elected to their position. After 2001, the province amalgamated the boards into twelve boards and eliminated elections, due in part to extremely low voter turnout. In British Columbia, fifty-two regional health authorities that were created in the 1990s were reorganized into one provincial and five geographical areas in 2001. Alberta created seventeen health regions in 1994, which were reduced to nine in 2004, then dissolved to create one superboard in 2008. In contrast, Nova Scotia created four regional health boards (RHBs) in 1996, but replaced these with nine district health authorities in 2001 that functioned similarly to the RHBs but covered a smaller geographic area. In each instance, changes were implemented as a means of attaining greater efficiency and accountability in health care.

How did all of these changes affect health care? On one hand, polls showed that the confidence of Canadians in their health care system plummeted during this time period. Similarly, the breadth and rapidity of change not only threatened to destabilize the entire system but also alienated entire groups of health care workers, many of whom continue to distrust and resist the efforts of the provinces to engage in further health care reforms. Moreover, once the period of retrenchment subsided in 1998, pent-up demand for wage increases and competition between provinces in the face of nursing shortages as a result of past hiring freezes meant that health care costs increased rapidly (Tuohy, 2002). In fact, by 2001, the cost of health care was at the same level it would have been had it not undergone the severe budget cutbacks of the previous decade (Boychuk, 2002), raising questions about what the period of retrenchment had actually accomplished.

On the other hand, some have noted that reducing the number of hospital beds and closing hospitals during the 1990s actually brought Canada more in line with bed capacity in other countries (Barer, Morgan, and Evans, 2003). Moreover, even though there were about 25% fewer hospital beds in 1998 than in 1985, outpatient services increased three-fold during this same time period, suggesting Canada was beginning to move toward a continuum of care by shifting some services out of the hospital setting (CIHI, 2000). Finally, regionalization enabled provinces to gain control of the costs of health care as their data-gathering functions made it possible for funding to be allocated on the basis of future population projections for the region rather than physician-directed expenses (Boychuk, 2009). Importantly, data-gathering allowed administrators to develop indicators to measure and more effectively manage the performance of the health care system, although as we will see in Chapter 12, doing so has increasingly impinged on the autonomy of doctors and posed a threat to medical dominance.

Canada Health and Social Transfer (CHST)

In 1996, the federal government once again unilaterally changed the conditions under which funds were transferred to the provinces. EPF was replaced by a new act called the Canada Health and Social Transfer (CHST). As had been the case with EPF, the new agreement came with an enticement and a cost. It offered to give provinces more latitude in terms of how they spent federal funds but further reduced the amount transferred from the federal government to the provinces. Specifically, the notion of an annual increase was removed entirely from the agreement, leaving it up to the federal government to decide the amount by which it would increase funding each year. This presented the provinces with significant challenges: Without knowing what the level of funding would be from year to year, it would be nearly impossible to plan for the future health care needs of their population.

Although CHST was intended to reduce the amount of federal transfers, this is not what actually occurred. As the federal government got its own deficits under control, it began to supplement the amounts given to provinces through a series of one-time contributions. For example, in 1999, the federal government gave the provinces $3.5 billion over and above the annual amount to allow them to make investments in health care. Thus, instead of the harsh cutbacks of the earlier part of the decade, the end of the 1990s witnessed a turn toward reinvestment and launched a new period of steady growth. This represents the third stage of health care in Canada, which continues to the present day. Evidence of renewed growth can be seen in Figure 10.1, which displays annual increases in expenditures in health care from the late 1990s onward. The global economic recession that occurred in 2008 did result in a sharp increase in health care expenditures as a proportion of GDP, just as it did in the early 1980s, reflecting that economic growth stalled while costs were either constant or increasing.

In 2004, the federal government under Paul Martin once again changed funding arrangements by splitting the CHST into the Canada Health Transfer (CHT) and Canada Social Transfer (CST). The purpose was to provide greater transparency by identifying the specific amount of monies that the federal government allocated to health care. Although it allowed for a better estimate of the dollars flowing from federal coffers into provincial health care systems, the agreement did not otherwise interfere with how much money the provinces contributed to their respective health care systems or how they operated their systems, provided that they adhered to the principles of the Canada Health Act. In addition, CHT restored the clause pertaining to the annual increase in federal funding. Specifically, CHT committed the federal government to a 6% annual increase in funding for health care in each year until 2014. With this ten-year commitment in place, the provinces once again had a stable funding envelope on which to base their own planning.

During this time, the federal government also began to offer the provinces additional funding for programs aimed at achieving excellence in health care and in areas deemed to be of national importance. For example, the federal government established a program called the Wait Times Reduction Fund, which set aside $5.5 billion for the provinces to improve the responsiveness of the health care system. Provinces that committed to reducing wait times in five priority areas (cancer treatment, heart procedures, diagnostic imaging, joint replacement, and eye restoration) and made information on these wait times available to the public were eligible for this additional funding. The funding was mainly used to help the provinces to develop the capacity to measure, monitor, and report on patient wait times through electronic reporting systems. It also encouraged provinces to share information with one another in order to adopt best practices. Implementing a single standard for assessing wait times made it possible to compare the performance of the health care system not just across the provinces, but internationally. Armed with this information, provinces could then identify and address areas in which wait times needed to be improved.

Looking toward the Future

As the provinces began to prepare for negotiations with the federal government to renew the Canada Health Transfer (CHT), set to expire in 2014, the federal government pre-empted the entire process in December 2011 by announcing the terms of the new funding arrangement. First, the federal government agreed to increase health care transfers annually by 6% until 2016–2017. After that, annual increases would be tied to economic growth, including inflation, with a guarantee that it would never fall below 3%. The new agreement also revised the equalization component of the funding formula by moving toward distributing funds on a per capita basis rather than disproportionately transferring funds to poorer provinces. Finally, the federal government did not introduce any additional funding programs to achieve national goals for health care.

The provinces responded to the new agreement in a predictable manner: They were furious to have been presented with the terms of the agreement rather than having an opportunity to lobby the federal government for more funds. In large part, this was regarded as a brilliant strategy on the part of Prime Minister Stephen Harper, who effectively circumvented the widely expected efforts of provinces to gang up on the federal government to demand more money. The agreement itself, however, is a mixed bag. On one hand, the agreement extends the 6% annual increase in federal funding for health care for a few more years, providing short-term stability and giving the provinces time to prepare for reduced funding after 2016. On the other hand, the lack of funding for specific programs aimed at achieving excellence in health care or accomplishing national goals signals a new hands-off approach by the federal government to health care. Provinces that wish to innovate and improve their health care systems will now find themselves on their own, with no mechanisms in place to encourage the sharing of innovative and successful programs with one another. The implication is that key indicators of health care performance, such as wait times, that have been developed to date may no longer be comparable in the future as provinces independently make their own innovations, making it difficult to evaluate which provinces are leading and which are lagging. It also erodes past efforts to make collective improvements to health care and makes any future collaboration less likely. Whether and how this new agreement will affect Canada's health care system, however, will not be known for quite some time.

A Closer Look at the Distribution of Costs within the Canadian Health Care System

Whereas the total expenditure on health care in Canada over time was the focus of previous sections, we now examine changes in the distribution of those costs. As indicated earlier in this chapter, the formation of the health care system initially placed hospitals at the core. Hospital care, however, is designed to provide heroic interventions, using highly technical equipment to treat those with urgent life-threatening conditions. As such, it is incompatible with the current health needs of the population, which are primarily the prevention and management of chronic and degenerative diseases. Has the allocation of funding changed over time to reflect these new needs?

A glance at Table 10.1 provides support for a shift away from hospital care over time. In 1975, hospitals accounted for 45% of all health care expenditures in Canada; by 2009, hospitals remained the single largest cost category but accounted for only 29.1% of health care expenditures. This proportion has been stable at around 29% since 2001 (CIHI, 2011a). The share of expenditures on physicians has also remained fairly stable over time, accounting for 15% in 1975 and 13.6% in 2009. Nonetheless, their ranking has slipped: In 1975, physicians were the second-largest cost category but by 2009 occupied the third-largest cost category, after hospitals and drugs. Correspondingly, the share allocated for drugs has increased dramatically between 1975 and 2009, with costs for drugs accounting for 6.0% of health care expenditures in 1975 but 16.2% in 2009. Drugs succeeded physicians as the second-largest category in 1997 (CIHI, 2011a).

A second issue with regard to shifting costs is the divide between expenditures that are public and those that are private. Those expenditures that are public represent services covered through provincial health insurance plans, whereas private costs are borne by individuals, who either pay out of pocket or have their expenses reimbursed through commercial for-profit insurance. Canadians are generally concerned that the costs of health care are slowly being privatized and that they are being asked to shoulder a greater burden of health care costs over time.

To see if this is indeed the case, it is important first of all to recognize that the share of public versus private costs differs depending on the health care expenditure. As Figure 10.2 demonstrates, the average share borne by the public sector represents 70.9% of all expenditures, with 29.1% borne by the private sector. This average, however, does not reveal the wide variability in the share of public and private expenditures across different health care services. Specifically, for hospitals (90.8%), physicians (98.4%), and public health (100%), the overwhelming burden falls on the public sector. In contrast, for drugs (39.0%) and other

Cost Category	1975	2009
Hospitals	45.0	29.1
Physicians	15.0	13.6
Drugs	6.0	16.2

TABLE 10.1 Shifting the Share of Costs, 1975 and 2009, Top Three Health Care Expenditures in Canada.

Adapted from: CIHI, *National Health Expenditure Trends, 1975 to 2011*, 2011.

health care professionals, including dentists, chiropractors, psychologists, and massage therapists (8.2%), the public sector plays a very small role. Combining the observation that the share of expenditures on drugs has increased the most rapidly since 1975 and the fact that the bulk of costs for drugs falls on the private sector, one might conclude that health care costs are increasingly being shifted onto individuals. The reality, however, is a little more complex. Whereas the share of private spending on health care increased in the early 1990s, the split between public and private since 1997 has consistently been 70–30. Thus, although the growing costs of drugs do fall more heavily on the private sector, reinvestment in health care since the late 1990s has seen the public sector pick up costs in other areas. Whether this will be true in the future remains to be seen.

Nonetheless, it is also the case that Canadians have increasingly turned to private insurance companies for their health care needs. Currently, approximately 66% of Canadians hold some form of private health insurance (Flood and Haugan, 2010). Moreover, costs in private insurance are rising rapidly. In 1988, the per capita expenditure on private health insurance was $139.40, increasing to $648.90 by 2009 (CIHI, 2011a) (both amounts reported in constant 1997 dollars).

That the public-private split in health care costs has been stable since 1997 does not, however, fully address the issue of privatization. As noted in the opening vignette, Canada's health care system is currently facing challenges in two provinces, Ontario and Alberta, where the decisions of two court cases may, in the future, decide whether Canadians will experience privatization in the form of a parallel private health care system that is allowed to compete with the province's public health care system. That is, the plaintiffs in these two court cases are arguing that Canadians are being denied their constitutional rights because the Canada Health Act forbids Canadians from purchasing health care services outside of the public health system.

The experience of Québec may (or may not) provide clues to what the future holds. In the 1990s, two plaintiffs, Dr. Chaoulli and Mr. Zeliotis, took the Québec government to

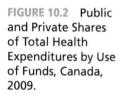

FIGURE 10.2 Public and Private Shares of Total Health Expenditures by Use of Funds, Canada, 2009.

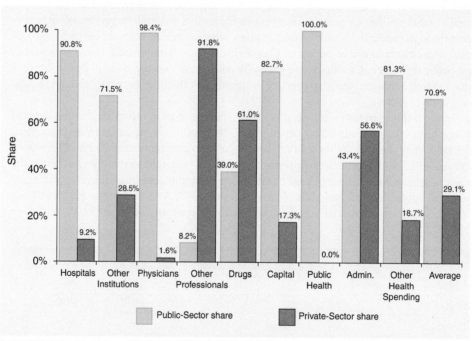

Source: CIHI, *National Health Expenditure Trends, 1975 to 2011*, Fig. 14, Pg. 19, 2011.

court. Dr. Chaoulli wanted the ability to offer services for health care outside the public system, and Mr. Zeliotis, who waited more than a year for hip replacement surgery, wanted to receive services more quickly without having to pay for the surgery at his own expense in another country. The plaintiffs lost their case at each level in Québec but appealed their rulings all the way to the Supreme Court of Canada. In June 2005, the Supreme Court of Canada unexpectedly sided with the plaintiffs, ruling that forcing Quebeckers to wait excessive amounts of time to receive needed health care was a violation of their rights and that the government has an obligation to provide these services in a timely manner. In essence, the ruling opened the door to private for-profit insurance, but only in the province of Québec.

The ruling itself was controversial and narrowly decided (4:3). The three dissenting judges strongly believed that the court should not rule on the issue of wait times, stating that wait times are a social not a legal issue, and further noting that the lack of accurate information on wait times in Canada precluded any objective assessment of whether they were indeed unfairly excessive. Experts in health care policy have also weighed in on the Court's ruling, suggesting that the decision did not appropriately take into account the complexity of the regulatory framework under which Canada's health care system operates and that courts, counsel, and litigants will need to be better apprised of these issues as they are called upon to make decisions in the future (Flood and Haugan, 2010).

For its part, Québec was given a year to comply with the court's ruling and responded by enacting two reforms: It implemented a guaranteed wait time for certain procedures, and it allowed private health insurance on certain procedures provided that doctors who performed those procedures opted out of the public health system. That is, doctors would not be allowed to operate in both the public health care system and a private for-profit system at the same time, but must choose between the two. Forcing doctors to make the choice to operate in either the public or the private system is important. First, doing so meant that Québec remained in compliance with the basic principles of the Canada Health Act, which does contain an opt-out clause for physicians who do not want to be part of the public health care system (less than 1% of doctors across Canada have ever made the choice to opt out). Second, by forcing doctors to choose between the two systems, the government removed any incentive for doctors operating in the public system to increase wait times in that system as a means of persuading the public to pay higher fees for more rapid service in a private system. As we will see in the next chapter, the decision by the Québec government was guided by lessons learned in other jurisdictions that allowing a private system to compete with a public system may have the contradictory effect of increasing wait times in the public system.

Nonetheless, the Supreme Court ruling that "access to a wait list is not access to health care" has laid the foundation for the two other pending lawsuits. In both cases, the litigants are using the ruling as a basis for extending the option of a private parallel health care system to the rest of Canada. There is no guarantee that the Supreme Court of Canada will agree to hear these two cases, and since the composition of the courts has changed dramatically in recent years, it is also impossible to determine in advance how the Court would rule. Nonetheless, these two court cases could fundamentally change Canada's health care system.

These events suggest that Canadians should be contributing their voices to the debate about what Canada's health care system should look like in the future. The key issue is deciding how Canada should ration health care. **Rationing** health care is a morally charged issue because it suggests that withholding health care will have tragic consequences for health and well-being (Ubel and Goold, 1998). The reality is that all systems ration health care, only differing in their approach. As we observed in the previous chapter, the demand for health is inexhaustible, whereas resources to provide health care are finite. Thus, all health care systems must confront choices about what should and should not be covered.

rationing:
Any mechanism that allows people to go without beneficial health care services.

The Canada Health Act states that provincial governments must provide public coverage of all medically necessary services. This is the current mechanism by which health care in this country is rationed. But, who should decide what is medically necessary? By choosing to delist certain services, provinces have clearly exercised authority on this issue. Given the evidence that provinces have made these decisions arbitrarily or simply as a cost-cutting measure, and that, in the case of sexual reassignment surgery, some provinces have been forced to reinstate coverage, it is clear that more guidance is needed.

Alternative options fall between two extremes. At one end of the spectrum, Giordano (2012) makes the argument that any procedure that is potentially beneficial becomes an obligation on the part of the public to provide. Yet, this standard is just as problematic as covering all medically necessary services because it still doesn't address the issue of who decides what is potentially beneficial. Moreover, any procedure that makes one better than well can be argued to be potentially beneficial, so that the public is necessarily obliged to provide a limitless supply of health care. It is certain that no society could withstand the burdens that satisfying such obligations would entail. At the other end of the spectrum, a fully private health care system would mean that rationing would occur on the basis of ability to pay for health care services. Those who could not afford a given procedure would be priced out of the market, whereas those with financial means would be able to purchase whatever procedure they were willing to pay for. Choosing this path would bring Canada closer to a U.S.-type health care system.

As can be appreciated, Canadians are confronted with difficult choices, with competing claims about what is best for Canadians. Perhaps comparing Canada's health care system with health care systems in other countries may help us to better understand the range of choices that are available. In the next chapter, we provide a broad framework for evaluating the performance of a health care system and then examine how Canada's health care system performs relative to those of other countries.

IMPLICATIONS

Canadians have historically expressed pride in their health care system, citing it as a remarkable national achievement. Yet, all too often, media reports and those with vested interests claim that our health care system is in crisis. The reality of the Canadian health care system surely lies somewhere between these two extremes, and it is only when we gain a glimpse into the history of our health care system that we understand how these different positions evolved.

The development of a national health insurance program appears to be the result of pivotal moments in history, when actions that were or were not taken altered the trajectory of what was considered possible at that time. When Tommy Douglas moved ahead to establish hospital-based insurance independent of the federal government, the enormous success and popularity of his vision laid the foundation for others to believe that a national health care system was attainable. Similarly, Emmett Hall twice played an instrumental role in shaping Canada's health care system. His recommendations, appearing in two different commission reports, for how the system should operate continue to reverberate today, including the consequences to Canadians when the federal government chose not to proceed with his recommendation that pharmaceuticals and home care be covered under provincial health insurance. Because of their immense contributions, both Tommy Douglas and Emmett Hall have been lauded as forefathers of our health care system.

Outside of a short period in the 1990s when provinces engaged in radical strategies to control spending, health care costs as a proportion of GDP have exhibited steady growth from the mid-1970s to the present day. Despite repeated proclamations that our health care system is in crisis, there is no evidence to suggest that Canadians can no longer afford their health care system, leading some to suggest that the crisis has been politically constructed (Boychuk, 2002). As we will see in the next chapter, however, that does not mean that Canada's health care system is without blemish—indeed, Canada lags behind other countries in a number of areas. Sadly, recent signals by the federal government to withdraw from a leadership role in encouraging and supporting provinces to achieve higher standards of care suggest that Canada may soon find itself slipping even farther down the international rankings.

SUMMARY

LO-1 1. Prior to the twentieth century, most Canadians received their health care from relatives, neighbours, or any of a variety of poorly trained and poorly respected practitioners. Regular doctors, or allopathic doctors—the forerunners of modern medical doctors—knew little of science. Their use of "heroic medicine" and ignorance of antisepsis, anaesthesia, and drugs left doctors at least as likely to harm as to heal.

LO-1 2. The main competitors to allopathic medicine were homeopathic doctors and eclectics, each with their own unique healing philosophy. Early attempts to consolidate power by allopathic doctors were not successful, and when the Ontario College of Physicians and Surgeons was formally recognized, it initially included eclectics and homeopaths.

LO-2 3. Two hundred years ago, the apprenticeship system was the main route to becoming a medical doctor. In such a system, the quality of training depended solely on the skill of the preceptor physician. Things began to change gradually over the course of the nineteenth century as the emergence of university-affiliated medical schools in Ontario and Québec paved the way for medical students to receive formal training.

LO-2 4. The Flexner Report, whose recommendations led to the closing of many poorly run schools in the United States, provided the needed impetus in Canada to eliminate the apprenticeship system and introduce new standards for medical education. By bestowing on allopathic doctors the right to control who entered the practice of medicine, the 1912 Canada Medical Act assured physicians of medical dominance: freedom from control by other occupations and ability to control the work of others in the health care field.

LO-3 5. As early as 1919, Canadians engaged in debate over a national health care system; however, several decades would pass before it was successfully brought to fruition.

LO-3 6. Having failed to reach consensus on a national health insurance program in the 1945 Dominion-Provincial Conference on Reconstruction, the premier of Saskatchewan, Tommy Douglas, decided to proceed independently with a plan to bring hospital insurance to the province. Municipal rolls were used to enrol residents, and an annual premium of $5 per person to a maximum of $30 per household made it possible for residents of Saskatchewan to receive care in a hospital without charge.

LO-3 7. In 1957, the federal government introduced the Hospital Insurance and Diagnostic Services Act (HIDSA), which proposed a joint funding agreement to share the costs of hospital-based medical care. In exchange for assuming half the costs, the federal government stipulated that provinces must provide hospital services to all residents of their respective provinces without condition, submit to an annual audit of hospital expenses, and adhere to mutually agreed upon standards of care.

LO-3   8.   Having secured funding from the federal government for hospital care, Premier Tommy Douglas turned his attention to implementing insurance for physician services. His proposal for medical insurance would cover all citizens of Saskatchewan regardless of ability to pay, be funded through annual premiums, and be administered by a public body. The government also promised to make necessary investments in health care and to proceed only with the approval of the public and provincial doctors. When the Saskatchewan Medical Care Insurance Act was introduced in 1961 and passed in 1962, it was clear that physicians were not in favour of medical insurance. When the doctors went on strike, however, few supported them and, within twenty-three days, the doctors conceded defeat.

LO-3   9.   Tasked with evaluating existing and future health care needs of Canadians and making recommendations for providing health care to all Canadians, the Royal Commission on Health Services, headed by Supreme Court Justice Emmett Hall, issued a two-volume report that recommended that the Saskatchewan model of medical insurance be adopted across the country. It also recommended covering other types of health care services, including pharmaceuticals, home care, dental care, and eye care.

LO-3   10.   The Medical Care Act, introduced in 1966 by the federal government, proposed to share the costs of medical care equally with the provinces, provided that they adhered to four principles. Each province would be required to create an insurance plan that provided universal access to citizens of that province, was administered by a public authority on a non-profit basis, offered comprehensive coverage by including all medically necessary services, and was portable so that those who moved from one province to another could still receive care.

LO-3   11.   In 1984, the federal government introduced the Canada Health Act. The bill replaced HIDSA and the Medical Care Act by harmonizing them into a single piece of legislation but also added a fifth principle, accessibility, that eliminated the practice of user fees and extra-billing.

LO-4   12.   Although many Canadians might cite the 1990s as the time when Canada's health care system first fell into crisis, in actuality, the perception that the system was unsustainable began as early as the 1970s. In many ways, the seeds for crisis were sown as a result of how the health care system came into being: The system privileged the input of medical doctors over that of other health care workers, lacked formal mechanisms for controlling the costs of health care, and focused on curative functions rather than preventative measures.

LO-5   13.   In 1977, the federal government changed the funding arrangements for health care through the Established Programs Financing Act (EPF) by shifting from shared funding to block funding. Block funding allowed the federal government to transfer a fixed amount of money to the provinces, with annual increases tied to economic growth. As such, provinces that spent more money on health care would be forced to cover any shortfall themselves. In return, the provinces were given extended powers. The net result of EPF was that the federal share of health care declined over time from 50% to approximately 25%.

LO-5   14.   The period from 1975 to 1991 represents a time of stable growth in Canada's health care system; however, as the federal government began to reduce annual increases in transfers to the provinces, provinces found themselves struggling to contain the costs of health care. Once the federal government froze annual increases to transfer payments to the provinces in 1991, the provinces were forced to implement harsh changes to their respective health care systems.

LO-5   15.   During the 1990s, provinces made significant reforms to health care by slashing health care budgets, laying off and/or freezing the wages of health care workers, closing hospital beds and entire hospitals, delisting services that had previously been covered, and creating regional health authorities to oversee health care services in a geographic area. This tumultuous period was accompanied by sharp declines in Canadians' satisfaction with their health care system and set the tone for acrimonious relations between the provinces and their health care workers that persist to the present day. Yet, reforms were not uniformly disastrous, as the reduction in hospital beds rid the system of excess capacity and brought Canada to a level that was comparable to other nations, helped to facilitate a shift toward a broader continuum of care, and provided provinces with the administrative tools needed to control the costs of health care in their own jurisdictions.

LO-5   16.   In 1996, the federal government again changed the nature of transfers to the provinces with the Canada Health and Social Transfer Act (CHST). The bill was intended to further reduce the federal share of funding to the provinces; however, once the federal government had eliminated the federal deficit, it began to make significant investments in health care.

LO-5   17.   In 2004, the provinces and federal government reached a ten-year agreement that brought greater stability to health care by guaranteeing a fixed annual increase in funding for the next ten years, and by allocating funding to achieve goals in health care that were of national interest. This agreement is set to expire in 2014, and the Conservative federal government has already established the terms of the new agreement: It will begin to reduce federal contributions after 2016–2017 and no longer offers funding to achieve national goals, signalling a new hands-off approach that will make it difficult to maintain comparability or to foster collaboration among provinces.

LO-5   18.   The issue of whether Canada will eventually introduce a parallel private health care system that competes with the public health care system continues to be debated. In 2005, the Supreme Court of Canada ruled that access to a waiting list was not access to health care, opening the door for private health insurance in the province of Québec. That decision has been the driving force behind two lawsuits, one in Ontario and the other in Alberta, which may one day lead the Supreme Court of Canada to extend that ruling to the rest of Canada. Such a decision would forever change the landscape of health care in this country, making it imperative that Canadians collectively participate in the process by expressing what values they wish to uphold in determining how health care is rationed in the future.

REVIEW QUESTIONS

1.   What were the differences between allopathic doctors and their main competitors, homeopathic doctors and eclectics?
2.   How were physicians in Canada trained in the early 1800s, and what could a doctor offer patients in the 1800s? In the early 1900s?
3.   How did the Flexner Report change medical education in the United States and in Canada?
4.   When did allopathic doctors in Canada achieve medical dominance?
5.   Why did Tommy Douglas, premier of Saskatchewan, move forward with his own plan to bring hospital insurance to his province?
6.   What did the Hospital and Insurance Diagnostic Services Act (HIDSA) accomplish?
7.   Describe doctors' efforts to halt government-sponsored hospital and medical insurance, and evaluate the success of these efforts.

8.   What were the major recommendations of the first Hall Commission Report, and which of these recommendations were eventually taken up by the federal government?
9.   Describe the four principles of the Canada Medical Care Act of 1966.
10. What were the two intended purposes of the Canada Health Act? Why was it necessary to add the fifth principle?
11. Describe three ways in which the founding of Canada's health care system laid the groundwork for the crises that later followed.
12. Describe how the Established Programs Financing Act (EPF) changed the federal government's funding for health care.
13. Describe the changes in the cost of health care as a proportion of GDP from 1975 to 2009.
14. What strategies did the provincial governments use to contain the costs of health care in the 1990s?
15. How did CHST in 1996 and CHT in 2004 change the nature of federal funding for health care? How did these changes affect how provinces delivered health care in their respective jurisdictions?
16. What are the implications of the new funding agreement for health care between the federal government and the provinces reached in December 2011?
17. What are the implications of lawsuits contending that banning private health insurance for health services offered in the public sector is a violation of Canadians' constitutional rights?

CRITICAL THINKING QUESTIONS

1.   Given what you now know about Canada's health care system, how might you respond if you were to read in the newspaper today that Canada's health care system is in crisis?
2.   On what basis should the decision to ration health care be made? Should it be rationed according to one's ability to pay? Should health care services be provided on the basis of need, and, if so, how will need be defined? Should health care services be provided on the basis of potential benefit, and, if so, what level of benefit will be sufficient to guarantee provision? Who should be given the authority to make such decisions?

KEY TERMS

allopathic doctors (p. 231)
delisting (p. 244)
eclectics (p. 232)
extra-billing (p. 239)
fee-for-service compensation (p. 237)
financially progressive (p. 240)
first dollar coverage (p. 239)
Flexner Report (p. 234)
harm reduction (p. 241)
heroic medicine (p. 233)

homeopathic doctors (p. 231)
irregular practitioners (p. 231)
medical dominance (p. 235)
privatization of health care (p. 244)
rationing (p. 251)
regionalization (p. 246)
regular doctors (p. 231)
single-payer system (p. 240)
user fee (p. 239)

11

Health Care in Other Countries

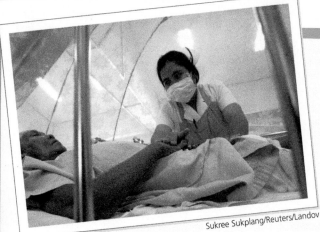

Sukree Sukplang/Reuters/Landov

The Accident

The accident happened on 7 October 2006. Narin Pintalakarn came off his motorcycle going into a bend. He struck a tree, his unprotected head taking the full force of the impact. Passing motorists found him some time later and took him to a nearby hospital. Doctors diagnosed severe head injury and referred him to the trauma centre, 65 km away, where the diagnosis was confirmed. A scan showed subdural haematoma with subfalcine and uncal herniation. Pintalakarn's skull had fractured in several places. His brain had bulged and shifted, and was still bleeding; the doctors decided to operate. He was wheeled into an emergency department where a

surgeon removed part of his skull to relieve pressure. A blood clot was also removed. Five hours later, the patient was put on a respirator and taken to the intensive care unit where he stayed for 21 days. Thirty-nine days after being admitted to hospital, he had recovered sufficiently to be discharged.

What is remarkable about this story is not what it says about the power of modern medicine to repair a broken body; it is remarkable because the episode took place not in a country belonging to the Organisation for Economic Cooperation and Development (OECD), where annual per capita expenditure on health averages close to US$ 4000, but in Thailand, a country that spends US$ 136 per capita, just 3.7% of its gross domestic product (GDP). Nor did the patient belong to the ruling elite, the type of person who … tends to get good treatment wherever they live. Pintalakarn was a casual labourer, earning only US$ 5 a day.

"Thai legislation demands that all injured patients be taken care of with standard procedure no matter what their status," says Dr Witaya Chadbunchachai, the surgeon who carried out the craniotomy on Pintalakarn at the Khon Kaen Regional Hospital in the country's northeastern province. According to Chadbunchachai, medical staff do not consider who is going to pay for treatment, however expensive it might be, because in Thailand, everyone's health-care costs are covered.

World Health Organization, *World Health Report: Health Systems Financing: The Path to Universal Coverage*, WHO, Switzerland, Pg. 3, 2010.

In this chapter, students should be able to:

LO-1 **Understand** why sociologists have an interest in cross-national comparisons of health care systems.

LO-2 **Describe** the convergence hypothesis and the factors that underlie it.

LO-3 **Understand** how the concepts of equity, cost, efficiency, and responsiveness are used to evaluate the performance of health care systems and **describe** how Canada's health care system compares to those of other countries on these criteria.

LO-4 **Understand** the unique aspects of the health care systems of the United States, Germany, United Kingdom, and China and **describe** how each has approached health care reform.

In the previous chapter, we discussed the history of Canada's health care system and described some of its current challenges. In this chapter, we use a comparative approach to evaluate how well Canada's health care system performs relative to that of other countries. We begin by looking at basic measures for evaluating health care systems, using some of these indicators to compare Canada's ranking with other OECD countries, most of which are high-income countries. Finally, we examine in more detail the systems of four other countries—the United States, Germany, the United Kingdom, and China.

EVALUATING HEALTH CARE SYSTEMS

We start by first exploring why sociologists have an interest in engaging in cross-national comparisons of health care systems. After all, these kinds of comparisons might seem to belong more properly to the sphere of health economics and political science. Yet, issues of power are also central to understanding why and with what consequence countries vary in the organization of their health care systems. For example, Tuohy (2012) distinguishes between the focus of economists who conduct comparative analyses in order to recommend policies that are aimed at system-level improvements and the work of sociologists who draw on detailed contextual descriptions of different health care systems to identify patterns that may have an impact on other outcomes, including the social distribution of illness and disease. In illuminating the role of power, some sociologists may evaluate discourses that are adopted by different governments to show how a policy change that implies better patient care may be used to serve institutional goals, such as altering the public's expectations. Still other sociologists may study how individuals in different countries interpret and respond to changes in health care systems, looking to the unique cultural, political, and social contexts that shape how citizens engage with these changes (Schlesinger, 2010). Thus, while the topic is of interest to many disciplines, cross-national comparisons of health care systems also bring into visibility many issues that have sociological relevance.

Our comparison begins with the recognition that differences in health care systems around the world are becoming less apparent over time. Mechanic and Rochefort refer to this as the **convergence hypothesis**, which argues that health care systems become increasingly similar over time due to a combination of "scientific, technological, economic, and epidemiological imperatives" (1996: 242).

First, Mechanic and Rochefort argue, doctors always seek the most current medical knowledge and technology, both to improve the services they offer and to increase their incomes and prestige. In recent decades **globalization** has expanded access to such knowledge, as doctors increasingly use medical journals and Internet resources from around the world and as medical and pharmaceutical corporations market new technologies

convergence hypothesis:
The thesis that health care systems become increasingly similar over time because of similar scientific, technological, economic, and epidemiological pressures.

internationally. Thus, doctors in many different countries are adopting the same technologies and placing similar economic pressures on their health care systems. In turn, these systems have adopted similar strictures to limit both specialization and the use of technological interventions whose benefits do not justify their costs.

Economic pressures can also push health care systems inadvertently toward convergence. Whether a country's economy is booming or faltering, and whether its health care system is largely capitalist or largely socialist, the cost of health care can eventually lead governments to conclude that they need to reduce those costs. Countries with largely capitalist health care systems may do so by *restricting* the role of the market in health care, while countries with largely socialistic health care systems may do so by *encouraging* the role of the market in health care. The latter situation, in which countries begin encouraging the private purchase of health care, encouraging the private practice of medicine for profit, and more generally encouraging the operation of market forces in health care, is referred to as the **privatization of health care**. Both sets of countries, therefore, move toward convergence, in the form of health care systems in which market forces play a role, but that role is restricted by the state.

Demographic changes also promote convergence. As populations have aged around the world, health care systems have had to shift more toward treating chronic degenerative diseases rather than treating acute diseases. At the same time, the globalization of knowledge has increased people's expectations regarding health and health care because they now compare themselves not only to their neighbours but also to those they see in the mass media. This shift has forced health care systems to pay greater attention to patient satisfaction and choice, while providing support for parallel systems that allow the wealthy to buy care unavailable to others.

Although comparative analyses of health care systems are useful for sociologists and many other disciplines, Marmor (2012) reminds us that there are instances when cross-national comparisons of health care systems can be misleading. He cautions against two types of errors. The first error, naive transplantation, occurs when it is assumed that an idea that works well in one country can be adopted successfully and with the same positive results in another country. The opposite error, labelled by Marmor the fallacy of comparative difference, is the mistaken assumption that countries have nothing to learn from one another simply because they differ in their health care systems on one or more major dimensions.

With these caveats in mind, we outline some basic indicators that we can use to compare how well Canada's health care system performs in terms of equity, cost, efficiency, and responsiveness relative to other countries (see Key Concepts 11.1).

KEY CONCEPTS 11.1 Four Indicators for Evaluating the Performance of a Health Care System

Equity	Fairness of the distribution of health care resources in the population.
Cost	The amount of money spent on health care.
Efficiency	Achieving optimal health-related outcomes with the best possible use of resources.
Responsiveness	The ways in which the health care system meets the needs and expectations of its citizens. Examples include respect, confidentiality, timeliness of care, perceived quality of care, and choice.

Equity

Equity in health care is a complex concept, essentially referring to the fairness of the distribution of health care resources in a given society. **Equity in access** occurs when all citizens are able to obtain services on the basis of need rather than ability to pay, social class, geography, or any other characteristic (Bevan, Helderman, and Wilsford, 2010). Countries that provide **universal coverage**, by guaranteeing health care to their citizens and legal residents, view health care as a social good that should be accessible to those who need it. With the exception of the United States, all high-income countries provide a level of universal health care coverage; however, as discussed further in Box 11.1, the idea that health care is a right is not unanimously endorsed by all countries.

equity in access:
The ability to obtain health care services on the basis of need rather than ability to pay or any other characteristic.

universal coverage:
Health care systems that provide access to health care for all legal residents of a nation.

BOX 11.1

ETHICAL DEBATE

Is There a Right to Health Care?

The Universal Declaration of Human Rights, adopted by the United Nations in 1948, recognizes the right to health care as a basic right of citizens. Yet, it is far from assured that most people around the world enjoy or have access to these rights. An analysis of the constitutions of the world's countries found that only 67.5% had a provision addressing health or health care, and less than half of these used the language of entitlement when referring to health and health care (Kinney and Clark, 2004). Enshrining the right to health care in law remains a controversial and hotly debated issue.

Those who argue against a right to health care draw on the language of autonomy and individualism, stressing the rights of individuals over any socially imposed rights accruing to all members of a society (Daniels and Roberts, 2008). Those who take this position note that in affirming individuals' rights to health care, we implicitly assert that health care workers have a duty to provide that care. In so doing, therefore, we restrict the rights of health care workers to control their time and resources. If we would not force a baker to give bread to the hungry, how can we force doctors to give their services away or restrict what patients doctors see, what services they provide, and what charges they assess?

Similarly, in upholding a right to health care, we implicitly obligate all members of a society to pay the costs of that care. When we subsequently use tax dollars to pay for health care, we restrict the rights of individuals to spend their money as they please. Some individuals, both rich and poor, might consider this a good investment, but many others would prefer to choose for themselves how to spend their money.

Moreover, according to those who take this position, asserting a right to health care fails to differentiate between unfortunate circumstances and unfair ones

(Daniels and Roberts, 2008). Although it is certainly unfortunate that some individuals suffer pain, illness, and disability, it is not necessarily unfair. Society may have an obligation to intervene when an individual unfairly suffers disability because another acted negligently, but society cannot be expected to take responsibility for correcting all inequities caused by biological or social differences in fortune.

Finally, if we assert that individuals have a right to demand certain social goods from a society, where do we draw the line? Do individuals have a right only to a minimum level of health care, or do they have a right to all forms of health care available in a given society? That is, does the right to health care extend to cosmetic surgery, infertility treatments, and expensive experimental treatment? And, if we grant individuals a right to health care, how can we deny them a right to decent housing, education, transportation, and so on?

Those who argue in favour of a right to health care, on the other hand, draw on the language of social justice (Rawls, 1971). Believing each individual has inherent worth, they reject the distinction between unfortunate and unfair circumstances and the idea that health care is a privilege, dependent on charity or benevolence. Instead, they argue that each individual has a right to at least a minimum level of health care. Moreover, they argue that all members of a society are interdependent in ways that a rhetoric of individualism fails to recognize. For example, doctors who believe they should have full control over how and to whom they provide services fail to recognize the many ways they have benefited from social generosity. Medical training relies heavily on tax dollars, as do medical research projects, technological developments, hospitals, and other health care facilities. In accepting these benefits of tax support, therefore, doctors implicitly accept an obligation to repay society through the health care they provide.

continued

Similarly, those who support a right to health care argue that to consider the decision to purchase health care as simply an individual choice misrepresents the nature of this decision, for it hardly makes sense to define something as a choice when the alternative is death or disability. Nor does it make sense to talk about the purchase of health care as a choice when individuals can do so only by giving up other essentials, such as housing or food.

Finally, those who support a right to health care recognize that society could never afford to provide all available health services to everyone but argue that this should not limit society's obligation to provide a decent minimum level of care to all. Doing any less denies the basic worth of all humans.

SOCIOLOGICAL QUESTIONS

1. What social views and values about medicine, society, and the body are reflected in the debate over a right to health care? Whose views are these?
2. Which social groups are in conflict over this issue? Whose interests are served by offering universal health care? Whose interests are harmed?
3. Which of these groups has more power to enforce its view? What kinds of power do they have?
4. What are the intended consequences of rejecting the idea that individuals have a right to health care? What are the unintended social, economic, political, and health consequences of this choice?

Because Canada has a universal health care system and the United States does not, there are numerous studies comparing how health care resources are distributed by income in both countries. Several decades of research have clearly shown that in the United States, those who are wealthy have, on average, more doctor visits than those who are poor. Canada generally displays the opposite pattern, such that those who are poor more frequently visit their doctor than those who are wealthy (Katz, Hofer, and Manning 1996; Roos and Mustard, 1997). These differences suggest that health care resources in Canada are more equitably distributed according to need (where those who are poor are often in worse health than those who are more advantaged), whereas resources in the United States flow disproportionately to those who are wealthier (and healthier). Moreover, once individuals in both countries become sick, inequity in access to health care services plays a role in whose health improves. For example, a recent study that compared colon cancer survival rates in both Toronto and San Francisco reported that there was a significant association between income and survival in the American city, but not in the Canadian city (Gorey et al., 2011).

Equity in access is often desirable in principle, but, in practice, it can attract strong opposition. That is, equity in access may conflict with the interests of those who wield the most power in society. When health care is financed though graduated taxation, the costs of health care are borne mainly by the young, healthy, and rich, who effectively subsidize care for those who are old, ill, and poor. That is, in a graduated tax system, wealthier citizens pay a larger proportion of their income than those who are poor. As noted in the previous chapter, this type of system is considered **financially progressive**. Equity of access may impose a further cost if spreading resources equally means that citizens are guaranteed neither immediate service nor every service they want. The wealthy then incur additional out-of-pocket expenses if they travel to other countries to receive health services they cannot obtain in Canada. As such, these restrictions may motivate those who are wealthy to contest the argument that health is a social good and to lobby instead that health care should be determined by ability to pay.

Moreover, because the link between socioeconomic disadvantage and health outcomes is so strong and enduring, equity in access does not translate into equity in health outcomes. That is, evidence suggests that the greater utilization of health care resources by the poor ameliorates some of the observed differences in health in Canada due to socioeconomic position, but access to health care does not fully eliminate the socioeconomic gradient in health in either Canada or the United States (McGrail et al., 2009; Prus, 2011) nor does it play a major role in the health of the population (Williams, McClellan, and Rivlin, 2010). Thus, equity in access to health care is an important principle but is not the only factor or even the most important factor in improving the health of the population or in reducing socioeconomic inequalities in health.

Finally, equity in access to health care involves more than simply establishing a universal health care system (Starfield, 2009). Indeed, most high-income countries, including Canada, exhibit a similar pattern whereby access to **primary care** is distributed on the basis of need and thus used more heavily by the poor, yet **specialist** services remain more heavily utilized by the wealthier segments of society (Pilote et al., 2003; van Doorslaer, Masseria, and Koolman, 2006; Veugelers and Yip, 2003). Why those who are poor are more likely to see a primary care doctor but less likely to see a specialist remains a mystery but hints at inequities that persist despite a universal health care system. It also appears that Canada has been moving toward greater inequity over time. An analysis of twenty-five years of health care utilization among Canadians shows that while health status remains the strongest predictor of health care utilization, there is an emerging trend that suggests that the wealthy and more educated have been increasing their use of health care services at a higher rate than more disadvantaged segments of society, and that the pattern has become particularly strong for specialist services (Curtis and MacMinn, 2008). Not surprisingly, then, research has shown that Canada's health care system is more equitable than that of the United States; however, it fares more poorly when compared to most European nations (van Doorslaer et al., 2006).

Cost

The cost of a health care system is another criterion by which overall performance is evaluated. In 2001, the estimated amount of money spent on health care globally was more than $3 trillion, representing about 7.9% of the world's economic output (WHO, 2002). There is wide variation, however, in what countries spend on their health care systems. One in four countries, most of which are low-income countries, spend less than 4% of their GDP on health care (WHO, 2002). In contrast, countries belonging to the Organization for Economic Cooperation and Development (OECD), as shown in Figure 11.1, spend far more on health care. In general, high-income countries make up around 19% of the world's population but consume 85% of the world's health care (WHO, 2002). Among high-income countries, health care in the United States is the costliest, accounting for 17.4% of GDP in 2009 (Canadian Institute for Health Information (CIHI), 2011a).

Relative to other high-income countries, Canada's health care system ranks as the sixth most costly and at 11.4% of GDP is well above the OECD average of 9.7%. Containing costs is more often an issue for countries where health care systems rely on multiple insurers, as is the case for both the United States and Germany. Countries that rely on a **single-payer system**, such as Canada and Britain, typically encounter fewer challenges with cost containment but, as we will see, are more likely to struggle with issues of responsiveness. Nonetheless, the cost of health care in Canada relative to that in other OECD countries suggests that cost is also a problem in the Canadian health care system.

What a country spends on its health care system should not be confused with the health of its population. Japan spends a far lower percentage of its GDP on health care, yet its citizens enjoy the highest life expectancy in the world. Conversely, not only does the United States spend more money than any other country in the world on its health care system but Americans live shorter lives on average than most citizens in high-income countries. Thus, spending more money on one's health care system does not necessarily translate into better health for the population.

primary care:
Health care provided by physicians (such as family care doctors) and others who are trained to offer treatment and prevention services when individuals first seek health care and, ideally, as part of an ongoing provider-patient relationship.

specialist:
A medical doctor whose practice focuses on certain disease categories, types of patients, or methods of treatment that have been recognized as specialized areas in medicine.

FIGURE 11.1 Health Expenditure as a Percentage of GDP, Twenty-Nine OECD Countries, 2009.

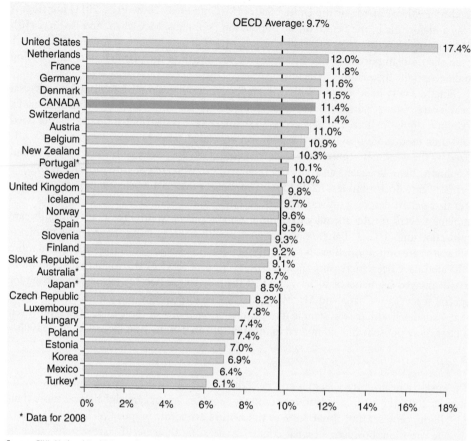

OECD Average: 9.7%

United States	17.4%
Netherlands	12.0%
France	11.8%
Germany	11.6%
Denmark	11.5%
CANADA	11.4%
Switzerland	11.4%
Austria	11.0%
Belgium	10.9%
New Zealand	10.3%
Portugal*	10.1%
Sweden	10.0%
United Kingdom	9.8%
Iceland	9.7%
Norway	9.6%
Spain	9.5%
Slovenia	9.3%
Finland	9.2%
Slovak Republic	9.1%
Australia*	8.7%
Japan*	8.5%
Czech Republic	8.2%
Luxembourg	7.8%
Hungary	7.4%
Poland	7.4%
Estonia	7.0%
Korea	6.9%
Mexico	6.4%
Turkey*	6.1%

0%   2%   4%   6%   8%   10%   12%   14%   16%   18%

* Data for 2008

Source: CIHI, *National Health Expenditure Trends, 1975 to 2011*, 2011.

Before we turn to the issue of efficiency (making the best possible use of resources to achieve health), we make one final comparison in terms of how countries differ in distributing the costs of health care between public and private sources. As we indicated in the previous chapter, the public share of health care in Canada has historically been around 70%. In Figure 11.2, we see that this percentage places Canada below the OECD average of 72.8% and in the bottom half of the distribution. As with overall costs, the public share of total health care costs across OECD countries varies widely, with the highest public share of health care occurring in Denmark (85.0%) and the lowest in the United States (47.7%).

Efficiency

technical efficiency:

The maximum possible improvement in an outcome that can be obtained from a set of resource inputs.

Related to the costs of a health care system is the issue of whether it operates efficiently, that is, whether the resources allocated to health care are spent in the best possible way to achieve health-related outcomes. **Technical efficiency** occurs when health care providers can produce equal or better outcomes at lower cost. Thus, low-cost and high-impact interventions should be preferred over high-cost and low-impact interventions. Although the WHO recommends that the optimal rate of caesarean sections in a given country be between 10 and 15%, some high- and middle-income countries, such as the United States, China, and Brazil, have rates that far exceed this. To the extent that excess rates point to procedures that are not only more costly than natural childbirth but medically unnecessary, these countries exhibit inefficiencies in their health care systems (Gibbons et al., 2010).

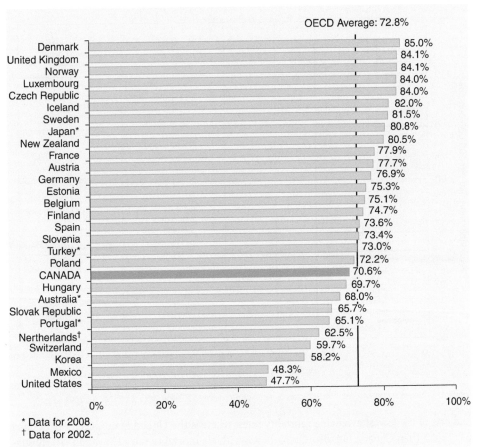

FIGURE 11.2 Public Share of Total Health Expenditure, Twenty-Nine OECD Countries, 2009.

OECD Average: 72.8%

Denmark	85.0%
United Kingdom	84.1%
Norway	84.1%
Luxembourg	84.0%
Czech Republic	84.0%
Iceland	82.0%
Sweden	81.5%
Japan*	80.8%
New Zealand	80.5%
France	77.9%
Austria	77.7%
Germany	76.9%
Estonia	75.3%
Belgium	75.1%
Finland	74.7%
Spain	73.6%
Slovenia	73.4%
Turkey*	73.0%
Poland	72.2%
CANADA	70.6%
Hungary	69.7%
Australia*	68.0%
Slovak Republic	65.7%
Portugal*	65.1%
Nertherlands†	62.5%
Switzerland	59.7%
Korea	58.2%
Mexico	48.3%
United States	47.7%

* Data for 2008.
† Data for 2002.

Source: CIHI, *National Health Expenditure Trends, 1975 to 2011*, 2011.

Similarly, cheap but equally effective generic drugs are more efficient than expensive patented drugs. For example, France saved more than 1.3 billion euros in health care costs in 2008 by adopting a policy of substituting generics for brand name drugs (WHO, 2010b).

Whereas technical efficiency is about how to provide health care at lower cost, **allocative efficiency** reflects decisions about whether something should be done and how much of it should be done. As such, allocative efficiency occurs when there is an optimal mix of services that maximizes the well-being of the community. This includes decisions about allocating resources within the health care system, such as how much should be devoted to preventative care, curative and rehabilitative functions, and medical research, as well as the optimal number of doctors and other health care workers.

Canadian doctors have long lobbied the government to increase the number of doctors in the country. In 2008, the Canadian Medical Association launched the "More Doctors, More Care" campaign to address a doctor shortage that was argued to present a crisis for the Canadian health care system and that, if left unaddressed, would erode the health of the Canadian population. To rebut this claim, Watson and McGrail (2009) evaluated the physician-to-population ratio in Canada and eighteen other high-income countries relative to the avoidable mortality rate in each country. Figure 11.3 presents their findings, showing that having a higher proportion of doctors in the population is not associated with achieving lower rates of avoidable mortality. Relative to Canada, Japan has both a lower physician-to-population ratio

allocative efficiency: The distribution of resources that maximizes the welfare of the community.

FIGURE 11.3
Avoidable mortality by physician supply, Nineteen Selected High-Income Countries, 2002.

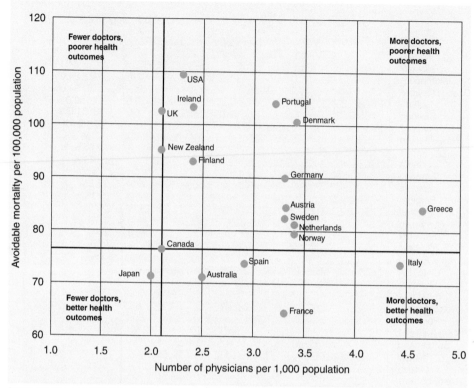

Source: D.E. Watson & K.M. McGrail, "More doctors or better care?" *Healthcare Policy*, Vol. 5 (1), Pg. 26-31, 2009.

and one of the lowest avoidable mortality rates, whereas the United States has more doctors per capita than Canada but also the highest avoidable mortality rate. The graph clearly suggests that Canada would be unlikely to reduce its avoidable mortality rate simply by increasing the number of doctors in the health care system.

Allocative efficiency is about not just the right mix within the health care system but also the allocation of resources spent on health care relative to other areas of government spending. For example, if a country spends so much on its health care system that it cannot afford to invest in education, pension plans, defence, and other areas of national interest, then resources are not being efficiently allocated. Similarly, heavily indebted poor countries have historically been forced to divert much of their revenue to repay international loans and thus have been unable to make critical investments in their own health care infrastructure.

Other countries may lack the means or the will to invest sufficiently in their health care systems. The second-poorest country in Latin America, Nicaragua, has a highly inefficient health care system. Inefficiency stems from a poorly administered social insurance program that creates disincentives for citizens to enrol in the plan, fails to collect contributions for those who are enrolled, and has a payment mechanism that encourages providers to skim off the healthiest citizens (Mathauer et al., 2010). Thus, the way in which the financing of the health care system in Nicaragua has been designed and implemented means that resources are both inequitably distributed (less than 18% of the population is covered by the plan, with resources flowing to those who are wealthier and healthier) and inefficient (under-resourced to provide the health care that is needed).

On a number of fronts, Canada's health care system is more efficient than that of the United States. First, Canada's single-payer system generates enormous savings compared to the United States, where the multitude of private and public insurers substantially drives up the administrative costs of the health care system. A recent analysis suggests that administrative costs in Canada's health care system are a quarter of the administrative costs in the United States (Morra et al., 2011). Stated differently, the United States could save as much as $28 billion a year if its administrative costs were more like Canada's.

Canada also achieves greater efficiency when provinces are able to negotiate directly with pharmaceutical manufacturers for lower prices. For instance, the Ontario Drug Benefit (ODB) plan, the public plan in Ontario and the largest plan in Canada, has successfully reduced the price of generics by more than 20% since 2006 (Silversides, 2009). Interestingly, the public drug plan in Québec has legislation that stipulates it pay no more for prescription drugs than the lowest price paid by any other province. In the long term, such tactics may undermine the efforts of other provinces to lower their drug costs and smaller provinces may end up paying higher prices because they have less purchasing power than the more populous provinces (Grootendoorst and Hollis, 2011). Nonetheless, the ability to negotiate directly with pharmaceutical manufacturers has produced greater efficiency than in the United States, where a fragmented health care system is less able to realize significant cost savings for its pharmaceuticals.

While it may be efficient relative to the United States, Canada's health care system is not as efficient as those of other countries. In 2000, the WHO ranked France and Italy as the best-performing health care systems in the world; however, Canada placed thirtieth, well behind most European nations (WHO, 2000). The United States ranked even farther behind at thirty-seven.

Responsiveness

A final criterion to evaluate the performance of a health care system is its responsiveness, which refers to how the health care system meets the needs and expectations of its citizens. Dimensions of responsiveness include respect for persons, confidentiality, prompt attention in emergencies and reasonable waiting times for non-emergency care, perceived quality of care, and whether one has choice.

Health care systems that are based on a single-payer system and that have control over capacity, as is the case in Canada and the United Kingdom, tend to perform well on cost containment but often struggle with responsiveness. This is evident in Table 11.1, which compares wait times in Canada, the United Kingdom, Germany, and the United States for different health care services. Of these four countries, the percentage waiting more than one hour for emergency care, more than six days to obtain a medical appointment, and more than four weeks to see a specialist is highest in Canada.

TABLE 11.1 Timeliness of Care in Four Countries, 2007–2008

	Canada	United Kingdom	Germany	United States
Percentage waiting more than one hour for emergency care	62	50	27	48
Percentage waiting more than six days for a medical appointment	34	14	26	23
Percentage waiting more than four weeks to see a specialist	60	58	32	26
Percentage waiting more than four months for elective/non-emergency surgery	27	30	5	8

Source: Adapted from: Karen Davis, Cathy Schoen, & Kristof Stremikis, *Mirror, Mirror on the Wall: How the Performance of the U.S. Health Care System Compares Internationally*, New York: The Commonwealth Fund, Exhibit 5, 2010.

The United Kingdom has the highest percentage waiting more than four months for elective or non-emergency surgery, but also the lowest percentage waiting more than six days for a medical appointment. The U.K. government has over the past few decades made numerous attempts to reduce the length of wait lists. Early efforts involved introducing a private parallel system whereby doctors in the public non-profit sector could also work in the private for-profit system. The rationale behind the parallel private system was to provide a safety valve that would release pressure and thus reduce the size of the waiting lists for the public system. Unlike Québec, which required doctors to work in either the public or the private system but not both, the United Kingdom allowed doctors to work in both systems. Because doctors were paid more for the same procedure in the private system, they had an incentive to keep public wait lists long as a means of increasing demand for more lucrative private services. An **unintended negative consequence** of introducing a private parallel system in Britain was that wait times actually began to increase. It took large funding boosts to the public system to produce substantial declines in wait lists, raising the question why the government hadn't simply invested in the public system in the first place (Tuohy, Flood, and Stabile, 2004; Willcox et al., 2007). As Table 11.1 demonstrates, wait times remain an issue for some services in the United Kingdom.

Table 11.1 also reveals that Germany and the United States, whose health care systems are both characterized by multiple insurers and fewer opportunities to constrain supply, have fewer of its citizens waiting for health care services. It is important to recognize, however, that the optimal wait time is never zero. That is, a health care system becomes massively inefficient when there is too much capacity; therefore, maintaining queues can contribute to the efficiency of a health care system, although determining what is optimal is likely to vary by country (Hurst and Siciliani, 2003).

In sum, on most of these criteria, Canada fares relatively well compared to the United States. The comparison is frequently made because of the close proximity and assumed similarities between the two countries. Yet, when Canada's health care system is compared to those of many other high-income countries, it is apparent that there is still room for improvement.

HEALTH CARE IN OTHER COUNTRIES

Having made some general comparisons between Canada and other OECD countries, we now take a closer look at the history and challenges of the health care systems of the United States, Germany, the United Kingdom, and China. Table 11.2 summarizes the characteristics of these systems.

The United States: Expensive and Inefficient

As the previous discussion has already suggested, the health care system of the United States is an outlier, different in almost every way from the health care systems of other high-income countries.

Structure of the Health Care System

Health care in the United States is primarily organized as an **entrepreneurial system**, that is, a system based on private enterprise and the search for profit. Consequently, health care is a complex and fragmented system of federal programs and private, for-profit insurance programs. Initiated in 1965 by the federal government, **Medicare** covers health care for virtually all Americans over age 65, as well as for some permanently disabled persons. Also begun in 1965, **Medicaid** is a means-tested program for the poor that is jointly funded by the federal

entrepreneurial system:
A system based on capitalism and free enterprise.

Medicare:
The federal insurance program, based on the Social Security system, that offers hospital insurance and medical insurance to those over age 65 and to permanently disabled persons.

Medicaid:
The joint federal-state health insurance program that pays the costs of health care for people with incomes below a certain (very low) amount.

TABLE 11.2
Characteristics of
Health Care Systems
in Other Countries.

Characteristics	Canada	United States	Germany	United Kingdom	China
Nature of system	National health insurance	Entrepreneurial	Social insurance	National health system	In flux
Role of private enterprise	Moderate	Very high	Moderate	Low but rising	Moderate and rising
Primary care doctors paid by:	Government, via fee-for-service payments	Wide variety of payers and mechanisms (private, government, capitation salary, etc.)	Government-regulated, non-profit social insurance, via fee-for-service and capitation payments	Government, via a form of capitation	Primarily individuals, as fee-for-service
Universal coverage	Yes	No	Yes	Yes	No, but good access for urban residents
Payment mechanism for hospital doctors	Salaried	Salaried and fee-for-service	Salaried	Salaried	Salaried
Payment mechanism for hospital expenses	Lump sum from government	Varied	Lump sum from government and social insurance	Lump sum from government	Lump sum from government, plus income from selling drugs a nd services

government and the states, but managed by the states. The **Children's Health Insurance Program (CHIP)** was implemented in 1997 to provide health care coverage for children who live in families whose incomes are modest but too high to be eligible for Medicaid.

A range of different commercial insurance schemes also exist in the U.S. health care system. During the Depression of the 1930s, the American Hospital Association and the American Medical Association (AMA) founded the nation's first major insurance programs: Blue Cross to cover individuals' hospital bills and Blue Shield to cover medical bills. These two plans have evolved into an association of private and independently operated companies that insure about one-third of all Americans (Blue Cross and Blue Shield Association, 2012). Americans enrolled in these plans pay for health care as they receive services and then seek reimbursement from their insurance plans. To maximize profits, these plans sell their insurance to people likely to be healthy (such as workers at major businesses), charge premiums based on an individual's predicted health risk (known as **actuarial risk rating**), and cover members' expenses only until preset yearly or lifetime limits are reached.

Health maintenance organizations (HMOs) also emerged during the 1930s. Early HMOs, such as Kaiser Permanente and the Group Health Cooperative of Puget Sound, were founded not to protect the incomes of doctors or hospitals but to provide affordable health

Children's Health Insurance Program (CHIP):
The joint federal-state health insurance program for children in families whose incomes are modest but too high to be eligible for Medicaid.

actuarial risk rating:
A system in which insurers try to maximize their financial gain by identifying and insuring only those populations that have low health risks.

health maintenance organizations (HMOs):
Organizations that provide health care based on prepaid group insurance. Patients pay a fixed yearly fee in exchange for a full range of health care services, including hospital care and doctor's services.

care. Unlike Blue Cross and Blue Shield, which reduced their costs by avoiding unhealthy members, HMOs reduced costs by requiring HMO members to use only HMO doctors who were paid on salary rather than through fee-for-service, keeping members healthy through preventive care, and monitoring doctors' behaviour to avoid unnecessary care.

Soaring health care costs in the 1980s led to a major reorganization of health care insurance and the emergence of managed care. **Managed care** refers to any system that controls costs through closely monitoring and controlling the decisions of health care providers. Most commonly, managed care organizations (MCOs) monitor and control costs through **utilization review**, in which doctors must obtain approval from the insurer before they can hospitalize a patient, perform surgery, order an expensive diagnostic test, or refer to a specialist outside the insurance plan. Those doctors who keep costs down are typically rewarded financially by MCOs. Although the terms *HMO* and *managed care* are often used interchangeably, HMOs represent only one form of managed care, and most insurers now also use managed care. Most Americans who have private insurance, and many who have government insurance, now belong to some form of managed care plan.

Purchasing Care

The kind of care Americans can access depends on the type of insurance plan. Currently, wealthy Americans can purchase any care they want from any willing provider. Americans who have **fee-for-service insurance** can seek care from any provider as long as they can afford the copayments and deductibles and, if their plan uses managed care, as long as their insurer approves the care. Finally, those who have Medicaid or Medicare coverage can obtain care only from providers willing to accept the relatively low rates of reimbursement offered by these programs, and those who have no health insurance can obtain care only from the few places willing to provide care on a charity basis.

Paying Doctors and Hospitals

Because of the complicated network of insurance schemes, there are many ways in which doctors in the United States are compensated for their work. These include **fee-for-service compensation** arrangements, where doctors are paid for each procedure they perform; **capitation**, where doctors are paid for each patient on their roster, regardless of how often they provide treatment to that patient; and salary, where doctors are paid an annual amount for their work.

Similarly, hospitals may be categorized into for-profit hospitals, which are generally privately owned, as well as non-profit hospitals and public hospitals, which serve the poor and underinsured, with the latter typically owned by the government. It appears that cost-containment programs at the state and federal levels have especially squeezed funding for public hospitals. Under any circumstances, it is difficult for these hospitals to make ends meet, because so many of their patients go to public hospitals only because they cannot afford to pay. To cover these costs, public hospitals rely on funding from state and local governments. This funding, however, has declined substantially in recent years, forcing hospitals to cut staff; close altogether; or, more often, close their emergency rooms (which are especially likely to lose money for hospitals).

Access to Care

Health insurance in the United States is typically linked to employment, with the majority of Americans receiving insurance through their employer or a family member's employer. As the economy tumbled in the mid-2000s, a growing number of newly unemployed Americans found themselves suddenly without insurance. Consequently, the proportion of

managed care:
A system that controls health care spending by monitoring closely how health care providers treat patients and where and when patients receive their health care.

utilization review:
A process in which insurance companies require doctors to get approval before ordering certain tests, performing surgery, hospitalizing a patient, or keeping a patient hospitalized more than a given number of days.

fee-for-service insurance:
Insurance that reimburses patients for all or part of the costs of the health care services they have purchased.

capitation:
A system in which doctors are paid a set annual fee for each patient in their practice, regardless of how many times they see their patients or what services the doctors provide for their patients.

Americans with employer-sponsored insurance declined from 63.5% to 58.8%; conversely, the proportion of uninsured Americans increased from 16.6% to 18.5% (49 million people) in 2011 (Kaiser Commission on Medicaid and the Uninsured, 2011). Increased enrolment in Medicaid and CHIP as a result of changes in federal legislation partially offset losses in private coverage. Even though more children were able to access health care through these two programs, many children continue to face numerous challenges in receiving the health care they need. Deamonte Driver's story, recounted in Box 11.2, illustrates the needless loss of life and inefficient use of resources that result when poor children are denied access to basic services.

BOX 11.2

IN THE NEWS

The Death of Deamonte Driver

Deamonte Driver grew up poor and, at the age of 12, died poor, when a tooth abscess led to a fatal brain infection (Otto, 2007).

Deamonte intermittently had Medicaid coverage, but neither he nor his brother ever received regular dental care. Most dentists across the country refuse to accept Medicaid patients; in Maryland, where Deamonte lived, less than 20% accept Medicaid and only about one-third of children on Medicaid receive dental care in any given year. In fact, for months before Deamonte fell ill, his mother, Alyce, had been trying to get dental care for his 10-year-old brother, DaShawn, whose teeth caused him constant pain. DaShawn finally got to see a dentist on October 5, 2006. That dentist informed his mother that six of DaShawn's teeth had abscesses and needed to be extracted. But no dental surgeon who accepted Medicaid would be available until January 16, 2007—three months later.

Even worse, on January 8, Alyce Driver learned that the boys' Medicaid insurance had lapsed, probably because some of the paperwork needed for annual renewal had mistakenly been sent to a homeless shelter where they used to live. Three days later, Deamonte (who had not complained about tooth problems, perhaps because his brother's problems seemed so much worse) came home from school with a headache. His health deteriorated rapidly, and the next day he received emergency brain surgery for an infection caused by an abscessed tooth—an infection that would probably never have developed if Deamonte had received regular dental care. Two weeks later, Deamonte died. The cost of his hospital care was more than $200,000—enough to buy a year's worth of preventive dental care for 2,000 children.

In response to Deamonte's death, the state of Maryland has raised reimbursement rates to encourage dentists to accept Medicaid patients, made it easier for Medicaid patients to find dentists, and earmarked funds for dental treatment and screening in schools (Otto, 2008). But around the nation, one-third of all Americans continue to lack access to affordable dental care (Berenson, 2008). Some of these will die as a result, not only due to brain infections but also due to heart disease and stroke exacerbated by gum disease and to oral cancers that could have been identified and treated successfully if the individuals had received routine dental care (Wu et al., 2000).

In addition to those who have no coverage, many more Americans have insurance that leaves them with more medical bills than they can afford to pay. These problems stem from required and increasingly expensive premiums, deductibles, and **copayments** (unreimbursable fees paid out of pocket each time one sees a doctor); long waiting periods before insurance covers preexisting conditions; caps on insurance reimbursement per treatment, per drug, per year, or per lifetime; and costs not covered by insurance, such as nursing-home care and prescriptions. About 25 million Americans are underinsured—20% of all insured adults under age 65 (Schoen et al., 2008). These numbers have increased by 60% since 2003, primarily because so many middle-class Americans now lack good insurance.

Just over half of underinsured Americans could not afford to seek needed medical care at some point during 2007, and just under half are already suffering financial stress because of medical bills (Schoen et al., 2008). Medical bills are responsible for between one-third and one-half of all personal bankruptcies in the United States, even though most people who file for bankruptcy have health insurance (Sered and Fernandopulle, 2005). Finally, in addition to the millions of Americans who are uninsured or underinsured, many more are

copayment:
Under some forms of health insurance, an unreimbursable fee that individuals must pay each time they see a health care provider. Fees can range from nominal sums to 20% of all costs.

precariously insured—liable to lose their insurance coverage at any time. Those who receive Medicaid lose their coverage once their income rises above a specified ceiling. Those who receive their insurance as part of a family plan can lose their insurance following divorce. Those who are covered through their own employment can lose coverage if they change to a job that does not offer insurance or where the insurance does not cover health problems they developed earlier. Finally, those whose employers either self-insure (thus avoiding state insurance regulations) or negotiate new insurance contracts yearly may have their insurance dropped if they or a family member becomes ill.

Controlling the Costs of Care

As we noted earlier, the United States vastly outspends every other country on its health care system. What accounts for the rising and unusually high costs of health care in the United States? If you ask the typical American, he or she is likely to respond with one of three popular myths about U.S. health care (Starr, 1994).

The first myth is that Americans receive more and better care than do citizens of other nations. Yet, on average, the reverse is true. Although Americans spend far more than other countries on health care, there are fewer hospital beds and fewer doctors per capita than in most high-income countries, so that Americans actually receive fewer days of inpatient hospital care and receive on average fewer and shorter doctor visits than citizens in other countries (Anderson et al., 2005).

A second myth attributes high health care costs to the uniquely American propensity for filing malpractice suits. Malpractice suits can raise prices both because doctors have to pay malpractice insurance premiums and because they may engage in **defensive medicine**—performing tests and procedures primarily to protect themselves against lawsuits. Federal researchers estimate, however, that the costs of the malpractice system account for no more than 2% of total U.S. health care costs (Beider and Hagen, 2004). Moreover, their data suggest that changing the malpractice system would not significantly reduce the number of unnecessary tests and procedures.

A third myth is that health care costs are so high in the United States because of its advanced technologies. Although these technologies certainly play a role in health care costs, they account for only a small fraction of all health care costs. Moreover, the same technologies exist in the other industrialized nations without producing equally high health care costs. Thus, the mere existence of technology cannot explain these costs.

If patient demand, malpractice costs, and advanced technology do not explain the rising costs of health care in the United States, what does? Research points to two underlying factors: a fragmented system that multiplies administrative costs and the fact that health care providers (doctors, hospitals, pharmaceutical companies, and so on) have greater power to set prices than do health care consumers, whether individuals, the government, or insurers (Reinhardt, Hussey, and Anderson, 2004; Bodenheimer, 2005a, 2005b, 2005c).

In addition to the question of why health care costs are so high in the United States, we must also ask why the United States is the only high-income country that lacks a universal health care system. Historically, opposition to national health care has come from numerous powerful sources (Quadagno, 2005). During the first half of the twentieth century, probably the most important opponent of national health care proposals was the AMA, which feared that such proposals might reduce doctors' incomes or autonomy. More surprisingly, labour unions opposed national health insurance because it would eliminate one of the major benefits they could offer members: the ability to press employers to offer health insurance. In addition, national health care was opposed by conservative politicians, who considered it socialistic, and by Southern politicians, who feared it would force racial integration of

defensive medicine:
Tests and procedures that doctors perform primarily to protect themselves against lawsuits rather than to protect their patients' health.

health care facilities. Meanwhile, the development of Blue Cross and Blue Shield in the mid-1930s freed most middle-class Americans from worrying about paying their health care bills. As a result, popular support for national health care among this important segment of the voting public declined, leaving insufficient stakeholder mobilization in favour of national health care to defeat its opponents (Quadagno, 2005; Rothman, 1997). Economic crises that arose in the 1980s and 1990s eroded the security of the middle class but failed to sway public opinion, particularly as antitax sentiment and distrust of "big government" became a powerful force in U.S. politics, making it difficult to generate support for any governmental programs (Rothman, 1997; Skocpol, 1996). Thus, a long history of attempts to reform health care in the United States have met with failure because powerful interest groups opposed it and the American public saw no reason to support it.

By 2008, however, with the election of Barack Obama, the time for health care reform seemed to have arrived. With the economy spinning out of control, the ranks of uninsured and underinsured rose rapidly, increasing public support for reform. Moreover, as the cost of insurance soared, many major employers who had traditionally paid most of their employees' insurance costs concluded that they could not compete in the global market unless these costs fell. As a result, the business community also came to support health care reform.

Health care reform was finally achieved in 2010 with the passage of the Patient Protection and Affordable Care Act (ACA), although it did not accomplish what many hoped for: the introduction of a universal health care system. Compromises to get the bill passed into law meant that practically speaking, as various parts of the bill are phased in (with complete implementation expected in 2018), Americans will have more ways to access health care than in the past. The main aspects of the bill are an individual mandate that requires each U.S. citizen and legal resident to obtain health insurance or face fines and an employer mandate that requires employers to subsidize health insurance for their workers. States are required to establish non-profit or state-run "health exchanges" through which individuals and small businesses can purchase coverage (helped by subsidies and tax credits for middle- and working-class individuals). The aim is to lower the cost of insurance by combining many individuals together in these exchanges, thus sharing and presumably reducing the health risks as a whole. Finally, the ACA imposes new restrictions on insurance companies, prohibiting them from capping annual or lifetime benefits, refusing to cover those with pre-existing health problems, or charging higher premiums to such individuals.

There is mixed reaction to the potential benefits of ACA. On one hand, millions of Americans will finally have access to health care, yet, frustratingly, nearly 6% of the American population will still lack insurance (Williams et al., 2010). Because the system remains entrepreneurial, for-profit insurers must still find ways to make a profit, which may produce **unintended negative consequences**. For example, new ACA regulations require insurance companies that sell individual health insurance policies for children to cover children with preexisting conditions. In response, several of the largest insurance companies have stopped selling *any* individual policies for children. It is also anticipated that, in the long term, the costs to the government and thus consumers are likely to expand dramatically. The ACA continues the nation's reliance on a vast web of insurers, thus guaranteeing huge administrative costs and inefficiencies. Moreover, provisions to impose cost control mechanisms were dropped from the bill before it was passed, weakening the ability of the government to contain costs.

It will be some time, however, before the full impact of the ACA becomes known. Whether it is ever fully implemented is also debatable. In June 2012, the U.S. Supreme Court ruled in a narrow 5–4 decision on the constitutionality of the individual mandate that the federal government does have the right to compel individuals to purchase health insurance. Nonetheless, the country remains fiercely divided on what is increasingly referred to as Obamacare, and Republicans have vowed to abolish it in the future should they be in a position to do so.

Health Outcomes

Not only is the U.S. health care system costly and inefficient, but the health of the American people ranks well behind and often last compared to most high-income countries (Kaplan and McFarland, 2004; UNICEF, 2007). Moreover, Americans appear to be falling farther and farther behind other high-income countries on most health indicators (Williams et al., 2010). These trends have led some social scientists to make an astounding observation: It is possible that the pattern of increased life expectancy that Americans have experienced over the past two centuries is about to come to an end (Olshansky et al., 2005). From this vantage point, Americans need to make some fundamental changes, including the organization of their health care system, to catch up to the health status of other countries and to improve the health of their population.

Germany: Social Insurance for Health Care

Modern Germany is the product of a tumultuous twentieth-century history, including more than a decade of Nazism and the division of the country in two following its defeat in World War II. Yet, despite the destruction wrought by two World Wars and the economic stresses that accompanied the reunification of East and West Germany in 1990, the nation is a stable constitutional democracy that enjoys one of the strongest economies, amidst ongoing economic turmoil in the European Union.

Structure of the Health Care System

Germany has a universal, multi-payer health care system whereby citizens must purchase health care through social insurance. Social insurance refers to the banding together of social groups, such as cities, occupations, or industries, to provide insurance for their residents or members. This system was adopted in 1883 by politicians who hoped that by offering workers accessible health care, as well as housing, unemployment, and retirement benefits, they could diffuse political tensions that might otherwise have led to a more radical redistribution of power and wealth in German society (Lassey, Lassey, and Jinks, 1997).

Purchasing Care

sickness funds:
German insurance programs offered by non-profit groups to serve a given occupation, geographic location, or employer.

Whereas in the United States, insurance providers compete in a profit-driven market, in Germany about 90% of health insurance is provided by government-regulated non-profit social insurance groups known as **sickness funds**. The cost of belonging to a sickness fund is about 15% of income (half paid by the individual for his or her entire family, half paid by the employer). Because costs are based on income, the system is financially progressive, placing the heaviest financial burdens on those who can best afford it. Private health insurance is available for the self-employed and high-income earners who may opt out of the sickness funds; however, private funds are also heavily regulated by the government. Approximately 10% of Germans purchase private health insurance (Or et al., 2010).

Paying Doctors and Hospitals

ambulatory care doctors:
Physicians whose work takes place outside of hospitals, whether specialists or primary care practitioners.

German doctors are sharply divided into hospital doctors and **ambulatory care** doctors (i.e., those who work outside of hospitals). Hospital doctors are paid on salary, based on specialty and seniority, but can earn extra income by running outpatient clinics or performing outpatient surgery. In contrast, ambulatory care doctors typically work in solo practice and are generally paid on a fee-for-service basis, although some are paid by capitation, where doctors are paid a set annual fee for each patient in their practice, regardless of how many times they see their patients or what services the doctors provide. In such a system, doctors lose income when they provide more services.

To pay doctors for their services, the sickness funds each year give their regional medical associations most of the premiums the funds collect from individuals, employers, and the government. In turn, the medical associations each year set fee schedules and then reimburse the doctors in their region according to those schedules. Hospital operating expenses are paid by the sickness funds, and their capital expenses, such as new MRI machines or surgical suites, are paid by the government in yearly lump sums.

Access to Care

All Germans receive a comprehensive package of health care benefits. With the exception of minimal copayments, insurance covers all costs of dental care, maternity care, hospitalization, ambulatory care, prescription drugs, preventive measures such as vaccinations, and income lost because of illness. As a result, Germans have few incentives to put off obtaining needed care but must get referrals to see hospital-based specialists.

Controlling the Costs of Care

Compared to other OECD countries in 2009, Germany has one of the more expensive health care systems (see Figure 11.1). A major factor driving up costs of health care in Germany is the oversupply of doctors. To control this, Germany forbids doctors over age 68 from working for the sickness funds, forbids doctors from opening practices in overserved areas, and shifted from paying doctors on a fee-for-service basis to paying by capitation. Finally, to control drug costs, the sickness funds encourage doctors and consumers, through both education and economic incentives, to adopt more cost-effective drugs.

Health Outcomes

Whether because of its health care system or because of its high standard of living and commitment to providing social services to its population, Germany enjoys a very high standard of health. Although conditions in the former East Germany remain poorer than in the former West Germany, these differences are rapidly disappearing. Life expectancy in Germany now averages 80 years, and infant mortality is among the lowest in the world: 3.4 per 1,000 live births (Population Reference Bureau, 2012).

The United Kingdom: National Health Service

As the home of the Industrial Revolution, Britain for many decades was a leading industrial power. Along with its industrial strength came a strong labour movement, as workers united to gain political power within Britain's parliamentary government. As a result, a commitment to protecting its citizens, including a commitment to universal health care coverage, has long been central to Britain's identity. During the 1980s and into the 1990s, however, the nation's economy declined while health care costs rose. In response, the government (led at the time by the Conservative Party) instituted a series of reforms that introduced market principles into the health care system. Successive governments (both Labour and Conservative) have instituted further market reforms, while assuring the public of their commitment to universal health coverage. Our discussion focuses on the structure of the National Health Service in England, which is part of the United Kingdom.

Structure of the Health Care System

Since 1948, England has provided care through its **National Health Service (NHS)**. The NHS is one of the world's largest employers, with 1.3 million people in its workforce. Thus, physicians as well as other health care workers are employed by the state, typically on a contract basis.

National Health Service (NHS):
A system in which the government directly pays all costs of health care for its citizens.

Purchasing Care

The NHS uses tax revenues to pay virtually all costs for a wide range of health care services, including medical care, visiting nurses for the homebound, homemakers for chronically ill persons, and some aspects of long-term care. Thus, more health care services are covered in England than in Canada. As is the case in Canada, the health care system is paid for through graduated income taxes and thus is financially progressive.

Paying Doctors and Hospitals

As in Germany, almost all medical specialists work as salaried employees of the NHS at hospitals or other health care facilities, although they can earn extra income by seeing private patients. In contrast, most English general practitioners work as private contractors, increasingly in large group practices. General practitioners are paid by a version of capitation: They receive a set fee from the government at the beginning of the year based both on the number of patients they have in their practice and on the specific services they agree to offer directly to their patients or to purchase for their patients (such as hospital care). In addition, general practitioners receive financial supplements if they have low-income or elderly patients; practise in medically underserved areas; or meet government targets for preventive services, such as immunizing more than a certain percentage of children in their practices.

The vast majority of hospitals in England belong to the government (although some now include beds for private patients). However, these hospitals operate semiautonomously, raising funds to support their operations by bidding against each other for contracts to cover hospital care for patients from a given area.

Access to Care

Under the NHS, individual financial difficulties do not keep English citizens from receiving necessary medical care. In addition, the NHS has substantially reduced the geographic inequities that for generations made medical care inaccessible to many rural dwellers, although access to care remains a problem in poor, inner-city neighbourhoods.

Controlling the Costs of Care

As noted earlier, the United Kingdom spent about 9.8% of its GDP on health care in 2009—well below what was spent in Canada (CIHI, 2011a). England has made its health funds go farther than they otherwise would through national and regional planning and by keeping salaries relatively low. Because the government owns a large proportion of health care facilities and employs a large proportion of health care personnel, it can base decisions about developing, expanding, and locating high-technology facilities on a rational assessment of how best to use available resources and can avoid the unnecessary proliferation of expensive facilities. Such decisions are made by a semiautonomous government body called the Institute for Innovation and Improvement.

In addition, England has attempted to restrain government health care expenditures by promoting privatization. Doctors can now take private patients as well as NHS patients, private companies can now run primary care practices funded by the NHS, private hospitals can compete for NHS contracts against public hospitals, and individuals can purchase private health insurance to pay for care outside the NHS. As we noted earlier in this chapter, this has produced unintended negative consequences, such that competition between private and public sources initially increased wait times for those in the public system, with reductions only occurring after the government increased funding to the public system (Tuohy et al., 2004).

Health Outcomes

Despite some access problems in the NHS, health outcomes have remained good. Infant mortality is lower than in Canada (4.3 versus 5.1), although life expectancy for Canadians is one year higher, with Britons living on average for 80 years compared to 81 for Canada (Population Reference Bureau, 2012).

China: Good Health at Low Cost

Although many observers view the health care systems of Germany, Canada, and the United Kingdom as models for other countries, few would seriously propose China (officially known as the People's Republic of China) as a viable model. China's culture differs greatly from that of Canada, and so its citizenry has very different values regarding what constitutes an acceptable health care system. Nevertheless, China's past successes suggest how focusing on primary care and public health can make it possible for poor countries to provide their citizens with good health care (Riley, 2007).

China's health care system reflects its unique history and situation (Lassey et al., 1997). When, after many years of civil war, the Communist Party in 1949 won control of mainland China, it found itself in charge of a vast, poverty-stricken, largely agricultural, and densely populated nation. Most lived in abject misery, while a small few enjoyed great wealth. Malnutrition and famine occurred periodically, life expectancies for both men and women were low, and infant and maternal mortality were shockingly high. In urban areas, only the elite could typically afford medical care, whereas in rural areas, where most of the population lived, Western medical care barely existed.

Structure of the Health Care System

In 1950, one year after winning control of mainland China, the Communist government announced four basic principles for the new nation's health care system (Anson and Sun, 2005: 10). First, the primary goal of the health care system would be to improve the health of the masses rather than of the elite. Second, the health care system would emphasize prevention rather than cure. Third, to attain health for all, the country would rely heavily on mass campaigns. Fourth, the health care system would integrate Western medicine with traditional Chinese medicine.

These principles reflected both the political climate and the practical realities of the new People's Republic of China. The first goal—improving the health of the masses—stemmed directly from the communist political philosophy underpinning the revolution. The years of bloodshed were to be justified by a new system that would more equitably redistribute the nation's wealth and raise the living standards and health status of China's people. The second and third goals reflected unignorable facts about China's situation. Lacking both a developed technological base and an educated citizenry, China's greatest resource was the sheer labour power of its enormous population, which could be efficiently mobilized because of its now-centralized economy. Focusing on prevention through mass campaigns promised to deliver the quickest improvements in the nation's health. Finally, the decision to encourage both Western and traditional medicine similarly recognized the difficulties China would face in developing a Western health care system, as well as the benefits of including traditional medicine in any new system. By encouraging traditional as well as Western medicine, China could take advantage of its existing health care resources and gain the support of the peasantry, who remained skeptical of Western medicine. At the same time, incorporating traditional medicine into the new, modernized Chinese health care system offered a powerful statement to the world regarding the new nation's pride in its traditional culture. Simultaneously encouraging the growth of Western medicine, meanwhile, would help bring China into the scientific mainstream.

Given its large and poverty-stricken population and its lack of financial resources and medically trained personnel, China needed to adopt innovative strategies if it were to meet its goal of improving the health of the common people. Two of these strategies were the use of mass campaigns and the development of physician extenders.

Mass Campaigns

One of the more unusual aspects of China's health care policy has been its emphasis, especially in the early years of the People's Republic, on mass campaigns (Horn, 1969). For example, to combat syphilis, which was **endemic** in much of China when the Communists came to power, the government first closed all brothels, outlawed prostitution, and retrained former prostitutes for other work. Second, the government began the process of redistributing income and shifting to a socialist economy so that no young women would need to enter prostitution to survive. During the next decade, the government trained thousands of physician extenders to identify persons likely to have syphilis by asking ten simple questions, such as whether the person had ever had a genital sore. By so doing, the government made manageable the task of finding, in a very populous country, the small percentage that needed to be tested and treated for syphilis.

To convince people to come to health centres for testing, these physician extenders held mandatory political meetings in villages, performed educational plays in marketplaces, and gave talks around the country, all to explain the importance of eradicating syphilis and attempting to reduce the stigma of seeking treatment for syphilis by defining the disease as a product of the corrupt former regime rather than a matter of individual guilt. Those identified as likely to have syphilis were tested and treated if needed. These methods—coupled with testing, among others, persons applying for marriage licenses, newly drafted soldiers, and entire populations in areas where syphilis was especially common—dramatically reduced the **prevalence** of syphilis in China.

Physician Extenders

The second innovative strategy for which China has won acclaim is its use of **physician extenders**, in addition to medical doctors trained in Western and (rarely) traditional medicine. In urban areas, **street doctors** offer both primary care and basic emergency care, as well as health education, immunization, and assistance with birth control. Street doctors have little formal training and work in outpatient clinics under doctors' supervision.

In rural areas, **village doctors** played a similar role. Village doctors were first used in 1965 during China's Cultural Revolution, a political movement started by students and fostered by some members of the national government to uproot the new bureaucratic elite

physician extenders:
Health care providers who have less education than physicians but who can, at lower costs, take over some of the tasks traditionally done by physicians.

street doctors:
Chinese health care workers with little formal training who work in urban outpatient clinics under the supervision of a doctor.

village doctors:
Chinese agricultural workers who receive a few months of training in health care and provide basic health services to members of their agricultural production team.

and the last vestiges of the old class structure (as well as to eliminate political dissidents). Village doctors, it was hoped, would alleviate the continued lack of health care providers in rural areas as well as reduce the political power of urban medical doctors, who were a reminder of the precommunist elites. Novice village doctors were selected for health care training by their fellow workers based on their aptitude for health work, personal qualities, and political "purity." Following about three months of training (supplemented yearly by continuing education), village doctors returned to their rural communes, dividing their time between agricultural labour and health care. Since the end of the Cultural Revolution in 1976, however, the number of village doctors has declined substantially, and rural areas are now substantially underserved.

Above village doctors in the Chinese health care hierarchy are **assistant doctors**. These individuals receive three years of postsecondary training similar to that received by medical doctors, during which they learn both Western and traditional Chinese medicine. Assistant doctors can both provide primary care and perform minor surgery.

assistant doctors: Chinese health care workers who receive three years of postsecondary training, similar to that of doctors, in both Western and traditional Chinese medicine.

Purchasing Care

As China's economy changed from a largely socialized and centrally controlled system toward a more decentralized, economically heterogeneous model, so did its health care system (Chen, 2001; Lassey et al., 1997; Wang, Xu, and Xu, 2007). For the majority of urban residents, these shifts brought few changes. As in the past, the government pays most costs of health insurance and health care for government employees, military personnel, and students. Public industries and urban industrial collectives also pay for care for their workers. The growing and now significant numbers of urban residents who work in private enterprises, however, often lack any health insurance.

For rural Chinese—about 60% of China's population—reforms served to dramatically reduce access to health care (Wang et al., 2007). Before the 1980s, rural residents received their care at little or no cost through the agricultural communes where they lived and worked. Within these communes, members shared all profits and costs, including those for health care. Each commune had between 15,000 and 50,000 members, several village doctors, and a clinic staffed by assistant doctors.

Beginning in the early 1980s, most agricultural communes reverted to their original non-communal village structures, with each family given land to farm by the village. Families were able to keep their profits but became responsible for their own welfare should costs exceed profits. Due to this shift in financing, the former communes could no longer earn sufficient revenues to continue providing health care. Many village doctors returned to full-time agricultural work, and most rural assistant doctors moved to township or city clinics. Almost all rural residents received their primary health care on a fee-for-service basis, and financial difficulties forced many to cut back on needed care. Consequently, only 21% of rural dwellers had health insurance by 2004 (Manning, 2011).

Paying Doctors and Hospitals

Currently, ambulatory care doctors in China work primarily on a fee-for-service basis and hospital doctors work on salary. In addition, many townships (made up of six or more rural villages) have a clinic where doctors work on salary but are allowed to divide among themselves any profits that the clinic generates. As a result, doctors have an incentive to order unnecessary tests and procedures (Wang et al., 2007).

Hospitals have also been subject to restriction as budgets have been cut and great pressure has been placed on hospitals to generate income through selling drugs and services and by starting other enterprises. Privatization of hospitals has also occurred.

Access to Care

Because of the changes in China's health care system, prices for health care have risen and access has diminished, especially in rural areas, where fewer hospital beds and doctors are available per capita. Although primary care remains affordable, even for those who lack health insurance, hospital care is not.

To equalize access to care, the government has established a national fund to supplement the health care budgets of poorer regions and an insurance program for childhood immunizations. Those who, for a small premium, purchase this insurance receive free immunization for children to age 7 and free treatment if a child develops one of the infectious diseases the immunization program is supposed to prevent. More than half of all children in the country belong to this program. Finally, a similar insurance program offers prenatal and postnatal care to women and infants; it is not known how many are covered by this program.

China's health care problems have been recognized for some time. The same report that ranked Canada and the United States thirtieth and thirty-seventh, respectively, in terms of the performance of the health care system, ranked China at 144th out of 191 countries. In April 2009, China formally announced plans to reform its health care system, with five specific elements (Manning, 2011). First, the government aims to reverse the pattern of declining coverage and availability of health care services in rural areas by increasing coverage to 90% of the rural population by 2020. Second, the government plans major investments in the hospital system that will reverse the trend toward privatizing the system and bring costs back under government control. A third element is to bring pharmaceutical drugs under government control by taking them out of the operations of hospitals and administering them through a government-sponsored insurance program. Fourth, China intends to move from an expensive hospital-based system to a locally organized system that makes use of lower-cost family doctors and nurses. Finally, the government aims to develop a public health system to promote better surveillance of diseases in the population.

As with recent reforms in the United States, it will be some time before the effects of these changes are known and there is some uncertainty as to whether any or all parts of the plan will come to pass. Several decades of failure have diminished trust in the government, and China's health care system has already been so heavily deregulated and privatized that implementation of some of these reforms will pose significant challenge to the Chinese government.

Health Outcomes

As a middle-income country, China spends only 4.6% of its GDP on health care (OECD, 2011). In the past, China's commitment to equalizing both income and health care allowed it to attain health outcomes far greater than its economic status or investment in health care might predict. Whereas in 1960 infant mortality was 150 deaths per 1,000 and life expectancy was 47 years, currently infant mortality is 17 per 1,000 and life expectancy is 75 (Population Reference Bureau, 2012).

As we described in Chapter 6, three factors seem to explain how China (like Sri Lanka, Costa Rica, Vietnam, and Cuba) achieved excellent health outcomes at low cost (Caldwell, 1993; Riley, 2007). Not surprisingly, health outcomes improved when access to medical care improved. But improved health outcomes depended much more strongly on emphasizing family planning; raising education levels among men; and, especially, raising education levels among women. Once women's educational levels increased, their power in the family increased, giving them greater control over family planning. Women's lives thus were less often cut short by childbirth, and their babies were born healthier. In addition, as women's status rose, they and the children who depended on them more often received a fair share of the family's food, thus reducing malnutrition and increasing life expectancies.

IMPLICATIONS

As the costs of health care continue to rise in Canada and most countries, it is helpful to examine how other countries have tried to deal with these challenges. All the countries described in this chapter illustrate how establishing government control over both operating and capital budgets for hospitals and other facilities can restrict the duplication of services and proliferation of technologies that have driven up the costs of the existing system. While Canada has had some success in this regard, a rigorous comparison of Canada's health care system with those in other countries suggests that Canada may fare less well than many high-income countries in managing the costs of health care.

Interestingly, efforts to contain costs may sometimes produce unintended negative consequences. Thus, both the United States and China have encountered powerful resistance in realizing reforms that aim to establish universal coverage for all their citizens. This suggests that to achieve true change, the citizens of these countries must be willing to challenge the power dynamics underlying their current systems. Similarly, introducing market reforms in England has at times exacerbated the very problem (long waiting lists) that such changes were meant to fix.

We also recognize that what a country spends on health care is not a very strong predictor of the overall health of the population, suggesting that more money spent on health care does not always translate into better health. The United States, a country that spends more on health care than any other in the world, appears to receive little for its investment given that the health of the American population ranks more poorly on all health indicators than in most other OECD countries. Conversely, China has historically achieved substantial improvements in population health with much fewer resources.

SUMMARY

LO-1 1. Sociologists maintain an interest in cross-national comparisons of health care systems for a variety of reasons, including that issues of power are often central to understanding why and with what consequence countries vary in the organization of their health care systems.

LO-2 2. According to the convergence hypothesis, scientific, technological, economic, and epidemiological forces compel largely capitalist countries to *restrict* market forces in health care, while pressing largely socialist countries to *increase* market forces.

LO-3 3. With a universal health care system, Canada achieves greater equity in access to health care services than does the United States, where health care services are based on ability to pay rather than need. Nonetheless, Canada's health care system exhibits some issues with equity as evidenced by the higher utilization of specialist services among more advantaged segments of society and an emerging trend that suggests that the wealthy and more educated have been increasing their use of health care services at a higher rate over the past twenty-five years than poorer Canadians.

LO-3 4. The cost of a health care system is typically evaluated in terms of what a country spends in a given year on health care relative to its economic output for that year. As a percentage of GDP, Canada spent more on its health care system (11.4%) in 2009 than many other OECD countries. Similarly, the public share of health care expenditures in Canada in 2009 was approximately 70%, which is lower than in many OECD countries.

LO-3   5.   A health care system is efficient when the resources allocated to health care are spent in the best possible way to achieve health-related outcomes. With strict government control on supply, including the number of physicians, Canada has a relatively efficient system; however, there is room for improvement.

LO-3   6.   Responsiveness refers to how the health care system meets the needs and expectations of its citizens. Canada continues to face significant challenges in wait lists, with a higher proportion of Canadians waiting substantially longer periods of time for health care services than citizens in the United Kingdom, Germany, and the United States.

LO-4   7.   Health care in the United States is inequitable, costly, and inefficient. Although the system is generally more responsive with shorter waiting lists for health care services than many countries, the short queues contribute to higher inefficiency.

LO-4   8.   Health care reform through the Patient Protection and Affordable Care Act will give millions of Americans access to health care, but 6% of the population will still lack health insurance. Moreover, the lack of cost containment measures makes it likely that health care costs will continue to rise, even as the health status of Americans lags farther behind those of other high-income countries.

LO-4   9.   Health care in Germany is overwhelmingly obtained through non-profit social insurance plans known as sickness funds. Germany is also a costly health care system, and efforts to control costs have meant increased government control over physician supply and shifting compensation for medical services from fee-for-service to capitation.

LO-4   10.   The United Kingdom provides universal access to health care through its government-run National Health Service. Due in part to its single-payer system, health care costs in England are lower than in other high-income countries, but efforts to improve responsiveness by reducing waiting lists have met with mixed success.

LO-4   11.   By emphasizing mass campaigns and physician extenders, China was able to improve access to care and quality of care for millions of poor citizens. Life expectancy also rose because the government committed to family planning and to public education for men and, more importantly, women.

LO-4   12.   As China's economy has become more capitalistic and decentralized, it has moved toward a fee-for-service system. Access to care has declined, especially in rural areas and among urban residents who work for private businesses. An announcement in 2009 to move toward universal health care coverage would reverse this trend if followed through, but it will be some time before the success of this initiative can be fully evaluated.

REVIEW QUESTIONS

1.   How might the interests of sociologists differ from those of health economists and political scientists when conducting cross-national comparisons of health care systems?

2.   What is the convergence hypothesis? What evidence of convergence can be found in the histories of health care in Great Britain and China?

3.   Evaluate how Canada's health care system performs relative to those in other high-income countries in terms of equity, cost, efficiency, and responsiveness.

4.   How does access to health care in Canada compare with access in the United States, and what are the consequences of these differences for health?

5. What prevents some countries from attaining allocative efficiency in their health care systems?
6. In what ways can a health care system become more responsive to the needs of its citizens? What impact might these changes have on the cost and efficiency of health care?
7. In what ways will the Affordable Care Act make the health care systems in the United States and Germany more similar? In what ways will they remain different?
8. What aspects of the health care systems in the United States and England have helped them to restrain costs? What aspects have kept costs high?
9. How has the rise of market forces affected health care in England and China?

CRITICAL THINKING QUESTIONS

1. Compare and contrast the health care system in Canada with the system in one other country. Explain which system you would prefer.
2. What areas of Canada's health care system do you think should be reformed, and how might this be accomplished?

KEY TERMS

actuarial risk rating (p. 269)
allocative efficiency (p. 265)
ambulatory care doctors (p. 274)
assistant doctors (p. 279)
capitation (p. 270)
Children's Health Insurance Program
    (CHIP) (p. 269)
convergence hypothesis (p. 259)
copayment (p. 271)
defensive medicine (p. 272)
entrepreneurial system (p. 268)
equity in access (p. 261)
fee-for-service insurance (p. 270)
health maintenance organizations (HMOs)
    (p. 269)

managed care (p. 270)
Medicaid (p. 268)
Medicare (p. 268)
National Health Service (NHS) (p. 276)
physician extenders (p. 278)
primary care (p. 263)
sickness funds (p. 274)
specialist (p. 263)
street doctors (p. 278)
technical efficiency (p. 264)
universal coverage (p. 261)
utilization review (p. 270)
village doctors (p. 278)

12

Health Care Professions

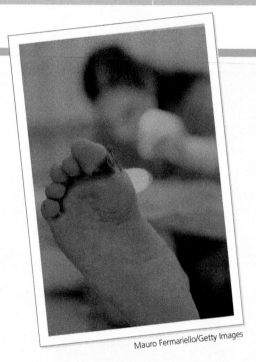

Mauro Fermariello/Getty Images

The Autopsy: Training to Be Doctors

The three students stood beside the wrapped body lying on the metal table. They all wore clean, new laboratory coats that still had creases down the arms and over the breast pockets from being folded and stacked in a box. These white coats were the same size, even though the wearers were of varying build. All three medical students were size medium, but differently framed. Ming had her cuffs rolled up twice.

They had come in from the hot early afternoon of an autumn day, a remnant of summer. They had entered the basement by an unmarked inner staircase, and then approached the lab through a plain, combination locked door. There were fourteen dissection rooms, eight tables per room, three students assigned per table, checking the tags to find their cadaver, whispering and shuffling like white-coated ghosts in the basement anatomy lab. No windows. Instead, a dry fluorescent light flattened every surface....

Dr. Harrison, their anatomy demonstrator, appeared at their table, congratulated them upon entering the study of medicine, and said, "This fine cadaver is your first patient. Dignity and decorum are crucial. You must be mindful of this gift you are given, and treat your patient nobly." He paused. "Nobility. You may give him... or her?" Harrison checked the tag. "Ah, him, a name if you like. Or not. That's up to you. No frivolous names. Questions? No? Very well. Continue, then." All of this he managed to say with his hands crossed neatly in front of himself, and then he was at the next table, nodding seriously....

Sri now held the scalpel like a pen. He looked at the manual. The manual was very particular, and Sri wanted to follow it with clarity. The incision should begin at the top of the sternum, extend downward to the xiphoid. A central incision it said. Ming opened the fabric, pulled it to either side, the nipples purple on the rubber-cold skin. Still not moving, Sri stared at the manual's exact instructions. There was a dotted line from the top of the sternum in the illustration, an arrow pointing toward the navel but stopping short of it. Sri straightened the veil, covered the nipples. He gripped the scalpel hard, like a dull pencil.

"Right down the middle," said Ming. "Like a zipper. But if you're going to take forever—"

Sri grabbed the scalpel handle like a stick and buried the short, triangular blade in the midline of the chest. Flesh gripped the blade, and through the handle Sri felt its texture—thick and chalky. Steel scraping on sternum. Sri thought of a beach—of writing with a stick in hard sand thrown halfway up from the tide, with the water not far away. Through his knuckles, Sri felt fibres tearing. The cadaver's flesh pulled hard at him now. Halfway there. It ripped at Sri, to cut this skin. He tore it, forced his way through. He pulled open the cotton shroud. This old, wrung-out chest with small lopsided man breasts. Above the left nipple were four tattooed hearts in purple, the shape of the designs twisted by the skin's movement through its years. A clean, jagged tear through the centre—the sternum white beneath. Sri was amazed by the pale ivory of this man's bone.

The three of them stood erect at the shining cold table. The man now lay slightly unwrapped. The cloths wound around themselves up and over his neck, then tenderly wrapped the face. They had been told the heads would all be shaved. The table was indented, and the indentation traced down to a hole between the feet. The hole opened into a spout over a bucket so fluids could escape as they ran down the table. On the steel was the man-form in soaked cloth. His chest was gashed now. The chest was not shaved but thick with cold hair. Hair parted now by one crooked stabbing cut that peeled open the front.

"Good job, Sri," said Chen.

Excerpted from *Bloodletting and Miraculous Cures* by Vincent Lam. Copyright © 2006 Vincent Lam. Reprinted by permission of Doubleday Canada.

LEARNING OBJECTIVES

In this chapter, students should be able to:

LO-1 **Describe** the characteristics of a profession and **understand** that medicine has become the premier example of a profession.

LO-2 **Identify** the sources of threat to medical dominance and **describe** how each is eroding physicians' power and autonomy.

LO-3 **Describe** the process of professional socialization that transforms medical students into medical doctors and **evaluate** the consequences of adopting medical norms for medical practice.

LO-4 **Recognize** that professionalization is an ongoing process, whereby structural change offers opportunities for those occupations seeking to elevate their status and challenges for those occupations seeking to maintain dominance.

LO-5 **Describe** how occupations such as nursing, pharmacy, midwifery, and chiropractic have historically attempted to attain professional status, and **evaluate** the current status of each.

LO-6 **Identify** characteristics associated with complementary and alternative medicine (CAM) and **describe** the efforts of medicine to co-opt and control CAM.

In this chapter, we look more broadly at the social organization of the health care occupations, describing the relative power of those who work in the health care industry and evaluating the ways in which **professionalization** is an ongoing process, so that one's status in the occupational hierarchy is never assured and thus may fluctuate over time. We start by investigating whether the power of allopathic doctors persists in the twenty-first century, identifying contemporary sources of threat to medical dominance. We also explore the process through which new doctors learn medical skills and are socialized into their profession. We then turn our attention to other health care occupations both within and outside the mainstream health care system, including nurses, pharmacists, midwives, and chiropractors, showing how ongoing struggles can lead to gains in power for some professions (pharmacy) and losses for others (chiropractic). Finally, we discuss complementary and alternative medicine (CAM) and describe how mainstream medicine has used science to co-opt and control various aspects of CAM.

professionalization: The process through which an occupation achieves professional status.

MEDICINE AS A PROFESSION

In Chapter 10, we traced the history of the efforts by allopathic physicians to achieve **medical dominance,** noting that this goal was reached in 1912 with the passage of the Canada

Medical Act, which freed doctors from control by other occupations and gave them the ability to control other health occupations. From this point forward, medical doctors have enjoyed almost complete control over all aspects of medicine. Thus, most doctors worked in private practice (whether solo or group), where they set their own conditions of work. Those who worked in hospitals or clinics were typically supervised by other doctors, not by non-medical administrators. Moreover, doctors regularly supervised the members of other health care occupations. It was common for doctors to serve on boards charged with judging the education and qualifications of other health care occupations, but members of other occupations had little say in setting standards for medical education and licensing.

On the basis of their position at the top of the health care occupational structure, doctors have become the premier example of a **profession** (Parsons, 1951). Although definitions of a profession vary, sociologists generally define an occupation as a profession when it is considered by most to have three characteristics:

profession:
An occupation that (1) has the autonomy to set its own educational and licensing standards and to police its members for incompetence or malfeasance; (2) has its own technical, specialized knowledge, learned through extended, systematic training; and (3) has the public's confidence that it follows a code of ethics and works more from a sense of service than from a desire for profit.

1. The autonomy to set its own educational and licensing standards and to police its members for incompetence or malfeasance;
2. Technical, specialized knowledge, unique to the occupation and learned through extended, systematic training; and
3. Public confidence that its members follow a code of ethics and are motivated more by a desire to serve than a desire to earn a profit.

For much of the twentieth century, doctors clearly met this definition of a profession. Doctors' autonomy was evidenced in the fact that they, rather than consumers or judges, were legally responsible for deciding whether to remove the license of any doctors accused of incompetence. That doctors held highly specialized knowledge, and that they spent many years acquiring that knowledge, was well known. Finally, the public placed great trust in the medical field and believed that physicians placed their patients' interests first.

Despite doctors' past achievements in attaining medical dominance and becoming the leading example of a profession, there is growing evidence that medicine may no longer wield as much power and influence as it has in the past. Whether and how medicine has lost some of its grip on the reins of power is an issue we turn to next.

THREATS TO MEDICAL DOMINANCE

The power and prestige of medicine remain intact in many ways, but there are also indications that medical dominance is under threat. We examine, in turn, threats from the state, the public, other health care professions, and from within medicine itself.

The Rise of Government Control over Medicine

It is the state that has ultimate authority to legitimize the claims of an occupation and confer the status of a profession, and thus the state also has within its capacity to revoke the professional status of an occupational group. Although the legitimacy of medicine as a profession has never been questioned, at different points in time, the state has acted to limit the scope of medical authority.

Nowhere has this been more evident than in health care reforms enacted by federal and provincial governments during the 1990s and 2000s. As we noted in Chapter 10, during this period, the federal government initiated various programs to contain the costs of health care as well as to improve efficiency and responsiveness. Clawing back physician income over a certain threshold and ceding to other health care occupations powers that were previously granted only to medical doctors (e.g., the right to prescribe) were aimed at reducing costs but also impinged on the power of medical doctors. Imposing limits on medical school applicants to control the number of physicians in the population and dictating that medical schools produce more family physicians and fewer specialists represent instances where the state has intervened in issues around physician training that were previously left to the discretion of medical doctors.

While these changes have meant that medical doctors have lost some of their power, it is two more recent interventions by the state that have tremendous implications for physician autonomy. We discuss these two programs, a pan-Canadian initiative to establish electronic health records (EHRs) and the Wait Times reduction program, in turn.

Created in 2001 as a non-profit corporation operating at arm's length from government, Canada Health Infoway is charged with funding, advising, and monitoring provinces and territories to help them develop their own independent electronic health records systems. All provinces and territories are expected to have a fully functioning system in place by 2016. Currently, 16% of all physicians in Canada rely exclusively on EHRs in their practice (Biro, Barber, and Kotecha, 2012). An **electronic health record (EHR)** is a lifetime health record of an individual that is accessible online from many separate, interoperable automated systems within an electronic network. At a practical level, this means that all test results, prescription histories, doctor visits, and medical procedures—virtually every encounter with the health care system—are now collected and stored in a secure online system that can be accessed by medical doctors and other health care professionals. The system is expected to generate substantial efficiencies in time and cost. For example, rather than waiting for an X-ray result to be transferred from the laboratory to a doctor's office and perhaps subsequently to the office of a specialist, the X-ray can be uploaded to the system as soon as it has been completed and accessed instantly by doctors and health care workers across the province. Similarly, doctors who are seeing a patient for the first time can now review the patient's past health care history by accessing his or her EHR instead of beginning a new file.

The public has expressed concern over the privacy issues associated with EHRs, but less attention has been given to the ways in which EHRs will influence how doctors practise medicine. That is, by assigning unique identifiers to physicians, it becomes possible to measure, monitor, and evaluate every task that a physician performs on the job. Placed under such scrutiny, doctors may in the future find themselves under pressure to change their behaviour. For example, those doctors who are identified through EHRs as being above average in terms of the number of X-rays or other types of tests ordered within a given period may be sent correspondence by the provincial health ministry alerting them of their above-average use of tests. If the doctor consistently orders tests in excess of the provincial average, they may get a visit from the health ministry, advising them on methods that will help them to eliminate unnecessary tests (and reduce costs).

If this seems a somewhat far-fetched application of the EHR system, one need only observe the increased scrutiny that has been given to medical procedures as a result of the Wait Times reduction program. As noted in Chapter 10, this program was implemented in 2004 when the federal government was making strategic investments in the health care system. Provinces received block funding to help them reduce wait times for certain types of procedures. To evaluate whether reductions in wait times were actually occurring, the provinces were required to establish wait times registries that could be accessed by the public. The wait times registry not only provides an average wait time at a city or regional level but also records the average wait time for each physician performing that particular procedure. For example, on its website, waittimes.alberta.ca, the Alberta Wait Times Registry lists specialists according to the procedures they perform and compares their wait times to the provincial average. That this information can be used to motivate doctors to reduce their wait times by performing procedures more quickly is clear. For example, the Ontario Ministry of Health website site

electronic health record:
A lifetime health record of an individual that is accessible online from many separate, interoperable automated systems within an electronic network.

encourages visitors to "Share the results with your doctor and request a referral to the health care option with the shortest wait time that is most convenient for you" (Ontario Ministry of Health and Long-Term Care, 2012).

It is not uncommon for workers in many different types of occupations to be under pressure to complete their respective tasks within a given time frame. For example, salespersons may have monthly quotas, bus drivers are often monitored on their routes to ensure that they stay on schedule, and the work pace in a car manufacturing plant is determined solely by the speed of the assembly line. Yet, these pressures are more likely to occur in blue-collar occupations. In contrast, professionals are typically assumed to enjoy a high level of autonomy and to be freed of such time constraints. To the extent that doctors are under greater pressure to perform their tasks more quickly, the work conditions of medical doctors may now be said to more closely resemble those of workers in less-skilled occupations.

The increased surveillance of medical practice by both federal and provincial governments suggests that the ability of doctors to monitor and police their own activities is being eroded. While physicians still find themselves at the top of the occupational hierarchy in the health care industry, it is clear that they can no longer resist the intrusion of the state into their workplace. Moreover, as governments engage in the ongoing struggle to keep the costs of health care down, it is likely that in the future there will be even greater scrutiny and control over the work that doctors perform.

The Decline of Public Support

From the beginnings of Western medicine, medical culture has stressed a paternalistic value system in which only doctors, and not patients or their families, are presumed capable of making decisions about what is best for a patient (Katz, 1984); this chapter's ethical debate on truth-telling in health care (Box 12.1) gives an example of such a situation. In the past, this paternalism might have been reinforced by patients who prefer to let their doctors make all decisions; indeed, at least part of doctors' efficacy comes simply from patients' faith in doctors' ability to heal.

BOX 12.1

ETHICAL DEBATE

Truth Telling in Health Care

Jeffrey Monk, an unmarried, 26-year-old accountant, goes to see Dr. Fisher because of recurrent headaches that have made it difficult for him to concentrate at work. Jeffrey generally enjoys good physical health, although he has experienced bouts of severe depression since his mother died a few months ago.

After a series of tests, Dr. Fisher discovers that Jeffrey has an inoperable brain tumour, which will probably kill him within the year. Because no treatments are available, telling Jeffrey of his diagnosis would seem to serve little purpose at this point. Jeffrey has no dependents, so he need not make a will or other financial arrangements immediately. Moreover, telling him might cause his health to deteriorate

more rapidly, spark another depressive episode, or even lead him to commit suicide. Anyway, Dr. Fisher believes, few patients truly want to know they have a fatal illness. He therefore merely tells Jeffrey that the headaches are not serious and prescribes a placebo, counting on the fact that placebos significantly reduce patient symptoms in about 30% of cases.

Do doctors have an obligation to tell their patients the truth? Answering this question requires us to look at several significant ethical issues. The most central ethical issue in this case is individual autonomy. According to the philosophical principle of autonomy, each rational individual is assumed capable of making his or her own choices if given sufficient information, and each health care worker has the obligation to provide that information. Consequently, each individual has the right to decide what is in his or her own best interest and to act upon those decisions without coercion from others. Counterbalancing this is the idea (derived from medical culture) that only doctors have the expertise needed to decide what is in their patients' best interest.

Evaluating this situation requires us to weigh the benefits of disclosure against those of dissembling. Will hiding his diagnosis from Jeffrey protect him from depression or suicide, or will the anxiety caused by not knowing the meaning of his symptoms increase his emotional problems? Is it best for a doctor to give a patient a placebo, which may offer some physical and emotional relief, or to let the patient know the truth, so the patient may make his or her own choices—from seeking unconventional treatments or a second opinion to choosing how to spend his last months? The final

question, then, is can doctors know what is in their patients' best interest, and when if ever should they be given the authority to act on those judgments?

SOCIOLOGICAL QUESTIONS

1. What social views and values about medicine, society, and the body are reflected in the debate over truth-telling in medicine? Whose views are these?
2. Which social groups are in conflict over this issue? Whose interests are served by requiring doctors to fully inform their patients? By giving doctors discretion in these decisions?
3. Which of these groups has more power to enforce its view? What kinds of power do they have?

As we first noted in Chapter 8, growing public awareness that unquestioning obedience to doctors can sometimes harm patients' health over time helped foster **health social movements**. These movements both reflected and created more egalitarian ideas about how doctors and patients should interact, giving patients greater voice in decisions about their own care and making it more difficult for doctors to unilaterally impose their own decisions upon the patient. Indeed, from a postmodern perspective, the authoritarian role of the physician has more or less evaporated to the extent that equal and sometimes greater value has been assigned to the experiential knowledge of the sick person relative to the empirical, technical knowledge of the doctor.

At the same time that the knowledge of doctors and patients has achieved equal footing in the medical encounter, the information that sustains medical practice has become increasingly accessible. Historically, medical tomes have been located in university and hospital libraries, placing them out of reach for all but the privileged few. Similarly, academic journals that communicated the most recent advances within the field of medicine have been traditionally restricted to medical doctors who subscribed to such journals. In the past few decades, however, the Internet has fundamentally changed the ability of physicians to cloister their knowledge and to restrict the dissemination of medical advances to other medical doctors. There are now specific websites that post medical information to help people recognize symptoms, reach a diagnosis, and evaluate different treatment options long before they arrive at the doctor's office. The general public can also learn about the latest medical advances in the same instant this information is delivered to health care professionals as a result of a new trend toward open access. **Open access** is the practice of providing unrestricted access via the Internet to peer-reviewed scholarly journal articles. Facilitated by the low costs associated with posting information on the Internet, many major medical journals in Canada and around the world have made the transition to open access. The perceived advantages are that it speeds research progress, productivity, and knowledge translation and generally makes available to the public material that is largely supported and paid for already through their taxes. The cost to medical doctors is in their potentially reduced medical authority—their

open access:
The practice of providing unrestricted access via the Internet to peer-reviewed scholarly journal articles.

practices are likely to be exposed to greater scrutiny and their decisions more frequently challenged by an informed public.

The valuing of experiential knowledge and the greater accessibility to medical knowledge have made possible the transformation of what was a passive and compliant patient into an informed and empowered consumer who can effectively challenge the previously unquestioned authority of the medical doctor. The inducement to respond as a consumer comes from many sources that increasingly frame the public's expectations about what the medical encounter should look like. As noted earlier in this chapter, provinces have provided information to the public on wait times, with the expectation that it will be the consumer who applies the pressure on doctors to perform procedures more quickly. Similarly, **direct-to-consumer advertising (DTCA)**, which allows drug manufacturers to advertise their products directly to the public, is based on the expectation that the consumer can change doctors' behaviours around prescribing medications. Thus, medical authority has become more difficult for doctors to retain as the public redefines itself as consumers of health care services and not merely recipients of medical treatment.

That the public has taken to the role of informed and empowered consumer in its interactions with physicians is clear. As has already happened with nearly every other consumer product and service, patients can now go online to register their level of customer satisfaction with their doctor. Thus, websites such as ratemymd.ca are used by the public to rate their doctors and, if dissatisfied, to review the ratings of other doctors as a means of finding a new physician. That the behaviour of doctors can now be routinely evaluated and posted for anyone to see speaks volumes about the ways in which the decisions and practices of doctors are no longer uncritically accepted by the public. Indeed, in addition to the demands of technical proficiency, customer approval hinges on whether or not a doctor exhibits empathy, caring, and attentiveness to the patient's needs. Together, these shifts point to the declining power of medicine and the rising influence of the public in medical decision-making and practice.

What do these changes suggest for public confidence in medicine? In 2010, *Maclean's Magazine* revealed that 40% of respondents said they believe Canadian doctors care less about their patients than they did ten years ago; only 6% said physicians care more (Gillis, Belluz, and Dehaas, 2010). Similarly, an Ipsos Reid poll conducted in 2011 found that 75% of Canadians trusted doctors, a decline from 85% in 2003 (Ipsos Reid, 2011). Despite this decline, however, it should be noted that doctors still ranked near the top of all professions on trustworthiness, second only to pharmacists. Thus, although Canadians have been losing faith in their doctors over time, the medical profession as a whole continues to instil more confidence among Canadians than most other professions.

The Rising Power of Other Health Care Professions

As medical knowledge has proliferated and other practitioners have stepped in to fill the niches created by this new knowledge, doctors have encountered greater difficulty in maintaining control and exerting influence over other professions that operate in the area of health. Thus, gains in status for other professions have come at the expense of medical dominance, chipping away at territory that had been held exclusively by medicine. For example, doctors are no longer in charge of hospital administration. Rather, hospital administration has emerged as a profession, with its own specialized knowledge and specific educational and licensing standards. Medical doctors who lack training in hospital administration may still wield influence in the affairs of the hospital, but their influence is much more muted than in the past. Similarly, some professions have acquired privileges that were once the sole jurisdiction of medicine. The right to prescribe medication is no longer limited to medical doctors but has been extended to nurse-practitioners and to pharmacists. Later on in this chapter, we will discuss in greater detail the efforts of specific health occupations to professionalize and evaluate whether these gains have encroached on medical dominance. For now, we simply acknowledge that medicine has not always been successful in fending off threats to its territory and that losses necessarily translate into diminished power and influence over an aspect of health care.

Divisions within Medicine Itself

In Chapter 10, we noted that the efforts of allopathic doctors to be recognized as a profession were successful once they had quashed internal division, producing a homogeneous membership united by shared interests. That is, medical doctors at the time shared similar ideologies (medicine as a scientific endeavour) and demographic characteristics (mostly male, Caucasian, and middle- to upper-class composition). Since that time, medicine has grown in complexity and diversity, creating the potential for division and conflict among the membership and making it more difficult to present a united front.

One of these divisions in medicine distinguishes those who are specialists from those who are general practitioners. **Specialization**, defined as professional attention to a particular branch of medicine or surgery that is recognized by a board of physicians, requires several years of training beyond the requirements to become a medical doctor. The number of specialties and even subspecialties has grown exponentially over the course of the twentieth century. When the Royal College of Physicians and Surgeons of Canada was first established in 1929, two specialties were recognized. Currently, there are sixty-seven specialties and subspecialties, including ophthalmology, psychiatry, cardiology, anaesthesiology, dermatology, rheumatology, urology, pediatrics, and geriatric medicine. Specialization may focus attention on one particular body part or biological process in the body (e.g., cardiology, dermatology, and urology) or may focus on health problems that are specific to a stage in the life course (e.g., pediatrics, adolescent medicine, and geriatric medicine). Subspecialization often combines elements of both (e.g., pediatric surgery and geriatric psychiatry).

From a **structural-functionalism** perspective, specialization is regarded as a natural progression that reflects growing complexity in medical knowledge and the emergence of new roles to perform these functions. To the extent that some of these new roles have greater social value or require more effort to attain, there is an assumed consensus among doctors that greater rewards should flow to those who take on these specialized tasks within medicine. From a **conflict theory** perspective, however, recognition as a specialty is the outcome of a struggle for resources and power that allows some groups within medicine to reap benefits that are at the expense of other medical doctors. Exerting monopolistic control over a specific area in medicine is used to garner greater prestige and economic benefit relative to other areas in medicine.

Given the greater rewards and prestige associated with specialization, it is not surprising that, during their training, many medical students choose to specialize. In 2010, there were approximately 70,000 active physicians, nearly equally split between general practitioners and specialists (Canadian Institute for Health Information (CIHI), 2011c). Interestingly, Canada fares better in managing the balance between general practitioners and specialists than other high-income countries, where there are typically two specialists for every general practitioner (Fujisawa and Lafortune, 2008). Nonetheless, the fragmentation of care and the narrow scope of practice associated with the increase in the number of specialties and the growing number of medical students who are attracted to them are viewed as problems not only by the Canadian government, which, as we noted earlier, implemented policies to increase the number of general practitioners, but also within medicine itself (Wilson et al., 2011). One of the concerns for the profession of medicine as a whole is that there is a growing divide between general

specialization:
Professional attention to a particular branch of medicine or surgery that is recognized by a board of physicians.

practitioners, who are seen to be toiling in the trenches, and specialists, who may occupy elite positions in universities and hospitals and whose job content may be more likely to involve research rather than seeing patients. As the work experiences and rewards associated with being a general practitioner and a specialist continue to diverge, finding common ground may be more elusive and there may be greater opportunity for internal discord to occur.

Not only has medicine become more occupationally differentiated, but also the demographic composition of medical doctors has been transformed. The most dramatic difference has been in the growing number of women in the field of medicine. Once dominated nearly exclusively by men, the gender composition of medical students in Canada now favours women. As noted in Table 12.1, only one in five first-year medical students were female in 1970; however, by 2010, more than half (56.5%) of first-year medical students were female. Thus, although there continue to be more male doctors than female doctors in Canada (63.9% versus 36.1% as of 2011), in the future, there will be more female doctors than male doctors.

The changing gender composition has implications for the profession as a whole. That is, female physicians tend to have different values and preferences than male doctors. Female medical students are less likely than male medical students to enter into a specialty, preferring instead to become general practitioners. This may serve to further fracture the interests of general practitioners and specialists. Moreover, female doctors work fewer hours on average than male doctors and are more likely to take time off to be with family (Canadian Collaborative Centre for Physician Resources, 2011).

Other demographic shifts in the characteristics of physicians have also occurred. There is greater racial diversity in medical schools than there has been in the past. Further, nearly one in five doctors in 2010 were trained abroad. Whereas the majority of doctors coming to Canada thirty years ago were trained in England and Ireland, today, South Africa and India account for the majority of internationally trained doctors. Nonetheless, those from First Nations, Inuit, and Métis communities continue to be underrepresented in medicine. Finally, although medical schools have made it possible for those with less advantaged backgrounds to become doctors, medical students are still typically drawn from Canada's wealthiest families (AFMC, 2010).

The Continued Strength of Medical Dominance

The debate as to whether medical dominance has declined significantly in recent decades remains unresolved among sociologists. We have presented evidence to suggest that medical doctors face threats to medical dominance on at least four fronts, but to the extent that medicine has responded adaptively to these challenges, it remains unclear whether medical dominance has actually eroded. Freidson (1985, 1986) has argued that medicine has retained control of critical areas of professional status (such as setting licensure regulations and practice standards) and thus has preserved its dominance as a field, even as the autonomy of many individual physicians has eroded. Moreover, Freidson argues, although individual

TABLE 12.1 Percentage of Women Enrolled in First Year in Canadian Faculties of Medicine, 1970–2010

Year	Percentage Female
1970	20.2
1980	40.0
1990	45.5
2000	54.1
2010	56.5

Adapted from: Association of Faculties of Medicine of Canada (AFMC), *Canadian Medical Statistics 2011*. Ottawa, Canada, Table 1, 2011.

doctors working in specific situations have lost some professional prerogatives, the power and dominance of doctors relative to other health care occupations have remained largely intact. Freidson notes, for example, that the rhetoric of health care "teams" hides the fact that doctors have by far the most power on these teams. By the same token, the use of medical technology by other health care workers tells us little about the relative power of those occupations. For example, nurses now use stethoscopes and blood pressure cuffs, but that has not increased their power relative to doctors. Similarly, although the rise of practice protocols could decrease the autonomy of individual doctors, supporters of protocols argue that only through such self-regulation can medicine preserve public faith and, in the end, its professional autonomy (Good, 1995). Taking all of this evidence into consideration, Timmermans and Oh (2010) concluded that medicine remains well positioned to survive future threats without irreparable harm. Whether this will always be the case is undoubtedly an important empirical question for sociologists to investigate in the years to come.

MEDICAL EDUCATION AND MEDICAL VALUES

Despite the assaults on medical dominance, becoming a doctor remains an attractive option, offering public prestige, the emotional rewards of service, and relatively high income. It is also highly competitive, with only one in four qualified applicants accepted into a medical school in Canada (AFMC, 2011). In this section, we look at how doctors-in-training acquire both medical knowledge and medical values, as well as the consequences of this training for both doctors and patients.

The Structure of Medical Education

Becoming a doctor is not easy. Most prospective doctors first earn a bachelor's degree (application to some medical schools can be made after two years of university) and then complete four years of training at a medical school. Before they can enter practice, however, and depending on their chosen specialty, they must spend another three to eight years as **residents**. Residents are doctors who are continuing their training while working in hospitals. (The term *intern,* referring to the first year of a residency, is no longer commonly used.) As a result, most do not enter practice until age 30.

Becoming a doctor carries tremendous financial and time burdens. Tuition costs for medical students are much higher than for most other university programs: Only dentistry has higher tuition costs. Medical students also graduate with high student debts that take many years to pay off. Medical students also work long hours. In the United States and the European Union, there are strict regulations about how many hours a resident may work. No such regulations exist in Canada, although some provinces have contractual agreements with residents that stipulate maximum work hours, such as forbidding two consecutive nights where residents are on call. Nonetheless, residents may spend up to eighty hours a week on the job. The heavy workload does not diminish once one enters the profession, as doctors work an average of 51.4 hours per week, which increases to eighty-three hours per week if one factors in hours on call (Canadian Collaborative Centre for Physician Resources, 2011). These time pressures, coupled with the financial pressures of training, encourage novice doctors to defer marriage, children, and other personal pursuits and to choose specialties requiring less training over those they otherwise might prefer.

Learning Medical Values

During their long years of training, doctors learn both a vast quantity of technical information and a set of **medical norms**—expectations about how doctors should act, think, and

residents:
Individuals who have graduated medical school and received their MD degrees but are now engaged in further on-the-job training needed before they can enter independent practice.

medical norms:
Expectations doctors hold about how they should act, think, and feel.

**professional
socialization:**
The process of learning
the skills, knowledge, and
values of an occupation.

feel. The transformation from medical student to medical doctor does not happen overnight. As medical students become immersed in the culture of medical school and master the skills they need to practise medicine, they slowly shed old identities and acquire new identities as medical doctors (Shapiro, 1987). This process of **professional socialization** teaches students that doctors should value emotional detachment, trust clinical experience more than scientific evidence, master uncertainty, adopt a mechanistic model of the body, trust intervention more than normal bodily processes, and prefer working with rare or acute illnesses rather than with typical or chronic illnesses.

Emotional Detachment

Undoubtedly most doctors enter the profession because they want to help others. Yet perhaps the most central medical norm is to maintain emotional detachment from patients. Given doctors' daily confrontations with illness, trauma, and death, emotional detachment can be a necessary coping mechanism. Some, such as Talcott Parsons, have regarded affective neutrality as an obligation of the medical profession. Indeed, just as the **sick role** carried with it a set of obligations and privileges for the patient, as described in Chapter 7, structural-functionalists theorized that the physician had a complementary set of obligations and privileges (Parsons, 1951). The privileges of being a physician included autonomy and the ability to self-regulate as well as unlimited access to the patient's body. Physicians were awarded these privileges through fulfilling their obligations to acquire technical proficiency in medicine and to maintain emotional distance from their patients. Maintaining emotional distance allowed the doctor to touch patients without fear of creating a sexually charged or otherwise uncomfortable environment and to conduct their work without becoming emotionally invested in the outcome. Affective neutrality also deepened the patient's trust of the doctor by assuring the patient that the doctor's ministrations were in the best interests of the patient and not the self-interests of the doctor.

This structural-functionalist viewpoint of the role of the doctor, along with its assumed privileges and obligations, has been largely discredited. As we have seen throughout this text, doctors have historically acted in their own interests and continue to do so to the same extent as other professionals. Moreover, the unequal social class and gender distribution of admissions to medical school that existed at the time Parsons expressed these ideas made it clear that technical proficiency alone did not determine who became a doctor. Despite these critiques, there can be no question that the development of emotional detachment remains a critical aspect of the professional socialization of medical students into the practice of medicine (Hafferty, 1991).

One of the most recognizable steps in the process of becoming a doctor, which also delivers a powerful lesson in emotional detachment, occurs when medical students conduct their first dissection of a human cadaver. For most medical students, it is the first time that they have touched a dead body. Thus, not only must students overcome the taboos associated with viewing naked bodies in mixed company and with desecrating human remains, but also they must learn to manage their emotional responses.

How students respond to the learning experience of the human cadaver lab has changed as perceptions about what it means to be a medical doctor have shifted. In the 1970s and 1980s, sociologists who observed how medical students responded to the demands of the cadaver lab found discrepancies between what students felt and what they displayed to others. That is, while medical students were generally privately reflective and sometimes quite distressed by human dissection, they publicly maintained a norm of silence and typically exhibited indifference. By remaining emotionally detached as they mastered the skills of dissection, medical students passed the test of emotional competence, conveying to their superiors their future success as medical doctors.

More recent analyses of responses to the rigours of the human dissection lab suggest that medical students are now expected to share their stories and that doing so is viewed as a practical demonstration of one's sensitivity and enlightenment (Dyer and Thorndike, 2000; Madill and Latchford, 2005). Thus, the contemporary test of emotional competence requires that medical students balance emotional detachment with a genuine empathy for the patients that they will one day treat. To facilitate this process, some medical schools have even incorporated sessions where medical students are invited to talk about their feelings to help them confront and develop their attitudes around death and dying.

Nonetheless, some students find that emotional detachment makes it easier for them to ridicule their patients. The use of medical slang, which peaks during the highly stressful residency years, allows students and residents to turn their anxieties and unacceptable emotions into humour by using terms such as "crispy critters" for severe burn patients. Medical slang also enables doctors and residents to avoid emotionally distressing interactions with patients and their families by using terms that laypersons cannot understand, such as "adeno-CA" for cancer (Coombs et al., 1993). According to Terry Mizrahi, who spent three years observing, interviewing, and surveying residents in internal medicine, by the end of their training, most held "attitudes towards patients ranging from apathy to antipathy" (Mizrahi, 1986: 122). These attitudes are reflected vividly in the many slang terms residents use (sometimes within earshot of patients) to describe those they dislike treating, including "train wrecks" (seriously ill or injured patients who might not seem worth spending resources on); and "scumbags" (dirty, smelly patients). Such terms help doctors vent frustrations regarding the difficulties of their situation and maintain needed emotional distance, but they also implicitly reinforce disparaging attitudes toward patients (Coombs et al., 1993).

Emotional detachment is emphasized often during medical school and residencies, as faculty and students implicitly or explicitly minimize the emotional aspects of medical practice (Haas and Shaffir, 1987: 85–99; Hafferty, 1991; Holmes and Ponte, 2011). During daily rounds of the wards, faculty members grill residents on highly technical details of patients' diagnoses and treatments. Except in family practice residencies, however, faculty members rarely ask about even the most obviously consequential psychosocial factors. Rounds and other case presentations also teach residents to describe patients in depersonalized language. Residents learn to describe individuals as "the patient," "the ulcer," or "the appendectomy" rather than by name. As Renee Anspach (1997: 328) has described, using language like "the vagina and the cervix were noted to be clear" rather than "I noted that Mrs. Simpson's vagina and cervix were clear" reinforces the impression "that biological processes can be separated from the persons who experience them."

The structure of the residency years largely prevents residents from emotionally investing in patients (Mizrahi, 1986). Long hours without sleep often make it impossible for residents to provide much beyond the minimum physical care necessary (Christakis and Feudtner, 1997). When combined with the norm of emotional detachment, such long hours can even encourage doctors to view their patients as foes. In her interviews with medical doctors, Tanya Luhrmann recorded this doctor's recollection of his experience during medical residency:

> I came in one morning to rounds and heard one of my classmates discussing his previous night on call. "Oh," he said, "a woman came in, and we did such and such and such and such but luckily she died by morning." What appalled me was that I understood how he felt: If she had lived, he would have had someone else to take care of. (2000: 84)

The desire to get rid of patients grew as residents came to realize that many patients suffer from illnesses or social problems that medicine cannot cure. Doctors reserved their most negative attitudes for such patients, as well as for those the doctors deemed morally or socially unworthy of their time. The latter include patients whose illnesses seemed linked to self-destructive behaviours; who sought treatment for minor illnesses; who were poor, non-Caucasian, female, or old; or who suffered from common illnesses that the doctors, trained in research-oriented medical schools, found uninteresting.

Clinical Experience

In addition to teaching doctors certain attitudes toward patients, medical culture also teaches, at a more abstract level, a set of attitudes toward medical care, illness, the body, and what makes humans truly human. Ironically, given that doctors' prestige rests partly on their scientific training, medical culture values clinical experience more than scientific research and knowledge (Bosk, 2003; Ludmerer, 1985; Millenson, 1997).

Along with teaching skills, students' clinical training also teaches them to base treatment decisions more on their personal experiences with a given treatment rather than on scientific research (Becker et al., 1961; Ludmerer, 1985: 260–271). For example, Knafl and Burkett describe the following incidents observed during surgical rounds at a hospital they studied:

> After the residents finished presenting the case to the audience, one of the attendings [senior doctors who supervise residents] asked, "What 'bout doing a cup arthroplasty on him?" Morrison replied, "There's some literature to back it up but it's *my experience* that 'cups' just aren't that successful on young people." (1975: 399)

In this way, residents have learned to value their own intuition and idiosyncratic clinical experience over scientific research. This partially explains why standard clinical procedure varies enormously from community to community and from doctor to doctor, producing high rates of medical error.

Recent events, however, suggest that scientific research may be growing in value within medical training and the medical world in general. The practice protocols described earlier are part of a broader push for **evidence-based medicine**: the idea that medical care should be based on a thorough evaluation of the best available data from randomized, controlled clinical research. The trend toward evidence-based medicine reflects not only the concerns about cost control mentioned earlier but also the growing recognition that less than half of modern medical treatments—and only a small fraction of surgical procedures—have good scientific support (Naylor, 1995).

Almost all medical schools now explicitly incorporate evidence-based medicine into their curricula. But this does not mean that doctors now base their practices solely on scientific evidence rather than on their personal clinical experience (Timmermans and Berg, 2003a). When doctors are working on a case, they rarely have time to obtain the latest research findings on the topic, let alone to evaluate that research fully. Instead, they must often settle for reading a single research article in a prestigious journal, or a single review article. In addition, because practice protocols cannot cover all the specific circumstances of each patient, doctors must rely on their clinical judgment rather than simply follow practice protocols. Finally, medical training and practice remain hierarchical environments, in which doctors and medical students are expected to defer to more senior doctors and thus are unlikely to challenge orders from senior doctors even if those orders go against practice protocols. On the other hand, because junior doctors are increasingly turning to the research literature for answers, more senior doctors must do so as well to retain their reputations and status. In sum, evidence-based medicine has affected medical care but has not supplanted clinical experience as a decision-making tool.

evidence-based medicine:
The use of medical therapies whose efficacy has been confirmed by large, randomized, controlled clinical studies.

Mastering Uncertainty

One reason medical culture values clinical experience over scientific knowledge is that there is simply too much knowledge for students to ever learn it all. As a result, students can never be certain that they have diagnosed or treated a patient correctly. Moreover, because the answers to so many medical questions remain unknown, even a student who somehow learned all the available medical knowledge would still on occasion face uncertainty about diagnoses and treatments. From the start of medical school, then, students must learn how to cope emotionally with uncertainty and how to reduce uncertainty where possible (by, for example, focusing on memorizing the discrete facts most likely to show up on examinations) (Fox, 2000). Students must also learn to question whether their difficulties in treating patients stem from a lack of available knowledge in the field or from their lack of familiarity with the available knowledge. Simultaneously, however, students' experiences in medical school classes and on the wards where they study also teach them that they must hide their sense of uncertainty if they are to be regarded as competent by their professors and patients (Holmes and Ponte, 2011; Lingard et al., 2003).

Mechanistic Model

Along with learning to master uncertainty, medical students also learn to consider the body analogous to a machine or factory and to view illness as a mechanical breakdown (Martin, 1987; Mishler, 1981; Osherson and Amara Singham, 1981; Waitzkin, 1993). The mechanistic model of the body and illness leads naturally to a distrust of natural bodily processes. Doctors learn to always look for signs that the body is breaking down and to view changes in the body as causes or consequences of such breakdowns. As a result, doctors typically view pregnancy and menopause as diseases, try to stop the effects of aging if possible, use drugs to control minor fevers (the body's natural process for fighting infection), and so on (e.g., Barker, 1998; Martin, 1987).

Intervention

Learning to distrust natural processes is intimately interwoven with learning to value medical intervention. During the preclinical years, doctors receive only minimal instruction in using tools such as nutrition, exercise, and biofeedback to prevent or treat illness; during the rest of their training, such tools are rarely—if ever—mentioned. Meanwhile, those medical specialties that rely most heavily on intervention receive the most prestige and financial rewards. For example, the average income in 2008 of orthopedic surgeons in Canada was $208,634, whereas the average income of primary care doctors was $125,104 (Laugesen and Glied, 2011). Similarly, medical school faculties routinely disparage general and family practitioners and discourage students from entering those fields (Block et al., 1996; Mullan, 2002). Taken together, these forces support a **technological imperative**—a belief that it is always best to use all available technological tools and interventions.

Emphasis on Acute and Rare Illnesses

As a natural corollary of valuing intervention (and a natural result of locating medical training within research-oriented universities), medical culture teaches doctors to consider **acute illness** more interesting than **chronic illness**. This is not surprising, for doctors can often perform spectacular cures for acute illnesses (such as appendicitis) but can do little for chronic illnesses (such as lupus). Similarly, medical culture teaches doctors to consider common diseases less interesting than rare ones, for the latter require complex and well-honed diagnostic skills even if no treatments are available.

The Consequences of Medical Values

In sum, medical training teaches doctors to value emotional detachment, trust their clinical experience, master uncertainty, adopt a mechanistic model of illness, rely on interventions, and prefer working with rare or acute illnesses. Although each of these values serves a purpose, each can also work against the provision of high-quality health care. Emotional detachment can lead doctors to treat patients insensitively and to overlook the emotional and social sources and consequences of illness. In addition, it can cause doctors to feel disdain for patients.

Meanwhile, the emphasis on clinical experience, although sometimes useful, can lead doctors to adopt treatments that have not been tested through controlled clinical trials and that lack scientific validity, such as treating ulcers (which are now known to be caused by bacteria) with a bland diet (Millenson, 1997). In addition, the desire for clinical experience sometimes encourages medical students and residents to perform procedures, from drawing blood to doing surgeries, even if they lack sufficient training or supervision or if the procedures cause unnecessary pain. Medical students and doctors are most likely to do so if they can define a patient as "training material" rather than as an equal human being.

Mastering uncertainty is necessary if physicians are to retain enough confidence in their clinical decisions to survive emotionally. And presenting an image of authoritative knowledge undoubtedly increases patient confidence and stimulates a placebo effect, if nothing else. At the same time, the desire for certainty—or at least an aura of certainty—also probably contributes to authoritarian relationships with patients. This is particularly problematic when proper treatment really is uncertain. For example, doctors are particularly uncomfortable with patients whose diagnoses are unclear or whose treatment is unsuccessful. Similarly, even though for years evidence has indicated that routine mammograms for healthy women below age 50 are ineffective and hormone replacement therapy for menopause is dangerous, many doctors—unwilling, perhaps, to give up their aura of certainty—continue to dismiss concerns about these practices and to recommend them to their patients.

Other problems stem from medicine's mechanistic model of the body. This model leads doctors to rely on **reductionistic treatment**. This term refers to treatment in which doctors consider each bodily part separately from the whole—reducing it to one part—in much the same way that auto mechanics might replace a spark plug without checking whether the issue was caused by problems in the car's fuel system. In contrast, sociologists (as well as a minority of doctors) argue for a more holistic image of how the body works and of how illness should be treated (Waitzkin, 1993). **Holistic treatment** refers to treatment that assumes that all aspects of an individual's life and body are interconnected. For example, rather than performing wrist surgery on typists who have carpal tunnel syndrome, it might be better to recommend using a wrist rest while typing or changing the height of the typist's desk. And rather than simply excising a tumour when someone has cancer, perhaps doctors and other health care workers should also explore how their patients' social and environmental circumstances contributed to cancer growth and how psychological and financial support might improve their odds of recovery.

Finally, emphasizing intervention can foster unnecessary diagnosis and treatment. One example is the meteoric rise in use of full-body scans, genetic testing, and increasingly detailed mammograms in apparently healthy patients. Through such testing, many individuals learn that they have biological characteristics (such as unusual cells or genes) that doctors cannot explain, diagnose, or treat—a situation guaranteed to produce great anxiety with little benefit. Others are diagnosed and treated based on these tests, even though the conditions these tests identify—referred to as **pseudodisease** by some sociologists—may never harm their health (Mechanic, 2006).

reductionistic treatment:
Treatment based on the assumption that each part can be treated separately from the whole.

holistic treatment:
Treatment based on the premise that all aspects of an individual's life and body are interconnected, so that to treat a sick individual effectively, health care workers must look at all aspects of the body, as well as at the individual's psychological and social functioning.

pseudodisease:
A condition diagnosed as disease based solely on test results but that will never cause health problems for the diagnosed individual.

A culture of intervention can also lead to overtreatment among those who are clearly ill. An individual who has a cold, for example, will likely recover regardless of treatment. Often, however, doctors will prescribe antibiotics because either they or their patients psychologically need to do something. Yet, antibiotics cannot cure colds but can cause unpleasant or even life-threatening health problems. Moreover, in the long run, unnecessary antibiotic treatment can foster drug-resistant bacteria.

All of these values, and the problems they create, are probably stronger during medical training than afterward. Once doctors enter practice, pressure from their patients may encourage them, willingly or unwillingly, to show at least somewhat more sensitivity to patients' needs. In addition, those who consistently work with the same pool of patients—a situation that, as described earlier, has become less common—can develop more meaningful relationships with them. Thus, over time, doctors may recoup some of their initial, more positive, attitudes toward patients and patient care (Mizrahi, 1986).

OTHER HEALTH CARE PROFESSIONS

Nursing: A Semiprofession

In everyday conversations, it is not uncommon to hear people equate health care workers with doctors. Similarly, although many sociologists have researched doctors, very few have researched nurses. Yet, nurses form the true backbone of the health care system, and hospital patients quickly learn that it is nurses who make the experience miserable or bearable and whose presence or absence often matters most. The history of nursing demonstrates the difficulties of achieving professional status for a "female" occupation.

The Rise of Nursing

Before the twentieth century, most people believed that caring came naturally to women and, therefore, that families could always call on any female relative to care for any sick family member (Reverby, 1987). Hospitals, meanwhile, relied on the labour of lower-class women for custodial nursing care, whereas religious hospitals were typically staffed by nuns. These beginnings in home and hospital created the central dilemma of nursing: Nursing was considered a natural extension of women's character and duty rather than an occupation meriting either respect or rights (Reverby, 1987). Nevertheless, increasingly during the nineteenth century, unmarried and widowed women sought paid work as nurses in both homes and hospitals. With the exception of French-speaking Canada, where nuns received training in nursing through the church and state-sanctioned midwives learned their skills through apprenticeship, few had any training.

The need to formalize nursing training and practice did not become obvious until the Crimean War of the 1850s, when the Englishwoman Florence Nightingale demonstrated that trained nurses could alleviate the horrors of war (Reverby, 1987). The acclaim Nightingale garnered for her war work subsequently enabled her to open new training programs and establish nursing as a respectable occupation.

Like most of her generation, Nightingale believed that men and women had inherently different characters and thus should occupy "separate spheres," playing different roles in society. To Nightingale, women's character, as well as their duty, both enabled and required them to care for others. She thus conceived of caring as nursing's central role. In addition, because her war work had convinced her of the benefits of strict discipline, she created a hierarchical structure in which nurses and nursing students would follow orders from their nursing supervisors. This structure, she hoped, would provide nurses with a power base within women's separate sphere parallel to that of doctors within their sphere. These principles became the foundation of British nursing and soon spread to the rest of Europe and North America.

The first nursing school in Canada was established in 1874 in St. Catharines, Ontario. As hospital administrators discovered that running a nursing school provided a ready pool of cheap labour, such schools opened up across Canada. Within these hospital-based schools, education was often secondary to patient care. A 1912 survey found that almost half of these schools had neither paid instructors nor libraries (Melosh, 1982: 41). Students worked on wards ten to twelve hours daily, with work assignments based on hospital needs rather than on educational goals. Formal lectures or training, if any, occurred only after other work was done.

This exploitative training system stemmed directly, if unintentionally, from the Nightingale model and its emphasis on caring and duty. As historian Susan Reverby notes (1987: 75), "Since nursing theory emphasized training in discipline, order, and practical skills, the ideological justification explained the abuse of student labour. And because the nursing work force was made up almost entirely of women, altruism, sacrifice, and submission were expected and encouraged."

Those women who, by the beginning of the twentieth century, sought to make nursing a profession by raising educational standards, establishing standards for licensure or registration, and improving the field's status found their hands tied by the nature of the field. According to Reverby, to raise its status, nursing reformers

> had to exalt the womanly character and service ethic of nursing while insisting on the right of nurses to act in their own self-interest, yet not be "unladylike." They had to demand higher wages commensurate with their skills and position, but not appear "commercial." Denouncing the exploitation of nursing students as workers, they had to forge political alliances with hospital physicians and administrators who perpetrated this system of training. While lauding character and sacrifice, they had to measure it with educational criteria in order to formulate registration laws and set admission standards. In doing so, they attacked the background, training, and ideology of the majority of working nurses. Such a series of contradictions were impossible to reconcile. (1987: 122)

Political weaknesses also hamstrung nurses' attempts to increase their status. The British North America Act only permitted men over the age of 21 to vote; women were not extended these rights throughout Canada until 1918. Moreover, nurses faced formidable opposition from doctors and hospitals that feared losing control over this cheap workforce.

The position of nursing began to improve slowly during the two World Wars, when nurses began to be included in the military establishment, and upon returning home, were able to access benefits that would otherwise have been denied to women. As women began to stay in the labour market in the post–World War II economic boom, they formed unions to demand better pay and working conditions. During these years, unionization proved more effective than professionalization in enhancing the status and pay of nursing (Strong-Boag, 1991).

Current Status of Nursing in Canada

Today, nursing is highly stratified, with nurses sorted according to their educational qualifications. On the lower rungs are **licensed practical nurses (LPNs)**, who have at least one year and often two years of classroom and clinical training and provide mostly custodial care to patients. On the top tier are **registered nurses (RNs)**, with further differentiation by level of educational attainment. At the bottom of this hierarchy are diploma nurses, who receive their training through two- or three-year community college diploma programs. Next are nurses who hold bachelor's degrees in nursing from universities. Finally, at the top of the RN

licensed practical nurses (LPNs): Individuals, not registered nurses, who assist nurses primarily with the custodial care of patients. LPNs have usually completed approximately one or two years of classroom and clinical training.

registered nurses (RNs): Individuals who have received at least two years of nursing training, and more commonly a four-year bachelor's degree, and passed national licensure requirements.

hierarchy are **advanced practice nurses**, such as **nurse-midwives** and **nurse-practitioners** (see Box 12.2), who have postgraduate training in specialized fields. All advanced practice nurses enjoy considerably more autonomy, status, and financial rewards than do other nurses, including hospital privileges and the right to diagnose illness and prescribe medication (CIHI, 2011b). Standing somewhat outside this hierarchy, but equivalent in power to university-trained nurses, are **registered psychiatric nurses (RPNs)**, who are regulated as a separate profession by four provinces and one territory.

The educational requirements to become a nurse have increased in recent years. Most provinces have phased out diploma programs for RNs so that the bachelor's degree in nursing is now the minimum standard for entry into nursing. Similarly, the one-year programs for LPNs have been replaced with two-year diplomas from community colleges. In 2010, LPNs

BOX 12.2
Nurse-Practitioners

Nurse-practitioners have existed in Canada since the 1970s, but their roles during this early period were much different than they are today. At the time, nurse-practitioners typically worked alongside doctors in community settings and had relatively little independence, except when they operated in remote settings where there were no practising physicians. The early efforts of nurse-practitioners to professionalize encountered numerous setbacks. Refusing to relinquish their privileges, medical doctors sought to limit the role of nurse-practitioners, lobbying legislators to withhold professional status from nurse-practitioners. The efforts of doctors were largely successful throughout the 1980s, with the lack of government support forcing many nurse-practitioner programs across Canada to close their doors. It was not until the 1990s, when health care reforms were under way, that sentiments began to change and nurse-practitioners were formally recognized by the state. Between 1997 and 2005, every provincial and territorial government (with the exception of Yukon) enacted nurse-practitioner legislation, providing legitimacy to the profession. In 2008, the title nurse-practitioner became protected, meaning that only those who had received training through an approved nurse-practitioner program could use the designation.

There are now more than 3,000 nurse-practitioners in Canada, with the majority located in Ontario, Alberta, and British Columbia. Twenty-eight nursing schools offer nurse-practitioner programs, graduating almost 400 students annually. Although they are still located in community settings, increasingly nurse-practitioners are shifting their location of practice to hospitals, with nearly 40% based in a hospital setting in 2010 (CIHI, 2011a).

Nurse-practitioners provide front-line health care and can do any of the following: make diagnoses, discuss diagnoses with clients, order and interpret diagnostic and screening tests, perform procedures, prescribe medications, and make referrals to specialists. There are, however, variations in practice standards. For example, some provinces still require nurse-practitioners to work in consultation with a physician (British Columbia), whereas other provinces allow nurse-practitioners to function autonomously (Ontario).

Research published in major medical journals and based on experiments in which patients were randomly assigned either to doctors or to nurse-practitioners suggests that care provided by nurse-practitioners is at least as good as that provided by doctors (Mundinger et al., 2000; Safriet, 1992; Sakr et al., 1999). Moreover, care provided by nurse-practitioners is considerably less expensive than medical care, both because nurse-practitioners are paid less and because they typically use fewer expensive tests, treatments, and medications.

advanced practice nurses:
Individuals who, after becoming registered nurses, additionally receive specialized postgraduate training. Includes nurse-midwives and nurse-practitioners.

nurse-midwives:
Registered nurses who receive additional formal, nationally accredited training in midwifery.

nurse-practitioners:
Registered nurses who are prepared, through advanced education and clinical training, to provide a wide range of health care services that would normally be performed by a medical doctor.

registered psychiatric nurses (RPNs):
Registered nurses who are trained to deal specifically with clients with mental illness.

Education	2001	2010
Diploma	74.0	57.7
Bachelor's	24.3	38.8
Master's/Doctorate	2.7	3.5

Adapted from: Canadian Nurses Association, *Workforce Profile of Registered Nurses in Canada*, Ottawa, Canada, Pg. 4, 2008. © Canadian Nurses Association. Reprinted with permission. Further reproduction prohibited; CIHI, 2011a, *Regulated Nurses: Canadian Trends, 2006–2010*, Table 12, Pg. 28.

constituted 22.9% of the nursing workforce in Canada, with RNs and RPNs accounting for 75.7% and 1.5%, respectively (CIHI, 2011b). As can be seen from Table 12.2, the proportion of nurses with a bachelor's degree in nursing increased between 2001 and 2010, due in part to incoming cohorts of highly trained nurses and the retirement of older generations of nurses with less training.

Although the educational qualifications of nursing have changed over time, nursing remains a feminized profession, with women making up 94% of the nursing population. Because nursing is so strongly identified with femininity, working as a nurse can present men with a serious conflict between their gender identity and their work identity. Men typically respond to this conflict by stressing the differences between what they do and traditional nursing—deemphasizing nurturing while emphasizing technical skills and quick thinking. As in other occupations, male nurses tend to be promoted more rapidly than similarly qualified female nurses.

Despite the increase in nurses' education, caring has remained central to nurses' work. Caring is considered a critical aspect of recovery but continues to be devalued within the health care system. When we apply the three criteria for a profession as outlined at the beginning of this chapter, it is clear that nurses have yet to establish technical, specialized knowledge that is unique to nursing or to convince others that caring requires extended, systematic training. As such, we must conclude that, with the exception of advanced practice nurses such as nurse-practitioners, most nurses continue to struggle to attain professional status.

Pharmacy: The Push to Reprofessionalize

Unlike nursing, pharmacy meets the three criteria that define a profession: the autonomy to set its own educational and licensing standards and to police its members for incompetence or malfeasance; a body of specialized knowledge, learned through extended, systematic training; and public faith that its work is grounded in a code of ethics. A brief look at the history of pharmacy illustrates how the fortunes of pharmacy have fluctuated over time.

Gaining Education, Losing Professional Prerogatives

A few centuries ago, pharmacists identified with a larger group known as apothecaries and competed directly with allopathic physicians to diagnose and treat illness. As allopathic doctors became more powerful, they successfully limited the practice of pharmacists to the dispensing of medication that was prescribed by a medical doctor. Even so, pharmacy remained an important occupation, requiring complex skills to store, compound, and dispense the drugs that doctors prescribed. Because pharmacists generally operated in small, independent pharmacist-owned enterprises, they also retained control over their working conditions.

Over the course of the twentieth century, the skill and prestige of the occupation declined, even as the educational skills to become a pharmacist increased (Birenbaum, 1982). Pharmaceutical companies adapted their production lines to deliver drugs in forms suitable for dispensing, leaving pharmacists with few tasks other than counting, selling, and occasionally advising on drugs to consumers or health care providers. Similarly, regulatory changes in Canada allowed non-pharmacists to own and operate pharmacies, paving the way for the large-scale corporate entities that now dominate the market (Dobson and Perepelkin, 2011). Consequently, most pharmacists became employees of drugstore chains, supermarket chains, or hospitals. Incomes for pharmacists remained high, but working conditions could be poor, especially in chain stores, where twelve-hour shifts, staffing shortages, and pressure to fill prescriptions quickly became common complaints (Stolberg, 1999).

As pharmacists' role shrank, however, their education expanded. All pharmacy schools now offer bachelor's degree programs, as well as postgraduate programs leading to doctorates in pharmacy. These advanced degrees place less emphasis on technical aspects of drug manufacturing and more on the complex subject of drug effects and interactions. These changes in education, combined with changes in pharmacists' role, created an identity crisis: Pharmacists considered themselves professionals but increasingly found their professional autonomy constrained (Birenbaum, 1982; Broadhead and Facchinetti, 1985).

The Growth of Clinical Pharmacy

This identity crisis stimulated interest among pharmacists in regaining their former level of professional status, or **reprofessionalization**. To do so, since the early 1970s, pharmacists have called attention to research documenting high rates of dangerous drug errors and have argued that such errors could be reduced by giving pharmacists authority to review doctors' and patients' use of pharmaceutical drugs. This led to the development of the new field of clinical pharmacy. **Clinical pharmacy** is the practice of educating and employing pharmacists to advise doctors and patients on the use of pharmaceutical drugs (Franklin and van Mil, 2005).

Pharmacists obtained the right to prescribe medication in the United Kingdom in 2003 and in France in 2009, despite the objections of medical doctors. The Patient Protection and Affordable Care Act in the United States also extends nationally the practice of a small number of states that have permitted pharmacist-delivered health care. Similarly, in 2007, the Alberta government amended the Pharmacists Regulation of the Health Professions Act to allow pharmacists to renew, modify, and in some cases prescribe medications. For the first time, pharmacists can see patients who come to them for advice about a minor or self-limiting condition and prescribe medication to treat that condition without prior consultation with a physician. Fears that other provinces would follow Alberta may have motivated an advertising campaign by the Ontario Medical Association in 2010 to promote the idea that only physicians should be permitted to prescribe medication (Barry and Pearson, 2010). Even so, in October 2012, Ontario pharmacists gained the right to renew non-narcotic prescriptions, administer flu shots and advise patients with chronic conditions. Clearly, the expanded scope of duties that has elevated pharmacists from dispensers of medication to front-line health care workers has been an important achievement in the reprofessionalization process.

Direct-Entry Midwives: Limited Practitioners

The history of direct-entry midwifery (as differentiated from nurse-midwives, who specialize in midwifery subsequent to a nursing degree) shows the difficulties members of an occupation face in gaining acceptance as **limited practitioners**. Until the Medical Act of 1912 eliminated midwifery practice in Canada, midwives had been historically responsible for

reprofessionalization:
The process of regaining former professional status.

clinical pharmacy:
A subfield of pharmacy in which pharmacists participate actively in decisions regarding drug treatment.

limited practitioners:
Occupational groups, such as chiropractors, midwives, and optometrists, that confine their work to a limited range of treatments and certain parts of the body.

all aspects of childbirth. Medical doctors, who subsequently took over the practice, retained their monopoly for most of the century but were never able to completely squelch the practice of midwifery. In the last decade of the twentieth century, several provinces began to recognize midwifery as a legitimate profession. In this section, we consider how these changes came about and how direct-entry midwives regained their lost position.

The Struggle to Control Childbirth

Until well into the nineteenth century, childbirth was considered primarily a woman's affair (Wertz and Wertz, 1989). Almost all women gave birth at home, attended by a midwife and "gossips"—female friends or relatives. Although a few local governments licensed midwives, nearly anyone who wanted to call herself a midwife could practise essentially without legal restrictions. Midwives received no formal training but rather learned their skills through experience and, sometimes, through apprenticeships. Typically, they served only women from their geographic or ethnic community. Doctors played almost no role in childbirth and had little to offer childbearing women beyond the ability to destroy their unborn child when prolonged labour threatened women with death (Wertz and Wertz, 1989: 97–98). Midwives, meanwhile, could offer only patience, skilled hands, and a few herbal remedies.

Over the course of the nineteenth century, male medical doctors began to express interest in attending childbirth. Equipped with medical forceps as a technological invention that could assist in the delivery process, they began to offer their services to women who anticipated a difficult childbirth. Facilitated by the public's growing faith in science and medicine during the late nineteenth century, the upper classes became the first to make use of male medical doctors and subsequently began to portray this as fashionable. To expand their clientele, doctors attempted through speeches and publications to convince women that childbirth was inherently and unpredictably dangerous and therefore required medical assistance. In particular, doctors began to discredit midwives, holding them responsible for endangering the lives of the mother and unborn child. Moreover, as childbirth began to be seen as a process that could be improved by science, social perceptions shifted so that childbirth was no longer seen as a respectable or appropriate occupation for Victorian women. Consequently, late nineteenth century middle- and upper-class women seeking a childbirth attendant had only two options: lower-class lay midwives or doctors of their own social class. Having a doctor attend one's childbirth thus could both reflect and increase one's social standing (Leavitt, 1986: 39; Wertz and Wertz, 1989). Ironically, however, doctors threatened women's health more than did midwives. Although inexperienced or impatient midwives could certainly endanger women, the surgical and manual interventions preferred by male medical doctors more frequently caused permanent injuries and deadly infections (Ehrenreich and English, 2005b; Leavitt, 1983: 281–292, 1986: 43–58; Rooks, 1997).

Doctors' desire to obtain a monopoly on childbirth care led them to escalate their attacks in the early twentieth century (Sullivan and Weitz, 1988: 9–14). Their efforts were rewarded in the Canada Medical Act of 1912, which eliminated the practice of midwifery as an accepted way for women to give birth in Canada.

The Resurgence of Direct-Entry Midwifery

By the second half of the twentieth century, childbirth had moved almost solely into hospital wards under medical care. Although childbearing women were grateful for the pain relief and safety that doctors promised, all too often women found the experience painful, humiliating, and alienating. Despite the absence of scientific support for such practices, doctors routinely shaved women's pubic area before delivery, strapped them on their backs to labour and delivery tables (the most painful and difficult position for delivering a baby), isolated them from their husbands during delivery and from their infants afterwards, and gave them drugs to speed up their labours or make them unconscious—all practices that scientific research would eventually find unnecessary or dangerous (Sullivan and Weitz, 1988).

Objections to such procedures sparked the growth of the natural childbirth movement during the 1970s and 1980s and forced numerous changes in obstetric practices. Most hospitals, for example, began to offer natural childbirth classes. Critics, however, argued that the real purpose of these classes was to make women patients more compliant and convince them that they have had a natural childbirth as long as they remain conscious, even if their doctors used drugs, surgery, or forceps (Sullivan and Weitz, 1988: 39).

Efforts to train and certify midwives during this time period met with fierce opposition. Thus, programs in midwifery that were established at universities and colleges in various provinces were shortly thereafter discontinued. For many years, midwives operated in a grey zone, legally unable to practise their birthing skills, but often granted exemptions on religious grounds or employed by the state to practise in underserved areas (Bourgeault, 2006). Medical doctors remained opposed to midwifery, as noted by directives issued by the College of Physicians and Surgeons of Ontario in 1982 that threatened to revoke the professional status of medical doctors who were allowing midwives to assist them (Paterson, 2011).

Struggles between midwives and doctors persisted until the early 1990s, when Ontario became the first province to pass legislation recognizing midwifery as a profession. This was an important milestone for the profession, allowing midwives to "catch" babies in homes, birthing clinics, and hospitals (Paterson, 2011). In addition, the term *midwife* became a protected title that could only be used by those registered with the College of Midwives. Ironically, the bestowing of legitimacy as a profession did not always have the desired result. For example, Alberta became the second province to recognize midwifery as a profession, allowing midwives to practise autonomously in homes and birthing clinics; however, unlike Ontario and later British Columbia, which allowed midwives to bill the provincial government for their health services, Alberta did not. The net result was that midwifery virtually ceased to exist in Alberta in the years immediately following its recognition as a profession (McKendry and Langford, 2001). It took until 2009 for midwifery services to be fully funded in Alberta. Midwifery is now recognized as a profession in all provinces and territories, with the exception of Prince Edward Island and Yukon, which are both currently considering legislation regulating midwifery as a profession.

Currently, a handful of universities in Canada offer a four-year midwifery program. Students take basic courses in anatomy, physiology, and sociology of the family as well as practical instruction and placement in a clinical setting. In several provinces, aboriginal women who practise as midwives are exempted from registering with the provincial regulating college and are permitted to call themselves aboriginal midwives. Those who are trained outside Canada are required to take a bridging program that instructs them on the practice of midwifery in Canada.

Working as a direct-entry midwife means long and uncertain hours with little pay. Most midwives, however, are motivated by humanitarian and philosophical concerns rather than by financial gain (Simonds, Rothman, and Norman, 2007). Although midwives recognize the need for obstetricians to manage the complications that occur in about 10% of births, they fear the physical and emotional dangers that arise when obstetricians employ interventionist practices, developed for the rare pathological case, during all births. Like nurse-midwives, lay midwives strongly believe in the general normalcy of pregnancy and childbirth and in the benefits of individualized, holistic maternity care in which midwife and client work as partners (Gallo-Cruz and Rutherford, 2011).

In provinces where direct-entry midwifery is legal, midwives must typically abide by regulations restricting them to "low-risk" clients (such as women under age 35) and restricting the techniques they can use (such as forbidding them from suturing tears following deliveries). Thus, licensure has given midwives some degree of freedom to practise but requires that they refer their clients to a physician for services they are prohibited from performing (Sullivan and Weitz, 1988: 97–111).

Research consistently suggests that home births conducted by experienced lay midwives working with low-risk populations are as safe as or safer than doctor-attended hospital births, even taking into account the small number of midwifery clients who develop problems needing medical attention (Hutton, Reitsma, and Kaufman, 2009; Johnson and Daviss, 2005). For example, one Canadian/American study compared 5,418 women who chose home birth with a licensed midwife with a similar group of low-risk women who chose hospital deliveries (Johnson and Daviss, 2005). In the end, both groups had similar (very low) rates of maternal and infant mortality and morbidity. However, the home-birthing women received less than half as many medical interventions. For example, only 3.7% of those delivered at home had caesarean deliveries, compared to 19% of those delivered in hospitals. As a result, those who delivered at home avoided the lingering discomfort, pain, and loss of energy that plagues many who experience medical interventions during birth. Nonetheless, midwifery in many ways still operates on the periphery: Midwives typically deliver less than 2% of all babies nationally (Benoit et al., 2005).

In sum, midwifery has made tremendous gains in the past three decades, having attained the status of a profession, with all of the rights and obligations that such a title confers. Nonetheless, midwifery retains the status of limited practitioner, as more difficult cases and complications require them to transfer care to a physician. And though it has gained greater acceptance, relatively few Canadian women choose to deliver their babies through a midwife, with the majority of women continuing to seek out the services of a medical doctor.

Chiropractors: Limited Practitioners with an Uncertain Future

The history of chiropractic illustrates the dynamic status of an occupation that has attained status as a profession despite the concerted opposition of allopathic medicine, but in recent years, has experienced substantial setbacks.

Early History

chiropractors:
Health care practitioners who specialize in spinal manipulation, trace illness and disability to misalignments of the spine, and believe spinal manipulation can cure a wide range of acute and chronic health problems.

Loosely translated from the Greek, chiropractic means "done by hand." The field of chiropractic was founded in 1895 by Daniel David Palmer, who was born in Port Perry, Ontario, but moved to the United States as a young man. Having studied magnetic healing and spinal manipulation, Palmer concluded that spinal manipulation could both prevent and cure illness. In 1896, Palmer founded the first school, to train **chiropractors** in his techniques of spinal manipulation. After his son, B. J. Palmer, took over the school in 1907, chiropractic began to grow in popularity.

Although from the beginning, some allopathic doctors studied chiropractic and taught at chiropractic schools, B. J. Palmer attempted to sharply separate chiropractic and allopathic medicine. Those who shared his philosophy and used only spinal manipulation became known as "straights." Most chiropractors, however, found Palmer's theory of illness too simplistic and limiting and so adopted a wide variety of therapeutic techniques. These "mixers" treated not only musculoskeletal problems but also other illnesses, as well as providing obstetrical and mental health care (Wardwell, 1988: 162–165).

The Fight against Medical Dominance

As chiropractic took root in both Canada and the United States, the medical establishment responded with hostility and open condemnation. Palmer himself was once arrested and jailed in the United States for practising medicine without a licence. In Canada, medical doctors also sought every opportunity to ban chiropractic. These efforts ensured that chiropractic operated on the outskirts of mainstream medicine, but allopathic doctors were never successful in eliminating it altogether.

Stagnation in the field of chiropractic in Canada prior to World War II may have been due in part to the lack of training schools within its own borders. To receive training in chiropractic, Canadians had to travel to the United States. Once the first chiropractic school in Canada was established in 1945, chiropractic began to exhibit steady growth. Legitimacy was conferred as provinces gradually granted chiropractic professional status as a self-governing occupation and the public increasingly relied on its services (Coburn, 1994). The workers' compensation boards of most provinces also began to recognize chiropractic as a legitimate form of care.

Although chiropractic meets the three criteria of a profession, its acceptance as a profession may be said to be incomplete in many respects. That is, chiropractic is a profession because it has established its own educational and licensing standards and controls who enters the profession; has technical, specialized knowledge that is imparted in schools of chiropractic; and has developed public confidence in its treatments. Moreover, chiropractors have the right to diagnose illness, do not need the referral of a doctor to see patients, and enjoy the right to use the term *doctor*. On the other hand, chiropractors still lack hospital privileges, and schools for chiropractic are separate institutions that remain unaffiliated with universities (Coburn, 1994). Attacks on the profession of chiropractic by medicine have lessened, but they have not disappeared entirely. Only 5% of chiropractic patients are referred by a medical doctor, clearly indicating that doctors do not regard chiropractors as colleagues (Mootz et al., 2005). Perhaps most importantly, the legitimacy that chiropractic gained appears to be at the expense of narrowing their scope of practice. Insurers who pay for chiropractic services typically do so only for treating specific conditions in specific ways (Tindle et al., 2005). Despite many chiropractors' desire to treat a broader range of problems, most patients visit them solely for treatment of acute back, head, or neck pain.

Current Status

There are currently 7,000 chiropractors in Canada, with approximately half based in the province of Ontario, providing services for nearly 4 million Canadians annually. All chiropractors in Canada identify as mixers. Two chiropractic schools operate in Canada, one in Ontario and one in Québec. Both schools require three years of university for admission, with four years of schooling followed by appearance before a board of examiners to receive licensure as a doctor of chiropractic.

Despite the fact that chiropractic is a regulated health profession in all provinces and territories, and on the surface meets all the criteria of a profession, there are indications that the profession is in jeopardy. First, the profession has experienced threats to its legitimacy as a profession. In 2004, the Ontario government **delisted** chiropractic services from the Ontario Health Insurance Plan. In essence, services provided by chiropractors were no longer reimbursable under the provincial health plan, even though a medical doctor who performed the same services could receive compensation. In 2009, the Alberta government also delisted chiropractic services, followed by Saskatchewan in 2010. These changes have repercussions in that the anticipated loss of income and damage to chiropractors' reputation may pose threat to their status as a profession.

In addition, several high-profile lawsuits have been levied against the field of chiropractic in Canada in recent years. The plaintiffs in these cases have alleged that chiropractic therapy is dangerous because of the increased risk for stroke that left one woman paralyzed and another dead. Such incidents have increased public awareness about the possible negative consequences of spine manipulation and may erode public confidence in chiropractic as a profession.

Finally, there are signs within the profession itself that all is not well. A recent survey of the profession concluded that there is a long-term oversupply of chiropractors relative to a relatively flat demand for chiropractic services (Mior and Laporte, 2008). Forced to compete with one another, chiropractors have begun to report declining levels of income, even as graduates are entering the profession with higher student debt. To remain viable, chiropractic must find ways to increase the demand for their services even as Canadians increasingly pay for their services out of pocket and are uncertain about its benefits. Whether chiropractic can weather these challenges remains to be seen.

COMPLEMENTARY AND ALTERNATIVE MEDICINE

The occupations described to this point all basically share allopathic medicine's understanding of how the body works, and all enjoy significant roles within the mainstream health care system. The occupations described in the remainder of this chapter are sufficiently divorced from mainstream medicine to be considered **complementary and alternative medicine (CAM)**—neither widely used nor taught in medical schools or other medical institutions, even if they are sometimes covered by health insurance. Those who offer health care services that fall under the rubric of CAM are **marginal practitioners**, whose health-related services are treated with some skepticism in the public realm and who typically have low social status.

marginal practitioners: Occupational groups that offer health care services and have low social status.

CAM: In Defiance of a Medical Model Approach

On a number of different levels, CAM has positioned itself in direct contradiction to the assumptions of a **medical model of illness** approach. For example, rather than endorsing mind-body dualism, CAM asserts that attempts to forge a deeper relationship between mind and body are necessary for healing. This holistic approach runs contrary to the reductionistic approach of the medical model, which focuses simply on the diseased part of the body and pays less attention to the rest of the body, let alone the psychosocial aspects of disease. Thus, the assumption of a medical model approach that the body operates similarly to a machine, where disease represents the malfunctioning of a given body part, is rejected by CAM practitioners in favour of the view that illness occurs when there is disharmony among the physical, psychological, social, spiritual, and other facets of one's being. CAM also embraces the idea that all bodies heal differently and thus questions the assumption in a medical model of illness approach that a cure that works in one body should work similarly in other bodies. Finally, CAM values the experiential knowledge of the individual, positing that clients must be actively engaged in the healing process, rather than passive recipients of heroic medical interventions (Hughes, 2004).

The National Center for Complementary and Alternative Medicine in the United States has identified five different types of CAM. Biologically based therapies use substances found in nature, such as herbs, foods, and vitamins, to treat illness. These include megavitamins, herbal products, and other dietary supplements. Manipulative and body-based therapies involve manipulation and/or movement of one or more parts of the body as a means of facilitating healing. Examples include feldenkrais, reflexology, rolfing, and therapeutic touch. Chiropractic is also a manipulative and body-based therapy. Mind-body interventions use a variety of techniques designed to enhance the mind's capacity to affect bodily function and symptoms. Energy therapies are based on the belief that there are energies in the environment that can be harnessed by the individual to achieve healing. They can be further distinguished into two types: Biofield therapies are intended to affect energy fields that purportedly surround and penetrate the human body. Some forms of energy therapy manipulate biofields by applying pressure and/or manipulating the body by placing the hands in, or through, these fields. Examples include Qiqong and Reiki. A second type of energy therapy involves unconventional use of electromagnetic fields that are passed over the body to bring healing to the body. Finally, alternative medical systems represent complete systems of theory and practice. Examples include Ayurveda, acupuncture, and traditional Chinese medicine.

Approximately one in nine Canadians reported using the services of CAM in the previous twelve-month period (Metcalfe et al., 2010). CAM use is more common among women than men and more likely among those with higher levels of education (McFarland et al., 2002). CAM use is also more likely for those who are between the ages of 20 and 64, with lower rates of utilization for those under age 20 and those over age 65 (Metcalfe et al., 2010).

History of Efforts to Suppress CAM

Historically, allopathic medicine has fiercely opposed CAM. Winnick (2005) distinguishes three phases in efforts by medical doctors to quash or manage the threat of CAM. The first phase, which occurred as medicine enjoyed medical dominance and lasted most of the twentieth century, was characterized by condemnation of CAM practitioners. Derided as quacks, CAM practitioners were subjected to vicious attacks by medical doctors, who used their positions of power to publicly express their skepticism of CAM practices and to lobby the provinces to ban CAM. Such efforts were successful initially, but after the 1970s, medicine began to lose key battles as some CAM practitioners became legitimized by the state (e.g., chiropractors).

During the second phase, lasting from the 1970s through to the mid-1990s, medical doctors engaged in reassessment. During this time period, doctors refrained from openly attacking CAM practitioners, turning inward instead to evaluate whether growing consumerism and dissatisfaction with conventional medicine accounted for the rising popularity of CAM. In the third phase, doctors launched a strategy of integration that involved accepting those aspects of CAM that could be shown to demonstrate evidence of safety and efficacy and proclaiming as fraudulent those aspects of CAM that did not hold up to scientific scrutiny. Thus, acceptance of CAM on medicine's own terms allowed medical doctors to control and co-opt CAM for their own purposes.

That CAM practitioners have largely consented to validating their practices on the terms of medicine was made clear in a Canadian study that described strategies CAM practitioners employed to attain professional status in the province of Ontario (Welsh et al., 2004). The authors identified four strategies: improving educational standards, improving practice standards, engaging in peer-review research, and increasing group cohesion. While these strategies worked to varying degrees, depending on the history and characteristics of the different CAM practitioners considered in the analysis, the authors found that employing these strategies inevitably required CAM practitioners to adhere more closely to the scientific method and to abandon some of the underlying principles of CAM. For example, conducting peer-reviewed research to evaluate the efficacy of CAM was viewed with consternation by those who eschewed the scientific method in favour of what they experientially learned through their own practice and others who worried how their individualized treatments could ever be evaluated in a clinical trial. Similarly, improving educational standards often translated into establishing programs that relied heavily on a science-based curriculum. In short, professionalizing required CAM practitioners to negotiate the boundaries with regard to how they were positioned relative to the rhetoric of science, where they discovered that attaining legitimacy invariably meant compromising and adapting to a more medical worldview. Whether CAM practitioners see this as an acceptable cost on the path to legitimacy remains both an open question and an issue that sociologists will continue to follow closely.

IMPLICATIONS

Over the course of the twentieth century, allopathic medicine attained and then enjoyed unprecedented autonomy and dominance, becoming the premier example of a profession. In the last few decades of the twentieth century and into the twenty-first century, however, doctors' social status has become somewhat diminished. Nonetheless, despite challenges to their power from the state, the public, other professions, and within medicine itself, doctors continue to wield considerable influence in the health care field.

Doctors' professional socialization has implications for the profession and the delivery of health care. A medical culture that emphasizes emotional detachment allows doctors to remain objective when they come into contact with their patients' bodies and to work in the patients' best interests rather than their own, but also has unintended negative consequences when doctors also learn ways of interacting with patients and thinking about illness that can encourage overly aggressive, scientifically unjustified, or simply discourteous treatment.

In this chapter, we have shown that the health care arena is much broader than we usually recognize and have highlighted the struggles of other health care occupations to gain and hold on to professional autonomy in the face of medical dominance. As the examples of pharmacy and direct-entry midwifery have shown, strict licensing laws, even when devised by doctors opposed to an occupation's growth, in the end can help occupations gain professional autonomy by forcing them to increase standards and thereby enabling them to gain additional status and freedom to practise. Not surprisingly, developing professional autonomy seems most difficult for those, like nurses, who work directly under medical control. On the other hand, groups such as chiropractors, who have considerably more leeway to develop their practices without interference from medical doctors, may be at risk for losing their professional status. These varied histories reaffirm that professionalization is an ongoing process, and that one's position is never certain but always open to contestation.

As an alternative to mainstream medicine, CAM has enjoyed growing popularity, which can be attributed to its focus on holistic rather than reductionist treatment, as well as the valuing of experiential knowledge over technical knowledge. As CAM moves to the mainstream, where its claims will be subject to the rigours of the scientific method, it is far from certain that it can retain its unique identity or resist being co-opted by medicine.

SUMMARY

LO-1 1. The three criteria to be characterized as a profession are (a) the autonomy to set educational and licensing standards and to police members for incompetence or malfeasance; (b) technical, specialized knowledge, unique to the occupation and learned through extended, systematic training; and (c) a code of ethics that increases public faith that activities are motivated more by a desire to serve than a desire to earn a profit.

LO-1 2. Medicine is the premier example of a profession: It sits at the top of the health care occupational structure, retains unparalleled access to the human body on the basis of its specialized knowledge, and adheres to a code of ethics that has long instilled and inspired the highest levels of public confidence.

LO-2 3. The achievements of medical dominance and becoming a profession happened in the previous century, and many now believe that medical dominance is in decline. Threats

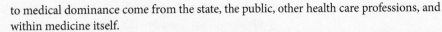

to medical dominance come from the state, the public, other health care professions, and within medicine itself.

LO-2   4.   Under pressure to contain the rising costs of health care, the state began to place limits on physician autonomy and intervened in areas that were once the exclusive jurisdiction of physicians. More recent interventions in EHRs and wait list reductions exemplify the growing influence of the state in the day-to-day work lives of medical doctors.

LO-2   5.   Having made the shift from passive recipient of medical care to empowered consumer, the public is expected and encouraged to wield greater influence in the medical encounter, changing the balance of power in a way that makes doctors more accountable and more responsive to the needs of patients.

LO-2   6.   The gains made by other health care occupations to be recognized as professions have chipped away at territory that was once exclusively held by allopathic doctors, eroding the ability of medicine to determine unilaterally what happens in the field of health care.

LO-2   7.   As the field of medicine has expanded, it has become much more hierarchically organized and heterogeneous, making it difficult for those within the field to find common ground and to present a united front to the outside world. To the extent that medical doctors may compete with one another for limited resources, there is potential for internal dissent and conflict to grow.

LO-3   8.   Through their medical training, students learn a set of cultural norms: to value emotional detachment, trust clinical experience more than scientific evidence, master uncertainty, adopt a mechanistic model of the body, trust intervention more than normal bodily processes, and prefer working with rare or acute illnesses than with typical or chronic illnesses.

LO-3   9.   The consequence of acquiring these medical norms is that doctors may begin to assume that they are the only ones who are capable of making decisions about what is best for the patient and may perform procedures that are either unnecessary or harmful to their patients.

LO-4   10.   The power of a profession is fragile: Those who have attained it must continually defend threats to their territory, whereas those who aspire to professional status must struggle to claim their own territory. How health care occupations adapt and respond to ongoing structural changes in health determines success and failure in the ongoing process of professionalization.

LO-5   11.   Nursing as a field has tried to improve its status primarily by increasing educational requirements. It has been held back by its status as a "female" occupation and by public expectations that women are naturally caring and thus do not need professional salaries, professional status, or good work conditions in exchange for their care-giving.

LO-5   12.   Increased educational qualifications have enabled nursing to achieve semiprofessional status; however, for the most part, nurses have yet to develop the truly independent knowledge base needed to obtain full professional status, and so they remain subordinate to doctors.

LO-5   13.   Pharmacy meets the three criteria of a profession. The history of pharmacy illustrates the changing fortunes of a profession: Once autonomous, pharmacy was reduced to a marginal status in the health care system over the course of the twentieth century, but efforts to reprofessionalize over the past decades have resulted in newly granted authority in Canada and elsewhere to prescribe medications and to provide front-line health care.

LO-5   14.   Prior to the nineteenth century, lay midwives delivered babies for almost all pregnant women. Lay midwives lost this status due to the growing public belief in science, competition from doctors, their low status as women, and the lack of strict licensing and educational requirements. Lay midwifery has reappeared due to dissatisfaction with medicalized childbirth, and increasingly in Canada it has attained the status of a profession, albeit limited to childbirth.

LO-5   15.   After protracted battles with medicine, chiropractors gained occupational status in exchange for remaining limited practitioners; however, in recent years, the status of chiropractic as a profession has been jeopardized as several provinces have delisted their services, as visible court cases suggest that chiropractic may be harmful, and as oversupply relative to a flat demand for services has eroded the economic rewards of practising chiropractic.

LO-6   16.   Rejecting the principles of a medical model of illness approach and embracing a holistic approach, CAM can be distinguished into five categories: biologically based therapies, manipulative and body-based therapies, mind-body interventions, energy therapies, and alternative medical systems. CAM has grown in popularity in Canada, although it is disproportionately used by women and those with higher levels of education.

LO-6   17.   The efforts of medical doctors to deal with the threat of CAM proceeded in three phases: condemnation, reassessment, and integration. In exchange for legitimacy, CAM has opened up its practices to greater scientific scrutiny, paving the way for medical doctors to co-opt and exert greater control over CAM in the future.

REVIEW QUESTIONS

1. What are the three criteria that elevate an occupation to the level of a profession?
2. In what ways have the state, the public, other professions, and medicine itself presented challenges for doctors' professional dominance?
3. What are the major medical norms, how do doctors learn them, and how do they affect patient-doctor relationships?
4. How did the early history of nursing make it difficult for nurses to increase their status or improve their working conditions?
5. How have nurses attempted to professionalize? Why haven't these strategies succeeded?
6. What does it mean to reprofessionalize?
7. What are the similarities and differences in the history of pharmacy and direct-entry midwives and their efforts to attain the status of a profession?
8. What are the current challenges faced by chiropractors, and what strategies might be employed to retain professional status in the future?
9. In what ways might CAM be considered a victim of its own success?

CRITICAL THINKING QUESTIONS

1. What factors have helped doctors to gain power in Canadian society? What factors are causing them to lose power? On balance, is the power of doctors growing or shrinking?
2. Identify two concepts that you have learned in this course so far, and explain why medical students need to be taught these concepts.
3. How might the growing popularity of CAM change the practice of medicine?

KEY TERMS

advanced practice nurses (p. 301)
chiropractors (p. 306)
clinical pharmacy (p. 303)
electronic health record (p. 287)
evidence-based medicine (p. 296)
holistic treatment (p. 298)
licensed practical nurses (LPNs) (p. 300)
limited practitioners (p. 303)
marginal practitioners (p. 308)
medical norms (p. 293)
nurse-midwives (p. 301)
nurse-practitioners (p. 301)

open access (p. 289)
profession (p. 286)
professionalization (p. 285)
professional socialization (p. 294)
pseudodisease (p. 298)
reductionistic treatment (p. 298)
registered nurses (RNs) (p. 300)
registered psychiatric nurses (RPNs) (p. 301)
reprofessionalization (p. 303)
residents (p. 293)
specialization (p. 291)

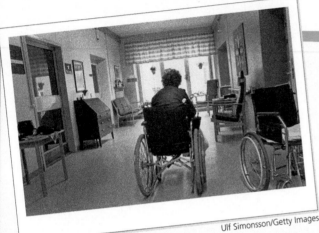

Ulf Simonsson/Getty Images

The Care-Cost Dilemma

Timothy Diamond, a sociologist who spent several years working as a nursing aide in a variety of nursing homes, recounts the following experience:

> Mary Ryan, like many others, spent all day in the day room, secured to her chair with a restraint vest. "How y' doin' today, Mary?" I once asked in passing.
>
> She answered the question with a question. "Why do I have to sit here with this thing on?"
>
> I responded automatically with a trained answer, "That's so you won't fall. You know that."

"Oh, get away from me," she reacted with disgust. "I don't trust anyone in white anymore."

Stunned by her rejection, and not completely confident of my own answer, I passed the question on to Beulah Fedders, the LPN [licensed practical nurse] in charge.

"Beulah, why does she have to wear that thing all the time?" Beulah accompanied her quick comeback with a chuckle. "That's so they don't have to hire any more of you."

We snickered together at the humour of her explanation, but an explanation it was, and more penetrating than mine to Mary. It posed a relationship between technology and labour, and in that connection Beulah explained that the use of one could mitigate the need for the other. A different kind of answer to the same question was given during our orientation [by the home's administrator]. "The restraint vests save on incidents...."

Beulah's answer was more accurate than "so you won't fall" and "vests save on incidents," because she connected them both to a common denominator—available labour. If no nursing assistant was there to be with Mary, to walk with her or anticipate her dizziness, and if she sat in the chair without a restraint and without anyone to keep an eye on her, she might have fallen, thus generating an incident. Her restraint vest saved on incidents while it saved on labour costs. (Diamond, 1992: 182)

Timothy Diamond, *Making Gray Gold: Narratives of Nursing Home Care*, Chicago: University of Chicago Press, 1992.

In this chapter, students should be able to:

LO-1 **Describe** the history of the hospital in Canada and **identify** how the hospital has transformed over time.

LO-2 **Describe** the history of mental hospitals in Canada and **identify** the causes and consequences of deinstitutionalization.

LO-3 **Recognize** differences among long-term care facilities, assisted living facilities, and home care.

LO-4 **Describe** the evolution of the hospice and palliative care movement in Canada.

LO-5 **Recognize** the social process that underlies and guides which potential technologies should be pursued and which should not be adopted.

As this story suggests, a central dilemma in health care is how to provide care in a system that is under pressure to reduce costs and seems designed to meet the needs of the institution rather than the patient. In this chapter, we look at several settings where health care is provided: hospitals, mental hospitals, long-term care facilities, assisted living facilities, home care, and hospices. We also consider a sociological analysis of the technologies that have become such a central part of care in these different settings, exploring what exactly we mean when we talk of "technology" and how society decides which potential technologies should be developed and adopted.

THE HOSPITAL

The hospital as we know it is a modern invention. Before the twentieth century, Canadians, whether rich or poor, typically preferred and received health care at home from friends, relatives, and assorted health care providers. Because these providers used only a few small and portable tools, hospitals were unnecessary.

Yet hospitals and other institutions have existed in Canada since the arrival of European settlers. Religious institutions operated hospitals known as Hôtels-Dieu, or hostels of God, offering custodial and basic social services on a charity basis. Such places, however, were few in number. For those who were not close to a hospital and lacked friends or relatives to provide care at home or the means to purchase such care, the option of last resort was the **almshouse**. Here they—along with orphans, the destitute, the disabled, the insane, and other public wards—would receive essentially custodial care. Conditions in almshouses were generally appalling. Hunger was common and blankets and clothing scarce, making almshouses ideal breeding grounds for disease (Rosenberg, 1987: 31–32).

It was not until the mid-nineteenth century that there was a general desire to distribute hospitals more broadly throughout Canada. The establishment of hospitals grew out of the converging interests of different segments of society. Not surprisingly, doctors who were eager to demonstrate their medical knowledge and to expand their client base were early advocates of hospitals. They hoped to offer care for the poor, but also envisioned private beds for those who could pay for medical treatment. Moreover, physicians recognized that the home was unsuited for aseptic techniques, which were increasingly recognized as an important standard of care, and viewed the hospital as an opportunity to create a suitable environment. Finally, the introduction of new technologies such as the X-ray machine made it unwieldy for doctors to visit their patients in their homes, helping doctors make the case that the hospital was a more appropriate setting than the home.

Church organizations and religious leaders also rallied behind the hospital movement, seeing hospitals as a central location for dispensing charity and social services. Similarly, other community leaders also perceived the political benefits of establishing a hospital

almshouse:
An institution, also known as a poorhouse, in which all public wards, including orphans, criminals, the disabled, and the insane, received custodial care.

This photograph, taken in 1894, of a men's ward at Royal Victoria Hospital in Montréal illustrates the emerging role of hospitals as they began to offer care based on the patient's ability to pay for services.

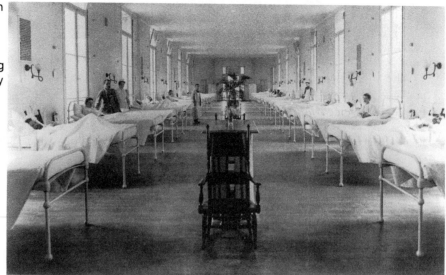

© McCord Museum. II-105912.

to ensure the survival and continued growth of their community. Though the public was sometimes reluctant to support these initiatives, fearing the costs of financing hospitals through their own taxes, they were eventually persuaded that these services could also provide them with benefit.

While small towns built small hospitals containing no more than a handful of beds staffed with one or two nurses, larger cities constructed more sizable hospitals with wings that separated the poor from the paying customers. The cost of care charged to the rich was used to subsidize the care provided to the poor. Conditions in these hospitals were better than what had been provided in the almshouse, although, of course, the poor did not receive the added services that transformed the institution into a homelike setting for those could afford them.

The Transformation to a Temple of Science

With the recommendation that hospitals become centres of learning for medical doctors, the Flexner Report created an opportunity for doctors to hasten and solidify the transformation of the hospital from a place of charity to a temple of science (Gagan, 1989). That is, the Flexner Report broadly affirmed the notion that the hospital was to be envisioned as a place where the best diagnostic and therapeutic technologies would be housed and where doctors could engage in leading-edge medical practice.

As the hospital gained broader recognition as a source of medical care rather than the dispensing of charity, the public began to rely more heavily on its services. This trend, already underway at the end of the nineteenth century, gained momentum following the Flexner Report. This was evidenced in subsequent increases in the revenues flowing into hospitals, particularly from patients who paid for the care they received. Moreover, to the extent that the custodial functions associated with warehousing the poor and indigent were no longer seen as the central focus of hospitals, there was a steady increase in the number of admissions and a corresponding decrease in the average length of stay. Table 13.1 illustrates the changing nature of hospitals as they made the transition from dispensers of charity to temples of science in the province of Ontario between 1880 and 1946.

	1880	1900	1920	1946
Admissions (per 1,000)	2.8	13.6	45.1	75.1
Average length of stay (days)	35	24	15	12
Average cost (patient day)	$0.57	$0.76	$2.84	$5.03
Percentage of revenue from patient fees	9.0	35.3	64.8	75.7

TABLE 13.1 Public General Hospital Characteristics in the Province of Ontario, 1880–1946

Source: Adapted from: David Gagan, "For patients of 'moderate' means: The Transformation of Ontario's Public General Hospital, 1880-1950," *The Canadian Historical Review*, LXX, Pg. 151, 1989.

During this time period, the physical and social organization of hospitals began to exhibit greater differentiation. For example, whereas nurses would have lived in rooms scattered throughout the hospital during the nineteenth century, there was a move to segregate nurses into their own quarters. Thus, hospitals constructed wings or entire buildings that functioned specifically as nurse residences. Moreover, the general-purpose tasks that nurses performed were delegated to other support staff, who assumed responsibility for various functions, including record-keeping, cleaning, and laundry. This freed nurses to provide more direct care to their patients. More importantly, these changes reflected the emergence of an occupational hierarchy, whereby different tasks in the hospital were assigned to different groups of workers, who had varying levels of skills and received varying levels of compensation for their work. Finally, hospitals themselves became oriented toward serving different segments of the population, with some hospitals devoted entirely to the needs of women (e.g., Toronto's Women's College Hospital) and other hospitals serving only children (e.g., Children's Memorial Hospital in Montréal).

By opening up a new market for health care, where the laws of supply and demand influenced the price of health care, hospitals also acquired the hierarchical structure that existed more broadly in Canadian society. That is, as the public embraced and increasingly utilized hospital care, its cost structure reflected and reinforced the social class divisions of the day. The wealthiest paid a steep price for the luxury of a private room, whereas middle-class patients purchased semiprivate accommodations, and the poorest, who could not be turned away, were afforded the lowest-quality care.

The uneasy tension between the philanthropic underpinnings of the hospital and its new mandate to provide scientific, market-oriented care would eventually produce its own crisis. As the hospital transformed itself by acquiring new technologies and creating new hierarchies of hospital workers, the costs of hospital care began to escalate. As costs rose, it became more difficult to shift the burden onto the middle and upper classes. Importantly, middle-class customers, who had flocked to hospitals convinced that preferential treatment elevated them above the level of care still provided on a charity basis to the poor, now found themselves increasingly unable to afford hospital care. In danger of losing critical support from the middle classes, hospitals desperately needed to solve the problem of looming budget deficits. As historian David Gagan (1989) notes:

> Hospital boards of trustees, comprised of citizen volunteers, were struggling to maintain highly complex, costly, and socially indispensable health-care facilities with essentially the same funding mechanisms, and operating under the same rules as they had at their disposal in 1880. Faced with a shortage of more than 10,000 acute-treatment beds, and rapidly increasing costs of construction, employment and medical technology, these voluntary, community-based and community-supported organizations had inherited, by the end of the Second World War, the whirlwind effects of a scientific and social revolution that their merely local resources could no longer contain. (p. 156)

From Temple of Science to Complex Bureaucracy

As World War II drew to an end, the ensuing postwar boom exacerbated the pressures that hospitals faced in their ability to provide care at the leading edge of medicine at an affordable price. These budget crises began to be resolved as federal and provincial governments stepped in with funding. For example, as part of the rebuilding effort, the federal government committed substantial funds in 1948 to launch hospital construction throughout Canada. As noted in Chapter 10, Saskatchewan was at the forefront of this trend, having forged ahead in 1947 and at its own expense to invest in hospital-building and to introduce government hospital insurance. The annual hospital premium that was charged to each household covered the bulk of the cost of hospital care in the province, paving the way for residents to obtain care at the hospital without paying for any of the services they received. This plan was also popular with Saskatchewan physicians as it allowed them to admit patients to hospital without concern for cost (Houston, 2002).

Saskatchewan's template for absorbing the costs of hospital care began to be applied across Canada, eventually culminating in the shared funding agreement for hospital care between the federal government and the provinces. With these new funding mechanisms in place, hospitals abandoned the remnants of their quasi-charity status as well as their market-oriented ambitions. Instead, hospitals were newly conceived as a large-scale collective investment that would exist as a public good to benefit the entire population.

In the process, hospitals underwent further transformation from small, relatively simple, locally administered organizations to large and complex bureaucratized institutions (Torrance, 1998). For example, one of the implications of the shared funding arrangements for hospitals was that new administrative technologies reporting back to provincial and federal governments had to be developed. This ushered a whole new set of workers into the hospital to process the growing amount of paperwork. These ranged from a veritable army of low-level clerical workers to new professional groups to handle finance, personnel, and public relations. At the top of this occupational group, the graduates of newly established university programs in hospital administration began to oversee the daily operations of hospitals, taking much of the control away from local, physician-dominated hospital boards.

Moreover, the intensified pace of government investment allowed hospitals to offer a wide range of new diagnostic and therapeutic instruments and techniques that required not only more staff but also a new type of worker who was highly trained and specialized. The growth of specialized technicians in the hospital setting can be evidenced in the nearly ten-fold increase in laboratory technicians between 1948 and 1982 in the province of Ontario (Torrance, 1998). Similar differentiation also occurred in other areas of hospital work as separate departments were established for housekeeping, dietetics, laundry, and maintenance. Unionization allowed nurses and other occupational groups not only to improve their wages but also to define and protect their roles within the hospital system. Thus, larger numbers of workers were employed to meet the expanding needs of the hospital, each with their own unique tasks and stratified position within the occupational hierarchy. Consequently, hospital costs surged in ensuing decades. These rising costs, not surprisingly, would be seen as unsustainable by the 1990s, making hospitals a primary target of subsequent health care reforms.

The bureaucratic nature of hospitals also began to be reflected in their physical architecture. Hospitals of the late nineteenth century were built as unique structures that were lavished with ornamental features. Throughout Canada, these hospitals were recognized as landmarks. By the middle of the twentieth century, however, hospitals were bland buildings, constructed with similar layouts across the different floors of the hospital. Unremarkable in almost every way, they represented the institutional environment of the hospital, imposing conformity and routinization even in their physical appearance.

Hospitals Today

Hospitals no longer terrify and endanger patients in the same way as they did in the nineteenth century. Nevertheless, a hospital stay often remains alienating and frightening. The bureaucratic nature and large size of modern hospitals, coupled with the highly technological nature of hospital care, often mean that the patient as an individual person, rather than just a diseased body, gets lost.

The reasons behind this are obvious and, to some extent, unavoidable. First, patients increasingly enter hospitals needing emergency care. Often, health care workers must respond immediately to their needs and have no time to talk with them to ascertain their preferences—which many are physically incapable of expressing in any case. Second, the highly technical nature of hospital care encourages staff to focus on the machines and the data these machines produce rather than on the patient as a whole person. In the modern obstetric ward, for example, workers often focus much of their attention on the electronic fetal monitor rather than on the labouring woman (Rothman, 2000). Third, as we noted in the previous chapter, medical training encourages doctors to focus on biological issues much more than on patients' psychological or social needs. At the same time, short stays make it less likely that patients will develop a personal relationship with either hospital staff or other patients. Fourth, as large institutions necessarily concerned with providing efficient care, hospitals are not geared toward offering individualized care. Instead, hospitals rely on routines and schedules that leave little leeway for individual needs or desires, resulting in such ironies as nurses awakening patients from needed sleep to take their temperature or blood pressure.

Importantly, the changes in the hospital that started more than a century ago persist to the present day. In the twenty-first century, a hospital stay is now a matter of only a few hours or days. Indeed, many services that would have once required admission to hospital are now performed on an **outpatient** basis. Moreover, decreases in the average length of stay over the course of the twentieth century continue such that the average length of stay of twelve days in 1946 had further reduced to 7.6 days in 2009 (Canadian Institute for Health Information (CIHI), 2010a). Similarly, the occupational hierarchy has continued to become more complex and stratified as new occupational categories are created to perform specific tasks within the hospital. Thus, the greater specialization of physicians, discussed in the previous chapter, continues to be matched by greater differentiation in the other occupations in the hospital system.

outpatient:
A hospital patient who is neither formally admitted nor kept overnight.

In other ways, the hospital of the twenty-first century may be seen as having acquired undesirable characteristics that make it more similar to hospitals prior to the twentieth century. Thus, although Canadians still flock to the hospital to receive health care services, the hospital is increasingly seen as a place to avoid if at all possible.

Deep cuts to hospital budgets in the past few decades have fuelled unfavourable perceptions of the hospital. First, budget cuts reduced the overall size of the workforce and eroded the working conditions and morale of hospital workers. These changes have had implications for the health and well-being of hospital workers. Moreover, awareness of these cutbacks created the public perception of a declining quality of care received in the hospital, fomenting general feelings of wariness and distrust. In short, the public is caught between the long-held view of the hospital as a temple of science that houses the latest technologies to save and prolong life and a growing recognition that hospitals, under pressure to be efficient, are not necessarily effective and may even run roughshod over the real needs of patients. As such, the health of patients is seen to be at risk in the hospital. In the rest of this section, we discuss how efficiency-driven hospitals may put the health of workers and patients at risk.

The health care funding crises of the 1990s transformed hospitals yet again, but this time the change was much more subtle. Because hospitals were viewed as a public good, hospital workers enjoyed the benefits of being employed in the public sector, with high wages and good job security. Moreover, the purpose of hospital work was to provide care and service, without weighing these against cost and profit (Armstrong and Armstrong, 2005). The attempt to reign in the spiralling costs of hospitals changed these underlying principles. In implementing harsh budget cuts, hospital tasks associated with cooking, cleaning, and laundry were redefined so that they were no longer viewed as health care but instead became ancillary services. In essence, the work of cooks and cleaners (caring) was deemed unimportant relative to the other specialized and technical functions of the hospital (curing). Consequently, cooking, laundry, and cleaning services were privatized and contracted out to large, multinational, for-profit corporations that offered similar services in hotels and airports.

Now employed in the private sector, these ancillary hospital workers receive much lower levels of compensation for their work and have far less job security. Moreover, the need to create profit has intensified the labour process, forcing workers to perform their tasks within a shorter time frame (Zuberi and Ptashnick, 2011). As a result, workers experience greater stress in their work, are at greater risk for work injury, and report high levels of job dissatisfaction, all contributing to a high rate of turnover. High job turnover means that, when there are staff shortages, workers may be asked to take on additional tasks for which they have received little training, further increasing the likelihood of making mistakes and being injured on the job (Zuberi and Ptashnick, 2011).

Because caring tasks are deemed unimportant, many assume that these changes have no consequences for the health and well-being of patients. Yet, Armstrong and Armstrong (2005) contend that the standards for hotel cleaning are not the same as those for hospital cleaning and that mistakes in the hospital setting have much more serious repercussions. Unlike hotels, hospitals contain sick people with weakened or compromised immune systems; thus, it is critical that hospitals maintain sterile environments that reduce the transmission of infectious disease.

superbugs:
Bacteria that have become resistant to most antibiotic drugs.

Indeed, hospitals have become well known for the threats posed by **superbugs**, bacteria that are resistant to most forms of antibiotic treatment. These superbugs, which include methicillin-resistant staphylococcus aureus (MRSA), clostridium difficile (C. diff.), and vancomycin-resistant enterococci (VRE), are highly infectious, can live for extended periods of time on flat surfaces, and are extremely difficult to treat. Every year, more than 200,000 Canadians contract these superbugs as a result of being hospitalized and as many as 8,000 die as a result (CIHI, 2008a). Moreover, the threat of superbugs has been increasing over time. Zoutman and Ford (2008) reported that rates of MRSA and VRE nearly doubled in Canadian hospitals between 1999 and 2005. Importantly, the evidence suggests that superbugs continue to be a major health risk in Canadian hospitals, with many blaming the privatization of cleaning services in the hospital system as well as a more generalized complacency about the importance of cleanliness in health care (Bourgeault et al., 2001; Dancer, 2012).

Because health care in the hospital setting involves hard physical work as well as interacting with patients who are ill and possibly disoriented and distressed, there are many ways in which the health and well-being of workers can be jeopardized. These include musculoskeletal injury as a result of heavy lifting, health risks associated with constant exposure to infectious disease as well as the chemical and biological agents used to detect and treat disease, mental health problems that can result from increased workloads and rapidly changing work demands, and injuries sustained as a result of violence in the workplace (Health Canada, 2004).

As hospitals strive to be more efficient, there is a need to ensure that workplace health and safety are not eroded. Importantly, risks to health are not spread equally across the hospital occupational hierarchy but occur disproportionately among those who have the least power in the system. This includes not only ancillary workers but also nurses, who provide much of the front-line care to patients.

A survey of nearly 7,000 nurses in British Columbia and Alberta revealed the extent to which hospital nurses are exposed to threats to their well-being (Hesketh et al., 2003). In the survey, nurses were asked if in the past five shifts they had worked, they had experienced physical assault (being spit on, hit, pushed, or bitten); threat of assault (verbal or written threats); or emotional abuse (insults, humiliation, coercion) and to identify whether the source of violence was a patient, family member or visitor, physician, nursing co-worker, or other hospital worker. The authors also distinguished the type of unit the nurse was assigned, creating different categories for those in medical/surgical wards, critical care, psychiatry, emergency, other types of units, or assigned across multiple units. Their findings, shown in Table 13.2, are disturbing because they suggest that hospital workplace violence is widespread. Emotional abuse is the most common form of workplace violence and occurs for the majority of nurses working in emergency (62.4%) and psychiatric units (55.0%). Physical assault was most common in emergency care (41.4%) and least common in critical care units (11.8%). Whereas the overwhelming majority of physical assaults and threats of physical assault were committed by patients, the sources of emotional abuse were much more diffuse, coming from patients, physicians, and co-workers.

In sum, hospitals have been continuously transforming from their earliest manifestation in Canadian history to the present day. What has not changed perhaps are the contradictions and challenges hospitals must manage when there are conflicting visions of what a hospital should be. On one hand, hospitals continue to embody the marvels of science, offering the promise of sophisticated technologies that miraculously save lives. For some, the depersonalizing aspects of hospital care that are part and parcel of large bureaucratic organizations may be a small price to pay for access to the wonders of modern medicine. More uneasy, however, is the current struggle to determine whether hospitals represent a public good or whether, under threat to perform more efficiently, hospitals are justified in quietly introducing for-profit companies to offer services that are seen as ancillary, and therefore irrelevant, to the curative functions of the hospital.

MENTAL HOSPITALS

The history of treatment for mental illness reveals the role social values play in medical responses to problematic behaviour. In this section, we trace the treatment of mental illness from the prescientific era to the present.

TABLE 13.2 Percentage of Nurses Experiencing Physical Assault, Threat of Assault, and Emotional Abuse in Hospitals in Alberta and British Columbia

Nursing Area	Physical Assault	Threat of Assault	Emotional Abuse
Medical/surgical	24.2	22.6	41.4
Critical care	11.8	8.9	39.9
Emergency	41.4	26.2	62.4
Psychiatry	20.3	43.3	55.0
Other units	14.4	12.8	30.3
Multiple units	18.1	18.6	36.9

Adapted from: Kathryn L. Hesketh, et al., "Workplace Violence in Alberta and British Columbia Hospitals," *Health Policy*, Vol. 63, Pg. 311, 2003.

Before the Scientific Era

Although the concept of mental illness is relatively new, all societies throughout history have had individuals whose behaviour set them apart as unacceptably and incomprehensibly different. However, premodern societies could more often find informal ways of coping with such individuals (Horwitz, 1982). First, premodern societies could offer acceptable, low-level roles to those whose thought patterns and behaviours differed from the norm. Second, because work roles rarely required individuals to function in highly structured and regimented ways, many troubled individuals could perform at marginally acceptable levels. Third, in premodern societies, work occurred within the context of the family, whether at home or in fields or forests. As a result, families could watch over those whose emotional or cognitive problems interfered with their abilities to care for themselves. These three factors enabled families to **normalize** mental illness by explaining away problematic behaviour as mere eccentricity. As a result, unless individuals behaved violently or caused problems for civil authorities, their families and communities could deal with them informally.

In some cases, however, individuals behaved too unacceptably or incomprehensibly for their communities to normalize. In these cases, and as is true with all illnesses (as described in Chapter 7), communities needed to find explanations to help them understand why such problems struck some people and not others. Such explanations helped to make the world seem more predictable and safe by convincing the community that such bad things would never happen to "good people" like themselves.

Until the modern scientific age, societies typically viewed disturbing behaviour as a punishment for sin or for violating a taboo, a sign that the afflicted individual was a witch, or a result of supernatural powers beyond the body. For example, the term **lunacy**, commonly applied to the mentally ill from the thirteenth until the mid-nineteenth century, reflected the belief that the movement of the moon exerted an influence on human behaviour. When the moon was full, it was expected that people would be most likely to behave in bizarre and even frightening ways.

Treatment might be delegated to religious authorities—whether shamans, witch doctors, or priests—who relied on prayer, exorcism, spells, and treatments such as bloodletting or trepanning (drilling a hole in the skull to let "bad spirits" out). Extreme measures, such as torture and fright, were also widely used by family members and various health practitioners, with the belief that these could effectively jolt the mentally afflicted back into the world of sanity. Thus, forcible confinement that left the mad chained or bound for extended periods of time and other equally degrading situations were justified as reasonable treatment regimens for those who were deemed to have lost their minds.

As a capitalist economy began to develop, both religious control and informal **social control** began to decline (Horwitz, 1982; Scull, 1977). Under capitalism, work moved from home and farm to workshops and factories, making it more difficult for families to care informally for problematic relatives. In addition, a capitalist economy could less readily absorb those whose productivity could not be scheduled and regimented. At the same time, widespread migration from the countryside to cities weakened families and other social support systems.

These changes fostered a need for new, formal institutions to address mental illness. Thus, **lunatic asylums**, as they were officially called, made their earliest appearance in eastern Canada and later spread westward. The first mental institution in North America, the Provincial Lunatic Asylum, opened its doors in Lancaster, New Brunswick, in 1835. In the west, mental hospitals were not established until much later (1872 in Victoria, British Columbia; 1911 in Ponoka, Alberta; and 1913 in North Battleford, Saskatchewan). During

normalize:
Make something seem like the normal course of events.

lunacy:
Intermittent periods of bizarre behaviour relieved by periods of reason that are assumed to be caused by the phases of the moon.

lunatic asylum:
The official name given to the first institutions in Canada that treated people with mental illness.

this period of expansion, however, new ideas about mental illness produced changes in both the name and the location of institutions. The label *lunatic asylum*, applied to all institutions built in Canada in the first half of the nineteenth century, was purposely abandoned in the latter half of the century. Thus, all mental institutions built west of Brandon, Manitoba, were opened under the title "Hospital for the Insane" at about the same time that mental hospitals in the east became similarly labelled. This was done to eliminate the association of mental illness with superstitious beliefs about its causes, and the use of the word *hospital* also allowed the emerging field of psychiatry to align its work with scientific principles and the practice of medicine (Reaume, 2002). Moreover, whereas mental institutions in the east tended to be built in or around major urban centres, those built several decades later in western Canada were located in the countryside, far from population. This change reflected the growing popularity of a new treatment philosophy for the mentally ill.

In late eighteenth century Europe, attitudes toward persons with mental illness underwent enormous change (Scull, 1989: 96–117). In place of terrorizing or simply warehousing those who were mentally ill, reformers proposed **moral treatment**: teaching individuals to live in society by showing them kindness and giving them opportunities to work and play. The stunning successes that resulted convinced many that mental illness was curable and changed the delivery of mental health care. The method of moral treatment, although it was short-lived in Canada, began to influence care for the mentally ill in Canada in the latter half of the nineteenth century.

moral treatment:
A nineteenth-century practice aimed at curing persons with mental illness by treating them with kindness and giving them opportunities for both work and play.

To ensure a pastoral environment in accordance with the principles of moral treatment, hospitals for the insane that were established in the latter half of the nineteenth century in western Canada were placed in rural farming communities. Hospitals that had been built earlier in eastern urban centres, such as the original lunatic asylum in Lancaster, New Brunswick, were also relocated to distant farmland during this time period. Not only was the pastoral setting seen as desirable to coax the mentally ill back to wellness, but also the mental hospital was designed to be self-sustaining. Built on large tracts of land, mental hospitals relied on farming to feed inhabitants of the institution and as a form of treatment. Male mental patients spent their time in agricultural tasks, tending to crops and livestock, whereas female patients performed domestic duties such as sewing. Thus, instead of spending their days in physical restraints, the mentally ill, under the principles of moral treatment, could be restored to sanity by being socialized to the positive influence of an agricultural existence.

That is not to say that treatments considered inhumane by current standards were ever fully abandoned. A system of punishments and rewards was implemented to motivate mental patients to choose reason over insanity, so that restraints and other forms of punishment were available when needed. Moreover, practices such as hydrotherapy were commonly applied during this time period. Intended to soothe troubled minds, hydrotherapy involved sitting in a bath of either cool or warm water for extended periods of time, ranging from hours to possibly days. Sometimes, hydrotherapy involved binding patients so that they would be forced to lie immobile in the bath.

Moral treatment exerted a lasting effect only on the location of mental hospitals in Canada—most of these facilities are still located in these same places to the present day, albeit under a different name. In the end, however, moral treatment proved unable to compete with medical models of mental illness (Scull, 1989: 137–161). As psychiatrists asserted their position in hospitals for the insane and as these institutions began to fill up and become overcrowded, custodial care began to replace moral treatment. In time, the only difference in the treatment of the mentally ill from a century ago was that instead of residing in institutions filled with a varied group of deviants, the mentally ill lived in large institutions officially devoted to their care.

Having acquired a ready population of patients at their disposal, psychiatrists had also begun to experiment with medical treatments to cure mental illness. Insulin therapy became immediately popular from its inception in 1933, followed by electroconvulsive (shock) therapy in 1938. These therapies caused comas or seizures, which psychiatrists believed improved mental functioning. Neither therapy had received scientific testing before becoming popular. Similarly, lobotomies—operations that permanently destroy part of the brain—became popular during the 1940s and 1950s. An estimated 50,000 people in North America received lobotomies, and the procedure's originator, Dr. Egas Moniz, received the Nobel Prize in Medicine in 1949. Yet, the only proven effects of lobotomies are diminished memory, intelligence, creativity, and emotional capacity (Valenstein, 1986). At any rate, therapy of any sort occupied only a minuscule proportion of patients' time in mental hospitals. Instead, patients spent most of their day locked in crowded wards with little other than radio or, later, television to ease their boredom. It would not be until later in the twentieth century that psychiatrists were able to claim any real success in treating mental disorder.

Deinstitutionalization

By the middle of the twentieth century, mental hospitals were seen as a huge and largely unsuccessful system (Mechanic, 1989). Consequently, between 1965 and 1980, the hospitalization rate for mental illness in Canada declined from 3.5 per 100,000 to 1 per 100,000 as treatment shifted from **inpatient** care (in hospitals) to outpatient care (Sealy and Whitehead, 2004). This process of moving mental health care away from large institutions and into community-based mental health centres, known as **deinstitutionalization**, gained further support during the 1970s and 1980s, as mental patients successfully fought in the courts against involuntary treatment, against hospitals that provided custodial care rather than therapy, and for the right to treatment in the "least restrictive setting" appropriate for their care.

It is also important to recognize that the process of deinstitutionalization was not confined to a few decades in the latter half of the twentieth century but is rather a process that has continued on and off to the present day. As can be seen from Table 13.3, the average length of stay in a mental hospital or on a psychiatric ward in a general hospital increased between 1982–1983 and 1992–1993 but declined precipitously between 2000–2001 and 2008–2009. Table 13.3 also shows that the length of stay is on average much shorter in a psychiatric unit of a general hospital than in a mental hospital. This is because the purpose in the former is to provide diagnostic and short-term crisis treatment, whereas mental hospitals serve as specialized facilities that treat those with serious chronic mental illness. Consequently, far more Canadians are admitted on an annual basis to a psychiatric unit in a general hospital than to a mental institution (CIHI, 2008b).

inpatient:

A hospital patient who is formally admitted and kept overnight.

deinstitutionalization:

The process of reducing the number of people treated in mental hospitals and the psychiatric wards of public hospitals by shifting their care to community-based mental health services.

TABLE 13.3 Average Length of Stay (in Days) for Mental Illness by Type of Hospital, Selected Years, Canada

Year	Psychiatric Hospital	General Hospital
1982–1983	193	27
1992–1993	326	33
2000–2001	160	36
2005–2006	100	16
2008–2009	80	18

Source: Canadian Institute for Health Information (CIHI), 2008b. Fig. E2, Pg. 7; Randhawa and Riley, 1996b; CIHI, 2011d.

There are a number of different explanations to account for disenchantment with the mental hospital system and consequent deinstitutionalization. Those who adopt a medical model of illness typically assume that deinstitutionalization was a natural result of the **psychopharmacological revolution** that began in the mid-1950s. There is no doubt that the psychopharmacological revolution represented a major turning point in the treatment of mental illness. Indeed, just as the discovery of antibiotics transformed the treatment of infectious disease, the discovery of antipsychotics in the early 1950s heralded a new era in the treatment of mental illness. These drugs, such as chlorpromazine and haloperidol, significantly reduced severe symptoms such as hallucinations. By 1954, they were used widely to treat schizophrenia, with stunning results. Many patients who had been relegated to the back wards of mental institutions experienced complete remission of symptoms and were released back into the community. The evidence that medication could so dramatically change behaviour fundamentally altered how psychiatrists viewed mental illness, providing what seemed to be incontrovertible evidence that mental illness was a biological condition of the brain.

The psychopharmacological revolution gained further momentum when, in 1954, a new tranquilizer by the name of Miltown appeared on the market, offering to ease the worries and anxieties of the population. Sales of Miltown subsequently began to skyrocket, with patients flooding doctors' offices demanding a prescription (Metzl, 2003). To these drugs would later be added other immensely popular medications, including antianxiety drugs such as diazepam (Valium), antidepressants such as fluoxetine (Prozac), and methylphenidate (Ritalin) to treat attention deficit/hyperactivity disorder (ADHD). Each reinforced the belief that mental illness was a biological condition of the brain and that chemical intervention was capable of changing behaviour and curing mental illness. Although faith in psychopharmacology has somewhat diminished, treating mental illness with pharmaceuticals remains the prevailing method today.

Although the psychopharmacological revolution did play a role in deinstitutionalization by making mental patients compliant enough for communities to tolerate their release, the number of patients in mental hospitals did not fall rapidly until long after these drugs were introduced. Thus, we must look to other explanations to understand why deinstitutionalization occurred.

Mental Hospitals as Antitherapeutic

Beginning in the 1960s, many voices began to challenge the existing mental hospital system. Civil rights, antiwar, and feminist movements all brought issues of individual rights to the forefront and stimulated a broader questioning of authority and social arrangements. These ideas contributed to a growing critique of mental health treatment by sociologists; psychologists; and even some psychiatrists, such as R. D. Laing (1967) and Thomas Szasz (1970, 1974).

One of the most powerful critiques of large mental institutions appeared in a classic study by sociologist Erving Goffman (1961). Goffman's work fell within the tradition of **symbolic interactionism** theory. According to this theory, individual identity develops through an ongoing process in which individuals see themselves through the eyes of others and learn through social interactions to adopt the values of their community and to measure themselves against those values. In this way, a **self-fulfilling prophecy** is created, through which individuals become what they are already believed to be. So, for example, children who constantly hear that they are too stupid to succeed in school might conclude that it is senseless to attend classes or study. They then fail in school, thus fulfilling the prophecies about them.

psychopharmacological revolution:
The dramatic change in the treatment of the mentally ill from the 1950s onward when the evidence of chemically induced behavioural change convinced psychiatrists that mental illness was primarily a biological condition of the brain that could be treated with medication rather than psychoanalysis and other forms of therapy.

symbolic interactionism:
A theoretical perspective arguing that identity develops as part of an ongoing process of social interaction, whereby individuals learn to see themselves through the eyes of others, adopt the values of their community, and measure their self-worth against those values.

self-fulfilling prophecy:
A situation in which individuals become what they are expected to be.

Goffman used symbolic interactionism theory to analyze mental hospitals and the experiences of mental patients. He pointed out that mental hospitals, like the military, prisons, and monasteries, were **total institutions**—institutions where a large number of individuals led highly regimented lives segregated from the outside world. Goffman argued that these institutions necessarily produced **mortification** of the self. Mortification refers to a process through which a person's self-image is damaged and is replaced by a personality adapted to institutional life.

Several aspects of institutional life foster mortification. Persons confined to mental hospitals lose the supports that usually give people a sense of self. Cut off from work and family, these individuals' only available role is that of patient. That role, meanwhile, is a **master status**—a status considered so central that it overwhelms all other aspects of individual identity. Within the mental hospital, a patient is viewed solely as a patient—not as a mother or father, husband or wife, worker or student, radical or conservative. According to Goffman's observations, all behaviour becomes interpreted through the lens of illness. In addition, because each staff member must manage many patients, staff members necessarily deal with patients en masse. In these circumstances, patients typically lose the right to choose what to wear, when to awaken or sleep, when and what to eat, and so on. Moreover, all these activities occur in the company of many others. Individuals thus not only experience a sense of powerlessness but also can lose a sense of their identity—their desires, needs, personalities—in the mass of others. As a result, patients experience **depersonalization**—a feeling that they are no longer fully human, or are no longer considered fully human by others. At the same time, the hierarchical nature of mental hospitals reinforces the distinctions between inmate and staff and constantly reminds both parties of the gulf between them. Consequently, patients can avoid punishment and eventually win release only by stifling their individuality and accepting the institution's beliefs and rules. Implicit in Goffman's work is the idea that once mental patients have experienced mortification and depersonalization, they are largely incapable of resuming life outside the institution, so that entering a mental hospital launches them into a lifetime career as a mental patient. As these sentiments began to be felt more widely, mental hospitals began to be perceived as one of the worst environments for treating mental problems, paving the way for the public to view deinstitutionalization as a more palatable alternative.

Decarceration

Attention has been most frequently drawn to the psychopharmacological revolution and the antitherapeutic critique of mental hospitals to explain why deinstitutionalization occurred. Rejecting both of these explanations as ideological camouflage, Scull (1976) offered a more controversial account. Taking a political economy approach, Scull suggested that the state, motivated by the rising costs of care rather than concern for patient well-being, abandoned expensive institutional care and pursued less costly forms of social control, reversing the long-standing practice of segregating deviant populations from the rest of society. Thus, the deinstitutionalization of the mentally ill was part of a broader movement, known as **decarceration**, that diverted into the community those who had previously been confined in prisons, reformatories for juvenile delinquents, and treatment facilities for the mentally retarded and disabled. To the extent that efforts to reduce the number of people in mental institutions were not accompanied by increased investment in community-based treatment, Scull (1976) argued that his interpretation not only was valid but was having a devastating impact on the lives of people with mental illness. Sadly, his perceptions about the unfolding consequences of deinstitutionalization continue to hold true today.

---

total institutions:
Institutions in which all aspects of life are controlled by a central authority and in which large numbers of like-situated persons are dealt with en masse. Examples include mental hospitals, prisons, and the military.

mortification:
A process, occurring in total institutions, through which a person's prior self-image is partially or totally destroyed and replaced by a personality suited for life in the institution.

master status:
A status viewed by others as so important that it overwhelms all other information about that individual.

depersonalization:
The process through which an individual comes to feel less than fully human or comes to be viewed by others as less than fully human.

decarceration:
The broad movement by the state to control the costs of institutional care by moving away from the residential segregation of deviant groups, including criminals, juvenile delinquents, and those with mental illness, and turning instead to less costly forms of social control.

The Consequences of Deinstitutionalization

Although persons with mental illness no longer found themselves locked for years in the often brutal conditions of large mental institutions, the promise that deinstitutionalization would herald a new era in which individuals would receive appropriate therapy in the community, avoiding the stigma, degradation, and mortification of mental hospitalization, has been met only partially. Although the community setting is still seen as preferable to institutional care, even by those who are mentally ill, the apparent benevolence of releasing the mentally ill from the depraved conditions of the mental hospital is difficult to reconcile in light of the absence of community-based services and ongoing neglect of people with mental illness (Sullivan, 1998). Then, as now, individuals released from mental hospitals to the community found few services to help them with their continuing problems. Where services were available, there was a tendency to locate them in marginal settings because the public didn't want these services offered in their communities. Consequently, the bricks and mortar of the institution were merely replaced with urban ghettos filled with the socially dependent, leaving intact the formidable barriers to social inclusion for people with mental illness. As such, deinstitutionalization succeeded in transforming the treatment of the mentally ill but produced concentrated landscapes of despair rather than anticipated landscapes of caring that integrated the mentally ill back into the community (Dear and Wolch, 1987).

As deinstitutionalization has proceeded, the consequences of this shift have become apparent in at least three ways. First, there is evidence to suggest that current practices in inpatient psychiatric care are producing what has been referred to as the **revolving door syndrome**. An extreme shortage of beds for people with mental illness means that only those who are in crisis are admitted to the psychiatric unit in a general hospital. Even then, there is continued pressure to reduce the length of stay and to use hospital treatment merely as a time to diagnose and stabilize the condition of the person with mental illness. Once stabilized, typically through medication, the person is released back into the community. With an inadequate level of services in the community and socially isolated, the person with mental illness is at risk for relapse, eventually producing another crisis and another short-term hospital stay. Evidence for the revolving door syndrome was provided in a Canadian study that reported nearly half of all those hospitalized for schizophrenia were readmitted within a year (Madi, Zhao, and Li, 2007).

The lack of community-based services for those with mental illness also means that many fall through the cracks after they are discharged from the hospital. Canadian researchers have reported that the lifetime prevalence of mental disorder in the homeless population approaches 66%, which is two to three times the rate in the general Canadian population (Riordan, 2004). Their needs strain the resources of homeless shelters, typically located in close proximity to other social service agencies and community mental health treatment centres.

Finally, deinstitutionalization has produced a phenomenon called **transinstitutionalization**, a process that occurs when people with mental illness are no longer sent to a mental institution but instead find themselves in other types of institutions that are not equipped to deal with mental illness and thus offer little opportunity for treatment. For example, long-term care facilities for seniors are typically designed to assist those with physical impairment but poorly equipped to deal with issues around cognitive impairment, dementia, and other forms of serious mental illness. Similarly, prisons increasingly house those with mental illness. Boe and Vuong (2002) show that even as the number of admissions to federal prisons in Canada decreased between 1997 and 2001, a growing proportion of those admitted had a current diagnosis of mental illness. The tragic story of Ashley Smith, recounted in Box 13.1, exemplifies the worst-case scenario when persons with mental illness are sent to institutions that are neither equipped nor willing to provide mental health services to inmates.

revolving door syndrome:

A continuing cycle in which short-term hospitalization in a psychiatric unit is followed by release into a community setting that lacks the appropriate resources, precipitating relapse and a new crisis situation requiring hospitalization.

transinstitutionalization:

The process by which people with mental illness are no longer placed in a mental hospital but instead are transferred to other types of institutions, such as prisons, where there is little opportunity to receive treatment.

BOX 13.1

IN THE NEWS

Ashley Smith and Transinstitutionalization

Adopted at birth in 1988, Ashley Smith had a childhood that initially appeared no different from that of others growing up in Moncton, New Brunswick. When Ashley reached age 10, however, she developed severe behavioural problems at home and at school that led to frequent school suspensions and finally transfer to an alternative school. Delinquent activities also got her in trouble with the police. Mental health professionals who saw her during this period applied different labels to her condition, including ADHD, borderline personality disorder, and oppositional defiant disorder.

By age 14, Ashley was no longer in school. Charged with numerous offences including assault and creating a public disturbance, she spent much of the next three years living in the New Brunswick Youth Centre, a facility for troubled children, where she continued to exhibit disturbing and violent behaviour. Her escalating behaviour resulted in continual surveillance, being placed in restraints, being pepper-sprayed, and spending time on the therapeutic quiet unit. None of these interventions slowed her behaviour; instead, they may have reinforced it.

Once Ashley reached the age of 18, she was no longer considered a minor and was transferred to a provincial correctional centre for adult women. Ashley's behaviour continued as before; however, now that she was in an adult women's prison, her refusal to comply resulted in her being subjected to more harsh treatment, despite her age. She was frequently strip-searched, she was tasered on a few occasions, and she spent most of her time in segregation (spending twenty-three hours a day in a nine by six foot cell, with one hour outside the cell reserved for showering and exercise). Moreover, her violent outbursts culminated in more criminal charges so that, several months later, she was transferred to a federal institution because the length of her sentence now exceeded two years.

It is likely that forced isolation and the lack of positive human contact began to wear on Ashley's mental health. Yet, throughout her time of incarceration, Ashley never received counselling services or had regular interaction with mental health professionals. It is also clear that the correctional officers monitoring her were not trained to deal with mental health issues, in particular her self-harming behaviour. Their frustration in dealing with her may explain why she was transferred seventeen times between different facilities in less than one year, further increasing her distress and discomfort.

On October 19, 2007, correctional officers at the Grand Valley Institution for Women in Ontario who had been told not to enter her cell unless she was not breathing watched while Ashley wrapped a ligature around her neck, cutting off her air flow. By the time they finally entered her cell, Ashley, at 19 years of age, was dead.

Her death may have finally brought needed attention to the issue of transinstitutionalization. Subsequent government inquiry has brought further insight; worryingly, such investigations have also revealed that Ashley Smith's story is not an isolated incident.

In summary, the treatment of mental illness and the settings in which those who are mentally ill receive care have undergone significant transformation throughout Canadian history. Yet, the public's desire to maintain social distance from those with mental illness continues to shape the social institutions developed to treat the mentally ill. Until these underlying social values change, it is unlikely that the care of those who are mentally ill will show visible signs of progress.

LONG-TERM CARE FACILITIES

Over the course of the twentieth century, average life expectancy increased and chronic rather than acute conditions accounted for the health problems of the population. Similarly, families grew smaller, more geographically dispersed, and less stable, and women less often worked at home. As a result of all of these changes, more and more Canadians began to rely on care from strangers. These emerging needs led to the creation of what are often referred to as nursing homes—facilities that primarily provide nursing and custodial care to groups of individuals over a long period of time—although a more accurate term would be **long-term care facilities**.

Unlike hospital care, long-term care facilities are not funded through the Canada Health Act. The federal government does provide, through the Canada Health Transfer, a limited

long-term care facilities:

Facilities that primarily provide nursing and custodial care to many individuals over a long period of time.

amount of funds to the provinces for extended health care but has not imposed any conditions or otherwise tied funding to delivery standards. Rather, each province unilaterally decides how to fund and deliver long-term care. The result is a fragmented system in which services and standards are regulated by each province, but not at the national level.

In the provinces, long-term care tends to be publicly subsidized but service delivery is provided by a mix of government-run, private non-profit, religious non-profit, and private for-profit organizations. Thus, the cost of long-term care, estimated at around $12 billion per year, is mostly borne by the public sector, with approximately 27% of the costs paid for privately or out of pocket (CIHI, 2005). The mix of private and public facilities differs across Canada. For example, nearly all long-term care facilities in Saskatchewan are publicly owned, whereas this is the case for less than half of the long-term care facilities in Ontario (CIHI, 2005).

Differences between private for-profit and non-profit long-term care facilities are important to the extent that researchers have identified systematic differences in the quality of care provided in these different types of settings. A national comparison found that for-profit facilities provide many fewer hours of direct care than non-profit and government-owned facilities (Berta et al., 2006). Other indicators of poor care quality, such as rates of pressure ulcers or bed sores and greater risk for acute hospitalization, are also found to be higher among residents in for-profit facilities (McGrail et al., 2007).

Who Receives Care in Long-Term Care Facilities?

The majority of those who receive care in a long-term care facility are seniors over the age of 65 (77%), with the remainder of facilities offering residential care to those of different ages who have physical, psychiatric, or developmental disabilities or are receiving treatment for substance abuse disorders. In those facilities specifically designed for seniors, women make up about two-thirds of the residents. The gender difference exists because women live longer and thus more often eventually need assistance. Moreover, women less often have a surviving spouse who can and will care for them, although the risk for moving into a long-term care facility increases for both men and women following the death of a spouse (Strohschein, 2011b).

Public wariness of institutional care also extends to long-term care facilities. Because most seniors now prefer to live independently for as long as possible, they tend to be much older when they move into a long-term care facility and spend less time in such settings before death occurs. Thus, the average age at admission to a long-term facility for seniors is approximately 86 years, which is an increase from 1972 when the average age at admission was 75 (Pitters, 2002). Nonetheless, there remain long waiting lists to find placement. For example, the average wait to obtain a placement in a long-term facility in Ontario is approximately 3.5 months (Ontario Health Quality Council, 2011).

Working in Long-Term Care Facilities

Work in a long-term care facility is extremely labour-intensive. Almost all workers in these settings are women and most are non-Caucasiann. Many come from Africa, Asia, or Latin America and are not native English speakers. Jobs in a long-term care facility may not be unionized and the pay is often lower than what hospital workers receive. These characteristics leave workers particularly vulnerable in today's shrinking job market, with little ability to fight for better working conditions.

To understand the life of residents of long-term care facilities and the staff who care for them, American sociologist Timothy Diamond (1992) became certified as a nursing assistant and worked for several years in a variety of nursing homes. He soon concluded that the core of working as a nursing assistant is caregiving, but that those who train nursing assistants do not recognize this basic fact. Instead, his instructors taught him to recite biological and anatomical terms, measure vital signs, and perform simple medical procedures. Instructors divorced these skills from any social context or any sense that their patients were people rather than inanimate objects. Moreover, the skills Diamond most needed he was never taught, such as exactly how you clean an adult who has soiled a diaper in a manner that preserves the individual's sense of dignity. Only by labelling this caregiving as mere physical labour could those who hire nursing assistants label them "unskilled" and treat them so poorly.

Life in Nursing Homes

Diamond's research underlines how the fates of nursing assistants and residents intertwine and how even in the best care facilities, the pressures to operate efficiently produce difficult conditions for both. According to Diamond, within nursing homes,

> caregiving becomes something that is bought and sold. This process involves both ownership and the construction of goods and services that can be measured and priced so that a bottom line can be brought into being. It entails the enforcement of certain power relations and means of production so that those who live in nursing homes and those who tend to them can be made into commodities and cost accountable units. (1992: 172)

In this process of **commodification**, or turning people into commodities, "Mrs. Walsh in Bed 3" becomes simply "Bed 3." To keep down the price of this "commodity," only the most expensive homes provide private rooms or separate areas for residents who are dying, incontinent, smelly, or insane. Privacy, then, also becomes a commodity that few residents can afford.

Staff, meanwhile, become budgeted expenses, which long-term care facilities try to keep to an absolute minimum. To justify these low staffing levels, administrators and owners may narrowly define the caregiving that assistants provide and residents need. For example, managers may hire only enough assistants to hurriedly spoon-feed residents rather than enough to allow assistants to chat with residents while feeding them or to help residents retain their dignity by feeding themselves. Similarly, managers can keep residents drugged, strapped to chairs, on a strictly regimented schedule, and in a single central room during the day so that a few assistants can supervise many residents. The same logic frequently leads long-term care facilities to reward aides who work quickly and efficiently (even if the aides must bully or coerce patients to do so) and to penalize aides who spend the time needed to offer true caring (Foner, 1994).

Problems such as these led Diamond to conclude:

> It made a certain kind of sense … that in the schooling and textbooks there had been no vocabulary of caring. There was no place for it in the records. Words that concerned how to be gentle with Arthur, firm with Anna, delicate with Grace; how to mourn with Elizabeth and mourn for Frances; how to deal with death and dying, loneliness and screaming; how to wait in responding to someone else's slow pace—these constituted much of the work as it went along, but nothing of the job. In the documentation there was nothing relational, no shadow of the passion, only a prescribed set of tasks a doer gave to a receiver. (1992: 163)

Ironically, in elite private long-term care facilities, the same process of commodification is now leading operators to encourage nursing assistants to emphasize caring and, indeed, to think of residents as their kin (Dodson and Zincavage, 2007). By so doing, nursing homes can both charge higher prices for their "family atmosphere" and get more and higher-quality work from assistants for the same low wages. But this "purchased intimacy"—similar to that offered by massage therapists, beauticians, and others—is a one-way transaction that may provide little benefit to the worker.

ASSISTED LIVING FACILITIES

Seen as a more preferable alternative to long-term care facilities, **assisted living facilities** have experienced explosive growth in recent years. Assisted living facilities provide fewer medical and nursing services than do long-term care facilities as well as greater independence and privacy. Unlike long-term care facilities, which typically consist of wards, assisted living facilities typically consist of small private or semiprivate apartments. Like long-term care facilities, they provide help with basic tasks of daily living (such as meal preparation and housecleaning) and with routine nursing tasks (such as administering medications). In addition, assisted living facilities offer local transportation and social activities for those who are reasonably healthy as well as the opportunity to transfer to nearby units with higher levels of care for those whose health deteriorates.

The promise of assisted living facilities is that they will allow residents to "age in place." In fact, however, residents stay an average of less than three years, with most who leave moving to long-term care facilities (Chapin and Dobbs-Kepper, 2001).

HOME CARE

As the discussion of long-term care facilities and assisted living facilities suggested, most individuals who experience chronic or acute health problems—whether children, working-age adults, or elderly, and whether the problems are physical or mental—receive and prefer to receive care for their condition at home. Care at home may be provided formally through the health care system or informally by family members. As such, **home care** is an array of services that enables clients who are incapacitated in whole or in part to live at home, often with the effect of preventing, delaying, or substituting for long-term care or acute care alternatives.

A confluence of technological, demographic, and policy changes has contributed to the provision of health care in the home. First, technological advances mean that babies born prematurely or with birth defects and persons who suffer severe trauma are increasingly likely to survive, although often with severe disabilities that require lifelong assistance. Much of this care is now given in the home rather than in an institution. Moreover, technological advances have made it possible for families to provide treatments at home that were previously available only in hospitals, ranging from chemotherapy to respiratory ventilation to kidney dialysis. Similarly, the rise in the numbers of frail elderly, many of whom suffer both multiple physical problems and cognitive impairments, has increased the number receiving care at home. For seniors who live alone, there are now electronic assistive technologies, such as virtual visiting, electronic sensors, and reminder systems, that prompt seniors to perform daily tasks and raise alerts when problems are detected (Percival and Hanson, 2006). These new technologies provide care remotely, making it possible for seniors with uncomplicated health problems to delay institutional care. Finally, as described earlier, policy changes now encourage hospitals to discharge patients to their homes "sicker and quicker," in essence replacing paid hospital workers with home care and unpaid family caregivers (Glazer, 1993).

assisted living facilities:
Institutions, typically consisting of small, private apartments, that offer two levels of services: (1) basic medical and nursing services and help with basic tasks of daily living for disabled residents and (2) comfortable living situations and social activities for healthy residents.

home care:
An array of services that enable clients who are incapacitated in whole or in part to live at home, often with the effect of preventing, delaying, or substituting for long-term care or acute care alternatives.

Growing awareness of the need to assist Canadians who require home care services and the recognition that such services could reduce the costs of hospitals and other forms of institutions prompted the federal government to begin funding home health services in the 1990s and then to boost funding levels in 2005 through the Canada Health Transfer. Funding also comes from the provinces and the Workers' Compensation Board. From these three funding sources, $3.4 billion was spent on home health care services in Canada in 2003–2004, with utilization rates of health care services averaging 26.1 per 1,000 nationally (CIHI, 2007). Although more recent statistics are not available nationally, concerns over the cost of hospital care have increased pressures to fund home care as a cheaper alternative that is also preferred by the public. For example, Ontario spent $1.9 billion on home health care in 2009, representing 4.1% of total health expenditures in that province (Ontario Home Care Association, 2010).

Informal Caregiving

One in five Canadians households includes someone who is providing care for a person over age 18 (Fast and Keating, 2001). Most of these are spouses and adult children caring for a senior. Moreover, the majority of caregivers are women and more than half of all caregivers are employed elsewhere (Cranswick and Dosman, 2008).

Those who care for the health needs of family members typically do so out of love and often reap substantial psychological rewards. Nevertheless, caregiving by family members should not be romanticized, nor should the financial, physical, social, or psychological costs of caregiving be underestimated (Fast and Keating, 2001; Hawranik and Strain, 2007).

The financial costs of caregiving are substantial. The demands of caregiving force many to shift to part-time work or even abandon paid employment. In addition, nearly all seniors (98%) who receive home care services also rely on the help of informal caregivers (CIHI, 2010b). Thus, caregivers must often negotiate issues of care with home health care workers. The physical costs can also be high. Caregiving often includes exhausting tasks such as lifting physically disabled or mentally incompetent individuals, some of whom either cannot help or resist being moved.

Taken together, the financial and physical burdens of caregiving often leave individuals with little time, energy, or money for social relationships. Caregiver stress is highest when it takes up more than twenty-one hours per week and lowest when providing less than ten hours of care per week (CIHI, 2010b). Caregivers often report feeling almost totally isolated from the world outside the household (Hawranik and Strain, 2007). Family relationships, too, can suffer. For example, a mother who spends hours each day caring for an ill child might feel guilty that she cannot spend more time with her other children, and those children might resent the attention given to their ill sibling. Problems are particularly acute when the person receiving care is mentally ill and throws family routines into chaos, embarrasses other family members, or physically threatens others' safety (Reinhard and Horwitz, 1996; Tessler and Gamache, 1994).

Family life also can suffer disproportionately when caregiving requires the use of high technology within the home. John D. Arras and Nancy Neveloff Dubler suggest that this

> invasion of the home by high-tech medical procedures, mechanisms, and supporting personnel exerts a cost in terms of important values associated with the notion of home. How can someone be truly "at home," truly at ease, for example, when his or her living room has been transformed into a miniature intensive care unit? … Rooms occupied by the paraphernalia of high-tech medicine may cease to be what they once were in the minds of their occupants; familiar and comforting family rituals, such as holiday meals, may

lose their charm when centered around a mammoth Flexicare bed; and much of the privacy and intimacy of ordinary family life may be sacrificed to the institutional culture that trails in the wake of high-tech medicine. (1995: 3)

Finally, caregiving brings with it numerous psychological costs. Caregivers can easily become depressed when their efforts cannot stop or even slow the disease process. This is especially true when caregivers must routinely inflict painful treatments on their charges or when the burdens of caregiving are unceasing, as when a parent must suction the lungs of a child with cystic fibrosis hour after hour, day after day, to keep the child from dying. Moreover, as this example suggests, caregivers also often bear the enormous psychological burden of being directly responsible for another person's life. In fact, family caregivers are now expected to manage in the home—often with little training or technical support—technology considered too complex for licensed practical nurses to manage in hospitals. Finally, caregivers of persons younger than themselves face anxieties about what will happen to their charges if the caregivers die first.

Summing up the burdens of caregiving, a woman whose husband has Parkinson's disease says:

> I need some help. I am burned out. I am locked in this house. I am used to going out to work and had to retire. I didn't plan to retire so soon. We had planned our retirement. We never did anything before because we didn't have the same vacation time. So you do all this and then bingo! … Two weeks ago I had a terrible pain in my ribs. But I can't run to the doctor for every little thing. How can I leave the house? I worry, what is going to happen to him, if I have to go to the hospital…. Medicare pays for only part of the things we need and doesn't pay for medications. That bottle of medication cost $130…. Sometimes he has to go to the bathroom just when I've finished eating. It is hard to get up at that instant to do it. You feel like everything [you just ate] is going to come up. You have all these things to contend with. People don't realize that unless they are in those situations themselves…. You have to really see it for yourself, be in it, to know what it is like. (Corbin and Strauss, 1988: 297)

HOSPICES

Origins of Hospice

Hospices emerged out of the awareness that there were no existing health care options that provided appropriate care for the dying. Hospice care, also referred to as palliative care, is a type of health care that provides physical, psychological, social, spiritual, and practical support to people, and their loved ones, living with progressive, life-threatening illness. It can be provided at home, in hospitals, in long-term care facilities, or in free-standing hospices. It is most effectively delivered by an interdisciplinary team of health care providers.

There are several factors that explain why hospice care began to be perceived as an unmet need in health care. First, changing patterns of death and disease meant that growing numbers of people required palliative care. At the beginning of the twentieth century, few individuals experienced a long period during which they were known to be dying. Instead, most succumbed quickly to illnesses such as pneumonia, influenza, tuberculosis, or acute intestinal infections, dying at home and at relatively young ages. Now, however, most Canadians live long enough to die from chronic rather than acute illnesses. In addition, as doctors and scientists have developed techniques for detecting illnesses in their earliest stages, they now more often identify individuals as having a fatal illness long before

hospices:
Institutions designed to meet the needs of the dying.

those individuals actually die. Thus, dealing with the dying is to some extent a uniquely modern problem.

Although modern medical care has proven lifesaving for many, its ability to prolong life raises other issues about what the end of life should look like (as this chapter's ethical debate on the right to die, Box 13.2, discusses in more detail). Importantly, this is an issue that most Canadians will have to negotiate at some point in their lives. Studies suggest that even though the majority of Canadians express the desire to die at home, most (more than 70%) spend their last moments in a hospital (Heyland et al., 2000). For various reasons, including legal concerns about restricting care, financial incentives for using highly invasive treatments, and a medical culture that emphasizes technological interventions, many dying patients receive intensive, painful, and tremendously expensive medical care that offers only a small hope of either restoring their quality of life or extending their lives. There appears then to be a large gap between what Canadians would like in terms of end-of-life care and what they actually receive.

right to die:

The right to make decisions concerning one's own death.

BOX 13.2

ETHICAL DEBATE

A Right to Die?

In 1992, Sue Rodriguez, a woman living in British Columbia who suffered from amyotrophic lateral sclerosis (also known as Lou Gehrig's disease), challenged the validity of the Canadian Charter of Rights and Freedoms, which banned assisted suicide. As someone with a terminal illness, she argued that she was being denied the right to determine the method, timing, and circumstances of her death. She took her battle all the way to the Supreme Court of Canada, but lost. In their decision upholding the prohibition against assisted suicide, the justices found that the law offered protection to the vulnerable, who might be convinced to commit suicide, and that opening the door to physician-assisted suicide would create a slippery slope leading to euthanasia. Two years later, with the help of an unknown doctor, Sue Rodriguez ended her life.

In 1993, Robert Latimer, a farmer in Saskatchewan, waited until his family left for church before placing his 12-year-old, severely disabled daughter, Tracy, in the cab of his truck. He then connected a hose from the exhaust pipe to the cab, leaving her to die of carbon monoxide poisoning. At first, Latimer tried to conceal what he had done, but when the police determined that his daughter had died of carbon monoxide poisoning, he confessed to killing her. He contended that his actions were motivated by love for Tracy and a desire to end her pain. Charged with first-degree murder, Latimer was convicted of second-degree murder and sentenced to life imprisonment, with no possibility of parole for ten years. He was released on day parole in 2008 and obtained full release from prison in 2010.

In the Netherlands and Belgium, meanwhile, doctors can legally practise active voluntary euthanasia (i.e., actively end a patient's life) for patients who are mentally competent, incurably ill, and suffering intolerable and unrelievable pain, and who authorize their doctors to do so in writing. In the United States, three states, Oregon, Washington, and Montana, permit physician-assisted suicide under limited conditions.

In April 2010, the Canadian Parliament rejected by a wide margin a private member's bill that would have made assisted suicide and euthanasia legal in Canada. In contrast, public opinion, assessed later that same year in an Angus Reid poll (2010), suggested that 63% of Canadians support euthanasia. This level of support, however, had declined from previous years. Indeed, 42% of Canadians expressed concern that vulnerable people would have little legal protection, such as might occur for older people who might be encouraged to accept euthanasia as a way to reduce health care costs.

The debate was renewed following a decision by the British Columbia Supreme Court that, in June 2012, ruled that the ban on physician-assisted suicide infringed on the rights of the individual. Although the ruling is certain to be appealed to the Supreme Court of Canada, Canadians will likely find themselves debating this issue for years to come. That the issue is both complex and contentious should not come as a surprise, given the strong arguments used to marshal opposing viewpoints.

Those who support a **right to die** argue that competent adults have the right to make decisions for themselves, including the ultimate decision of when to die. They argue that death can sometimes be a rational choice and that forcing individuals to suffer extreme physical or mental anguish is unwarranted cruelty.

If we accept that death can be a rational choice, then harder questions follow. Why is it rational only if one's condition is terminal? Doesn't it make even more sense to end the life of someone whose agonies may continue for another fifty years than to end the life of someone who will die soon regardless? Why should this choice be forbidden to individuals simply because they cannot, either physically or emotionally, carry it out themselves? And why should we allow individuals to choose death only through passive euthanasia, leaving them to languish in pain while awaiting death, if instead they could be killed quickly and painlessly?

Opponents of this view argue that the duty to preserve life overrides any other values and that euthanasia is merely a nice word for suicide or murder. They question whether those choosing to end their lives because of illness would have wanted to die if they had the resources needed to live independently and with dignity, and they wonder whether euthanasia is merely an easy way out for a society that wants to avoid responsibility for relieving the burdens imposed by illness and disability. Opponents who have studied euthanasia practices in the Netherlands and Belgium suggest that doctors there do not in fact always follow the legal guidelines but instead sometimes end patients' lives without their explicit consent and without first attempting to make the patients' lives worth living (Hendlin, Rutenfrans, and Zylicz, 1997; Chambaere et al., 2010). In addition, opponents question whether acceptance of euthanasia in the Netherlands explains why there are fewer hospices in the Netherlands than elsewhere in Europe and why Dutch doctors receive relatively little training in pain relief. Finally, opponents note that well over half of assisted suicides are women with chronic but not fatal illnesses, killed by their spouses (Bergner, 2007).

This raises the question of whether the women were pushed to suicide either by their husbands or by social norms that expect women to put others' needs before their own.

In sum, the use of euthanasia, whether active or passive, raises numerous difficult questions: What are the consequences of, in effect, declaring it reasonable for disabled people to choose death? What pressures does this place on individuals to end their own lives rather than burdening others? What responsibilities does this remove from society to make these individuals' lives less burdensome? Finally, given that social factors, such as age, gender, and social class, affect our perceptions of individuals' worth, how do we ensure that health care workers and courts will not be more willing to grant a right to die to those who belong to socially disvalued groups?

SOCIOLOGICAL QUESTIONS

1. What social views and values about medicine, society, and the body are reflected in the debate over a right to die? Whose views are these?
2. Which social groups are in conflict over this issue? Whose interests do the different sides of this issue serve?
3. Which of these groups has more power to enforce its view? What kinds of power do they have?
4. What are the intended consequences of recognizing a right to die? What are the potential unintended social, economic, political, and health consequences of doing so?

The perception, not just in Canada but elsewhere, that there was a lack of appropriate care for the dying fuelled the development of the hospice movement. The first modern hospice, St. Christopher's, was founded in England in 1968 by Dr. Cicely Saunders, specifically to address the needs of the dying and to provide an alternative to the often alienating and dehumanizing experience of hospital death. The hospice admitted only patients expected to die within six months and offered only palliative care (designed to reduce pain and discomfort) rather than treatment or mechanical life supports. The hospice provided care both in St. Christopher's and in patients' homes.

In Canada, the first hospice programs were established in 1975 in both Winnipeg and Montréal. Today, there are nearly seventy hospices spread across Canada, ranging in size. Only some of these receive funding; thus, hospices that are not funded through provincial health care rely on fundraising to support daily operations. For example, Ontario only began to provide funding for hospices in 2005. Little is known about hospice use in Canada. It is estimated that somewhere between 16% and 30% of Canadians who die have access to palliative care, suggesting that there remains an unmet need for hospice care (Canadian Hospice Palliative Care Association (CHPCA), 2010).

The Hospice Philosophy

The early hospice philosophy differed markedly from mainstream medical philosophy (Abel, 1986; Finn Paradis and Cummings, 1986). First, the hospice philosophy asserted that patients should participate in their own care, controlling as much as possible the process and nature of their dying. Hospices strove to give clients choices over everything from what they ate to where they would die. Most significantly, hospices allowed residents to decide when to receive pain medications, how much, and what kinds. To eliminate pain from the experience of dying, hospices used whatever drugs would work, including opiates such as heroin. In contrast, nursing home staff do not have the expertise to prescribe or supervise the drugs that dying patients need, and hospital staff often oppose using addictive drugs because their commitment to healing makes it difficult for them to acknowledge that certain patients are dying and therefore cannot be harmed by addictive drugs.

Second, the hospice philosophy forswore regimentation and stressed the importance of integrating hospice care into clients' everyday lives rather than integrating clients into hospice routines. Where possible, hospices would offer services in clients' homes. For those who needed care in the hospice, the hospice would offer a homelike environment, without the regulations regarding schedules, visitors, food, clothing, and so on that rule life in hospitals and nursing homes.

Third, the hospice philosophy emphasized a true team approach. Because hospices provided neither diagnosis nor treatment, doctors could claim little special expertise (Abel, 1986). As a result, within hospices, doctors had little more importance or influence than did social workers, nurses, ministers, psychotherapists, nutritionists, and others. Hospices explicitly worked to minimize the authority of doctors and to increase the role and status of non-professional volunteers.

Fourth, hospices focused not only on the dying person but also on his or her friends and relatives. Hospices attempted to involve these others in the process of dying and to meet their social and psychological needs. As a result, hospice care did not end with the client's death but extended to bereavement counselling for survivors.

Finally, hospices viewed dying "as a natural event rather than as technological failure" (Abel, 1986: 71). Workers viewed dying as an important phase of life, suitable for and worthy of open discussion. Neither the dying process nor the disease was to be hidden.

The history of hospice resembles the history of many other reform movements and organizations. As various sociologists have observed, successful social movements over time often come to resemble the very institutions they sought to reform (DiMaggio and Powell, 1983; McCarthy and Zald, 1973). These changes evolve gradually and naturally. For a movement to survive, it must mobilize people and develop sources of funding. To do so, the movement's reformers typically must develop hierarchies and rules, abandon their grassroots and voluntaristic approach, and hire professional staff. Whether these changes are forcing the Canadian hospice movement to abandon some of its earlier principles has not been researched in Canada; however, in the United States, there is evidence to suggest that hospice care is more cost oriented and less patient centred than in the past.

HEALTH CARE TECHNOLOGIES

Doctors and other healers have always used technologies in their work. Two hundred years ago, doctors used knives to cut veins and "bleed" patients of their illness, and they used strips of cloth to bandage the wounds afterward. One hundred years ago, doctors used mercury compounds and electricity in attempting to cure patients of masturbation or syphilis.

In modern medicine, health care technology includes everything from Band-Aids to computerized patient record systems to heart–lung machines.

The Nature of Technology

Technology refers to any human-made object used to perform a task. In addition, the term is often used to describe processes that involve such objects. For example, the term *technology* can refer both to the overall process of kidney dialysis and to the equipment used in that process.

Although we often talk about technology as if it is inherently either good or bad—"technology has made our lives easier," or "technology has depersonalized medical care"—the reality is more complex (Timmermans and Berg 2003b; Heath, Luff, and Svensson, 2003). It is true that the nature of a technology determines the *range* of ways in which it might be used, but whether it is harmful, helpful, or both depends on *who* uses it in *which* ways. Electricity is helpful when used by doctors to stimulate muscle healing and harmful when used by doctors who are poorly educated or are employed as torturers in dictatorships. Fetal monitors can depersonalize childbirth when nurses stare at the screens rather than pay attention to the pregnant woman. But ultrasound imaging of fetuses can *personalize* pregnancy when fathers see their future children as real for the first time. In addition, such technologies can create a setting in which fathers, mothers, and health care workers can discuss the emotional aspects of pregnancy and child-rearing.

Similarly, we often talk about technology as if it is either a blank slate, lacking any inherent nature, or a force outside of human control. Again, the reality is more complex. For example, there has been considerable pressure lately for doctors and hospitals to reduce medical errors by adopting computerized medical databases to standardize the collection of patient data (Timmermans and Berg, 2003a). The purpose of these databases is to eliminate human error and variability in this process. For this reason, computerized databases may prompt doctors to ask their patients a specific set of questions, in a specific sequence, with a specific set of prompts if the answers seem insufficient or inappropriate. In this way, the database program presses doctors to standardize their practices and encourages them to focus on certain areas to the exclusion of others and to organize the data they obtain in specific ways. At the same time, doctors quickly learn how to obtain at least partial control over the database through the way they ask their questions and the answers they record to the database's questions. Similarly, although patients are pressed by the nature of the database to respond within a narrow framework, they often sidestep the questions they are asked and instead address a different set of issues (Timmermans and Berg, 2003a).

When we study technologies sociologically, therefore, it is as important to study the cultural system that surrounds that technology and determines how it will be used, by whom, and for what purposes as it is to study the nature of the technology itself. In addition, we must study not only how society and social actors shape the use of technology but also how technology shapes society and social actors.

In this section, we will look at how technologies develop and become adopted. We will also consider how different groups within the health care world interact with technology—and with each other.

The Social Construction of Technology

In the same way that we have talked about the social construction of illness, we can talk about the **social construction** of technology: the process through which groups decide which potential technologies should be pursued and which should be adopted. This concept

technology:
Any human-made object used to perform a task, or a process using such objects.

in turn leads us to question who promotes and who benefits from the social construction of any given technology.

As is true for the social construction of illness, the social construction of technology is a political process, reflecting the needs, desires, and relative power of various social groups. These groups can include manufacturers, doctors, the government, and consumers. As a result, harmful technologies are sometimes developed and adopted, and needed technologies sometimes are not.

One fascinating example of the social construction of technology is the history of cardiopulmonary resuscitation (CPR) and associated resuscitation techniques. (Box 13.3 discusses another example, the rapid adoption of CT scans.) The purpose of CPR is to restore life to those whose hearts and lungs have stopped working. In earlier times, the very notion of such resuscitation would not have made any sense to doctors or the public. Death was considered to be in God's hands, and dead was dead. But since the rise of modern medicine, doctors have struggled to find ways to restore life to those who die suddenly.

At the same time, doctors have grown increasingly able to understand the slow trajectory of dying associated with cancer. And with the rise of the hospice movement (described earlier in this chapter), both doctors and the public have come to hold as an ideal the "good death," in which an individual comes to terms with his or her dying, has the time to make peace with family and friends, and receives appropriate terminal care to minimize physical and emotional suffering.

None of this, however, applies to the sudden—and common—deaths caused by stroke or heart disease. In his award-winning book *Sudden Death and the Myth of CPR*, sociologist Stefan Timmermans (1999) argues that CPR and associated resuscitation techniques have

BOX 13.3
CT Scans

The use of computed tomography (CT) scans (typically referred to as "cat scans") has exploded in recent years. Nearly 4.2 million CT scans were conducted in Canada in 2009–2010, representing nearly twice as many as were performed in 2003–2004 (Health Canada, 2010a).

The increase in screening is primarily attributed to asymptomatic, healthy people who hope screening will uncover any health problems while they are still treatable. Yet, according to an article that made international headlines when it appeared in the prestigious *New England Journal of Medicine* (Brenner and Hall, 2007), a single series of CT scans delivers as much radiation—and as much danger—as the atomic bombs dropped on people living about 1.5 miles (2.4 kilometres) from "ground zero" in Hiroshima and Nagasaki. For years afterwards, survivors of those bombs suffered substantially increased rates of illness and death from cancer. The risks to CT users will be even greater, since they are likely to get multiple scans over the years.

The widespread adoption of CT scans (including "full-body" CT scans) reflects the cultural belief—common among both doctors and the general public—that medical tests can do no harm. It also reflects the tendency in medicine to adopt procedures based on early information about their benefits and before sufficient information has accumulated about any potential dangers. Without question, CT scans are tremendously useful for diagnosing illnesses in certain circumstances. But when used unnecessarily, they expose people not only to dangerous radiation but also to the risk of great anxiety, for these tests often uncover tiny tumours or other tiny biological variations in the body that even doctors cannot interpret. For these reasons, the rapid rise in CT scans seems a case study in the social construction of technology.

become part of Western medical culture because they appear to offer a "good death" in these circumstances. Innumerable television dramas portray heroic doctors who save apparently dead patients through CPR, and millions of dollars have been spent teaching the general public to perform CPR and outfitting community emergency response teams and hospital emergency rooms with resuscitation equipment. Yet CPR is almost never effective except when otherwise healthy individuals drown or are struck by lightning. The typical person who receives CPR has *at best* a 1–3% chance—and probably much less—of surviving, at an estimated cost of $500,000 per survivor. Moreover, "survival" may be brief, and it may be accompanied by severe neurological damage. As a result, according to Timmermans, emergency room doctors and emergency medical technicians overwhelmingly regard resuscitation as futile, and so they joke, complain, or simply go through the motions when they have to use it.

Why, then, has CPR become so widely adopted? Timmermans argues that the widespread use of CPR reflects our modern discomfort with death. The real benefit of CPR, according to Timmermans, is that it "takes some of the suddenness of sudden death away" (1999: 110). CPR allows families and friends to believe they have done everything possible by getting their loved ones to treatment as fast as possible. It also gives families and friends time to gather and to recognize that death may be imminent, and it gives medical personnel a sense of technical accomplishment as they fight to keep their patients' bodily organs functioning as long as possible. The use of CPR, then, is part of the broader project of **death brokering**: the process through which medical authorities make deaths explainable, culturally acceptable, and individually meaningful, such as through pain management and "death counselling" in hospices or by orchestrating a gradual removal of life supports when death is certain in intensive care units (Timmermans, 2005). For these reasons, and despite all its emotional and financial costs, CPR has become a valued and expected ritual in North American culture.

Whereas the adoption of CPR in our society mainly reflects cultural forces, the adoption of many other technologies illustrates the economic and political forces that underlie the social construction of technology. Because there are almost no legal requirements for corporations to demonstrate the safety or effectiveness of technological devices, corporations with vested economic interests can promote their products to an unwitting consumer without penalty. Thus, doctors must depend on promotional materials from manufacturers and on their own clinical experiences in deciding whether to use a technology, and patients must rely on doctors' judgment.

For example, the **electronic fetal monitor (EFM),** introduced in the 1960s as a diagnostic tool to identify fetal distress during delivery, is a technology that visually correlates the second-by-second fetal heart rate with the strength and periodicity of uterine contractions on a screen or computer printout. Intended originally for high-risk pregnancies, EFM is now routinely used during the birthing process. Indeed, more than 90% of Canadian women who gave birth vaginally in 2006–2007 reported that EFM was used on them (the question was not asked of women who did not have a vaginal birth) (Public Health Agency of Canada, 2009).

The wide usage of EFM suggests that the technology exists because it has demonstrably improved health outcomes in the delivery process. Yet, as Devoe (2011) notes, four decades later, the benefits, if any, that may be attributable to EFM remain to be conclusively established. Similarly, Grimes and Peipert (2010) declare EFM to be a failed public health screening program that lacks empirical evidence of its clinical benefit. We must ask ourselves, then, whose interests are best served by the pervasive use of a technology that might be helpful for women with high-risk pregnancies, but serves little purpose for most women in labour.

death brokering:
The process through which medical authorities make deaths explainable, culturally acceptable, and individually meaningful.

electronic fetal monitor (EFM):
A technology that visually correlates the second-by-second fetal heart rate with the strength and periodicity of uterine contractions on a screen or computer printout.

IMPLICATIONS

In this chapter, we examined three difficulties inherent in the ways we provide care to those who are physically ill, mentally ill, or disabled. First, we looked at some of the inherent contradictions of trying simultaneously to provide care and to minimize the costs of that care. Health care workers—from medical students to home health aides—who labour long hours in difficult conditions to keep costs low, cannot provide the quality of care they might like. Even when operating on a non-profit basis, institutions must contend with the demands of a wider system that emphasizes efficiency.

Second, we considered the difficulty of providing individualized care in institutional environments. Almost by definition, large institutions must provide care en masse, ignoring individual preferences and desires. Patients must follow rules, schedules, and regimens established for the sake of efficiency, regardless of the impact on their quality of life. This tendency to ignore the individual is further reinforced because it is far cheaper to provide regimented rather than individualized care.

Third, we explored some of the inherent difficulties of treating health care as an individual or family responsibility rather than a social responsibility. As we have seen, the burdens of caregiving can be enormous. Yet, Canada lags behind other countries in offering support to those who take on this responsibility. Both Sweden and Finland, for example, allow parents of sick children to leave work for several months while still receiving most of their salaries, and they provide free or inexpensive assistance with domestic chores to elderly persons who might otherwise have to turn to family members for assistance (Swedish Institute, 1997, 1999; Zimmerman, 1993). There are signs of progress, as evidenced in the new Compassionate Care Benefit Program, which allows Canadians to take up to eight weeks of paid leave to care for a dying loved one; however, too few Canadians are even aware that they have access to such benefits (CHPCA, 2011).

In sum, the data presented in this chapter suggest the low priority our society places on caring for those who are weak or ill. Technology is not a panacea for these problems. Nor, for that matter, is it inherently dehumanizing or otherwise problematic. Rather, technology is a tool, adopted for a combination of cultural, medical, emotional, and financial reasons, that can be used for good or ill. Only when our underlying social values and commitments change can we expect the lives of ill persons, disabled persons, and their caregivers to improve significantly.

SUMMARY

LO-1 1. Prior to the twentieth century, most Canadians received their health care at home. Although hospitals had been in existence since the arrival of European settlers, services were mainly offered on a charity basis for those who were indigent.

LO-1 2. The converging interests of doctors, community and religious leaders, and the general public facilitated the emergence of hospitals more generally throughout Canada. The hospitals of small towns often had no more than a handful of beds, whereas in larger cities, hospitals were built on a grander scale, with the revenues generated from wealthy clients used to subsidize care for the poor.

LO-1 3. Following the Flexner Report, the hospital began to transform itself into a temple of science: a place where the best diagnostic and therapeutic technologies would be housed and where doctors would engage in leading-edge medical practice. By the end of World War II, however, the costs of hospital care had risen so rapidly that it created a crisis of affordability for the middle classes, threatening the long-term economic stability of the hospital.

LO-1   4.   Supported though federal investment, a period of hospital growth was launched by the postwar boom. Saskatchewan introduced a hospital insurance program that levied an annual household fee that allowed residents of the province to receive hospital services for free, a template that other provinces would soon follow. Government investment and oversight not only suggested that hospitals had become a public good but also required new systems of accounting and workers to manage these systems. Combined with greater specialization in the emerging hospital occupational hierarchy, hospitals took on the characteristics of a complex bureaucracy.

LO-1   5.   During the health care crises of the 1990s, hospitals quietly transformed once again, by redefining some functions of the hospital as ancillary and contracting these services to for-profit companies. Such changes undermine the idea of the hospital as a public good. Moreover, valuing curative functions over caring aspects of health care may have implications for the health and well-being of both hospital workers and patients.

LO-2   6.   Even though prescientific views of mental illness as caused by supernatural or external sources have given way to modern ideas that mental illness is to be understood as a biological condition, what has persisted in Canadian society is the desire to exert control and maintain distance from those who are mentally ill.

LO-2   7.   Lunatic asylums, later renamed hospitals for the insane to align the emerging field of psychiatry with medicine, shifted from offering custodial care for the mentally ill to moral treatment, but reverted back to custodial care when patient overcrowding made moral treatment impossible.

LO-2   8.   It has been suggested that deinstitutionalization occurred because of the psychopharmacological revolution and the antitherapeutic critique of mental hospitals; however, others more cynically contend that deinstitutionalization was simply part of a larger plan by the state to control the costs of care by moving deviant populations out of costly institutional care and implementing other, less expensive forms of social control.

LO-2   9.   The process of deinstitutionalization continues to unfold to the present day. Although community care is generally preferable to life in a mental institution, the undesirable consequences of deinstitutionalization include revolving door syndrome, whereby those who are mentally ill cycle between short-term hospitalization and community care; a lack of adequate services in the community, which allows many to fall through the cracks; and transinstitutionalization, which shifts care of the mentally ill to other types of institutions that lack training in mental health issues.

LO-3   10.   Long-term care facilities, also referred to as nursing homes, offer care to those who are unable to live on their own but do not require hospital care. In the absence of national standards of care in these facilities, each province must decide how to fund and deliver long-term care, creating a patchwork system with a mix of government-run, private non-profit, religious non-profit, and for-profit facilities.

LO-3   11.   More than three in four long-term care facilities provide residential care for the elderly. Because seniors prefer to age in place, most seniors delay the transition to institutional care for as long as possible, meaning that the average age at admission is higher now than it has been in the past.

LO-3   12.   Assisted living facilities serve individuals who require neither medical nor nursing care but do need assistance in routine daily tasks such as routine housekeeping chores and meal preparation. Assisted living facilities also offer greater independence and privacy. Throughout Canada, assisted living facilities are becoming a popular alternative to long-term care facilities for aging seniors.

LO-3 13. Home care enables clients who are incapacitated in whole or in part to live at home, often with the effect of preventing, delaying, or substituting for long-term care or acute care alternatives. Although the federal government has begun to offer funding for home care services, the burden still falls most heavily on spouses and family members, particularly women. Providing informal care to a loved one can be emotionally rewarding, but for some, the costs can outweigh these potential benefits.

LO-4 14. Hospices are institutions designed to serve the needs of the dying. Early hospice philosophy placed the patient's needs at the centre of care and viewed death as a natural process; however, there is concern that as the hospice movement has become more established, it may lose some of its philosophical underpinnings.

LO-5 15. Technology refers to any human-made object used to perform a task. Technology is never inherently good or bad. Its nature determines the range of ways it might be used, but whether it is harmful, helpful, or both depends on who uses it in which ways.

LO-5 16. The social construction of technology refers to the political process through which groups decide which potential technologies should be pursued and which should be adopted. This process reflects the needs, desires, and relative power of various social groups, including manufacturers, doctors, and consumers.

LO-5 17. Cardiopulmonary resuscitation (CPR) was designed to restore life to those whose hearts and lungs have stopped. It is almost never successful but has been widely adopted because it helps people come to terms with sudden death. Similarly, other medical technologies may be adopted, not necessarily because they improve health outcomes, but because of the vested economic interests of manufacturers and because neither the government nor doctors require manufacturers to prove the effectiveness of a given technology.

REVIEW QUESTIONS

1. What evidence suggests that hospitals evolved from dispensers of charity to a market-oriented institution in the first few decades of the twentieth century?
2. In what ways did Saskatchewan's introduction of hospital insurance change the function of hospitals in Canada?
3. How have cutbacks to hospital budgets increased the risks to health for both patients and hospital workers?
4. What were the causes and consequences of deinstitutionalization?
5. Who uses long-term care facilities?
6. What is the difference between long-term care facilities and assisted living facilities?
7. Why has home care grown? What are the difficulties faced by family caregivers?
8. How is palliative care different from typical care in a health care institution?
9. What is technology? What do sociologists mean when they say that technology is inherently neither good nor bad, and neither a blank slate nor a force outside of human control?
10. What is the social construction of technology? What does it mean to say that this is a political process?
11. Why was CPR so widely adopted even though it is so ineffective?

CRITICAL THINKING QUESTIONS

1. What are the burdens experienced by family caregivers, and how have these changed over time? If you were asked to be on a provincial task force on health care, what policies might you want to implement to lighten those burdens?
2. If you could go back into the past and change one thing in the history of hospitals, what would it be? Why?
3. How can society shape technology? How can technology shape society?

KEY TERMS

almshouse (p. 315)
assisted living facilities (p. 331)
death brokering (p. 339)
decarceration (p. 326)
deinstitutionalization (p. 324)
depersonalization (p. 326)
electronic fetal monitor (EFM) (p. 339)
home care (p. 331)
hospices (p. 333)
inpatient (p. 324)
long-term care facilities (p. 328)
lunacy (p. 322)
lunatic asylum (p. 322)
master status (p. 326)

moral treatment (p. 323)
mortification (p. 326)
normalize (p. 322)
outpatient (p. 319)
psychopharmacological revolution (p. 325)
revolving door syndrome (p. 327)
right to die (p. 334)
self-fulfilling prophecy (p. 325)
superbugs (p. 320)
symbolic interactionism (p. 325)
technology (p. 337)
total institutions (p. 326)
transinstitutionalization (p. 327)

Part V

Issues in Bioethics

The final part addresses the issue of ethics; however, its placement at the end of this text should not be taken to mean that it occupies a trivial place in the sociology of health and illness. Rather, the final chapter represents the culmination of an ongoing discussion of ethical issues that have been interspersed throughout the text.

In Chapter 14, we provide a broad overview of bioethics: the study of ethical issues involved in the biological sciences, health, and health care. We discuss how both bioethicists and sociologists can inform bioethical debate. We describe the historical events and contexts that have shaped greater attention to ethical issues in health care and research. Importantly, we draw attention to the role of power by critically evaluating the extent to which the institutionalization of ethics has actually changed adherence to ethics in health research and health care.

14

Issues in Bioethics

CP Photo/The Toronto Star-Rick Madonik

Dr. Nancy Olivieri

Dr. Nancy Olivieri: Whistleblower

In the mid-1990s, Dr. Nancy Olivieri, a medical doctor and well-respected researcher in blood disorders, found evidence that a drug being tested in her laboratory at Toronto's Hospital for Sick Children, an institution affiliated with the University of Toronto, was causing harmful liver toxicity in some of the study participants, who were also her patients. Instead of being supportive of her attempts to fulfill her ethical and legal obligations to warn others of the problems with the drug, Apotex Inc., the pharmaceutical company that was partially funding her research, responded harshly. Not only did Apotex dispute her findings and abruptly terminate its research contract with her, but on the basis of a non-disclosure clause in the rescinded contract, she was threatened with legal action if she divulged any further information about her work for the drug manufacturer, including her concerns about the drug. Dr. Olivieri refused to comply and

appropriately filed her findings about the drug with the federal department of health and welfare so that other physicians would be alerted to potential problems with the drug. She also published her findings in the *New England Journal of Medicine* in 1998, and soon after there was a flurry of lawsuits.

As the situation escalated, Dr. Olivieri turned to her institution for support; however, instead of coming to her defence, the University of Toronto distanced itself from the scandal and began to treat her with suspicion. On the basis of anonymous letters that made false allegations about Dr. Olivieri's research practices and were circulated around the university and to the media, the university formed an internal committee to investigate Dr. Olivieri. The committee, which collected evidence and testimony but failed to give Dr. Olivieri an opportunity to view evidence or contest claims, found fault with Dr. Olivieri and she consequently lost her position.

Six years after her ordeal began, Dr. Olivieri was vindicated in two separate reports issued by the Canadian Association of University Teachers and the Ontario College of Physicians and Surgeons that found no evidence of professional misconduct and instead praised her for her efforts to protect her patients. Following these reports, the University of Toronto absolved Dr. Olivieri of any wrongdoing. In time, DNA evidence revealed that the person who had written the anonymous letters and provided false information to the university committee was a colleague at the same institution whose research continued to receive funding from Apotex. It also came to light that the University of Toronto had been negotiating with Apotex for a sizable donation at the same time that university administrators were censuring Dr. Olivieri.

In this chapter, students should be able to:

LO-1 **Recognize** the ways in which the interests of bioethicists and sociologists both differ and converge.

LO-2 **Describe** the past historical practices of medical doctors in adhering to ethical principles and **identify** the turning points from the end of World War II through the 1970s that helped to facilitate the emergence of bioethics as a field of study.

LO-3 **Describe** changes that have occurred to the regulation of ethical principles in medical research and practice in Canada over the course of the twentieth century and into the twenty-first century.

LO-4 **Describe** the composition and function of research ethics boards and clinical ethics committees in contemporary Canadian society.

LO-5 **Evaluate** the extent to which establishing research ethics boards and clinical ethics committees has changed medical research, training and practice.

For centuries, doctors have formally recognized that health care should be based on ethical principles. The Hippocratic oath, for example, written in about 400 BCE, instructed doctors to take only actions that would benefit their patients and to forswear euthanasia, seducing patients, or divulging patients' secrets. Yet in practice, health care may fall far short of meeting ethical principles. In this chapter, we explore the history of **bioethics**, a growing field of study that evaluates all ethical issues related to human health, and analyze how bioethics has—and has not—affected health care and medical research.

To some students and faculty, it might seem odd to include a chapter on bioethics in a sociology textbook. Yet the issues raised by bioethics are sociological issues, for many of the issues bioethicists ponder revolve around the impact of power differences among social groups (most importantly, between physicians and patients). Even when exploring the same issues, however, bioethicists and sociologists do so through different lenses. Robert Zussman, a sociologist who has studied bioethics extensively, succinctly summarizes the difference:

> Medical ethics may be thought of as the normative study of high principles for the purpose of guiding clinical decisions. In contrast, the sociology of medical ethics may be thought of as the empirical study of clinical decisions for the purpose of understanding the social structure of medicine. Clearly then, medical ethicists and sociologists of medical ethics travel much of the same terrain, but they do so traveling in different directions. (1997: 174)

bioethics:
The study of the moral and ethical dilemmas that scientists and doctors encounter in medical research and in the treatment of patients.

A HISTORY OF BIOETHICS

Since 1868, the Canadian Medical Association (CMA) has required its members to subscribe to its code of ethics. The code, however, speaks more of medical etiquette—proper relations between doctors—than of medical ethics or, more broadly, bioethics. Indeed, throughout the nineteenth century and well into the twentieth century, doctors' ideas regarding bioethics remained ill defined and their commitment to bioethics remained minimal. Although doctors undoubtedly would have identified relieving human suffering as their primary goal, both in their research and in clinical practice, doctors sometimes behaved in ways that would horrify modern doctors and bioethicists. For example, Dr. J. Marion Sims, considered the father of modern obstetrics, achieved fame during the 1840s for developing a surgical procedure to correct vesicovaginal fistulae, tears in the wall between a woman's vagina and bladder usually caused by overaggressive medical intervention during childbirth (Barker-Benfield, 1976). Women who suffered these fistulae could not control the leakage of urine and often had to withdraw from social life altogether because of odour and the resulting social shame. To develop a surgical cure, Sims bought black women slaves who had fistulae and then operated on them as many as thirty times each, in an era before antibiotics and antisepsis and with only addictive drugs for anaesthetics. When Sims announced his new surgical technique, the medical world and the public greeted him with acclaim. No one questioned his research ethics.

A century later, Nazi doctors working in German concentration camps also used socially disvalued populations for equally barbaric—and even less justifiable—experiments. The world's response to these experiments would mark the beginnings of modern bioethics.

The Nazi Doctors and the Nuremberg Code

In 1933, the German people voted the Nazis, under Adolf Hitler's leadership, into power. At that time, Germany's medical schools and researchers were known and respected worldwide and its system of health care was considered one of the best and most comprehensive (Redlich, 1978).

Shortly after coming to power, the Nazi government passed the Law for the Prevention of Congenitally Ill Progeny (Lifton, 1986). This law required the sterilization of anyone considered likely to give birth to children with diseases that doctors considered genetic, including mental retardation, schizophrenia, manic depression, epilepsy, blindness, deafness, and alcoholism. Under this law, government-employed doctors sterilized between 200,000 and 300,000 persons. Two years later, in 1935, the government passed the Law to Protect Genetic Health, prohibiting the marriage of persons with certain diseases.

Both these laws reflected a belief in **eugenics**, the theory that the population should be "improved" through selective breeding and birth control. The eugenics movement has had many followers throughout the Western world. By 1920, twenty-five U.S. states and two Canadian provinces (Alberta and British Columbia) had passed laws allowing the sterilization of those believed (usually incorrectly) to carry genes for mental retardation or criminality.

As the power of the Nazis grew in Germany, and as public response to their actions both within and outside Germany proved mild, the Nazis adopted ever bolder eugenic actions (Lifton, 1986; Redlich, 1978). Beginning in 1939, the Nazis began systematically killing patients in state mental hospitals. Doctors played a central role in this program, selecting patients for death and supervising their poisoning with lethal drugs or carbon monoxide gas. Doctors and nurses also watched silently while many more patients starved to death. In total, between 80,000 and 100,000 adults and 5,000 children died (Lifton, 1986). Shortly after, the Nazi government began systematically killing Jews, Gypsies, and others whom they considered racially inferior. By the end of World War II, the Nazis had murdered between 5 million and 10 million people in their concentration camps.

At least 350 doctors played major roles in this genocidal policy (Lifton, 1986; Redlich, 1978). As prisoners entered the concentration camps, medical officers of the Nazi SS corps decided whom to kill immediately and whom to use for forced labour. When shooting those marked for death proved too expensive, doctors developed more efficient means of mass murder using carbon monoxide gassing. Medical corpsmen, supervised by doctors, conducted the murders. Those whom doctors selected for forced labour, meanwhile, usually died in a matter of weeks from starvation, overwork, or the epidemic diseases that ravaged the camps. In addition, doctors working in the concentration camps (including university professors and highly respected senior medical researchers) performed hundreds of unethical experiments on prisoners—such as studying how quickly individuals would die once exposed to freezing cold and seeing whether injecting dye into prisoners' eyes would change their eye

eugenics:
The theory that the population should be "improved" through selective breeding and birth control.

colour. Doctors also used prisoners to gain surgical experience by, for example, removing healthy ovaries or kidneys or creating wounds on which to practise surgical treatments.

Following the Nazi defeat, the Allied victors prosecuted twenty-three of these doctors for committing "medical crimes against humanity," eventually sentencing seven to death and nine to prison (Lifton, 1986). The decisions in these cases contained the basis for what is now known as the **Nuremberg Code**, a set of internationally recognized principles regarding the ethics of human experimentation (see Box 14.1). The code requires researchers to have a medically justifiable purpose, do all within their power to protect their subjects from harm, and ensure that their subjects give **informed consent**, that is, voluntarily agree to participate in the research with a full understanding of the potential risks and benefits.

The 1960s: The Rise of Bioethics

Because the trials received relatively little publicity outside Europe, and because Nazi doctors were viewed as *Nazis* rather than as doctors, few drew connections between Nazi practices and medical practices elsewhere in the world (Rothman, 1991). Moreover, although all countries that belonged to the United Nations at the time endorsed the Nuremberg Code, the principles

Nuremberg Code:
A set of internationally recognized principles regarding the ethics of human experimentation that emerged during the post–World War II Nuremberg trials for medical crimes against humanity.

informed consent:
Voluntary agreement to participate in medical research or to receive a medical procedure or treatment, with a full understanding of the potential risks and benefits.

BOX 14.1

Principles of the Nuremberg Code

1. The voluntary consent of the human subject is absolutely essential....
2. The experiment should be such as to yield fruitful results for the good of society, unprocurable by other methods or means of study, and not random and unnecessary in nature.
3. The experiment should be so designed and based on the results of animal experimentation and a knowledge of the natural history of the disease or other problem under study that the anticipated results will justify the performance of the experiment.
4. The experiment should be so conducted as to avoid all unnecessary physical and mental suffering and injury.
5. No experiment should be conducted where there is an a priori reason to believe that death or disabling injury will occur; except, perhaps, in those experiments where the experimental physicians also serve as subjects.
6. The degree of risk to be taken should never exceed that determined by the humanitarian importance of the problem to be solved by the experiment.
7. Proper preparations should be made and adequate facilities provided to protect the experimental subject against even remote possibilities of injury, disability, or death.
8. The experiment should be conducted only by scientifically qualified persons. The highest degree of skill and care should be required through all stages of the experiment of those who conduct or engage in the experiment.
9. During the course of the experiment, the human subject should be at liberty to bring the experiment to an end if [they have] reached the physical or mental state where continuation of the experiment seems to [them] to be impossible.
10. During the course of the experiment, the scientist in charge must be prepared to terminate the experiment at any stage if [they have] probable cause to believe, in the exercise of the good faith, superior skill and careful judgment required of [them], that a continuation of the experiment is likely to result in injury, disability, or death to the experimental subject.

Source: U.S. Dept. of Health & Human Services, The Office for Human Research Protections. Found at: http://www.hhs.gov/ohrp/archive/nurcode.html.

themselves were not legally binding. As a result, discussion of bioethics and adherence to the principles of the Nuremberg Code remained largely dormant in the years following the Nuremberg Trials. It wasn't until the 1960s that ethical questions regarding medical care and research became topics of popular discussion.

One reason for this was the rise of new technologies, such as life support systems for comatose persons. Of particular importance was the development of kidney dialysis, a technology that could keep alive persons whose kidneys had failed (Fox and Swazey, 1974). Demand for dialysis far outstripped supply, forcing selection committees made up of doctors and, in some cases, lay people to decide who would receive this life-saving treatment and who would die. Forced to choose from among the many who, on medical grounds, were equally likely to benefit from the treatment, these committees frequently based their choices on social criteria such as sex, age, apparent emotional stability, social class, and marital status. When news of these committees' work reached the public, the resulting outcry led to new regulations designed to allocate kidney dialysis more fairly.

whistleblower:
A person who reveals any wrongdoings or unethical practices that are taking place within his or her organization.

Although the dialysis issue sparked public concern about medical *practice,* medical *research* still remained outside the bounds of public discussion. In 1966, however, one article by a concerned **whistleblower** changed this. Writing in the *New England Journal of Medicine,* respected medical professor Henry Beecher (1966) described twenty-two research studies, published in top journals in the recent past, that had used ethically questionable methods. In one study, for example, soldiers sick with streptococcal infections received experimental treatments instead of penicillin, causing twenty-five soldiers to develop rheumatic fever. In another, doctors inserted catheters into the bladders of healthy newborns and X-rayed them, without parental consent, to study how bladders worked.

To determine the frequency of such studies, Beecher looked at 100 consecutive research studies published in a prestigious medical journal. In 12 of the 100 studies, researchers had not told subjects of the risks involved in the experiments or had not even told the subjects that they were in an experiment. Yet, no journal reviewer, editor, or reader had questioned the ethics of these studies.

Beecher's article sent ripples of concern not only through the medical world but also through the general public, as news of the article spread through the mass media. In the United States, this public concern translated into pressure on Congress and, in turn, pressure on the U.S. Public Health Service (PHS), the major funder of medical research. To demonstrate to Congress that they could deal with the problem on their own and to keep public concern from turning into budget cuts, the PHS in 1966 published guidelines for protecting human subjects in medical research (Rothman, 1991).

The responses to Beecher's article and the dialysis issue demonstrate the increased role that the mass media and the general public had begun to play in health care decision-making. Meanwhile, the growth of the civil rights and women's rights movements stimulated discussion both about patients' rights generally and about birth control and abortion specifically. Taken together, these changes led observers to proclaim the birth of a bioethics movement (Fox, 1974; Rothman, 1991). Despite greater public awareness of human rights in biomedical research and practice, however, there appears to have been little visible impact on the way researchers and doctors conducted their work throughout the 1960s and into the 1970s, with some ethical violations committed by the very institutions committed to upholding them. We discuss the often cited American example of the Tuskegee Syphilis Study, before turning our attention to a lesser known but equally egregious case in Canada.

The Tuskegee Syphilis Study

In 1972, the Tuskegee Syphilis Study made headlines around the world (Jones, 1993). Begun by the U.S. Public Health Service (PHS) in 1932, the study, which was still ongoing, was intended to document the natural progression of untreated syphilis in African American men. At the time the study began, medical scientists understood the devastating course of syphilis in the Caucasian population (which, in its later stages, can cause neurological damage and heart disease), but, reflecting the racist logic of the times, the scientists suspected its progression took a different and milder form in African Americans.

For this study, researchers identified 399 desperately poor and mostly illiterate African American men, all with untreated late-stage syphilis, who lived in the Tuskegee, Alabama, area. The men were neither told they had syphilis nor offered treatment. Instead, researchers informed them that they had "bad blood," a term used locally to cover a wide variety of health ailments. The researchers then told the men that if they participated in this study of bad blood, they would receive free and regular (if infrequent) health care, transportation to medical clinics, free meals on examination days, and payment of burial expenses—enormous inducements given the men's extreme poverty.

At the time the study began, treating syphilis was difficult, lengthy, and costly. The development of penicillin in the early 1940s, however, gave doctors a simple and effective treatment. Yet, throughout the course of the study, researchers not only did not offer penicillin to their subjects but also kept them from receiving it elsewhere. During World War II, researchers worked with local draft boards to prevent their subjects from getting drafted into the military, where the subjects might have received treatment. When federally funded venereal disease treatment clinics opened locally, researchers enlisted the support of clinic doctors to keep research subjects from receiving treatment. Similarly, they enlisted the cooperation of the all-white County Medical Society to ensure that no local doctor gave penicillin to their subjects for any other reason.

The Tuskegee Syphilis Study, which treated African American men as less than human guinea pigs, was not the work of a few isolated crackpots. Rather, it was run by a respected federal agency, the PHS, with additional funding from the widely respected Milbank Fund. The study received significant cooperation from the state and county medical associations and even from doctors and nurses affiliated with the local Tuskegee Institute, a world-renowned college for African Americans. Over the years, more than a dozen articles based on the study appeared in top medical journals, without anyone ever questioning the study's ethics. Yet the study patently flouted the Nuremberg Code and, after 1966, the PHS's own research ethics guidelines. Nevertheless, the study did not end until 1972, after a newspaper exposé resulted in public outrage. By that time, at least 28 and possibly as many as 100 research subjects had died of syphilis, and an unknown number had succumbed to syphilis-related heart problems (Jones, 1993). In addition, the study indirectly caused untold additional deaths by convincing many in the African American community to distrust public health workers and contributing to their suspicions that the U.S. federal government created **HIV/AIDS** to control population growth in their community (Jones, 1993; Thomas and Quinn, 1991).

The Alberta Sexual Sterilization Act

In the same year that the scandal over the Tuskegee Syphilis Study erupted, a newly elected government in the province of Alberta, as one of its first acts after assuming power and amid growing public awareness, repealed an act of legislation that for more than forty years had permitted the involuntary sterilization of patients in mental institutions. Passed originally in 1928, the Sexual Sterilization Act was grounded in the same mistaken ideas about eugenics that had generated many of the atrocities committed during World War II; however, in Alberta, the practice quietly continued long after the Nuremberg Trials had ended and the eugenics movement had been discredited. As was the case in Nazi Germany, the chief proponents and architects of the Act were some of the province's leading citizens, including university presidents, politicians, professors, and medical doctors.

The Act established the Eugenics Board, which, over its more than forty years of operation, approved the sterilization of 4,785 individuals judged to be mentally defective as a result of mental illness, low intelligence, epilepsy, or other conditions. Although 2,832 people (59% of those approved) actually underwent the sterilization procedure, archival analysis of the board's meeting minutes and patient records revealed that the board never once decided against sterilization (Grekul, Krahn, and Odynak, 2004). Initially, the board required the consent of the patient to proceed; however, frustration with the perceived inefficiencies of obtaining consent led to an amendment in 1937 that allowed the board to proceed without it. In subsequent years, the Act would be further revised to broaden the criteria under which patients could be considered for involuntary sterilization.

Although the repealing of the Act attracted some attention at the time, the public outcry was much louder in 1996 when details of Leilani Muir's encounter with the Eugenics Board came to light after she won a lawsuit against the Alberta government. As a child, Leilani had been placed by her mother in an institution in Red Deer known as the Provincial Training School for Mental Defectives (now called the Michener Centre). After undergoing intelligence tests, Leilani was determined to have a sufficiently low IQ to warrant sterilization, and her application, submitted on her behalf by the training school, was approved by the Eugenics Board. Told at the time that she was having her appendix removed, Leilani only discovered that she had been sterilized when, years later, she and her husband sought medical advice after trying unsuccessfully to have children. Tests at that time also revealed that Leilani's IQ fell within the normal range. Her court case and subsequent victory triggered a series of lawsuits as more than 700 others came forward with similar stories.

INSTITUTIONALIZING BIOETHICS

Beecher's revelations in 1966 coupled with the international uproar over the Tuskegee Syphilis Study a decade later made it clear that the medical community was not capable of regulating itself and provided needed impetus for establishing ethical guidelines that were legally binding. In 1976, a U.S. commission produced a report referred to as the Belmont Report that outlined three basic ethical principles for medical research and practice (respect for persons, beneficence, and justice). The Belmont Report also went further than previous ethical guidelines in mandating protection for people with diminished capacity or other vulnerabilities, while advocating for their inclusion in research. Shortly thereafter, these principles were codified into law in the United States.

In 1978, Canada also began to introduce regulatory mechanisms to oversee research ethics. Guidelines that were published that year (and revised in 1987) by the Medical Research Council of Canada (MRC) and in 1981 by the Social Sciences and Humanities Research Council (SSHRC) drew heavily on the Belmont Report. To ensure that there was national oversight of researchers' compliance with ethical guidelines, the National Council on Bioethics in Human Research (NCBHR) was created in 1989. When the mandate was broadened to include all human research in 1995, this body was renamed the National Council on Ethics in Human Research (NCEHR).

In 1998, all three federal funding agencies in Canada (MRC—soon to be renamed CIHR—as well as SSHRC and NSERC) adopted the Tri-Council Policy Statement: Ethical Conduct for Research Involving Humans (TCPS) as a national standard of ethical conduct for all research involving human subjects. To receive funding from these agencies, researchers and their respective institutions had to agree to be bound by the ethical guidelines outlined in the TCPS. Several years later, the Interagency Panel on Research Ethics (PRE) was established to respond to ongoing challenges and developments in research ethics. The accumulating policy changes as a result of the work of the PRE prompted the need to revise the TCPS, resulting in a second edition published in December 2010 (TCPS2).

Greater attention has also been paid to **conflict of interest** and other aspects of professional misconduct (e.g., falsification of data, plagiarism). In December 2011, a new regulatory body called the Panel on Responsible Conduct of Research (PRCR) was established. The mandate of the PRCR is to ensure a coherent and uniform approach to promoting the responsible conduct of research and addressing allegations of breaches of agency policies. Members of the PRCR are appointed for a three-year term by the presidents of the three federal funding agencies; receive no compensation for their work; are expected to have a wide range of expertise and experience in research ethics; are balanced in terms of gender, geography, and discipline; and are drawn from university administration as well as the broader community.

The creation of the PRCR coincided with the publication of a new document called the Tri-Council Framework of Responsible Conduct of Research. This document describes the policies for researchers, institutions, and funding agencies for ensuring the integrity of research as well as the means by which institutions promote responsible research and address breaches. An important shift in this document is that researchers (and their institutions) who have been found in violation of ethical principles and other procedural or administrative breaches (misuse of funds, invalid authorship, plagiarism) will now be publicly named and required to disclose their status in all future research proposal applications. Nonetheless, unlike in the United States, ethical guidelines in Canada have yet to be codified into law.

In contrast, legislation that protects the rights of patients in clinical settings has long been entrenched in Canadian law. From the beginning of the twentieth century, Canadian courts have reinforced the spirit of Justice Cardozo's famous quote that "every human being of adult years and sound mind has a right to determine what is done with his body" (cited in Robertson, 2008). This standard for informed consent remained in effect for most of the century; however, in 1980, the Supreme Court of Canada handed down a decision in the case of *Reibl v. Hughes* that essentially shifted the standard from one based on objective professional standards to a patient-based standard. Reibl, who had been left paralyzed as a result of a procedure to rid him of migraines, successfully argued that he would have delayed the surgery by a year if he had known that the full risks of surgery included the inability to return to work, which subsequently made him ineligible for a pension from his employer. The Supreme Court's decision of medical negligence on the part of Dr. Hughes led to the modified test for informed consent. The modified test no longer allowed doctors to be guided by their own inference as to what a reasonable person might decide but rather compelled them to take into account what each particular patient might decide given his or her unique situation.

Thus, in research settings such as universities and clinical settings such as hospitals, there are committees that ensure that health research and health care will be conducted ethically. We describe the specific functions of research ethics boards and clinical ethics committees in the following sections.

Research Ethics Boards

Research ethics boards (REBs) are federally mandated committees that are locally responsible for reviewing the ethics of research projects involving human subjects in their respective institutions. An institution may be a university or college or it may be a non-profit organization, such as the Heart and Stroke Foundation, that conducts research, or a government agency, such as Health Canada, that undertakes research projects on its own behalf. Academic researchers who receive government funding from one of the three federal granting agencies can conduct no research until they receive REB approval.

conflict of interest: Professional misconduct that occurs when professional judgment concerning a primary interest (such as a patient's welfare or the validity of research) tends to be unduly influenced by a secondary interest (such as financial gain).

research ethics boards (REBs): Federally mandated committees that are locally responsible for reviewing the ethics of research projects involving human subjects in their respective institutions.

To maintain the integrity of the review process, the REB operates independently but is subject to oversight by the highest office in its own institution and the national governing bodies mentioned in the previous section. The main role of REBs is to review all proposed research studies, sometimes referred to as protocols, to determine if they meet regulatory and ethical requirements for research involving human subjects as laid out in TCPS2. The review includes assessing the risk of harm to participants and weighing potential harms against the expected benefits of the research. REBs also have the responsibility of monitoring research that they have approved, which includes an annual review of ongoing research as well as ensuring that all adverse events are reported to them and passed on to the relevant authorities.

According to the TCPS2, each REB must consist of at least five members, including both men and women. In terms of representation, at least two members must have expertise in relevant research disciplines, one member must be knowledgeable in ethics, and one member must be knowledgeable in the relevant law (but does not provide legal counsel). In addition, at least one member must be from the community and cannot be affiliated in any way with the institution.

The REB must conduct regular face-to-face meetings where members discuss and make decisions on research proposals. All decisions are extensively and meticulously documented so that there is transparency in the process: All REBs need to act and to be seen to act in ways that are fair and reasonable. The workload can be enormous: Board members in mid-sized to large universities typically review and render decisions on anywhere between 300 and 2,000 proposed experiments yearly, depending on the size of their institution. Members are not compensated for their work, as this is part of their expected service contribution.

From the perspective of the researcher seeking ethics approval of his or her research, the task is equally daunting. Researchers who submit an application to the REB must master the language of research ethics and immerse themselves in its culture. Indeed, researchers quickly learn that they must produce a narrative that expresses familiarity with and adherence to a wide range of concepts and practices, including

> sensitivity to and awareness of the harm potential, to direct or indirect methods of recruitment, to careful access procedures, to the intricacies of formulating and claiming informed consent, to the propriety of questions to be asked, to proper approval from agencies and communities, to the complete identification of all the researchers to be involved, to the actual source of funding, to plans for future use, storage and ultimate destruction of the data, to the nature of any perceived risks, to the types of future benefits expected, to ways of protecting confidentiality and anonymity, to maintaining this promised confidentiality over time and, finally, to the plans for future feedback…. Without learning this story and reproducing it accurately, however, legitimate research cannot occur. (Whittaker, 2005, p. 526)

Clinical Ethics Committees

clinical ethics committees (CECs): Committees located within health care institutions such as hospitals and nursing homes whose purpose is to provide education, counsel, and support on ethical issues related to patient care.

In the 1980s, there was a systematic effort in Canada to establish ethics committees within hospitals and other health institutions, referred to as **clinical ethics committees (CECs)**. CECs exist within health institutions and act as an educational and advisory resource on ethical issues related to patient care. As advisory committees, CECs lack the ability to impose binding decisions on health care providers.

CECs are common in the United States but relatively new in other countries, such as Canada and most European nations. Only one in five Canadian hospitals had a CEC in 1984. Today, more than 80% of hospitals in Canada have CECs; however, many of these have been established in the past ten years. A recent study that collected information on the characteristics of CECs across Canada in 2008 noted few changes in their overall composition and function over the past two decades (Gaudine et al., 2010). CECs in 2008 were found to range in size from five to twenty-six members and comprised physicians, nurses, administrators, clergy or pastoral workers, community representatives, lawyers, bioethicists, and hospital board members. Over time, there appears to be a trend in which lawyers and bioethicists are increasingly represented in CECs. Comparing their findings with those from previous surveys on Canadian CECs, Gaudine and her colleagues found that, both then and now, CECs rarely got involved in end-of-life decisions.

THE IMPACT OF BIOETHICS

The growth of the bioethics movement and the institutionalization of bioethics in hospitals and universities in Canada and elsewhere have made ethical issues more visible than ever before. Articles on bioethics, virtually non-existent before the 1960s, now appear routinely in medical journals, while in both the clinical and research worlds, ethics committees have proliferated.

These developments have led some observers to conclude that the bioethics movement has fundamentally altered the nature of medical work. According to U.S. historian David Rothman:

> By the mid-1970s, both the style and the substance of medical decision-making had changed. The authority that an individual physician had once exercised covertly was now subject to debate and review by colleagues and laypeople. Let the physician design a research protocol to deliver an experimental treatment, and in the room, by federal mandate, was an institutional review board composed of other physicians, lawyers, and community representatives to make certain that the potential benefits to the subject-patient outweighed the risks. Let the physician attempt to allocate a scarce resource, like a donor heart, and in the room were federal and state legislators and administrators to help set standards of equity and justice. Let the physician decide to withdraw or terminate life sustaining treatment from an incompetent patient, and in the room were state judges to rule, in advance, on the legality of these actions. (1991: 2)

Other observers, however, contend that the impact of the bioethics movement has been more muted (Annas, 1991). These critics argue that these committees exist primarily to offer legal protection and social support to researchers and clinicians, not to protect patients or research subjects. Further, they argue, although clinicians have become more concerned with *documenting* their allegiance to ethics guidelines, they have not become any more concerned with *following* those guidelines. Finally, sociologist Daniel F. Chambliss (1996) argues that bioethics' emphasis on helping individual health care providers make more ethical decisions simply does not apply to health care workers like nurses, who often understand clearly what they should do ethically but lack the power to do so. For example, nurses often have a much better understanding than doctors of how much a patient is suffering and thus more often believe treatment should be discontinued unless it will improve quality of life, and not simply lengthen life. Yet nurses can rarely act on that belief because they lack the necessary legal standing, economic independence, and social status.

The following sections evaluate the impact of bioethics on medical research, medical education, and clinical practice.

The Impact on Medical Research

According to ethicist George Annas, the bioethics movement, as institutionalized in REBs, has affected medical research only slightly. In his words, their

> primary mission is to protect the institution by providing an alternative forum to litigation or unwanted publicity.… [For this reason] its membership is almost exclusively made up of researchers (not potential subjects) from the particular institution. These committees have changed the face of research … by requiring investigators to justify their research on humans to a peer review group prior to recruiting subjects. But this does not mean that they have made research universally more "ethical." In at least a few spectacular instances, these committees have provided ethical and legal cover that enabled experiments to be performed that otherwise would not have been because of their potentially devastating impact on human subjects. (1991: 19)

As an example, Annas cites the case of "Baby Fae" (not her real name), who died in 1984 soon after doctors replaced her defective heart with a baboon's heart. Although all available evidence indicated that cross-species transplants could not succeed, the doctors who performed the surgery had received approval from their hospital's ethics committee. A subsequent review found that Baby Fae's parents had not given truly informed consent, because the doctors had not suggested seeking a human transplant, had disparaged available surgical treatments, and had unreasonably encouraged the parents to believe that a baboon transplant could succeed.

Another concern arises over the wide variability in interpretation that can occur when REBs apply vaguely worded ethical guidelines to specific research projects. As noted earlier, REBs operate independently from one another and members are unpaid volunteers with a voluminous workload. Not only does this make it likely that errors will occur, but also there is no formal mechanism to ensure that the decisions rendered across the network of REBs are consistent. The extent of the problem was clearly revealed in a Canadian study that documented these divergences (de Champlain and Patenaude, 2006). In this study, seventy-seven REBs across Canada were asked to review a mock protocol using standard procedures, having been informed in advance that the protocol was fictional. The mock study proposed to use functional neuroimaging techniques to scan the brains of participants while they were exposed to three states: an ordinary state, where the respondent would be asked to think about everyday things; a meditation state, where the respondent would be asked to think introspectively; and a violent state, where the respondent would be shown photographs depicting extreme violence. Of the forty-three REBs that agreed to conduct the review and rendered a decision, three approved the project unconditionally, with two providing specific feedback that commended the study for its potential to produce interesting and valuable knowledge. Ten REBs conditionally approved the project, with the majority requesting further clarification as to whether consent was being properly obtained given that participants would be exposed to extremely violent photographs. The remaining thirty REBs rejected the project, with 70% voicing concern about the photographs depicting violence and nearly 80% discounting the scientific validity of the study. In their comments, many REBs expressed concern over deceiving subjects by assessing their responses to violent images without informing them in advance that they would be exposed to such pictures, with one REB remarking that this study reminded them of the "atrocious eugenics movement in the late nineteenth century." Importantly, the same concerns about violent images that led some REBs to conditionally approve their project motivated other REBs to issue an outright rejection. These discrepancies are troubling because they suggest that REBs have adopted unwieldy bureaucratic processes that increase the time researchers must spend to get their projects approved, without necessarily improving the protection of research subjects.

There also remain lingering questions about the ethical implications of industry-sponsored research in Canada, which now accounts for 60–70% of all research protocols in Canada. Tight budgets and greater pressure to commercialize research have prompted universities across Canada to rely even more heavily on industry-supported research. Ethical guidelines in Canada were revised following the debacle around Dr. Olivieri's whistle-blowing efforts (described in the opening vignette of this chapter) to ensure that the interests of research participants are always given greater weight than the interests of researchers and their industry sponsors. Thus, TCPS2 contains specific directives about industry-sponsored research and recommends that sponsors not impose restrictions on publication; however, responsibility for compliance is left to the individual institution. In addition, new opportunities to manipulate the system continue to emerge. For example, the finding that there was wide variability in the policies and practices of Canadian universities and hospitals in regard to conflicts of interest led Lexchin and his colleagues (2007) to speculate that these inconsistencies might create incentives for industry sponsors to shop around for institutions that have softer policies.

Others have noted that Dr. Olivieri's experiences may also send an unintended message to other researchers (Rhodes and Strain, 2004). To the extent that institutions have treated and continue to treat whistleblowers with hostility, Dr. Olivieri's experiences may serve to effectively warn and silence future whistleblowers from protesting unethical practices they observe in their own research environments. It is notable that a discussion of the protections that should be afforded whistleblowers is conspicuously absent in TCPS2. Indeed, there is little indication that Canada will, in the near future, follow the lead of the United States in creating a Whistleblowers Bill of Rights.

Finally, the growth of industry-sponsored research has created new ethical issues around for-profit drug testing, including competitive enrolment and guinea pigging (the latter is further described in Box 14.2). **Competitive enrolment** is a method of recruiting participants to

competitive enrolment:
A method of recruiting participants to a research study that induces competition amongst different research sites by rewarding those that are first to meet their targets for recruiting a specific number of participants within a given time period.

guinea pigging:
Healthy individuals participating in clinical drug trials for pay.

BOX 14.2

IN THE NEWS

Guinea Pigging

The term *guinea pigging* first entered the mainstream vocabulary in January 2008, when an article by that name was published in *The New Yorker* magazine (Elliott, 2008). **Guinea pigging** refers to healthy individuals (overwhelmingly poor, sometimes students) who participate in clinical drug trials for pay.

In the past, most participants in drug trials were either medical students and personnel who at least intellectually understood the risks they faced or persons struggling with illnesses who might benefit from the drugs they tested. Over the last ten years, however, as drug testing and development have exploded and have largely shifted from non-profit to for-profit operations, the need to quickly find large numbers of research subjects has led to the widespread use of healthy subjects for pay in early trials of drugs. (If the drugs prove safe with healthy subjects, they are then tested for efficacy on ill subjects.)

These human guinea pigs can earn large fees for participating in research; studies that last for several weeks can pay several thousand dollars. The risks, though, are high. The obvious dangers come from the drugs themselves. In March 2006, for

example, six volunteers who participated in tests of a potential treatment for immune disorders were almost killed, and apparently all are now permanently disabled (Elliott, 2008). In addition, testing sometimes involves invasive and potentially dangerous procedures such as biopsies and endoscopies. Moreover, most clinical trials do not cover medical costs—let alone compensation for pain or lost wages—when volunteers are injured or become ill as a result of the experiments. Participating in drug trials can also be extremely unpleasant, requiring subjects to wear rectal probes, experience food or sleep deprivation, live for weeks in hospital-like environs, or the like.

In addition to the risks faced by volunteers, the public is also placed at risk when drugs are tested in these circumstances. When subjects participate because they need money, they may feel no qualms about, for example, ignoring research protocols, such as sneaking food or alcohol when they are supposed to fast or abstain. Similarly, when researchers are employed by for-profit corporations, they may be inclined to interpret results optimistically or to recruit homeless alcoholics who need money rather than spending the time needed to recruit a more representative sample.

a research study that induces competition among different research sites by rewarding those that are first to meet their targets for recruiting a specific number of participants within a given time period. The practice is of concern to the extent that these strategies may encourage researchers to subvert the consent process, as could occur if researchers subtly pressure subjects to participate in the study or inappropriately broaden the inclusion criteria (Caulfield, 2005). Such issues raise new concerns not only about the safety of research subjects but also about the credibility of the research enterprise itself.

Nevertheless, and despite the limitations of REBs, the rise of bioethics has curbed the most egregious abuses of human subjects. According to David Rothman:

> The experiments that Henry Beecher described could not now occur; even the most ambitious or confident investigator would not today put forward such protocols. Indeed, the transformation in research practices is most dramatic in the area that was once most problematic: research on incompetent and institutionalized subjects. The young, the elderly, the mentally disabled, and the incarcerated are not fair game for the investigator. Researchers no longer get to choose the martyrs for mankind. (1991: 251)

The Impact on Medical Education

One obvious result of the bioethics movement has been the incorporation of ethics training into medical education, with courses now common at medical schools throughout Canada. As critics have noted, however, those courses are too often divorced from real life, aimed at teaching students abstract ethical principles and legal norms through classroom lectures rather than practical instruction on how to negotiate the everyday ethical situations they might face. Not surprisingly, surveys of medical students generally find that they are dissatisfied with ethics training and feel ill-prepared to handle ethical dilemmas. Recent efforts by the University of Toronto to draw on the knowledge of bioethics experts to help both faculty and students become more aware of ethical issues and to more fully integrate ethical care into medical training suggest that the situation may be slowly improving (Howard, McKneally, and Levin, 2010).

At the same time, other observers have noted that courses in ethics will have limited effects because students who are already undergoing socialization to medical culture may no longer be able to identify ethically problematic aspects of that culture (Hafferty, 1998; Hafferty and Franks, 1994). Moreover, this strategy does not challenge the ways in which ethics are discounted in the "hidden curriculum" of medical practice and culture. For example, a structure that expects students both to provide care for patients *and* to learn techniques on patients without the patients' knowledge inherently teaches students to view patients at least partly as objects rather than as subjects. From this perspective, only through "the integration of ethical principles into the everyday work of both science and medicine" can we expect new doctors to adopt more ethical approaches to care (Hafferty and Franks, 1994: 868).

The Impact on Clinical Practice

At a fundamental level, the bioethics movement challenges doctors' clinical autonomy, for it "substitutes principles and general rules for the case-by-case analysis that has long characterized medical practice … and attempts to reformulate medical problems as moral, rather than technical, issues" (Zussman, 1992: 10–11).

According to Annas (1991), professional ethics committees emerged to counter this challenge. Annas argues that the true purpose of these committees is not to foster more ethical behaviour but to protect professional autonomy by providing clinicians with legal protection against accusations of unethical behaviour. These sentiments have also been expressed in Britain, where, despite enthusiasm for introducing CECs into the health care system, reservations about their ability to effectively balance the voices of patients and health care providers in the decision-making process persist (McLean, 2007).

Relatively few studies have looked at the impact of bioethics on actual clinical practices. One series of studies in the United States looked at the impact of New York's 1987 law establishing formal policies for writing "do not resuscitate" orders (orders forbidding health care workers from intervening if the lungs or heart of a terminally ill patient stop functioning). These studies found that after the law's passage, doctors significantly altered how they *documented* their actions but not how they *acted* (Zussman, 1992: 162). Similarly, studies have found that hospitals sharply limit access of patients, family, and non-medical staff to ethics consultations. As a result, consultations primarily function to provide additional institutional support to doctors confronted by families or patients they consider disruptive, such as those who challenge doctors' decisions regarding how aggressively to treat a given condition (Kelly et al., 1997; Orr and Moon, 1993). These findings have led researchers to conclude that the true purpose of ethics consultations is to reinforce doctors' power.

The most extensive study of the impact of bioethics on clinical practice appears in *Intensive Care: Medical Ethics and the Medical Profession* (1992), by sociologist Robert Zussman. Zussman spent more than two years observing and interviewing in the intensive care units of two hospitals. His research suggests both the impact and the limitations of the bioethics movement.

Although it might seem that doctors often want to use aggressive treatment despite the objections of patients and families, Zussman found that on intensive care wards the reverse is usually the case. Knowing that most of their patients will die, doctors on these wards often hesitate before beginning aggressive treatment, which might only escalate costs, increase their work as well as their patients' suffering, and prolong the dying process. Patients, however—and, more important, their families (for, in most cases, the patients are incapable of communicating)—often face a sudden and unexpected medical crisis. Unable to believe the situation hopeless, they demand that health care workers "do everything." In these situations, the doctors Zussman studied expressed allegiance to the principle that families have the right to make decisions regarding treatment. In practice, however, doctors found ways to assert their discretion, if no longer the authority they had in years past.

Doctors asserted their discretion in several ways. First, doctors made decisions without asking the family on the assumption that the family would agree with their decisions. Second, doctors sometimes ignored a family's stated decisions, arguing that it was cruel to force a family to make life-or-death decisions that would later cause them guilt or grief. Third, doctors might respect a family's wishes, but only after first shaping those wishes through selectively providing information. This information included defining the patient as terminally ill or not—a highly significant designation, for ethical guidelines permit health care workers to withhold or terminate treatment only for terminally ill patients. Fourth, when doctors failed to shape a family's wishes, the doctors could discount those wishes on the grounds that the family was too emotionally distraught to decide rationally.

Finally, and perhaps most importantly, doctors continued to assert their discretion by defining the decision to withhold or terminate treatment as a technical rather than an ethical problem. The following example from Zussman's research demonstrates this process:

> The Countryside ICU [Intensive Care Unit] staff was considering whether or not to write a Do Not Resuscitate order for Mr. Lake, a 73-year-old man who had been admitted to the unit with acute renal [kidney] failure, a gastrointestinal

bleed, pneumonia, and sepsis [infection]. Ken [the medical director of the ICU] asked what they should do "if the family wanted a full court press." One of the residents started to say what he thought were the "interesting ethical issues." But Ken cut him off, arguing that the decision depended entirely on prognostics: "There are no ethical issues…. I'm not an ethicist. I'm a doctor." When the resident attempted to distinguish different circumstances preceding codes [decisions not to resuscitate], Ken broke in again: "A code is a code. It's a medical decision, not an ethical decision." (Zussman, 1992: 150; ellipses in original)*

Once doctors succeeded in defining treatment decisions as purely technical issues, they could define the family's stated wishes as uneducated and irrelevant. Doctors could end discussion regarding treatment decisions by declaring it simply a technical fact that any treatment would be futile. Similarly, doctors might acknowledge families' general wishes regarding how aggressively treatment should proceed, but then define each specific intervention as a technical decision best left to doctors. Because most treatment decisions involve not dramatically pulling a plug but rather a series of small, minute-to-minute actions, leaving doctors in control of these "technical" matters gives doctors power far outweighing families' general statements regarding whether to pursue aggressive treatment.

Summing up his findings, Zussman writes:

> The picture I have drawn corresponds neither to an image of unbridled professional discretion nor to one of patients' rights triumphant. As many observers of contemporary medicine have argued, the discretion of physicians in clinical decisions (like the discretion of professionals in other fields) depends on their ability to make successful claims to the exclusive command of technical knowledge. Yet, while … physicians … make such claims, they do not always succeed either in convincing themselves that they are legitimate or in converting them to influence over patients and their families, for the claims of physicians are met by the counterclaims of patients and, more important, families…. The institutionalization of patients' rights, in law and in hospital policy, … empower[s] families when they do insist on doing everything. In such a situation, physicians may continue to exercise considerable influence and enjoy considerable discretion. By no means have they been reduced to the role of technicians and nothing more. But at the same time, they must, at the very least, take the wishes of patients and families into account. (1992: 159–160)

Case Study: Baby Joseph and the Ethics of Medical Futility

In the past, challenges to medical decision-making typically revolved around the **right to die,** where doctors who wanted to do everything possible were pitted against patients who resisted intrusive technologies. In contrast, the new paradigm represents the opposite conflict: patients who want everything done to save life versus doctors who are reluctant to perform futile interventions. Increasingly, doctors must decide whether the use of technologies that prolong but do not save life offers false hope to the patient and their family members and inflicts harm without benefit to the patient. Doctors must also weigh broader issues of equity by making decisions that fairly distribute finite health care resources. In every situation, these are heart-wrenching decisions for families and for doctors. But do doctors have the right to make these decisions independent of what the patient and their family would like? Should doctors or the patient and their family have the final say?

---

* R. Zussman, *Intensive care: Medical ethics and the medical profession*, Chicago: University of Chicago Press, 1992.

In the spring of 2010, a family living in Windsor, Ontario, was devastated to learn that their four-month-old baby, Joseph, had been diagnosed with a rare neurological disorder that had previously claimed the life of an older sibling. The situation became desperate a few short months later when Joseph stopped breathing and was rushed to the London Health Sciences Centre. There, doctors inserted a breathing tube and began to discuss the possibility that Joseph might one day be removed from life support. In the beginning of 2011, Joseph was declared to be in a persistent vegetative state with no hope of recovery, and doctors recommended to the family that Joseph be removed from life support. The family in turn requested that doctors insert a tracheotomy tube so that Joseph could die peacefully at home with his family.

Although a similar procedure had been performed on the sibling who had previously died, this time doctors refused to perform the procedure on the grounds of **medical futility**. That is, the doctors made the determination that even though a tracheotomy could prolong life, it was an invasive procedure that would not change the course of the disease nor improve Joseph's quality of life. To resolve the dispute, the case was sent to the Consent and Capacity Board of Ontario, an independent body that renders decisions when there is disagreement between doctors and their patients over treatment. When the board sided with the medical doctors, the family hired a lawyer and told their story to the media, where it attracted international attention. Various right-to-life and other interest groups, who saw this as a perfect example of the imposition of medical values on the worth of a human life, began to get involved. One group, Priests for Life, raised enough money to have Joseph transferred to a U.S. hospital, where he received a tracheotomy. In April 2011, Joseph, breathing on his own, was returned to his family in Windsor. On September 27, 2011, Joseph died, as his parents had always wanted, in the arms of his loving family.

A similar case is currently making its way through the courts. The family of Hassan Rasouli, a man who suffered brain damage in October 2010 as a result of infection following surgery, has opposed the medical decision to remove life support. Doctors at Toronto's Sunnybrook Health Sciences Centre determined that Mr. Rasouli was in a persistent vegetative state and felt that there was no medical purpose in keeping him alive. When the family disagreed with this decision, the doctors took their case to court, but lost. In June 2011, the Ontario Court of Appeal upheld this decision, stating that doctors do not have the unilateral right to make decisions about medical treatment but require the consent of the patient and family. In a surprising twist, Mr. Rasouli has since moved out of a vegetative state and responds to some stimuli, although his doctors insist that he is still minimally conscious and will never regain full consciousness. This case is now before the Supreme Court of Canada, which is expected to render a decision on the issue of whether a doctor requires the consent of patient and family to proceed with treatment and to provide a legal framework under which a patient in a vegetative state can be withdrawn from life support.

medical futility:
A judgment made by a physician to withhold or withdraw treatment on the basis that therapy is unlikely to increase the patient's probability of survival, may inflict harm without benefit to the patient, or will only result in a poor quality of life.

IMPLICATIONS

As we have seen, bioethics and sociology have much in common. At a very basic, if typically unacknowledged, level, bioethics, like sociology, is about power. The abuses of the Nazi doctors, for example, not only illuminate the horrors possible when ethical principles are ignored but also illustrate both how social groups can obtain power over others and how individuals can be harmed or even killed when this happens. Conversely, sociology, in similarly unacknowledged ways, is at a basic level an ethical enterprise. Underlying abstract, technical sociological discussions about the nature of society often lurk hidden assumptions about what society *should* be like and how society should be changed. These assumptions often draw on philosophies regarding justice, autonomy, human worth, and other basic ethical issues. Yet, in the same way that bioethicists often ignore the sociological implications of their work, sociologists often ignore the ethical implications of the questions they ask, the research they conduct, and the findings their research generates.

It seems, then, that bioethicists and sociologists can provide each other with broader perspectives that can only enrich our understanding of both fields—encouraging bioethicists to see not only individual cases but broader social and political issues and encouraging sociologists to see the world and their work in it as ethical as well as political and intellectual enterprises. These are issues that all of us should keep in mind as we seek our place in the world. Box 14.3 provides some suggestions for readers who are interested in pursuing a career related to health and health care.

BOX 14.3

Choosing Your Career

By this point in the term, undoubtedly some of you are just grateful that it is almost over. But others of you may now find that you are fascinated by the topic and wondering how you can somehow make a difference in this field. For those who are interested, four broad career options exist: clinical practice, administration, research and teaching, and policy work.

Many students take a course on the sociology of health, illness, and health care because they intend to become a health care practitioner of some sort. Now that you have reached the end of this term, you probably have a better idea than when you started of the costs and benefits of entering the different health care fields. Perhaps you now recognize that you are attracted to the professional autonomy as well as the art and science of medicine, or realize that you would be more comfortable in a health care field that offers a more holistic approach to care. Perhaps you have second thoughts about entering nursing given its struggles for professional autonomy, or find it more appealing now that you understand the intellectual challenges and financial rewards available to those who obtain masters-level training. No matter what health care occupation you might enter, you should now bring to your work a greater understanding of the underlying sources of health and illness; the culture of medicine; and the experiences of persons who live with illness, and of other health care consumers, as well as the impact of the larger health care delivery system on both consumers and providers. Working as a compassionate, ethical, and educated health care provider is an important way of making a better world, one patient at a time.

Other readers of this book may realize, when they think about their personalities, skills, and interests, that they are not really suited for the "hands-on" work of dealing directly with patients. For those who enjoy the nitty-gritty details of the business world, there are many opportunities to work in health care administration or in health care economics and analysis. Your goal, as students of the sociology of health, illness, and health care, will be to find a position that allows you to help *others* deliver high-quality, equitable health care.

A third option is to enter a career in research or teaching. Such a career requires that you be primarily fascinated by the process of generating knowledge (research), evaluating research conducted by others, and figuring out how to communicate research findings to others, whether through publications or in the classroom. Research positions can be found at all levels of government (from city departments to federal agencies such as Health Canada or Statistics Canada, in colleges and universities, and in non-profit organizations and "think tanks" such as the Canadian Centre for Policy Alternatives). In some of these positions, you would have the freedom to develop your own research and teaching agenda, while in others you would be assigned to a general field of study or specific research tasks. But in all cases you would have the satisfaction of generating and communicating important knowledge about health, illness, and health care.

Finally, those of you who are most interested in effecting change on a broader scale, and who have the requisite personalities and skills, should consider careers in law, government, or political advocacy. Perhaps a reader of this book will some day direct a non-profit organization that advocates for the rights of persons with disabilities, argue a right-to-life or right-to-die case before the Supreme Court of Canada, or successfully defeat legislation that seeks to erode the principles of the Canada Health Act.

Whatever path you choose, you *can* make a difference.

SUMMARY

LO-1   1.   Bioethics is the field of study that evaluates the moral and ethical dilemmas that scientists and doctors encounter in medical research and in the treatment of patients. Many of the issues bioethicists ponder revolve, whether explicitly or not, around the use and impact of power—a central concern of sociologists.

LO-2   2.   Although Canadian doctors have been required to subscribe to a Code of Ethics since 1868, historically doctors in Canada and elsewhere have conducted research and practised medicine in ways that would horrify modern bioethicists. One example was Dr. J. Marion Sims's use of black slaves as surgical guinea pigs, which paved the way for what is now recognized as the modern field of obstetrics.

LO-2   3.   Following the Nazi defeat, Allied countries prosecuted twenty-three doctors as part of the broader war crimes trials held in Nuremberg. These trials resulted in the development of the Nuremberg Code, a set of internationally recognized principles regarding the ethics of human experimentation; however, the Nuremberg Code was not a legally binding document and there were few consequences for medical doctors and researchers when these principles were violated.

LO-2   4.   Interest in bioethics grew substantially during the 1960s, sparked by popular and medical articles on kidney dialysis selection committees and on unethical medical research practices.

LO-2   5.   In failing to treat syphilis in a sample of poor black American men over a forty-year period, the Tuskegee Syphilis Study is one of the most cited examples of blatant disregard for human life in medical research and represents a turning point in the establishment of enforceable ethical principles. Canada was not immune to scandal either, as evidenced by public reaction and the successful lawsuits of those who had been subjected to involuntary sexual sterilization in the province of Alberta between 1928 and 1972.

LO-3   6.   In Canada, the need to regulate medical research and practice has resulted in the proliferation of a number of national agencies that oversee and develop policies to guide researchers as well as apply sanctions for those who violate those ethical guidelines.

LO-3   7.   In the courts, the issue of informed consent changed during the twentieth century to reflect a patient-based standard in which physicians must now take into account the patient's specific circumstances in disclosing the potential risks of a given treatment or procedure.

LO-4   8.   As federally mandated committees that review the ethics of all research proposed at a given institution, research ethics boards (REBs) are staffed with volunteers drawn from that institution and from the community who have diverse expertise in medical research, bioethics, and law.

LO-4   9.   Clinical ethics committees (CECs) are becoming more common in Canadian hospitals, but although they comprise health professionals including bioethicists, their decisions are not binding on medical practice.

LO-5   10.   The growth of the bioethics movement and the institutionalization of bioethics in hospitals and universities have made ethical issues more visible than ever before, but it is not clear whether these have resulted in greater protection for research participants and patients.

LO-5   11.   Some have suggested that the institutionalization of bioethics has created a bureaucracy of REBs that simply erects more hurdles that researchers must jump over before they can conduct their work; lacks consistency from one committee to another; and by failing to offer any protection to whistleblowers, places the interests of institutions over those of researchers and research participants.

LO-5   12.   Doctors are more aware of their ethical obligations to their patients but arguably not more knowledgeable about how to apply these ethics in medical practice. As the field of bioethics expands and new challenges emerge (e.g., medical futility), it is likely that doctors will face even greater scrutiny of their work in the future.

REVIEW QUESTIONS

1. What is the Nuremberg Code, and how and why did it come into existence?
2. What factors led to the emergence of the bioethics movement?
3. Why do researchers now consider the Tuskegee Syphilis Study and the Sexual Sterilization Act to have been unethical?
4. What impact has bioethics had on health care, medical education and on medical research?

CRITICAL THINKING QUESTIONS

1. What role does doctors' professional dominance play in creating ethical problems in medical care? What role does bioethics, as institutionalized in the Canadian health care system, play in limiting doctors' professional dominance?
2. What notable similarities and differences do you see between the behaviour of the medical community in the Alberta Eugenics Board and in the Nazi genocide?
3. You now hold a position of power in our health care system. (You choose which position.) What three changes could you realistically attempt to make so that health care would be provided more ethically? Justify your decisions.

KEY TERMS

bioethics (p. 347)
clinical ethics committees (CECs) (p. 354)
competitive enrolment (p. 357)
conflict of interest (p. 353)
eugenics (p. 348)
guinea pigging (p. 357)

informed consent (p. 349)
medical futility (p. 361)
Nuremberg Code (p. 349)
research ethics boards (REBs) (p. 353)
whistleblower (p. 350)

acculturation:
The process by which immigrants increasingly adopt the lifestyles and habits of their host country. (p. 67)

actuarial risk rating:
A system in which insurers try to maximize their financial gain by identifying and insuring only those populations that have low health risks. (p. 269)

acute illness:
Any illness that strikes suddenly and disappears rapidly (within a month or so). Examples include chicken pox, colds, and influenza. (p. 18)

advanced practice nurses:
Individuals who, after becoming registered nurses, additionally receive specialized postgraduate training. Includes nurse-midwives and nurse-practitioners. See *registered nurses.* (p. 301)

aesthetic surgery:
See *cosmetic surgery.* (p. 210)

age-adjusted rates:
Epidemiological data that have been manipulated, using standard statistical techniques, to eliminate any effects that arise because some populations include more older or younger persons than do others. Age adjustment allows us to compare populations with different age distributions. (p. 19)

agency:
The ability of individuals to make their own choices, free of any limitations placed on them by other people, culture, or social forces. Similar to the concept of free will. (p. 29)

allocative efficiency:
The distribution of resources that maximizes the welfare of the community. (p. 265)

allopathic doctors:
Early forerunners of contemporary medical doctors. Also known as regular doctors. (p. 231)

almshouse:
An institution, also known as a poorhouse, in which all public wards, including orphans, criminals, the disabled, and the insane, received custodial care. (p. 315)

ambulatory care doctors:
Physicians whose work takes place outside of hospitals, whether specialists or primary care practitioners. (p. 274)

antiretroviral drugs (ARVs):
Treatment with drugs that inhibit the ability of the human immunodeficiency virus (HIV) or other types of retroviruses to multiply in the body. (p. 135)

ARVs:
See *antiretroviral drugs.* (p. 135)

assistant doctors:
Chinese health care workers who receive three years of post-secondary training, similar to that of doctors, in both Western and traditional Chinese medicine. (p. 279)

assisted living facilities:
Institutions, typically consisting of small, private apartments, that offer two levels of services: (1) basic medical and nursing services and help with basic tasks of daily living for disabled residents and (2) comfortable living situations and social activities for healthy residents. (p. 331)

avoidable deaths:
Deaths that could have been prevented with timely access to medical care. (p. 76)

baby boom generation:
Those born between 1946 and 1965 in Canada. (p. 50)

bioconservatism:
The belief that the use of science and technology to enhance and expand the capacities of humans may be morally problematic and may fundamentally erode what it means to be human. (p. 209)

bioethics:
The study of the moral and ethical dilemmas that scientists and doctors encounter in medical research and in the treatment of patients. (p. 347)

biographical disruption:
The process that occurs when, confronted with a serious or life-threatening condition, an individual (1) becomes aware of the ways in which the body asserts itself in daily life, (2) questions taken-for-granted explanatory frameworks for what life means and what one hopes to achieve in life, and (3) begins to respond and mobilize resources that are sensitive to their altered situation. (p. 186)

biological embedding:
Experiences that get under the skin and alter human biological processes. (p. 82)

biological reductionism:
One of four operating assumptions of a medical model approach that postulates that illness is an objective biological condition that is located within the body. (p. 4)

body as machine:
One of four assumptions of a medical model approach that contends that the body is comparable to a machine with unique functioning parts that can be fixed or replaced when broken. (p. 5)

body project:
The shaping of one's body to express identity and to meet cultural norms of beauty and health. (p. 205)

brain-technology interface device:
A device implanted within the brain that enables signals from the brain to direct some external activity, such as control of a cursor or a prosthetic limb. (p. 214)

CAM:
See *complementary and alternative medicine.* (p. 191)

capitation:
A system in which doctors are paid a set annual fee for each patient in their practice, regardless of how many times they see their patients or what services the doctors provide for their patients. (p. 270)

CECs:
See *clinical ethics committees.* (p. 354)

challenging:
Rejecting the social norms that attach stigma to a behaviour or condition, including illness or disability. See *stigma.* (p. 196)

chaos story:
One of Frank's three types of narrative reconstruction, which is about suffering that makes an individual unable to imagine a life that gets better. (p. 188)

Children's Health Insurance Program (CHIP):
The joint federal-state health insurance program for children in families whose incomes are modest but too high to be eligible for Medicaid. (p. 269)

CHIP:
See *Children's Health Insurance Program.* (p. 269)

chiropractors:
Health care practitioners who specialize in spinal manipulation, trace illness and disability to misalignments of the spine, and believe spinal manipulation can cure a wide range of acute and chronic health problems. (p. 306)

chronic illness:
Illness that develops in an individual gradually or is present from birth and that will probably continue at least for several months and possibly until the person dies. Examples include muscular dystrophy, asthma, and diabetes. (p. 18)

chronic obstructive pulmonary disease (COPD):
A progressive lung disease that makes it difficult to breathe. Chronic bronchitis and emphysema are common examples of COPD. (p. 129)

chronic strains:
Enduring stressors that have no specific moment of onset, but typically develop slowly, lying beneath the surface until they are recognized as problematic aspects of people's environments or roles. (p. 37)

clinical ethics committees (CECs):
Committees located within health care institutions such as hospitals and nursing homes whose purpose is to provide education, counsel, and support on ethical issues related to patient care. (p. 354)

clinical pharmacy:
A subfield of pharmacy in which pharmacists participate actively in decisions regarding drug treatment. (p. 303)

colonization:
The process of subjugating and dispossessing indigenous peoples by foreign peoples who settle and build colonies on the lands of indigenous peoples. (p. 61)

commodification:
The process of turning things or people into products that can be bought or sold. (p. 207)

community treatment orders (CTOs):
Legal provisions by which a physician can require a person who has a mental illness to follow a course of treatment (typically medication and regular doctor visits) while living in the community. (p. 169)

competitive enrolment:
A method of recruiting participants to a research study that induces competition amongst different research sites by rewarding those that are first to meet their targets for recruiting a specific number of participants within a given time period. (p. 357)

complementary and alternative medicine (CAM):
Diverse systems of diagnosis, treatment, and prevention based on philosophies and techniques other than those used in conventional Western medicine. (p. 191)

confirmation bias:
The tendency to selectively attend to and favour information that supports one's beliefs and discount information that does not fit in with one's beliefs. (p. 115)

conflict of interest:
Professional misconduct that occurs when professional judgment concerning a primary interest (such as a patient's welfare or the validity of research) tends to be unduly influenced by a secondary interest (such as financial gain). (p. 353)

conflict theory:
The view that society is held together by power and coercion, with dominant groups imposing their will on subordinate groups. (p. 8)

contested illness:
Any collection of distressing, painful symptoms that occur together and that laypeople assume constitute an illness, even though many doctors disagree. (p. 165)

control:
A process through which researchers statistically eliminate the potential influence of extraneous factors. For example, because social class and race often go together, researchers who want to investigate the impact of social class have to be sure that they are not really seeing the impact of race. To study the impact of social class on mental illness, therefore, researchers would have to look separately at the relationship between social class and mental illness among Caucasians and then at the relationship among Blacks to control for any effect of race. (p. 12)

convergence hypothesis:
The thesis that health care systems become increasingly similar over time because of similar scientific, technological, economic, and epidemiological pressures. (p. 259)

copayment:
Under some forms of health insurance, an unreimbursable fee that individuals must pay each time they see a health care provider. Fees can range from nominal sums to 20% of all costs. (p. 271)

COPD:
See *chronic obstructive pulmonary disease.* (p. 129)

cosmetic surgery:
Procedures that alter the surface or shape of the body for the purposes of enhancement. Also known as aesthetic surgery. (p. 210)

covering:
Attempting to deflect attention from deviance, including illnesses or disabilities. (p. 196)

critical period:
A window of opportunity during development in which a particular skill or characteristic is believed to be most readily acquired, and that if missed, will either not be as easily acquired or result in permanent deficit. (p. 82)

CTOs:
See *community treatment orders.* (p. 169)

cumulative advantage hypothesis:
The process by which initial comparative advantages in a certain domain beget subsequent advantages that systematically widen differences over time. (p. 92)

cyborg:
A hybrid entity that breaches established boundaries, such as those between life and death, or human and machine. (p. 209)

death brokering:
The process through which medical authorities make deaths explainable, culturally acceptable, and individually meaningful. (p. 339)

decarceration:
The broad movement by the state to control the costs of institutional care by moving away from the residential segregation of deviant groups, including criminals, juvenile delinquents, and those with mental illness, and turning instead to less costly forms of social control. (p. 326)

deconstruction:
A postmodern approach that dismisses singular understandings of the world, embracing interpretations that are fluid and multiple, including those that have an inherent contradiction. (p. 204)

defensive medicine:
Tests and procedures that doctors perform primarily to protect themselves against lawsuits rather than to protect their patients' health. (p. 272)

deinstitutionalization:
The process of reducing the number of people treated in mental hospitals and the psychiatric wards of public hospitals by shifting their care to community-based mental health services. (p. 324)

delisting:
The removal of a specific medical procedure or health care service from the list of services covered under a provincial health care plan. (p. 244)

demedicalization:
The process through which a condition or behaviour becomes defined as a natural condition or process rather than an illness. (p. 169)

depersonalization:
The process through which an individual comes to feel less than fully human or comes to be viewed by others as less than fully human. (p. 326)

depoliticize:
To define a situation in a way that hides or minimizes the political and social context of that situation. (p. 5)

deviance:
Behaviour that violates a particular culture's norms or expectations for proper behaviour and therefore results in negative social sanctions. See *negative social sanctions.* (p. 162)

deviance disavowal:
The process through which individuals attempt to prove that, despite their apparent deviance, they are no different from other people. (p. 196)

Diagnostic and Statistical Manual (DSM):
A manual published by the American Psychiatric Association and used by mental health workers to assign diagnoses to

clients. Generally, this manual must be used if mental health workers want to obtain reimbursement for their services from insurance providers. (p. 219)

direct-to-consumer advertising (DTCA):
The use of mass media (e.g., television, newspapers, magazines, and the Internet) by the pharmaceutical industry to promote drugs, medical devices, and other products that require a prescription to the general public. (p. 166)

disability:
A restriction or inability to perform an activity in the manner or within the range considered normal for a human being, mostly resulting from impairment (WHO definition). OR Restrictions or lack of ability to perform activities resulting from the interplay between physical, intellectual, and sensory limitations; social responses to these limitations; and the built or social environment. (p. 177)

disclosing:
Making one's deviance more widely known by telling others about it or making it more visible. (p. 183)

discrimination:
Differential and unequal treatment grounded in prejudice. See *prejudice*. (p. 180)

disease:
A biological problem within an organism. (p. 17)

doctrine of specific etiology:
One of four operating assumptions of a medical model approach asserting that for each disease there is a specific cause. (p. 4)

double burden of malnutrition:
A situation where high rates of undernutrition, particularly among children, persist even as there is a rapid increase in the rate of people who are overweight. (p. 143)

DSM:
See *Diagnostic and Statistical Manual*. (p. 219)

DTCA:
See *direct-to-consumer advertising*. (p. 166)

dysfunctional:
Threatening to undermine social stability. (p. 170)

eclectics:
Those who practised a form of botanical medicine in North America for nearly two hundred years, involving the complex combination of concentrated plant extracts to treat illness. (p. 232)

EFM:
See *electronic fetal monitor*. (p. 339)

electronic fetal monitor (EFM):
A technology that visually correlates the second-by-second fetal heart rate with the strength and periodicity of uterine contractions on a screen or computer printout. (p. 339)

electronic health record:
A lifetime health record of an individual that is accessible online from many separate, interoperable automated systems within an electronic network. (p. 287)

endemic:
Referring to diseases that appear at a more or less stable rate over time within a given population. (p. 19)

entrepreneurial system:
A system based on capitalism and free enterprise. (p. 268)

environmental dispossession:
The process through which aboriginal peoples' access to the resources of their traditional environments is reduced. (p. 64)

epidemic:
Either a sudden increase in the rate of a disease or the first appearance of a new disease. (p. 19)

epidemiological transition:
The shift from a society burdened by infectious and parasitic diseases and in which life expectancy is low to one characterized by chronic and degenerative diseases and high life expectancy. (p. 21)

epidemiology:
The study of the distribution of a disease within a population. (p. 17)

equity in access:
The ability to obtain health care services on the basis of need rather than ability to pay or any other characteristic. (p. 261)

ethnicity:
Cultural affiliation of a group sharing a common culture, language, ancestry, nationality or beliefs. (p. 67)

eugenics:
The theory that the population should be "improved" through selective breeding and birth control. (p. 348)

evidence-based medicine:
The use of medical therapies whose efficacy has been confirmed by large, randomized, controlled clinical studies. (p. 296)

extra-billing:
Billing patients for the difference between the amount provincial governments have agreed to pay for a given procedure and the amount the doctor desires to charge for that procedure. (p. 239)

false positive:
A test result that indicates a disease or condition is present, when in reality, there is no disease. (p. 59)

family instability hypothesis:
The hypothesis that the turbulence associated with multiple changes in family structure cumulatively erodes health and well-being to a greater extent and in a qualitatively different way than a single change in family structure. (p. 117)

family-to-work conflict (FWC):
The extent to which home life interferes with the responsibilities and expectations at one's place of work. (p. 118)

fee-for-service compensation:
The practice of paying doctors for each health care service they provide, rather than paying them a salary. (p. 237)

fee-for-service insurance:
Insurance that reimburses patients for all or part of the costs of the health care services they have purchased. (p. 270)

feminization of aging:
The steady rise in the proportion of the population that is female in each older age group. Manifested in the fact that women constitute a larger proportion of the elderly than of younger age groups. (p. 52)

fetal programming hypothesis:
The supposition that development of the fetus can be shaped by environmental events, such as maternal malnutrition, that will have a permanent impact on the health of the individual, including into adulthood. (p. 83)

financially progressive:
Describes any system in which poorer persons pay a smaller proportion of their income for a given good or service than do wealthier persons. (p. 240)

first dollar coverage:
An insurance plan under which the third-party payer assumes liability for covered services as soon as the first dollar of expense for such services is incurred. (p. 239)

Flexner Report:
The report on the state of American and Canadian medical education produced in 1910 by Abraham Flexner for the Carnegie Foundation. This report identified serious deficiencies in medical education and helped to produce substantial improvements in that system. (p. 234)

food security:
Physical and economic access for all individuals at all times to sufficient, safe, and nutritious food to meet their dietary needs and food preferences for an active and healthy lifestyle. (p. 86)

Fordism:
A method of producing goods that combines the principles of scientific management with an automated assembly line to achieve even greater efficiency. (p. 103)

fundamental cause:
Any social condition that (1) influences a wide range of health conditions, (2) operates through a number of different intervening mechanisms, (3) is associated with resources that can be used to protect health, and (4) maintains a persisting association with health over time even as intervening mechanisms are replaced and new ones take their place. (p. 35)

FWC:
See *family-to-work conflict*. (p. 118)

gender:
The social categories of masculine and feminine and the social expectations regarding masculinity and femininity that we are expected to follow based on our assigned sex. (p. 53)

germ theory:
A theory that proposes that infectious diseases are caused by the activity of microorganisms invading the human body. (p. 25)

globalization:
The process through which ideas, resources, and persons increasingly operate within a worldwide rather than a local framework. (p. 23)

guinea pigging:
Healthy individuals participating in clinical drug trials for pay. (p. 357)

harm reduction:
Public health programs, policies, and practices designed to reduce the harmful consequences associated with illicit drug use and other high-risk activities for people who are unable or unwilling to stop. (p. 241)

health belief model:
A model predicting that individuals will follow medical advice when they (1) believe they are susceptible to a particular health problem, (2) believe the health problem they risk is a serious one, (3) believe compliance will significantly reduce their risk, and (4) do not perceive any significant barriers to compliance. (p. 28)

health lifestyle theory:
A theory that attempts to predict why groups adopt patterns of healthy or unhealthy behaviour by showing how demographic circumstances and cultural memberships combine with socialization and experiences to produce both life chances and life choices. These life chances and choices in turn lead to habitual dispositions toward healthy or unhealthy behaviours, which then lead to actual behaviours. (p. 29)

health maintenance organizations (HMOs):
Organizations that provide health care based on prepaid group insurance. Patients pay a fixed yearly fee in exchange for a full range of health care services, including hospital care and doctor's services. (p. 269)

health promotion:
The process of enabling people to increase control over, and to improve, their health. (p. 31)

health social movements:
Informal networks of individuals who band together to collectively challenge health policy, politics, beliefs, or practices. (p. 194)

healthy immigrant effect:
A phenomenon in which new immigrants are in relatively better health than the native-born residents of the country to which they immigrate. (p. 67)

heroic medicine:
An aggressive system of treatment used by allopathic doctors during the nineteenth century that emphasized curing illnesses by purging the body through bloodletting, causing extreme vomiting, or using repeated laxatives and diuretics. See *allopathic doctors.* (p. 233)

HIV (human immunodeficiency virus):
The virus that causes AIDS. (p. 24)

HIV/AIDS:
The term that summarizes all stages of disease in humans caused by HIV infection. The disease harms individuals' health by gradually destroying their body's immune system. (p. 23)

HMOs:
See *health maintenance organizations.* (p. 269)

holistic treatment:
Treatment based on the premise that all aspects of an individual's life and body are interconnected, so that to treat a sick individual effectively, health care workers must look at all aspects of the body, as well as at the individual's psychological and social functioning. (p. 298)

home care:
An array of services that enable clients who are incapacitated in whole or in part to live at home, often with the effect of preventing, delaying, or substituting for long-term care or acute care alternatives. (p. 331)

homeopathic doctors:
Early health practitioners who treated illnesses with extremely dilute solutions of drugs that, at full strength, produced similar symptoms to a given illness. (p. 231)

hospices:
Institutions designed to meet the needs of the dying. (p. 333)

human immunodeficiency virus:
See *HIV.* (p. 23)

illness:
The social experience of having a disease. (p. 17)

illness behaviour:
The process of defining, interpreting, and otherwise responding to symptoms and deciding what actions to take. (p. 184)

illness behaviour model:
A model that predicts the circumstances in which individuals are most likely to seek medical care. According to this model, individuals are most likely to seek medical care if their symptoms are frequent or persistent, visible, and severe enough to interfere with daily activities and if they lack alternative explanations for the symptoms. (p. 184)

immersion, illness as:
A situation in which illness becomes so demanding that a person must structure his or her life around it. (p. 187)

impairment:
Any temporary or permanent loss or abnormality of a body structure or function, whether physiological or psychological (WHO definition). (p. 177)

in vitro fertilization:
A specialized technique by which an ovum (egg) is fertilized by sperm outside the body, with the resulting embryo later implanted in the uterus for gestation. (p. 216)

incidence:
The number of new cases of an illness or health problem occurring within a given population during a given time period (e.g., the number of Canadian children with asthma in 2012). (p. 18)

income inequality:
A measurement of the distribution of income that highlights the gap between those making most of the income in a population and those making the least. (p. 92)

income inequality hypothesis:
The supposition that for low-income countries, absolute measures of income are stronger predictors of the health of the population, but among high-income countries, relative income differences are the more important predictors of population health. (p. 93)

individualize:
To define a situation in a way that focuses attention only on the individual. (p. 5)

infant mortality rate:
The number of deaths of babies under one year of age per 1,000 live births. (p. 19)

informed consent:
Voluntary agreement to participate in medical research or to receive a medical procedure or treatment, with a full understanding of the potential risks and benefits. (p. 349)

inpatient:
A hospital patient who is formally admitted and kept overnight. (p. 324)

institution:
An enduring social structure that meets basic human needs, such as the family, education, religion, or medicine (taken in its entirety). (p. 164)

interruption, illness as:
A situation in which illness is experienced as only a small and temporary part of one's life. (p. 187)

intimate terrorism:
A form of intimate partner violence, committed mainly by men, in which repeated acts of physical aggression and abusive behaviour are used to dominate and control one's partner. (p. 60)

intrusion, illness as:
A situation in which illness demands time, accommodation, and attention and forces one to live from day to day. (p. 187)

irregular practitioners:
Nineteenth-century health care practitioners other than allopathic doctors, such as homeopaths, midwives, eclectics, barber-surgeons, bonesetters, and patent medicine makers. (p. 231)

job control:
The degree to which tasks in the workplace are varied and require skill and workers are able to decide for themselves how best to perform tasks. (p. 109)

job demands:
The extent to which workers feel that they are free from time constraints to perform a task and are not overwhelmed with too many or conflicting tasks. (p. 109)

latency:
The amount of time between exposure to a risk factor and the initial signs of illness. (p. 90)

licensed practical nurses (LPNs):
Individuals, not registered nurses, who assist nurses primarily with the custodial care of patients. LPNs usually have completed approximately one or two years of classroom and clinical training. (p. 300)

LICOs:
See *low-income cutoffs.* (p. 81)

life expectancy:
The average number of years that individuals in a given population and born in a given year are expected to live. (p. 19)

lifeworld:
The everyday needs of people and ways in which they interact and live their lives. (p. 192)

limited practitioners:
Occupational groups, such as chiropractors, midwives, and optometrists, that confine their work to a limited range of treatments and certain parts of the body. (p. 303)

long-term care facilities:
Facilities that primarily provide nursing and custodial care to many individuals over a long period of time. (p. 328)

low-income cutoffs (LICOs):
An income threshold, varying by family and community size, where a household is considered poor if it spends 20% more of its income on food, shelter, and clothing than the average household, leaving less income available for other expenses, such as health, education, transportation, and recreation. (p. 81)

LPNs:
See *licensed practical nurses.* (p. 300)

lunacy:
Intermittent periods of bizarre behaviour relieved by periods of reason that are assumed to be caused by the phases of the moon. (p. 322)

lunatic asylum:
The official name given to the first institutions in Canada that treated people with mental illness. (p. 322)

magic bullet approach:
To prevent or cure illness by attacking one specific etiological factor, usually with drugs. (p. 4)

malnutrition:
The condition that develops when the body does not get a sufficient amount of food or the right nutrients it needs to function properly. (p. 127)

managed care:
A system that controls health care spending by monitoring closely how health care providers treat patients and where and when patients receive their health care. (p. 270)

marginal practitioners:
Occupational groups that offer health care services and have low social status. (p. 308)

master status:
A status viewed by others as so important that it overwhelms all other information about that individual. For example, if we know someone as the local scoutmaster, know he is fluent in several languages and likes to play chess, and then learn he is gay, we might start thinking about him and interacting with him solely on the basis of his sexual orientation, essentially forgetting or ignoring the other information we know about him. (p. 326)

maternal mortality:
The death of a woman who was pregnant or within 42 days of termination of pregnancy, and whose death was caused or aggravated by the pregnancy or its management. (p. 19)

maternal mortality ratio:
The number of maternal deaths in the population per 100,000 live births during a given time period. (p. 133)

median:
The value or number representing the midpoint of a distribution that is ordered from lowest to highest. (ch. 3) (p. 62)

Medicaid:
The joint federal-state health insurance program that pays the costs of health care for people with incomes below a certain (very low) amount. (p. 268)

medical dominance:
The freedom of allopathic physicians from control by other occupations or groups and the ability to control other occupations working in the sphere of health care. (p. 235)

medical futility:
A judgment made by a physician to withhold or withdraw treatment on the basis that therapy is unlikely to increase the patient's probability of survival, may inflict harm without benefit to the patient, or will only result in a poor quality of life. (p. 361)

medical model of disability:
A model of disability that assumes disability stems solely from forces within the individual mind or body, rather than from constraints built into the environment or into social attitudes. (p. 177)

medical model of illness:
The belief that illness is a biological condition that occurs exclusively within the sphere of the human body, with the direct implication that one need look no further than the individual to determine cause and cure. As such, a medical model approach both individualizes and depoliticizes the problem of death and illness. See also *individualize* and *depoliticize*. (p. 4)

medical norms:
Expectations doctors have about how they should act, think, and feel. (p. 293)

medicalization:
The process through which a condition or behaviour becomes defined as a medical problem requiring a medical solution, or through which the definition of an illness is broadened to cover a wider population. (p. 164)

Medicare:
The federal insurance program, based on the Social Security system, that offers hospital insurance and medical insurance to those over age 65 and to permanently disabled persons. (p. 269)

menstrual suppression:
The off-label use of oral contraceptive pills in which, rather than following a twenty-one-day phase of active pills followed by seven days of placebo pills, active pills are continuously taken so as to reduce the frequency of menstruation or eliminate bleeding altogether. (p. 207)

miasma theory of disease:
A theory of disease causation that posits that disease is caused by foul smells that emanate from soil, water, or air. (p. 158)

mind-body dualism:
One of four operating assumptions of a medical model approach that refers to the Cartesian philosophy that bodies and minds are uniquely different entities in that bodies have a material presence, but minds do not. (p. 4)

minority group:
A group that, because of its cultural or physical characteristics, is considered inferior and subjected to differential and unequal treatment. (p. 179)

moderators:
Resources that can be mustered to combat stressors and minimize their impact on health. (p. 38)

moral status:
A status that identifies in society's eyes whether a person is good or bad, worthy or unworthy. (p. 161)

moral treatment:
A nineteenth-century practice aimed at curing persons with mental illness by treating them with kindness and giving them opportunities for both work and play. (p. 323)

morbidity:
Symptoms, illnesses, or impairments. (p. 18)

mortality:
Deaths. (p. 18)

mortification:
A process, occurring in total institutions, through which a person's prior self-image is partially or totally destroyed and replaced by a personality suited for life in the institution. See *total institutions*. (p. 326)

narrative reconstruction:
Stories that one tells about one's experiences of illness that not only act as a form of self-repair but, because stories draw on cultural understandings of illness, make it possible to create bonds and shared meanings with others about illness. (p. 188)

National Health Service (NHS):
A system in which the government directly pays all costs of health care for its citizens. (p. 276)

negative social sanctions:
Punishments meted out to those considered deviant by society. Can range from ridicule and isolation to imprisonment and execution. (p. 162)

new social movements:
Groups of individuals who reject modern society's emphasis on science and rationality, value human interaction, and hope to create a more humane society primarily by living their lives in ways that reflect their ideals rather than through organized political activity. (p. 192)

NHS:
See *National Health Service*. (p. 276)

normalize:
Make something seem like the normal course of events. In the context of medical error, this refers to emphasizing how medical errors can happen to anyone. In the context of mental illness, this refers to explaining to oneself and others how unusual behaviour is not really a sign of mental illness. (p. 322)

norms:
Social expectations for appropriate behaviour. (p. 161)

Nuremberg Code:
A set of internationally recognized principles regarding the ethics of human experimentation that emerged during the post–World War II Nuremberg trials for medical crimes against humanity. The code stipulates that researchers must have a medically justifiable purpose; do all within their power to protect their subjects from harm; and ensure that their subjects give voluntary, informed consent. (p. 349)

nurse-midwives:
Registered nurses who receive additional formal, nationally accredited training in midwifery. (p. 301)

nurse-practitioners:
Registered nurses who are prepared, through advanced education and clinical training, to provide a wide range of health care services that would normally be performed by a medical doctor. (p. 301)

off-label use:
Taking prescription medication for purposes other than the condition it has been approved to treat. (p. 207)

open access:
The practice of providing unrestricted access via the Internet to peer-reviewed scholarly journal articles. (p. 289)

organ transplant:
A surgical operation in which a failing or damaged organ in the human body is removed and replaced with a functioning organ. (p. 214)

outpatient:
A hospital patient who is neither formally admitted nor kept overnight. (p. 319)

overweight:
When an individual is above the average weight for height. (p. 143)

pandemic:
A worldwide epidemic. See *epidemic*. (p. 19)

pass:
To hide one's deviance (such as illnesses or disabilities) from others. (p. 195)

patent:
A legal monopoly that the state grants to an inventor, preventing others from using, making, or selling an invention for a set period of time. (p. 218)

peer-to-peer health care:
Going online to find others who have similar health concerns. (p. 194)

pharmaceutical determinism:
The existence of prescription medication for a condition is used to argue for the biological existence of that condition. (p. 165)

phenotype:
The observable physical or biochemical characteristics of an organism, as determined by both genetic makeup and environmental influences. (p. 53)

physician extenders:
Health care providers who have less education than physicians but who can, at lower costs, take over some of the tasks traditionally done by physicians. (p. 278)

placebo:
Anything offered as a cure that has no known biological effect. Approximately 30% of the time, placebos will produce cures through their psychological effects. (p. 192)

population health model:
A theory that posits that health and illness are determined by the full range of individual and collective factors and involve a complex interplay among biological, psychological, environmental, social, economic, and political factors. (p. 32)

positive social sanctions:
Rewards of any sort, from good grades to public esteem. (p. 162)

post-traumatic stress disorder (PTSD):
An anxiety disorder that develops following exposure to a stressful event and is generally characterized by intrusions, avoidance, and hyperarousal. (p. 219)

power:
The ability to get others to do what one wants, whether willingly or unwillingly. (p. 7)

preimplantation genetic diagnosis (PGD):
An assisted reproductive technology that allows an embryo created through in vitro fertilization to be tested for genetic abnormalities. (p. 217)

prejudice:
The unwarranted suspicion, dislike of, or disdain toward individuals because they belong to a particular group, whether defined by ethnicity, religion, or some other characteristic. (p. 179)

prevalence:
Total number of cases of an illness or health problem within a given population at a particular point in time (for example, the number of persons living in Canada who have arthritis). This includes both those newly diagnosed and those diagnosed earlier who still have the disease. See *incidence*. (p. 18)

primary care:
Health care provided by physicians (such as family care doctors) and others who are trained to offer treatment and prevention services when individuals first seek health care and, ideally, as part of an ongoing provider-patient relationship. (p. 163)

privatization of health care:
The shift toward encouraging the private purchase of health care; the private, for-profit practice of medicine; and, in general, the operation of market forces in health care. (p. 244)

profession:
An occupation that (1) has the autonomy to set its own educational and licensing standards and to police its members for incompetence or malfeasance; (2) has its own technical, specialized knowledge, learned through extended, systematic training; and (3) has the public's confidence that it follows a code of ethics and works more from a sense of service than from a desire for profit. (p. 286)

professional socialization:
The process of learning the skills, knowledge, and values of an occupation. (p. 294)

professionalization:
The process through which an occupation achieves professional status. (p. 285)

pseudodisease:
A condition diagnosed as disease based solely on test results but that will never cause health problems for the diagnosed individual. (p. 298)

psychopharmacological revolution:
The dramatic change in the treatment of the mentally ill from the 1950s onward when the evidence of chemically induced behavioural change convinced psychiatrists that mental illness was primarily a biological condition of the brain that could be treated with medication rather than psychoanalysis and other forms of therapy. (p. 325)

quest story:
One of Frank's three types of narrative reconstruction, which seeks to find meaning in illness, whether or not recovery is attainable. (p. 188)

racialization:
The process by which society attributes social significance to groups on superficial physical grounds, by pairing apparent physical characteristics with negative social attributes and creating the perception that there are natural differences between racialized groups. (p. 61)

rate:
The proportion of a population that experiences a given condition or certain circumstance. (p. 18)

rationing:
Any mechanism that allows people to go without beneficial health care services. (p. 25)

REBs:
See *research ethics boards*. (p. 353)

reconstructive surgery:
Surgical intervention to restore or repair function or normal appearance as a result of catastrophic injury or birth defect. (p. 210)

reductionistic treatment:
Treatment based on the assumption that each part can be treated separately from the whole, in the same way that an air filter can be replaced in a car without worrying whether the problem with the air filter has caused or stemmed from problems in the car's electrical system. (p. 298)

regionalization:
The organization of all health care institutions and agencies in a given geographical area under a single administrative board. (p. 246)

registered nurses (RNs):
Individuals who have received at least two years of nursing training, and more commonly a four-year bachelor's degree, and passed national licensure requirements. (p. 300)

registered psychiatric nurses (RPNs):
Registered nurses who are trained to deal specifically with clients with mental illness. (p. 301)

regular doctors:
Nineteenth-century forerunners of contemporary medical doctors. Also known as allopathic doctors. See *allopathic doctors*. (p. 231)

repetitive strain injury (RSI):
The injuries to tendons or nerves that often result from repetitive movements and that express themselves as pain, numbness and tingling in the affected body part. (p. 107)

reproductive technology:
Medical developments that allow doctors to control the process of human conception and fetal development. (p. 216)

reprofessionalization:
The process of regaining former professional status. (p. 303)

research ethics boards (REBs):
Federally mandated committees that are locally responsible for reviewing the ethics of research projects involving human subjects in their respective institutions. (p. 353)

residents:
Individuals who have graduated medical school and received their MD degrees but are now engaged in further on-the-job training needed before they can enter independent practice. (p. 293)

restitution story:
One of Frank's three types of narrative reconstruction, which celebrates triumph over illness, as achieved through both medical intervention and the personal perseverance of the person who has been healed. (p. 188)

restless leg syndrome:
A sleeping disorder characterized by twitchiness in the legs when one lies down. (p. 223)

revolving door syndrome:
A continuing cycle in which short-term hospitalization in a psychiatric unit is followed by release into a community setting

that lacks the appropriate resources, precipitating relapse and a new crisis situation requiring hospitalization. (p. 327)

right to die:
The right to make decisions concerning one's own death. (p. 334)

RNs:
See *registered nurses*. (p. 300)

role strain:
Any problem that individuals experience in fulfilling one of their social roles, including one's role as worker, parent, student, and so on. (p. 37)

RPNs:
See *registered psychiatric nurses*. (p. 301)

RSI:
See *repetitive strain injury*. (p. 107)

scientific management:
A method of producing goods that emphasized making people work more efficiently by breaking down a large task into its smallest components and assigning each component to a worker who had been instructed on how the work should be done and how long it should take. (p. 103)

second shift:
The daily chores that still awaited women when they returned home from a full day of paid work. (p. 105)

self-fulfilling prophecy:
A situation in which individuals become what they are expected to be. For example, when it is assumed that no girls can throw a ball properly, girls might never be taught to do so, might never think it worth trying on their own, and thus might never learn to do so. (p. 325)

sex:
The biological categories of male and female, to which we are assigned based on our chromosomal structure and physical appearance: those who have two X chromosomes and a vagina are sexually female; those with one X and one Y chromosome and a penis are sexually male. (p. 53)

sex role hypothesis:
The supposition that the consequences associated with enacting a given social role will depend on the sex of the incumbent. (p. 113)

sick role:
An institutionalized mechanism in which illness becomes recognized and legitimated through the interaction of doctor and patient, allowing the sick person to step away from their responsibilities for a temporary period to recover from illness. (p. 7)

sickness funds:
German insurance programs offered by non-profit groups to serve a given occupation, geographic location, or employer. Also known as social insurance. (p. 274)

single-payer system:
A health care system in which the medical costs of the entire population are financed by one source, usually the government. (p. 240)

situational couple violence:
The most common form of intimate partner violence, occurring when conflict between partners erupts into aggression and violence. This form of intimate partner violence is gender-symmetric, with men and women equally likely to resort to violence. (p. 60)

slum:
An informal settlement that is densely populated and characterized by substandard housing and inadequate access to clean water and sanitation. (p. 149)

social capital:
Those aspects of social ties that both provide and produce resources that can be used by individuals and groups within a social network. (p. 89)

social causation:
A theory holding that social factors are causally implicated in producing disease and death. (p. 85)

social construction:
Ideas created by a social group, as opposed to something that is objectively or naturally given. (p. 163)

social constructionism:
The view that reality is socially defined and created through meaning-making and interpretive practices. (p. 8)

social control:
Means used by a social group to ensure that individuals conform to social norms and to ensure that the existing balance of power is maintained. Social control can be formal (such as execution or commitment to a mental hospital) or informal (such as ridicule or shunning). See *norms*. (p. 60)

social control agents:
Those individuals or groups of individuals who have the authority to enforce social norms, including parents, teachers, religious leaders, and doctors. See *norms*. (p. 164)

social determinants of health:
The study of the range of social factors that influence the health status of individuals or populations. Equivalent to the term *social epidemiology*. See *social epidemiology*. (p. 17)

social epidemiology:
The study of the distribution of disease within a population according to social factors (such as social class, use of alcohol, or unemployment) rather than biological factors (such as blood pressure or genetics). Equivalent to the term *social determinants of health*. See *social determinants of health*. (p. 17)

social insurance:
See *sickness funds*. (p. 274)

social model of disability:
A model of disability that assumes that disability stems solely from constraints built into the environment or into social attitudes, rather than from the physical, intellectual, or sensory impairments of an individual. (p. 178)

social selection:
A theory holding that health causally influences socioeconomic position such that lower-class persons have higher rates of illness because middle-class persons who become ill drift over time into the lower class. (p. 84)

socioeconomic gradient in health:
The graded relationship between socioeconomic position (as measured by occupation, income, or education) and health (as measured by mortality and morbidity) in which an improvement in socioeconomic position is associated with a corresponding increase in health (i.e., lower risk for death and disease). (p. 74)

socioeconomic position:
A measure of one's relative location within the stratified structure of society based on access to valued resources such as money, power, knowledge, prestige, and social connections. (p. 35)

sociological perspective:
A perspective regarding human life and society that focuses on identifying social patterns and grappling with social problems rather than on analyzing individual behaviour and finding solutions for personal troubles. (p. 5)

sociology in medicine:
An approach to the sociological study of health, illness, and health care that focuses exclusively on research questions of interest to medical doctors. (p. 9)

sociology of medicine:
An approach that emphasizes using the area of health, illness, and health care to answer research questions of interest to sociologists in general. This approach often requires researchers to raise questions that could challenge medical views of the world and power relationships within the health care world. (p. 9)

son preference:
The cultural, economic, social, and ideological arguments that are marshalled to justify preferential treatment for men and boys as opposed to women and girls. (p. 147)

specialist:
A medical doctor whose practice focuses on certain disease categories, types of patients, or methods of treatment that have been recognized as specialized areas in medicine. (p. 263)

specialization:
Professional attention to a particular branch of medicine or surgery that is recognized by a board of physicians. (p. 291)

stem cells:
Cells that have the ability to differentiate into various other kinds of cells. (p. 215)

stereotypes:
Oversimplistic assumptions regarding the nature of group members, such as assuming that people who are obese are lazy and that people with mental illness are dangerous and unpredictable. (p. 179)

stigma:
The social disgrace of having a deeply discrediting attribute, whether a criminal record, a gay lifestyle, or a socially unacceptable illness. (p. 195)

street doctors:
Chinese health care workers with little formal training who work in urban outpatient clinics under the supervision of a doctor. (p. 278)

stress proliferation:
The process by which an initial stressor gives rise to other stressors. (p. 106)

stress relief hypothesis:
The supposition that a stressful life event may result in no adverse health effects or a positive effect on health because the stressful event represents escape from the chronic strain of a noxious environment. (p. 117)

stressful life events:
Discrete events that have an identifiable moment of onset. Examples include being a victim of a violent crime, experiencing a natural disaster, job loss, divorce, and death of a spouse. (p. 37)

stressors:
The broad range of problematic conditions and experiences that challenge the adaptive capabilities of individuals. (p. 37)

structural-functionalism:
The view that society is a harmonious system consisting of interdependent functioning parts that become more complex as societies themselves become more developed. (p. 7)

structure:
The social forces around us, including cultural pressures, economic standing, gender expectations, presence or absence of resources (time, money, prestige), and so on. When used as the opposite of agency, refers to the concept that individual choices are limited by all these social forces. See *agency*. (p. 29)

stunting:
A measure of height for age that is two standard deviations below the international standard and that reflects the consequences of chronic malnutrition. (p. 143)

superbugs:
Bacteria that have become resistant to most antibiotic drugs. (p. 320)

symbolic interactionism:
A theoretical perspective arguing that identity develops as part of an ongoing process of social interaction, whereby individuals learn to see themselves through the eyes of others, adopt the values of their community, and measure their self-worth against those values. (p. 325)

technical efficiency:
The maximum possible improvement in an outcome that can be obtained from a set of resource inputs. (p. 264)

technological imperative:
The belief that technology is always good, so any existing technological interventions should be used. (p. 59)

technology:
Any human-made object used to perform a task, or a process using such objects. Can refer both to the overall process of kidney dialysis and to the specific pieces of equipment used in that process. (p. 337)

total institutions:
Institutions in which all aspects of life are controlled by a central authority and in which large numbers of like-situated persons are dealt with en masse. Examples include mental hospitals, prisons, and the military. (p. 326)

transhumanism:
The philosophy that science and technology should be used to enhance and expand human mental and physical characteristics and capacities. (p. 209)

transinstitutionalization:
The process by which people with mental illness are no longer placed in a mental hospital but instead are transferred to other types of institutions, such as prisons, where there is little opportunity to receive treatment. (p. 327)

tuberculosis:
An infectious, airborne disease caused by the bacillus *Mycobacterium tuberculosis,* which attacks and destroys lung tissue. (p. 20)

unintended negative consequences:
Unplanned, harmful effects of actions that had been expected to produce only benefits. (p. 168)

universal coverage:
Health care systems that provide access to health care for all legal residents of a nation. (p. 261)

user fee:
A fixed amount charged at the time of use to an individual who receives a health care service or product. (p. 239)

utilization review:
A process in which insurance companies require doctors to get approval before ordering certain tests, performing surgery, hospitalizing a patient, or keeping a patient hospitalized more than a given number of days. (p. 270)

verbal autopsy:
A method of determining cause of death in resource-poor settings that involves interviewing family members and caregivers of the deceased with a structured questionnaire to identify signs and symptoms as well as other pertinent information that can be used to assign a cause of death. (p. 126)

village doctors:
Chinese agricultural workers who receive a few months of training in health care and provide basic health services to members of their agricultural production team. (p. 278)

violent resistance:
A form of intimate partner violence, committed mainly by women, who as victims of violence respond in kind, either as an instinctive reaction to protect themselves or as a strategy for preventing further assaults. (p. 60)

wasting:
A measure of weight for height that is two standard deviations below international standards and that reflects short-term exposure to acute food shortage or disease. (p. 143)

WFC:
See *work-to-family conflict.* (p. 118)

whistleblower:
A person who reveals any wrongdoings or unethical practices that are taking place within his or her organization. (p. 350)

widow inheritance:
A type of marriage arrangement whereby a widow is married to a male relative of her deceased husband. (p. 149)

work-life balance:
The subjective feeling that one is able to manage multiple roles in society and maintain the boundaries between work and home life so as to achieve satisfactory involvement in both. (p. 118)

work-to-family conflict (WFC):
The extent to which work life interferes with responsibilities and expectations at home, both consuming and depleting one's finite amount of time and energy. (p. 118)

xenotransplantation:
The transplantation, implantation, or infusion of cells, tissues, or organs from one species to another, including from non-human animal to human. (p. 214)

Abel, Emily K. 1986. "The hospice movement: Institutionalizing innovation." *International Journal of Health Services* 16: 71–85.

Abraham, Laurie Kaye. 1993. *Mama Might Be Better Off Dead: The Failure of Health Care in Urban America*. Chicago: University of Chicago Press.

Agardh, Emilie, Peter Allebeck, Johan Hallqvist, Tahereh Moradi, and Anna Sidorchuk. 2011. "Type 2 diabetes incidence and socio-economic position: A systematic review and meta-analysis." *International Journal of Epidemiology* 40: 804–818.

Albrecht, Gary L. 1992. *The Disability Business: Rehabilitation in America*. Newbury Park, CA: Sage.

Amato, Paul R. 2003. "Reconciling divergent perspectives: Judith Wallerstein, quantitative family research, and children of divorce." *Family Relations* 52: 332-339.

American Society of Plastic Surgeons. 2012. *2011 Plastic Surgery Statistics Report*. http://www.plasticsurgery. org/Documents/news-resources/statistics/2011-statistics/2011-cosmetic-procedures-trends-statistics. pdf, accessed February 2012.

Anderson, Gerard F., and Peter Sotir Hussey. 2000. "Population aging: A comparison among industrialized countries." *Health Affairs* 19: 191–203.

Anderson, Gerard F., Peter S. Hussey, Bianca K. Frogner, and Hugh R. Waters. 2005. "Health spending in the United States and the rest of the industrialized world." *Health Affairs* 24: 903–914.

Angus Reid. 2010. *Majority of Canadians Support Legalizing Euthanasia*. Montreal: Author.

Annas, George J. 1991. "Ethics committees: From ethical comfort to ethical cover." *Hastings Center Report* 21: 18–21.

Anson, Ofra, and Shifang Sun. 2005. *Health Care in Rural China*. Aldershot, U.K.: Ashgate Publishing.

Anspach, Renee R. 1997. "The language of case presentation." Pp. 320–338 in *The Sociology of Health and Illness: Critical Perspectives*, 5th ed., edited by Peter Conrad and Rochelle Kern. New York: St. Martin's Press.

Apovian, Caroline M. 2004. "Sugar-sweetened soft drinks, obesity, and type 2 diabetes." *Journal of the American Medical Association* 291: 978–979.

Armstrong, Elizabeth M. 1998. "Diagnosing moral disorder: The discovery and evolution of fetal alcohol syndrome." *Social Science and Medicine* 47: 2025–2042.

———. 2000. "Lessons in control: Prenatal education in the hospital." *Social Problems* 47: 583–605.

Armstrong, Pat, and Hugh Armstrong. 1998. *Universal Health Care: What the United States Can Learn from the Canadian Experience*. New York: New Press.

———. 2005. "Public and private: Implications for care work." *The Sociological Review* 53: 167–187.

Arras, John D., and Nancy Neveloff Dubler. 1995. "Ethical and social implications of high-tech home care." Pp. 1–34 in *Bringing the Hospital Home: Ethical and Social Implications of High-Tech Home Care*, edited by John D. Arras. Baltimore: Johns Hopkins University Press.

Aseltine, R. H., Jr. 1996. "Pathways linking parental divorce with adolescent depression." *Journal of Health and Social Behavior* 37: 133–148.

Association of the Faculties of Medicine of Canada (AFMC). 2010. *The Future of Medical Education in Canada (FMEC): A Collective Vision for MD Education*. Ottawa: Author.

———. 2011. *Canada Medical Education Statistics, 2011*. Ottawa: Author.

Association of Workers' Compensation Boards of Canada. 2012. *Number of Fatalities, by Jursidiction, 1993–2010*. http://www.awcbc.org/common/assets/nwisptables/ fat_summary_jurisdiction.pdf, accessed June 2012.

Atkinson, Michael. 2008. "Exploring male femininity in the 'crisis': Men and cosmetic surgery." *Body & Society* 14: 67–87.

Atkinson, Michael, and Kevin Young. 2001. "Flesh journeys: Neo primitives and the contemporary rediscovery of radical body modification." *Deviant Behavior* 22: 117–146.

Atzema, Clare L., Peter C. Austin, Thao Huynh, Ansar Hassan, Maria Chiu, Julie T. Wang, and Jack V. Tu. 2011. "Effect of marriage on duration of chest pain associated with acute myocardial infarction before seeking care." *Canadian Medical Association Journal* 183: 1482–1491.

Auger, N., G. Zang, and M. Daniel. 2009. "Community-level income inequality and mortality in Québec, Canada." *Public Health* 123: 438–443.

Ayo, Nike. 2012. "Understanding health promotion in a neoliberal climate and the making of health conscious citizens." *Critical Public Health* 22: 99–105.

Badalament, John. 2010. *The Modern Dad's Dilemma: How to Stay Connected with Your Kids in a Rapidly Changing World*. Novato, CA: New World Library.

Ballard, Karen, and Mary Ann Elston. 2005. "Medicalisation: A Multi-dimensional Concept." *Social Theory and Health* 3: 228–241.

Barbotte, Eric, Francis Guillemin, Nearkasen Chau, and the Lor Handicap Group. 2001. "Prevalence of impairments, disabilities, handicaps and quality of life in the general population: A review of recent literature." *Bulletin of the World Health Organization* 79 (11): 1047–1055.

Barer, Morris L., Steven G. Morgan, and Robert G. Evans. 2003. "Strangulation or rationalization? Costs and access in Canadian hospitals." *Longwoods Review* 1: 10–19.

Barker, Kristin 1998. "A ship upon a stormy sea: The medicalization of pregnancy." *Social Science and Medicine* 47: 1067–1076.

———. 2005. *The Fibromyalgia Story: Biomedical Authority and Women's Worlds of Pain*. Philadelphia: Temple University Press.

———. 2008. "Electronic support groups, patient-consumers, and medicalization: The case of contested illness." *Journal of Health and Social Behavior* 49: 20–36.

———. 2011. "Listening to Lyrica: Contested illnesses and pharmaceutical determinism." *Social Science and Medicine* 73: 833–842.

Barker-Benfield, Graham J. 1976. *The Horrors of the Half-Known Life: Male Attitudes toward Women and Sexuality in Nineteenth Century America*. New York: Harper.

Barnes, Colin, and Geof Mercer. 2003. *Disability: Key Concepts*. Cambridge, U.K.: Polity Press.

Barry, Arden R., and Glen J. Pearson. 2010. "Prescribing by pharmacist's [sic] and collaborative care: Are we ready to accept the baton and get in the race." *The Canadian Journal of Hospital Pharmacy* 63: 59.

Basch, Paul F. 1999. *Textbook of International Health*. 2nd ed. New York: Oxford University Press.

Bauman, Zygmunt. 1998. "Postmodern adventures of life and death." Pp. 217–231 in *Modernity, Medicine and Health*, edited by Graham Scambler and Paul Higgs. New York: Routledge.

Beck, Ulrich. 1992. *Risk Society: Towards a New Modernity*. London: Sage.

Becker, Howard S., Blanche Geer, Everett C. Hughes, and Anselm Strauss. 1961. *Boys in White: Student Culture in Medical School*. Chicago: University of Chicago Press.

Becker, Marshall H. (ed.). 1974. *The Health Belief Model and Personal Health Behavior*. San Francisco: Society for Public Health Education.

———. 1993. "A medical sociologist looks at health promotion." *Journal of Health and Social Behavior* 34: 1–6.

Beecher, Henry K. 1966. "Ethics and clinical research." *New England Journal of Medicine* 274: 1354–1360.

Beeson, Paul B. 1980. "Changes in medical therapy during the past half century." *Medicine* 59: 79–99.

Beider, Perry and Stuart Hagen. January 2004. *Limiting Tort Liability for Medical Malpractice*. Congressional Budget Office Economic & Budget Issue Brief.

Bell, Daniel. 1973. *The Coming of Post-industrial Society: A Venture in Social Forecasting*. New York: Basic.

Benoit, Cecilia, Sirpa Wrede, Ivy Bourgeault, Jane Sandall, Raymond De Vries, and Edwin R. van Teijlingen. 2005. "Understanding the social organisation of maternity care systems: Midwifery as a touchstone." *Sociology of Health and Illness* 27: 722–737.

Berenson, Alex. 2008. "Dental clinics meeting a need with no dentist." *New York Times* April 28: A1.

Beresford, Peter. 2000. "What have madness and psychiatric system survivors got to do with disability and disability studies?" *Disability and Society* 15: 167–172.

Bergman, Howard, Luigi Ferrucci, Jack Guralnik, David B. Hogan, Silvia Hummel, Sathya Karunananthan, and Christina Wolfson. 2007. "Frailty: An emerging research and clinical paradigm—Issues and controversies." *Journal of Gerontology: Medical Sciences* 62: 731–737.

Bergner, Daniel. 2007. "Death in the family." New York Times December 2. 6: 39+.

Bernard, Jesse. 1972. *The Future of Marriage*. New York: World.

Berta Whitney, Audrey Laporte, Dara Zarnett, Vivian Valdmanis, and Geoffrey Anderson. 2006. "A pan-Canadian perspective on institutional long-term care." *Health Policy* 79: 175–194.

Bevan, Gwyn, Jan-Kees Helderman, and David Wilsford. 2010. "Changing choices in health care: Implications for equity, efficiency and cost." *Health Economics, Policy and Law* 5: 251–267.

Bhalla K., M. Naghavi, S. Shahraz, D. Bartels, and C. J. L. Murray. 2009. "Building national estimates of the burden of road traffic injuries in developing countries from all available data sources: Iran." *Injury Prevention* 15: 150–156.

Biblarz, Timothy J., and Judith Stacey. 2010. "How does the gender of parents matter?" *Journal of Marriage and Family* 72: 3–22.

Billette, Jean-Michel, and Teresa Janz. 2011. *Injuries in Canada: Insights from the Canada Community Health Survey*. Cat. No. 82-624-X. Ottawa: Statistics Canada.

Bird, Chloe E., and Patricia P. Rieker. 2008. *Gender and Health: The Effects of Constrained Choices and Social Policies*. New York: Cambridge University Press.

Birenbaum, Arnold. 1982. "Reprofessionalization of pharmacy." *Social Science and Medicine* 16: 871–878.

Birken, Catherine S., Patricia C. Parkin, Teresa To, and Colin Macarthur. 2006. "Trends in rates of death from unintentional injury among Canadian children in urban areas: influence of socioeconomic status." *Canadian Medical Association Journal* 175: 867–868.

Birken, Catherine S., Patricia C. Parkin, Teresa To, Russell Wilkins, and Colin Macarthur. 2009. "Neighborhood socioeconomic status and homicides among children in urban Canada." *Pediatrics* 123: e815–e819.

Biro, Suzanne C., David T. Barber, and Jyoti A. Kotecha. 2012. "Trends in the use of electronic medical records." *Canadian Family Physician* 58: e21.

Black, Robert E., Simon Cousens, Hope L. Johnson, Joy E. Lawn, Igor Rudan, Diego G. Bassani, Prabhat Jha, Harry Campbell, Christa Fischer Walker, Richard Cibulskis, Thomas Eisele, Li Liu, Colin Mathers, and the Child Health Epidemiology Reference Group of WHO and UNICEF. 2010. "Global, regional, and national causes of child mortality in 2008: A systematic analysis." *The Lancet* 375: 1969–1987.

Blakeney, Allan. 2009. "The struggle to implement medicare." *Canadian Bulletin of Medical History* 26: 527–532.

Block, J. H., J. Block, and P. Gjerde. 1986. "The personality of children prior to divorce: A prospective study." *Child Development* 57: 827–840.

Block, Susan D., Nancy Clark-Chiarelli, Antoinette S. Peters, and Judith D. Singer. 1996. "Academia's chilly climate for primary care." *Journal of the American Medical Association* 276: 677–682.

Blue Cross and Blue Shield Association. 2012. "About the Blue Cross and Blue Shield Association." http://www.bcbs.com/about-the-association, accessed January 2012.

Bodenheimer, Thomas. 2005a. "High and rising health care costs. Part 1: Seeking an explanation." *Annals of Internal Medicine* 142: 847–854.

———. 2005b. "High and rising health care costs. Part 2: Technologic innovation." *Annals of Internal Medicine* 142: 932–937.

———. 2005c. "High and rising health care costs. Part 3: The role of health care providers." *Annals of Internal Medicine* 142: 996–1002.

Boe, Roger, and Ben Vuong. 2002. *Mental Health Trends among Federal Inmates*. Ottawa, Ontario: Correctional Service of Canada.

Bordo, Susan. 2003. *Unbearable Weight: Feminism, Western Culture and the Body*. London: University of California Press.

Bortolotti, Dan. 2004. *Hope in Hell: Inside the World of Doctors Without Borders*. Richmond Hill, ON: Firefly Books.

Bosk, Charles L. 2003. *Forgive and Remember: Managing Medical Failure*. 2nd ed. Chicago: University of Chicago Press.

Bourgeault, Ivy L. 2006. *Push! The Struggle for Midwifery in Ontario*. Montreal and Kingston: McGill-Queen's University Press.

Bourgeault, Ivy Lynn, Pat Armstrong, Hugh Armstrong, Jacqueline Choiniere, Joe Lexchin, Eric Mykhalovskiy, Suzanne Peters, and Jerry White. 2001. "Everyday experience of implicit rationing: Comparing the voices of nurses in California and British Columbia." *Sociology of Health and Illness* 23: 633–653.

Boychuk, Gerard W. 2002. *The Changing Political and Economic Environment of Health Care in Canada*. Discussion Paper 1: Commission on the Future of Health Care in Canada. Ottawa: Government of Canada.

Boychuk, Terry. 2009. "After medicare: Regionalization and Canadian health care reform." *Canadian Bulletin of Medical History* 26: 353–378.

Boyle, Michael H. 2002. "Home ownership and the emotional and behavioral problems of children and youth." *Child Development* 73: 883–892.

Braman Sidney S. 2006. "The global burden of asthma." *Chest* 130: 4S–12S.

Brandt, Allan M., and Paul Rozin. 1997. *Morality and Health.* New York: Routledge.

Brennan, Shannon. 2011. "Self-reported spousal violence, 2009." Family Violence in Canada: A Statistical Profile 2011. Catalogue No. 85-224-X. Ottawa: Statistics Canada.

Brenner, David J. and Eric J. Hall. 2007. "Computed tomography: An increasing source of radiation exposure." *New England Journal of Medicine* 357: 2277–2284.

Broadhead, Robert S., and Neil J. Facchinetti. 1985. "Drug iatrogenesis and clinical pharmacy: The mutual fate of a social problem and a professional movement." *Social Problems* 32: 425–436.

Brown, Ian. 2009. *The Boy in the Moon: A Father's Search for His Disabled Son.* Toronto: Random House Canada.

Brown, Ian, R. Renwick, and D. Raphael. 1995. "Frailty: Constructing a Common Meaning, Definition, and Conceptual Framework." *International Journal of Rehabilitation Research* 18: 93–102.

Brown, Phil, Stephen Zavestoski, Sabrina McCormick, Brian Myer, Rachel Morello-Frosch, and Rebecca Gasior Altman. 2004. "Embodied health movements: New approaches to social movements in health." *Sociology of Health and Illness* 26: 50–80.

Brownell, Marni D., Shelley A. Derksen, Douglas P. Jutte, Noralou P. Roos, Okechukwu Ekuma, and Lauren Yallop. 2010. "Socio-economic inequities in children's injury rates: Has the gradient changed over time?" *Canadian Journal of Public Health* 101: S28–S31.

Brownell, Marni D., Teresa Mayer, and Daniel Chateau. 2006. "The incidence of methylphenidate use by Canadian children: What is the impact of socioeconomic status and urban or rural residence?" *Canadian Journal of Psychiatry* 51: 847–854.

Brulle, Robert J., and David N. Pellow. 2006. Environmental justice: Human health and environmental inequalities." *Annual Review of Public Health* 27: 103–24.

Bullard, Robert D., Rueben C. Warren, and Glenn S. Johnson. 2001. Pp. 471–488 in *Health Issues in the Black Community,* edited by Ronald L. Braithwaite and Sandra E. Taylor. 2nd ed. San Francisco: Jossey-Bass.

Bunton, Robin, Sarah Nettleton, and Roger Burrows. 1995. *The Sociology of Health Promotion: Critical Analyses of Consumption, Lifestyle and Risk.* London: Routledge.

Burke, Mike, and H. Michael Stevenson. 1998. "Fiscal crisis and restructuring in Medicare; The politics of health in Canada." Pp. 597–618. In *Health and Canadian Society: Sociological Perspectives,* edited by David Coburn, Carl D'Arcy, and George M. Torrance, 3rd ed. Toronto: University of Toronto Press.

Burrows, Stephanie, Nathalie Auger, Philippe Gamache, Danielle St-Laurent, and Denis Hamel. 2011. "Influence of social and material individual and area deprivation on suicide mortality among 2.7 million Canadians: A prospective study." *BMC Public Health* 11: 1–11.

Bury, Michael. 1982. "Chronic illness as a biographical description." *Sociology of Health and Illness* 4: 167–182.

———. 1998. "Postmodernity and health." Pp. 1–28 in *Modernity, Medicine and Health,* edited by Graham Scambler and Paul Higgs. New York: Routledge.

Busfield, Joan. 2004. "Mental health problems, psychotropic drug technologies and risk." *Health, Risk and Society* 6: 361–375.

Bushnik, Tracey, Jocelynn L. Cook, A. Albert Yuzpe, Suzanne Tough, and John Collins. 2012. "Estimating the prevalence of infertility in Canada." *Human Reproduction* 27: 738–746.

Butler, Sandra, and Barbara Rosenblum. 1991. *Cancer in Two Voices.* San Francisco: Spinsters.

Cadman, D., M. H. Boyle, D. R. Offord, P. Szatmari, N. I. Rae-Grant, J. Crawford, and J. Byles. 1986. "Chronic illness and functional limitation in Ontario children: Findings of the Ontario Child Health Study." *Canadian Medical Association Journal* 135: 761–767.

Cairney, John, and Neal Krause. 2005. "The social distribution of psychological distress and depression in older adults." *Journal of Aging and Health* 17: 807–835.

Cakic, Vince. 2009. "Smart drugs for cognitive enhancement: Ethical and pragmatic considerations in the era of cosmetic neurology." *Journal of Medical Ethics* 35: 611–615.

Caldwell, John C. 1993. "Health transition: The cultural, social, and behavioral determinants of health in the Third World." *Social Science and Medicine* 36: 125–135.

Campbell, Jacquelyn C. 2002. "Health consequences of intimate partner violence." *The Lancet* 359: 1331–1336.

Canada Parliamentary Debates, House of Commons, Edited Hansard. 2008. Vol. 142, Number 100, Session 2, 39th Parliament, Wednesday, June 11, 2008. http://www.parl.gc.ca/HousePublications/Publication.aspx?DocId=3568890&Language=E&Mode=1&Parl=39&Ses=2, accessed August 2012.

Canada Parliamentary Debates, House of Commons. 2005. Session 1, 38th PARLIAMENT, Standing Committee on Aboriginal Affairs and Northern Development, meeting minutes, Thursday October 27, 2005. http://www.parl.gc.ca/HousePublications/Publication.aspx?DocId=2067775&Language=E&Mode=1&Parl=38&Ses=1.

Canadian Collaborative Centre for Physician Resources. 2011. *Trends in Physician Workload Based on Survey Data*. Ottawa: Canadian Medical Association.

Canadian Hospice Palliative Care Association. 2010. *Policy Brief on Hospice Palliative Care Quality End-of-Life Care? It depends on where you live ... and where you die.* Ottawa: Author.

———. 2011. *Fact Sheet: Hospice Palliative Care in Canada.* Ottawa: Author.

Canadian Institute for Health Information (CIHI). 2000. *Health Care in Canada: A First Annual Report.* Ottawa: Author.

———. 2005. *Exploring the 70/30 Split: How Canada's Health Care System Is Financed.* Ottawa: Author.

———. 2007. *Public-Sector Expenditures and Utilization of Home Care Services in Canada: Exploring the Data.* Ottawa: Author.

——— 2008a. *Health Care in Canada 2008.* Ottawa: Author.

———. 2008b. *Hospital Mental Health Services in Canada, 2005–06.* Ottawa: Author.

———. 2010a. *Highlights of 2008–2009 Inpatient Hospitalizations and Emergency Department Visits.* Ottawa: Author.

———. 2010b. *Supporting Informal Caregivers: The Heart of Home Care. Health Systems Performance.* Ottawa: Author.

———. 2011a *National Health Expenditure Trends, 1975 to 2011.* Ottawa: Author.

———. 2011b. *Regulated Nurses: Canadian Trends, 2006–2010.* Ottawa: Author.

———. 2011c. *Supply, Distribution and Migration of Canadian Physicians.* Ottawa: Author.

———. 2011d. Hospital Mental Health Database (http://apps.cihi.ca/MicroStrategy/asp/Main.aspx?&EVT=4001&REPORTid=F39FF73A42C66705C42F018455AC9512, accessed October 2012)

Canadian Institute for Health Information/Public Health Agency of Canada. 2011. *Obesity in Canada.* Ottawa: Author.

Canadian Nurses Association. 2008. *2006 Workforce Profile of Registered Nurses in Canada.* Ottawa: Author.

Cancian, Francesca M., and Stacey J. Oliker. 2000. *Caring and Gender.* Thousand Oaks, CA: Pine Forge.

Carr, Deborah. 2003. "A 'good death' for whom? Quality of spouse's death and psychological distress among older widowed persons." *Journal of Health and Social Behavior* 44: 215–232.

Caulfield, Timothy. 2005. "Legal and ethical issues associated with patient recruitment in clinical trials: The case of competitive enrolment." *Health Law Review* 13: 58–61.

CBC News, 2007a. "Kashechewan rejects Timmins move: survey." http://www.cbc.ca/news/canada/north/story/2007/03/16/kashechewan-survey.html (Friday, March 16, 2007), accessed August 2012.

———. 2007b. "Prentice turns down Kashechewan move request." http://www.cbc.ca/news/canada/story/2007/03/30/kashechewan.html (March 30, 2007), accessed August 2012.

Chad, Karen E., Bruce A. Reeder, Elizabeth L. Harrison, Nigel L. Ashworth, Suzanne M. Sheppard, Sandra L. Schultz, Brenda G. Bruner, Koren L. Fisher, and Joshua A. Lawson, 2005. "Profile of physical activity levels in community-dwelling older adults." *Medicine and Science in Sports and Exercise* 37: 1774–1784.

Chambaere, Kenneth, Johan Bilsen, Joachim Cohen, Bregje D. Onwuteaka-Philipsen, Freddy Mortier, and Luc Deliens. 2010. "Physician-assisted deaths under the euthanasia law in Belgium: A population-based survey." *Canadian Medical Association Journal* 182: 895–901.

Chambliss, Daniel F. 1996. *Beyond Caring: Hospitals, Nurses, and the Social Organization of Ethics.* Chicago: University of Chicago Press.

Chapin, Rosemary, and Debra Dobbs-Kepper. 2001. "Aging in place in assisted living: Philosophy versus policy." *Gerontologist* 41: 43–50.

Chappell, Neena L., and Marcus J. Hollander, 2011. "An evidence-based policy prescription for an aging population." *Healthcare* 11: 8–18.

Charles, Cathy, Jonathan Lomas, and Mita Giacomini. 1997. "Medical necessity in Canadian health policy: Four meanings … and a funeral?" *The Milbank Quarterly* 75: 365–394.

Charmaz, Kathy. 1991. *Good Days, Bad Days: The Self in Chronic Illness and Time*. New Brunswick, NJ: Rutgers University Press.

Chen, Meei-Shia. 2001. "The great reversal: Transformation of health care in the People's Republic of China." Pp. 456–482 in *The Blackwell Companion to Medical Sociology*, edited by William C. Cockerham. Malden, MA: Blackwell.

Chen, Wen-Hao, John Myles, and Garnett Picot. 2012. "Why have poorer neighbourhoods stagnated economically while the richer have flourished? Neighbourhood income inequality in Canadian cities." *Urban Studies* 49: 877–896.

Chen, Yue, Paula Stewart, Helen Johansen, Louise McRae, and Gregory Taylor. 2003. "Sex difference in hospitalization due to asthma in relation to age. *Journal of Clinical Epidemiology* 56: 180–187.

Cherlin, Andrew J., Paula L. Chase-Lansdale, and C. McRae. 1998. "Effects of parental divorce on mental health throughout the life course." *American Sociological Review* 63: 239–249.

Cherry, Mark J. 2005. *Kidney for Sale by Owner: Human Organs, Transplantation, and the Market*. Washington, DC: Georgetown University Press.

Chouinard, Vera. 2010. "Women with disabilities' experiences of government employment assistance in Canada." *Disability and Rehabilitation* 32: 148–158.

Christakis, Dmitri A., and Christopher Feudtner. 1997. "Temporary matters: The ethical consequences of transient social relationships in medical training." *Journal of the American Medical Association* 278: 739–743.

Clarke, Adele E., Janet K. Shim, Laura Mamo, Jennifer R. Fosket, and Jennifer R. Fishman. 2003. "Biomedicalization: Technoscientific transformations of health, illness, and U.S. biomedicine." *American Sociological Review* 68: 161–194.

Clarke, Philippa, Victor Marshall, James House, and Paula Lantz. 2011. "The social structuring of mental health over the life course: Advancing theory in the sociology of aging." *Social Forces* 89: 1287–1314.

Clow, Barbara, Ann Pederson, Margaret Howarth-Brockman, and Jennifer Bernier. 2009. *Rising to the Challenge: Sex- and Gender-Based Analysis for Health Planning, Policy and Research in Canada*. Halifax, NS: Atlantic Centre of Excellence for Women's Health.

Coburn, David. 1994. "Professionalization and proletarianization: Medicine, nursing, and chiropractic in historical perspective." *Labour* 34: 139–162.

Coburn, David, Keith Denny, Eric Mykhalovskiy, Peggy McDonough, Ann Robertson, and Rhonda Love. 2003. "Population health in Canada: A brief critique." *American Journal of Public Health* 93: 392–396.

Cockerham, William. 2005. "Health lifestyle theory and the convergence of agency and structure." *Journal of Health and Social Behavior* 46: 51–67.

Coleman, James S. 1988. "Social capital in the creation of human capital." *American Journal of Sociology* 94: 95–120.

Comeau, Tammy D., and Anton L. Allahar. 2001. "Forming Canada's ethnoracial identity: Psychiatry and the history of immigration practices." *Identity: An International Journal of Theory and Research*, 1: 143–160.

Conrad, Peter. 1985. "The meaning of medications: Another look at compliance." *Social Science and Medicine* 20: 29–37.

———. 1987. "The experience of illness: Recent and new directions." *Research in the Sociology of Health Care* 6: 1–32.

———. 2007. *The Medicalization of Society: On the Transformation of Human Conditions into Treatable Disorders*. Baltimore: Johns Hopkins University Press.

Conrad, Peter, and Joseph W. Schneider. 1992. *Deviance and Medicalization: From Badness to Sickness*. Philadelphia: Temple University Press.

Coombs, Robert H., Sangeeta Chopra, Debra R. Schenk, and Elaine Yutan. 1993. "Medical slang and its functions." *Social Science and Medicine* 36: 987–998.

Coontz, Stephanie. 2004. "The world historical transformation of marriage." *Journal of Marriage and Family* 66: 974–979.

Cooper, David K. C. 2012. "A brief history of cross-species transplantation." *Proceedings of Baylor University Medical Centre* 25: 49–57.

Corbin, Juliet M., and Anselm Strauss. 1988. *Unending Work and Care: Managing Chronic Illness at Home*. San Francisco: Jossey-Bass.

Council on Ethical and Judicial Affairs, American Medical Association. 1991. "Gender disparities in clinical decision making." *Journal of the American Medical Association* 266: 559–562.

Courtenay, Will H. 2000. "Behavioral factors associated with disease, injury and death among men: Evidence and implications for prevention." *The Journal of Men's Studies* 9: 81–142.

Cousineau, Michael R. 1997. "Health status of and access to health services by residents of urban encampments in Los Angeles." *Journal of Health Care for the Poor and Underserved* 8: 70–82.

Coutinho, Elsimar, and Segal, Sheldon J. 1999. *Is Menstruation Obsolete? How Suppressing Menstruation can Help Women Suffering from Anemia, Endometriosis, or PMS*. New York: Oxford University Press.

Craig, Cora L., Storm J. Russell, Christine Cameron, and Adrian Bauman. 2004. "Twenty-year trends in physical activity among Canadian adults." *Canadian Journal of Public Health* 95: 59–63.

Cranswick, Kelly, and Donna Dosman. 2008. "Eldercare: What we know today." *Canadian Social Trends* 82: 49–57.

Crawford, Robert. 1979. "Individual responsibility and health politics." Pp. 247–268 in *Health Care in America: Essays in Social History*, edited by Susan Reverby and David Rosner. Philadelphia: Temple University Press.

———. 2006. "Health as a meaningful social practice." *Health* 10: 401–420.

Critser, Greg. 2003. *Fat Land: How Americans Became the Fattest People in the World*. New York: Houghton Mifflin.

Crompton, Susan. 2011. "What's stressing the stressed? Main sources of stress among workers." Statistics Canada Catalogue no. 11-008-X, *Canadian Social Trends*: 44–51.

Crosby, Alfred J. 1986. *Ecological Imperialism: The Biological Expansion of Europe, 900–1900*. New York: Cambridge University Press.

Crossette, Barbara. 2001. "Wars enlist young legions, report says." *New York Times* June 14: A14.

Currie, Janet, and Mark Stabile. 2003. "Socioeconomic status and child health: Why is the relationship stronger for older children?" *American Economic Review* 93: 1813–1823.

Curtis, Lori J., and William J. MacMinn. 2008. "Health care utilization in Canada: Twenty-five years of evidence." *Canadian Public Policy* 34: 65–87.

Cutler, David M., Edward L. Glaeser, and Jesse M. Shapiro. 2003. "Why have Americans become more obese?" *Journal of Economic Perspectives* 17: 93–118.

Dancer, S. J. 2012. "Infection control 'undercover': A patient experience." *Journal of Hospital Infection* 80: 189–191.

Daniels, Norman, and Marc Roberts. 2008. "Health care reform." Pp. 83–88 in *From Birth to Death and Bench to Clinic: The Hastings Center Bioethics Briefing Book for Journalists, Policymakers, and Campaigns*, edited by Mary Crowley. Garrison, NY: The Hastings Center.

Davis, Devra. 2007. *The Secret History of the War on Cancer*. New York: Basic.

Davis, Fred. 1961. "Deviance disavowal: Management of strained interaction by the visibly handicapped." *Social Problems* 9: 120–132.

Davis, Karen, Cathy Schoen, and Kristof Stremikis. 2010. *Mirror, Mirror on the Wall: How the Performance of the U.S. Health Care System Compares Internationally*. New York: The Commonwealth Fund.

Davis, Kathy. 2002. "'A dubious equality': Men, women and cosmetic surgery." *Body & Society* 8: 49–65.

de Champlain, J., and J. Patenaude. 2006. "Review of a mock research protocol in functional neuroimaging by Canadian research ethics boards." *Journal of Medical Ethics* 32: 530–534.

De Jonge, Jan, Hans Bosma, Richard Peter, and Johannes Siegrist. 2000. "Job strain, effort-reward imbalance and employee well-being: A large-scale cross-sectional study." *Social Science and Medicine* 50: 1317–1327.

De Jongh, Reinoud, Ineke Bolt, Maartje Schermer, and Berend Olivier. 2008. "Botox for the brain: Enhancement of cognition, mood and pro-social behavior and blunting of unwanted memories." *Neuroscience and Biobehavioral Reviews* 32: 760–776.

De Maio, Fernando G. 2010. "Immigration as pathogenic: A systematic review of the health of immigrants to Canada." *International Journal for Equity in Health* 9: 27–47.

de Onis Mercedes, Monika Blössner, and Elaine Borghi. 2012. "Prevalence and trends of stunting among pre-school children, 1990–2020." *Public Health Nutrition* 15: 142–148.

Dear, Michael, and Jennifer Wolch. 1987. *Landscapes of Despair*. Princeton, NJ: Princeton University Press.

Dettwyler, Katherine A. 1995. "Beauty and the breast." Pp. 167–213 in *Breastfeeding: Biocultural Perspectives*, edited by Patricia Stuart-Macadam and Katherine A. Dettwyler. New York: Aldine De Gruyter.

Devoe, Lawrence D. 2011. "Electronic fetal monitoring. Does it really lead to better outcomes?" *American Journal of Obstetrics and Gynecology* 204: 455–456.

Dewey, Kathryn G., and Khadija Begum. 2011. "Long-term consequences of stunting in early life." *Maternal and Child Nutrition* 7: 5–18.

Dhejne, Cecilia, Paul Lichtenstein, Marcus Boman, Anna L. V. Johansson, Niklas Langstrom, and Mikael Landen. 2011. "Long-term follow-up of transsexual persons undergoing sex reassignment surgery: Cohort study in Sweden." *PLoS ONE* 6: e16885.

Diamond, Timothy. 1992. *Making Gray Gold: Narratives of Nursing Home Care.* Chicago: University of Chicago Press.

Dickason, Olive P. 1992. *Canada's First Nations: A History of Founding Peoples from Earliest Times.* Toronto: McClelland & Stewart.

Diller, Lawrence H. 1998. *Running on Ritalin: A Physician Reflects on Children, Society, and Performance in a Pill.* New York: Bantam.

DiMaggio, Paul J., and Walter W. Powell. 1983. "The iron cage revisited: Institutional isomorphism and collective rationalizing in organizational fields." *American Sociological Review* 48: 147–160.

DiPrete, Thomas A., and Gregory M. Eirich. 2006. "Cumulative advantage as a mechanism for inequality: A review of theoretical and empirical developments." *Annual Review of Sociology* 32: 271–297.

Dobash, Russell P., and Rebecca Emerson Dobash. 1998. *Rethinking Violence Against Women.* Newbury Park, CA: Sage.

Dobkin, Patricia L., and Lucy J. Boothroyd. 2008. "Organizing health services for patients with chronic pain: When there is a will there is a way." *Pain Medicine* 9: 881–889.

Dobson, Roy Thomas, and Jason Perepelkin. 2011. "Pharmacy ownership in Canada: Implications for the authority and autonomy of community pharmacy managers." *Research in Social and Administrative Pharmacy* 7: 347–358.

Dodson, Lisa, and Rebekah M. Zincavage. 2007. "It's like a family: Caring labor, exploitation, and race in nursing homes." *Gender & Society* 21: 905–928.

Dougherty, G., Barry Pless, and Russell Wilkins. 1990. "Social class and the occurrence of traffic injuries and deaths in urban children." *Canadian Journal of Public Health* 81: 204–209.

Drewnowski, Adam, and Nicole Darmon. 2005. "Food choices and diet costs: An economic analysis." *The Journal of Nutrition* 135: 900–904.

Dreze, Jean, and Amartya Sen. 1989. *Hunger and Public Action.* Oxford, UK: Clarendon.

Driver, Deana J. 2011. *Never Leave Your Wingman: Dionne and Graham Warner's Stoy of Hope.* Regina, SK: DriverWorks Ink.

Dubos, Rene. 1961. *Mirage of Health.* New York: Anchor.

Duffin, Jacalyn. 1994. "AIDS, memory and the history of medicine: Musings on the Canadian response." *Genitourinary Medicine* 70: 64–69.

Dunn, James R. and Michael V. Hayes. 2000. "Social inequality, population health, and housing: A study of two Vancouver neighborhoods." *Social Science and Medicine* 51: 563–587.

Dunn, Kyla. 2002. "Cloning Trevor." *Atlantic Monthly* 289 (6): 31–53.

Dupre, Matthew E. 2008. "Educational differences in health risks and illness over the life course: A test of the cumulative disadvantage theory." *Social Science Research* 37: 1253–1266.

Dutton, Donald G. 2012. "The case against the role of gender in intimate partner violence." *Aggression and Violent Behavior* 17: 99–104.

Dyck, Ronald, Nathaniel Osgood, Ting H. Lin, Amy Gao, and Mary R. Stang. 2010. "Epidemiology of diabetes mellitus among First Nations and non-First Nations adults." *Canadian Medical Association Journal* 182: 249–256.

Dyer, George S. M., and Mary E. L. Thorndike. 2000. "Quidne mortui vivis docent? The evolving purpose of human dissection in medical education." *Academic Medicine* 75: 969–979.

Ehrenreich, Barbara, and Deirdre English. 2005a. *For Her Own Good: Two Centuries of the Experts' Advice to Women.* 2nd ed. New York: Anchor Books.

———. 2005b. *Witches, Midwives, and Nurses: A History of Women Healers.* 2nd ed. New York: The Feminist Press at CUNY.

Elder, Glen H., Jr. 1998. "The life course as developmental theory." *Child Development* 69: 1–12.

Elliott, Carl. 2008. "Guinea-pigging." *The New Yorker* January 7: 36–41.

Elwert, Felix, and Nicholas A. Christakis. 2008. "The effect of widowhood on mortality by the causes of death of both spouses." *American Journal of Public Health* 98: 2092–2098.

Esserman, Laura, Yiwey Shieh, and Ian Thompson. 2009. "Rethinking screening for breast cancer and prostate cancer." *Journal of the American Medical Association* 302: 1685–1692.

Evans, Robert G. 2011. "Stumbling over iron rice bowls: The quest for integrated continuing care for the elderly." *Healthcare Papers* 11: 36–40.

Evans, Robert G., Morris L. Barer, and Theodore R. Marmor. 1994. *Why Are Some People Healthy and Others Not?* New York: Aldine de Gruyter.

Ezzati, Majid, Ari B. Friedman, Sandeep C. Kulkarni, and Christopher J. L. Murray. 2008. "The reversal of fortunes: Trends in county mortality and cross-county mortality disparities in the United States." *PLoS Medicine* 5 (4): e66 doi:10.1371/journal.pmed.0050066.

Fairfall, Nicola, Colleen Langron, Catherine Sherrington, Stephen R. Lord, Susan E. Kurrle, Keri Lockwood, Noeline Monaghan, Christina Aggar, Liz Gill, and Ian D. Cameron. 2011. "Treating frailty: A practical guide." *BMC Medicine* 9: 83.

Faris, R. L., and H. W. Dunham. 1939. *Mental Disorders in Urban Areas: An Ecological Study of Schizophrenia and Other Psychoses*. Chicago: University of Chicago Press.

Farmer, Paul. 1999. *Infections and Inequalities: The Modern Plagues*. Berkeley: University of California Press.

Fast, Janet, and Norah Keating. 2001. *Informal Caregivers in Canada: A Snapshot*. Ottawa: Health Canada.

Feinstein, Jonathan S. 1993. "The relationships between socioeconomic status and health: A review of the literature." *Milbank Quarterly* 71: 279–322.

Ferlay, Jacques, Hai-Rim Shin, Freddie Bray, David Forma, Colin Mathers, and Donald Maxwell Parkin. 2010. "Estimates of worldwide burden of cancer in 2008: GLOBOCAN 2008." *International Journal of Cancer* 127: 2893–2917.

Feshbach, Morris. 1999. "Dead souls." *Atlantic Monthly* 283 (1): 26–27.

Feshbach, Morris, and Alfred Friendly. 1992. *Ecocide in the USSR: Health and Nature Under Siege*. New York: Basic.

Fine, Michelle, and Adrienne Asch. 1988. "Introduction: Beyond pedestals." Pp. 1–38 in *Women with Disabilities: Essays in Psychology, Culture, and Politics*, edited by Michelle Fine and Adrienne Asch. Philadelphia: Temple University Press.

Finn Paradis, Lenora, and Scott B. Cummings. 1986. "The evolution of hospice in America toward organizational homogeneity." *Journal of Health and Social Behavior* 27: 370–386.

Flegel, Ken, Noni MacDonald, and Paul C. Hébert. 2011. "Binge drinking: All too prevalent and hazardous." *Canadian Medical Association Journal* 183: 1–2.

Flood, Colleen, and Amanda Haugan. 2010. "Is Canada odd? A comparison of European and Canadian approaches to choice and regulation of the public/private divide in health care." *Health Economics, Policy and Law* 5: 319–341.

Fomby, Paula, and Andrew J. Cherlin. 2007. "Family instability and child well-being." *American Sociological Review* 72: 181–204.

Foner, Nancy. 1994. *The Caregiving Dilemma: Work in an American Nursing Home*. Berkeley: University of California Press.

Food and Agriculture Organization. 2006. "Food Security." *FAO Policy Brief* (2): 1–4.

Food Banks Canada. 2012. *Food Banking in Canada*. http://www.foodbankscanada.ca/Learn-About-Hunger/Food-Banking-in-Canada.aspx, accessed June 2012.

Fox, Renee C. 1974. "Ethical and existential developments in contemporaneous American medicine: Their implications for culture and society." *Milbank Memorial Fund Quarterly* 52: 445–483.

———. 2000. "Medical uncertainty revisited." Pp. 409–425 in *The Handbook of Social Studies in Health and Medicine,* edited by Gary L. Albrecht, Ray Fitzpatrick, and Susan C. Scrimshaw. Thousand Oaks, CA: Sage.

Fox, Renee C., and Judith Swazey. 1974. *The Courage to Fail*. Chicago: University of Chicago Press.

Fox, Susannah. 2011. *Peer-to-peer healthcare*. Washington, DC: Pew Internet and American Life Project.

Frank, Arthur W. 1991. "From sick role to health role: Deconstructing Parsons." Pp. 205–216 in *Talcott Parsons: Theorist of Modernity*, edited by R. Robertson and B. S. Turner. Newbury Park, CA: Sage.

———. 1995. *The Wounded Storyteller: Body, Illness and Ethics.* Chicago: University of Chicago Press.

Frank, John W. 1995. "Why 'Population health'"? *Canadian Journal of Public Health* 86: 162–164.

Frankish, James C., Stephen W. Hwang, and Darryl Quantz. 2005. "Homelessness and health in Canada: Research lessons and priorities." *Canadian Journal of Public Health* 96: S23–S29.

Franklin, Byrony Dean, and J. W. Foppe van Mil. 2005. "Defining clinical pharmacy and pharmaceutical care." *Pharmacy World and Science* 27: 137.

Freidson, Eliot. 1970. *Profession of Medicine: A Study of the Sociology of Applied Knowledge.* New York: Dodd, Mead.

———. 1985. "The reorganization of the medical profession." *Medical Care Review* 42: 11–35.

———. 1986. "The medical profession in transition." Pp. 63–79 in *Applications of Social Science to Clinical Medicine and Health Policy,* edited by Linda Aiken and David Mechanic. New Brunswick, NJ: Rutgers University Press.

French, S. A., M. Story, D. Neumark-Sztainer, J. A. Fulkerson, and P. Hannan. 2001. "Fast food restaurant use among adolescents: Associations with nutrient intake, food choices and behavioral and psychosocial variables." *International Journal of Obesity* 25: 1823–1833.

Fujisawa, Rie, and Gaetan Lafortune. 2008. "The remuneration of general practitioners and specialists in 14 OECD countries: What are the factors influencing variations across countries?" *Directorate for Employment, Labour, and Social Affairs Health Committee: Organisation for Economic Co-operation and Development. Health Working Papers* 41: 1–63.

Furstenberg, Frank F., Jr. 2010. "On a new schedule: Transitions to adulthood and family change." *Future of Children* 20: 67–87.

Gagan, David. 1989. "For 'patients of moderate means': The transformation of Ontario's public general hospitals, 1880–1950." *Canadian Historical Review* 70: 152–179.

Galarneau, Diane, and Marian Radulescu. 2009. "Employment among the disabled." *Perspectives* (May 2009): 5–15. Catalogue No. 75-001-X. Ottawa: Statistics Canada.

Gallo-Cruz, Selina, and Markella Rutherford. 2011. "Great expectations: Legitimacy and emotions among out of hospital midwives." *Social Theory and Health* 9: 275–301.

Garcy, Anthony M., and Denny Vågerö. 2012. "The length of unemployment predicts mortality, differently in men and women, and by cause of death: A six year mortality follow-up of the Swedish 1992–1996 recession." *Social Science and Medicine* 74: 1911–1920.

Garg, Nitin, and Adnan A. Hyder. 2006. "Exploring the relationship between development and road traffic injuries: A case study from India." *European Journal of Public Health* 16: 487–491.

Garner, Rochelle, Gisèle Carrière, Claudia Sanmartin, and the Longitudinal Health and Administrative Data Research Team. 2010. *The Health of First Nations Living Off-Reserve, Inuit, and Métis Adults in Canada: The Impact of Socio-economic Status on Inequalities in Health.* Cat. No. 82-622-X. Ottawa: Minister of Industry.

Gaudine, Alice, Linda Thorne, Sandra M. Lefort, and Marianne Lamb. 2010. "Evolution of hospital clinical ethics committees in Canada." *Journal of Medical Ethics* 36: 132–137.

Geiger, H. Jack, and Robert M. Cook-Deegan. 1993. "The role of physicians in conflicts and humanitarian crises: Case studies from the field missions of Physicians for Human Rights, 1988 to 1993." *Journal of the American Medical Association* 270: 616–620.

George, Linda K. 1993. "Sociological perspectives on life transitions." *Annual Review of Sociology* 19: 353–373.

Gerace, Terence, and Valerie Anne George. 1996. "Predictors of weight increases among fire fighters and paramedics." *Preventive Medicine* 25: 593–600.

Gerber, J. 1990. "Enforced self-regulation in the infant formula industry." *Social Justice* 17: 98–112.

Gething, Lindsay. 1992. "Judgments by health professionals of personal characteristics of people with a visible physical disability." *Social Science and Medicine* 34: 809–815.

Gibbons, Luz, José M. Belizán, Jeremy A. Lauer, Ana P. Betrán, Mario Merialdi, and Fernando Althabe. 2010. "The global numbers and costs of additionally needed and unnecessary caesarean sections performed per year: Overuse as a barrier to universal coverage." In World Health Report 2010. Health systems financing: The path to universal coverage. Background paper. No 30. Geneva, Switzerland: World Health Organization.

Gilbert, Leah, and Terry-Ann Selikow. 2011. "The epidemic in this country has the face of a woman: Gender and HIV/AIDS in South Africa." *African Journal of AIDS Research* 10: 325–334.

Gilleard, Chris, and Paul Higgs. 2011. "Frailty, disability and old age: A re-appraisal." *Health* 15: 475–490.

Gillis, Charlie, Julia Belluz, and Josh Dehaas. 2010. "Do you trust your doctor? An exclusive Maclean's poll shows that an increasing number of Canadians don't." *Maclean's Magazine*. Monday, August 16, 2010.

Giordano, Simona. 2012. "Sliding doors: Should treatment of gender identity disorder and other body modifications be privately funded?" *Medical Health Care and Philosophy* 15: 31–40.

Glazer, Nona Y. 1993. *Women's Paid and Unpaid Labor: The Work Transfer in Health Care and Retailing*. Philadelphia: Temple University Press.

Goering, Paula N., David L. Streiner, Carol Adair, Tim Aubry, Jayne Barker, Jino Distasio, Stephen W Hwang, Janina Komaroff, Eric Latimer, Julian Somers, and Denise M. Zabkiewicz. 2011. "The At Home/Chez Soi trial protocol: A pragmatic, multi-site, randomised controlled trial of a Housing First intervention for homeless individuals with mental illness in five Canadian cities." *British Medical Journal* 1: 1–18.

Goffman, Erving. 1961. *Asylums*. Garden City, NY: Doubleday.

———, Erving. 1963. *Stigma: Notes on the Management of Spoiled Identity*. Englewood Cliffs, NJ: Prentice Hall.

Gold, E. Richard, and Julia Carbone. 2010. "Myriad genetics: In the eye of the policy storm." *Genetics in Medicine* 12: S39–S70.

Good, Mary-Jo DelVecchio. 1995. *American Medicine: The Quest for Competence*. Berkeley, CA: University of California Press.

Gorey, Kevin M., Isaac N. Luginaah, Emma Bartfay, Karen Y. Fung, Eric J. Holowaty, Frances C. Wright, Caroline Hamm, and Sindu M. Kanjeekal. 2011. "Effects of socioeconomic status on colon cancer treatment accessibility and survival in Toronto, Ontario, and San Francisco, California, 1996–2006." *American Journal of Public Health* 101: 112–119.

Gottfried, Robert S. 1983. *The Black Death*. New York: Free Press.

Goyal, Madhav, Ravindra L. Mehta, Lawrence J. Schneiderman, and Ashwini R. Sehgal. 2002. "Economic and health consequences of selling a kidney in India." *Journal of the American Medical Association* 288: 1589–1593.

Gray, Alastair M. 1982. "Inequalities in health: A summary and comment." *International Journal of Health Sciences* 12: 349–380.

Greaves, Lorraine. 2003. "Smoke screen: The cultural meaning of women's smoking". Pp. 261–91 in *High Culture: Reflections on Addiction and Modernity,* edited by Alexander and M. S. Roberts. Albany, NY: State University of New York Press.

Green, Carolyn J., Arminée Kazanjian, and Diane Helmer. 2004. "Informing, advising, or persuading? An assessment of bone mineral density testing information from consumer health websites." *International Journal of Technology Assessment in Health Care* 20: 156–166.

Green, Chris, James F. Blanchard, T. Kue Young, and Jane Griffith. 2003. "The epidemiology of diabetes in the Manitoba-registered First Nation population: Current patterns and comparative trends." *Diabetes Care* 26 (7): 1993–1998.

Grekul, Jana, Harvey Krahn, and Dave Odynak. 2004. "Sterilizing the 'feeble-minded': Eugenics in Alberta, Canada, 1929–1972." *Journal of Historical Sociology* 17: 358–384.

Grenier, Amanda. 2007. "Constructions of frailty in the English language: Care practice and the lived experience." *Ageing and Society* 27: 425–445.

Griffiths, Frances, and Eileen Green. 2003. "A normal biological process? Brittle bones, HRT and the patient-doctor encounter." Pp. 210–222 in *Debating Biology: Sociological Reflections on Health, Medicine and Society,* edited by Simon J. Williams, Lynda Birke, & Gillian A. Bendelow. London: Routledge.

Grimes, David A., and Jeffrey F. Peipert. 2010. "Electronic fetal monitoring as a public health screening program: The arithmetic of failure." *Obstetrics and Gynecology* 116: 1397–1400.

Grootendorst, Paul, and Aidan Hollis. 2011. *Managing Pharmaceutical Expenditure: An Overview and Options for Canada. Paper 2*. Ottawa: Canadian Health Services Research Foundation.

Grzywacz, Joseph G., and Brenda L. Bass. 2003. "Work, family and mental health: Testing different models of work-family fit." *Journal of Marriage and Family* 65: 248–261.

Gunby, Joanne, Francois Bissonnette, Clifford Librach, and Lisa Cowan. 2011. "Assisted reproductive technologies (ART) in Canada: 2007 results from the Canadian ART Register." *Fertility and Sterility* 95: 542–547.

Ha, Do T. P., Edith J. M. Feskens, Paul Deurenberg, Le B. Mai, Nguyen C. Khan, and Frans J. Kok. 2011. "Nationwide shifts in the double burden of overweight and underweight in Vietnamese adults in 2000 and 2005: Two national nutrition surveys." *BMC Public Health* 11: 1–9.

Haas, Jack, and William Shaffir. 1987. *Becoming Doctors: The Adoption of a Cloak of Competence.* Greenwich, CT: JAI.

Haas, Steven A., M. Maria Glymour, and Lisa F. Berkman. 2011. "Childhood health and labor market inequality over the life course." *Journal of Health and Social Behavior* 52: 298–313.

Habermas, Jürgen. 1981. "New social movements." *Telos* 49: 33–37.

Hafferty, Frederic W. 1991. *Into the Valley: Death and the Socialization of Medical Students.* New Haven, CT: Yale University Press.

———. 1998. "Beyond curriculum reform: Confronting medicine's hidden curriculum." *Academic Medicine* 73: 403–407.

Hafferty, Frederic W., and Ronald Franks. 1994. "The hidden curriculum, ethics teaching, and the structure of medical education." *Academic Medicine* 69: 861–871.

Hahn, Harlan. 1985. "Toward a politics of disability definitions, disciplines, and policies." *Social Science Journal* 22 (October): 87–105.

Hämmig, Oliver, Michaela Knecht, Thomas Läubli, and Georg F. Bauer. 2011. "Work-life conflict and musculoskeletal disorders: A cross-sectional study of an unexplored association." *BMC Musculoskeletal Disorders* 12: 60.

Hanna, Timothy P., and Alfred C. T. Kangolle. 2010. "Cancer control in developing countries: Using health data and health services research to measure and improve access, quality and efficiency." *BMC International Health and Human Rights* 10: 1–12.

Hanson, T. L. 1999. "Does parent conflict explain why divorce is negatively associated with child welfare?" *Social Forces* 77: 1283–1315.

Hawkes, Corinna. 2006. "Uneven dietary development: linking the policies and processes of globalization with the nutrition transition, obesity and diet-related chronic diseases." *Globalization and Health* 2: 1–18.

Hawranik, Pamela G., and Laurel A. Strain. 2007. "Giving voice to informal caregivers of older adults." *Canadian Journal of Nursing Research* 39: 156–172.

Health Canada. 2004. *Trends in Workplace Injuries, Illnesses, and Policies in Healthcare across Canada.* Ottawa: Author.

———. 2009. *A Statistical Profile on the Health of First Nations in Canada: Self Rated Health and Selected Conditions, 2002–2005.* Ottawa: Minister of Health.

———. 2010. Healthy Canadians—A federal report on comparable health indicators 2010. Ottawa: Author.

Heath, Christian, Paul Luff, and Marcus Sanchez Svensson. 2003. "Technology and medical practice." *Sociology of Health and Illness* 25: 75–96.

Heisz, Andrew. 2007. "Income inequality and income redistribution in Canada, 1976–2004." Analytical Studies Branch Research Series. Catalogue 11F0019MIE—No. 298. Ottawa: Statistics Canada.

Hendlin, Herbert, Chris Rutenfrans, and Zbigniew Zylicz. 1997. "Physician-assisted suicide and euthanasia in the Netherlands: Lessons from the Dutch." *Journal of the American Medical Association* 277: 1720–1722.

Hertzman, Clyde, and Tom Boyce. 2010. "How experience gets under the skin to create gradients in developmental health." *Annual Review of Public Health* 31: 329–347.

Hesketh, Kathryn L., Susan M. Duncan, Carole A. Estabrooks, Marlene A. Reimer, Phyllis Giovannetti, Kathryn Hyndman, and Sonia Acorn. 2003. "Workplace violence in Alberta and British Columbia hospitals." *Health Policy* 63: 311–321.

Hettiaratchy, Shehan, and Peter E. Butler. 2002. "Face transplantation: Fantasy or the future?" *The Lancet* 360: 5–6.

Heyland, Daren K., James V. Lavery, Joan E. Tranmer, S. E. D. Shortt, and Sandra J. Taylor. 2000. "Dying in Canada: Is it an institutionalized, technologically supported experience?" *Journal of Palliative Care* 16: S10–S64.

Higgins, Paul C. 1992. *Making Disability: Exploring the Social Transformation of Human Variation.* Springfield, IL: Charles C. Thomas.

Hitchcock, Christine L., 2008. "Elements of the menstrual suppression debate." *Health Care for Women International* 29: 702–719.

Hochschild, Arlie. 1989. *The Second Shift: Working Parents and the Revolution at Home.* New York: Viking.

Hogan, Margaret C., Kyle J. Foreman, Mohsen Naghavi, Stephanie Y. Ahn, Mengru Wang, Susanna M. Makela, Alan D. Lopez, Rafael Lozano, and Christopher J. L. Murray. 2010. "Maternal mortality for 181 countries, 1980–2008: A systematic analysis of progress towards Millennium Development Goal 5." *The Lancet* 375: 8–14.

Hogle, Linda F. 2005. "Enhancement technologies and the body." *Annual Review of Anthropology* 34: 695–716.

Hollingshead, A. B., and F. C. Redlich. 1958. *Social Class and Mental Illness: A Community Study*. New York: John Wiley and Sons.

Holmes, Seth M., and Maya Ponte. 2011. "En-case-ing the patient: Disciplining uncertainty in medical student patient presentations." *Culture, Medicine and Psychiatry* 35: 163–182.

Holmes, Thomas H., and Richard H. Rahe. 1967. "The Social Readjustment Rating Scale." *Journal of Psychosomatic Research* 11: 213–218.

Holt-Giménez, Eric, and Loren Peabody. 2008. "From food rebellions to food sovereignty: Urgent call to fix a broken food system." http://www.foodfirst.org/files/pdf/bgr%20spring%202008%20-Food%20Rebellions.pdf, accessed August 2012.

Horn, Joshua S. 1969. "*Away with all Pests…*": *An English Surgeon in People's China*. London: Paul Hamlyn.

Horwitz, Allan V. 1982. *Social Control of Mental Illness*. New York: Academic.

Horwitz, Allan V., and Jerome C. Wakefield. 2005. "The age of depression." *The Public Interest* 158: 39–58.

Houston, Clarence Stuart. 2002. *Steps on the Road to Medicare*. Montreal: McGill-Queen's University Press.

Howard, Frazer, Martin F. McKneally, and Alex V. Levin. 2010. "Integrating bioethics into postgraduate medical education: The University of Toronto model." *Academic Medicine* 85: 1035–1040.

Huey, Laura, and Eric Berndt. 2008. "'You've gotta learn how to play the game': homeless women's use of gender performance as a tool for preventing victimization." *The Sociological Review* 56: 177–194.

Hughes, Bill, and Kevin Paterson. 1997. "The social model of disability and the disappearing body: Towards a sociology of impairment." *Disability and Society* 12: 325–340.

Hughes, Kahryn. 2004. "Health as individual responsibility: Possibilities and personal struggle." In *The Mainstreaming of Complementary and Alternative Medicine: Studies in Social Context*, edited by Philip Tovey, Gary Easthope, and Jon Adams. New York: Routledge.

Hunt, Alison M., Angela da Silva, Steve Lurie, and David S. Goldbloom. 2007. "Community treatment orders in Toronto: The emerging data." *Canadian Journal of Psychiatry* 52: 647–656.

Hurst, Jeremy, and Luigi Siciliani. 2003. *Tackling Excessive Waiting Times for Elective Surgery: A Comparison of Policies in Twelve OECD Countries*. OECD Health Working Paper 6. Paris, France: Directorate for Employment, Labour, and Social Affairs.

Hutton, Eileen K., Angela H. Reitsma, and Karyn Kaufman. 2009. "Outcomes associated with planned home and planned hospital births in low-risk women attended by midwives in Ontario, Canada, 2003–2006: A retrospective cohort study." *Birth* 36: 180–189.

Huynen, Maud M. T. E., Pim Martens, and Henk B. M. Hilderink. 2005. "The health impacts of globalisation: A conceptual framework." *Globalization and Health* 1: 1–12.

Hwang, Stephen W., Tim Aubry, Anita Palepu, Susan Farrell, Rosane Nisenbaum, Anita M. Hubley, Fran Klodawsky, Evie Gogosis, Elizabeth Hay, Shannon Pidlubny, Tatiana Dowbor, and Catharine Chambers. 2011. "The health and housing in transition study: A longitudinal study of the health of homeless and vulnerably housed adults in three Canadian cities." *International Journal of Public Health* 56: 609–623.

Hwang, Stephen W., Russell Wilkins, Michael Tjepkema, Patricia J. O'Campo, and James R. Dunn. 2009. "Mortality among residents of shelters, rooming houses, and hotels in Canada: 11 year follow-up study." *British Medical Journal* 339: 1–9.

International Baby Food Action Network. 2007. "Breaking the Rules, Stretching the Rules 2007." http://www.ibfan.org/code_watch-btr.html, accessed August 2012.

International Diabetes Foundation. 2011. *IDF Diabetes Atlas, Fifth Edition*. Brussels, Belgium: Author.

Ipsos Reid. 2011. *A Matter of Trust*. Media Release: January 11, 2011. http://www.ipsos-na.com/news-polls/pressrelease.aspx?id=5100, accessed August 2012.

Jha, Prabhat, Vendhan Gajalakshmi, Prakash C. Gupta, Rajesh Kumar, Prem Mony, Neeraj Dhingra, Richard Peto, and RGI-CGHR prospective collaborators. 2006. "Prospective study of one million deaths in India: Rationale, design, and validation results." *PloS Medicine* 3: 192–200.

Jha, Prabhat, Maya A. Kesler, Rajesh Kumar, Faujdar Ram, Usha Ram, Lukasz Aleksandrowicz, Diego G. Bassani, Shailaja Chandra, and Jayant K. Banthia. 2011. "Trends in selective abortions of girls in India: Analysis of nationally representative birth histories from 1990 to 2005 and census data from 1991 to 2011." *The Lancet* 377: 1921–1928.

Jin, Robert L., Chandrakant Shah, and Tomislav J. Svoboda. 1995. "The impact of unemployment on health: A review of the evidence." *Canadian Medical Association Journal* 153: 529–540.

Johnson, David R., and Jian Wu. 2002. "An empirical test of crisis, social selection and role explanations of the relationship between marital disruption and psychological distress: A pooled time-series analysis of four-wave panel data." *Journal of Marriage and Family* 64: 211–224.

Johnson, Kenneth C., and Betty-Anne Daviss. 2005. "Outcomes of planned home births with certified professional midwives: Large prospective study in North America." *British Medical Journal* 330: 1416.

Johnson, Michael P. 2005. "Domestic violence: It's not about gender—or is it? *Journal of Marriage and Family* 67: 1126–1130.

———. 2011. "Gender and types of intimate partner violence: A response to an anti-feminist literature review." *Aggression and Violent Behavior* 16: 289–296.

Johnston-Robledo, Ingrid, Jessica Warnack, and Stephanie Wares. 2006. "'Kiss Your Period Good-Bye': Menstrual Suppression in the Popular Press." *Sex Roles* 54: 353–360.

Jones, James. 1993. *Bad Blood: The Tuskegee Syphilis Experiment.* Rev. ed. New York: Free Press.

Joung, Inez M., H. Dike van de Mheen, Karien Stronks, Frans W. A. Van Poppel, and Johan P. Mackenbach. 1998. "A longitudinal study of health selection in marital transitions." *Social Science and Medicine* 46: 425–435.

Kaiser Commission on Medicaid and the Uninsured. 2011. *Changes in Health Insurance Coverage in the Great Recession, 2007–2010.* Washington, DC: Kaiser Family Foundation.

Kale, Rajendra. 2012. "'It's a girl!'—could be a death sentence." *Canadian Medical Association Journal* 184: 387–388.

Kaplan, Mark S., Nathalie Huguet, David H. Feeny, and Bentson H. McFarland. 2010. "Self-reported hypertension prevalence and income among older adults in Canada and the United States." *Social Science and Medicine* 70: 844–849.

Kaplan, Mark S., and Bentson H. McFarland. 2004. "Spending more, feeling worse: Medical care expenditures and self rated health." *Journal of Epidemiology and Community Health* 58: 528–531.

Karasek, R. 1979. "Job demands, job decision latitude and mental strain: Implications for job redesign." *Administrative Science Quarterly* 24: 285–306.

Katz, Jay. 1984. *The Silent World of Doctor and Patient.* New York: Free Press.

Katz, Steven J., Timothy P. Hofer, and Willard G. Manning. 1996. "Physician use in Ontario and the United States: The impact of socio-economic status on health status." *American Journal of Public Health* 86: 520–524.

Kaysen, Susan. 1993. *Girl, Interrupted.* New York: Random House.

Keating, Daniel P., and Clyde Hertzman. 1999. *Developmental Health and the Wealth of Nations: Social, Biological and Educational Dynamics.* New York: Guilford Press.

Kellogg, J. H. 1880. *Plain Facts for Young and Old.* Burlington, IA: Segner and Condit.

Kelly, John. 2005. *The Great Mortality: An Intimate History of the Black Death, the Most Devastating Plague of All Time.* New York: HarperCollins.

Kelly, Mary Bess. 2012. "Divorce cases in civil court, 2010/2011." Statistics Canada Catalogue No. 85-002-X, *Juristat* March 2012: 5–23.

Kelly, Michael P., and David Field. 1996. "Medical sociology, chronic illness and the body." *Sociology of Health and Illness* 18: 241–257.

Kelly, Susan E., Patricia A. Marshall, Lee M. Sanders, Thomas A. Raffin, and Barbara A. Koenig. 1997. "Understanding the practice of ethics consultation: Results of an ethnographic multi-site study." *Journal of Clinical Ethics* 8: 136–149.

Kelm, Mary-Ellen. 1994. "Women, families and the provincial hospital for the insane, British Columbia, 1905–1915." *Journal of Family History* 19: 177–193.

Kesselheim, Aaron S., Jessica A. Myers, Daniel H. Solomon, Wolfgang C. Winkelmayer, Raisa Levin, and Jerry Avorn. 2012. "The prevalence and cost of unapproved uses of top-selling orphan drugs." *PLoS ONE* 7: e31894.

Kierans, Ciara. 2011. "Anthropology, organ transplantation and the immune system: Resituating commodity and gift exchange." *Social Science and Medicine* 73: 1469–1476.

Kiernan, Kathleen, and Kate E. Pickett. 2006. "Marital status differences in maternal smoking during pregnancy, breastfeeding and maternal depression." *Social Science and Medicine* 63: 335–346.

Kim, Anthony S., and S. Claiborne Johnston. 2011. "Global variation in the relative burden of stroke and ischemic heart disease." *Circulation* 124: 314–323.

Kinney, Eleanor D., and Brian Alexander Clark. 2004. "Provisions for health and health care in the constitutions of the countries of the world." *Cornell International Law Journal* 37: 285–305.

Kiple, Kenneth F. 1993. *Cambridge World History of Human Disease*. New York: Cambridge University Press.

Knafl, Kathleen, and Gary Burkett. 1975. "Professional socialization in a medical specialty: Acquiring medical judgment." *Social Science and Medicine* 9: 397–404.

Koehlmoos, Tracey Pérez, Shahela Anwar, and Alejandro Cravioto. 2011. "Global health: Chronic diseases and other emergent issues in global health." *Infectious Disease Clinics of North America* 25: 623–638.

Kolata, Gina. 2004. "Stem cells: Promise, in search of results." New York Times August 24: D1+.

Kramer, Peter D. 1993. *Listening to Prozac: A Psychiatrist Explores Antidepressant Drugs and the Remaking of the Self*. New York: Penguin Books.

Krause, Neil, D. R. Ragland, B. A. Greiner, S. Leonard Syme, and J. M. Fisher. 1997. "Psychosocial job factors associated with back and neck pain in public transit operators." *Scandinavian Journal of Work Environment and Health* 23: 179–186.

Krieger, Nancy. 2001. "Theories for social epidemiology in the 21st century: An ecosocial perspective." *International Journal of Epidemiology* 30: 668–677.

Krieger, Nancy, David H. Rehkopf, Jarvis T. Chen, Pamela D. Waterman, Enrico Marcelli, and Malinda Kennedy. 2008. "The fall and rise of U.S. inequities in premature mortality: 1960–2002." *PLoS Medicine* 5 (2): e46 doi:10.1371/journal. pmed.0050046.

Kurzweil, Ray. 2005. *The Singularity Is Near: When Humans Transcend Biology*. London: Viking.

Labonte, Ronald. 1995. "Population health and health promotion: What do they have to say to each other?" *Canadian Journal of Public Health* 86: 165–168.

Lacey, Marc. 2005. "Beyond the bullets and blades." *New York Times* March 20: WK1+.

Laing, Ronald D. 1967. *The Politics of Experience*. New York: Ballantine.

Lam, Vincent. 2005. *Bloodletting and Miraculous Cures*. Toronto: Anchor Canada.

Lappé, Frances Moore, Joseph Collins, and Peter Rosset. 1998. *World Hunger: Twelve Myths*. 2nd ed. New York: Grove.

Lassey, Marie L., William R. Lassey, and Martin J. Jinks. 1997. *Health Care Systems Around the World: Characteristics, Issues, Reforms*. Upper Saddle River, NJ: Prentice Hall.

Laugesen, Miriam J., and Sherry A. Glied. 2011. "Higher fees paid to US physicians drive higher spending for physician services compared to other countries." *Health Affairs* 30: 1647–1656.

Lawn, Joy E., Simon Cousens, and Jelka Zupan. 2005. "4 million neonatal deaths: When? Where? Why?" *The Lancet* 365: 891–900.

Leatherman Thomas L., and Alan Goodman. 2005. "Coca-colonization of diets in the Yucatan." *Social Science and Medicine* 61: 833–846.

Leavitt, Judith Walzer. 1983. "Science enters the birthing room: Obstetrics in America since the eighteenth century." *Journal of American History* 70: 281–304.

———. 1986. *Brought to Bed: Childbearing in America, 1750–1950*. New York: Oxford University Press.

Leavitt, Judith Walzer, and Ronald L. Numbers. 1985. *Sickness and Health in America*. Madison: University of Wisconsin Press.

Lester, Felicia, Nerys Benfield, and Mohamed M. F. Fathalla. 2010. "Global Women's Health in 2010: Facing the Challenges." *Journal of Women's Health* 19: 2081–2089.

Lesthaeghe, Ron. 2010. "The unfolding story of the second demographic transition." *Population and Development Review* 36: 211–251.

Lexchin, Joel, Melanie Sekeres, Jennifer Gold, Lorraine E. Ferris, Sunila R. Kalkar, Wei Wu, Marleen Van Laethem, An-Wen Chan, David Moher, M. James Maskalyk, Nathan Taback, and Paula A. Rochon. 2007. "National evaluation of policies on individual financial conflicts of interest in Canadian academic health science centers." *Journal of General Internal Medicine* 23: 1896–1903.

Li, Allanah, Naomi Dachner, and Valerie Tarasuk. 2009. "Food intake patterns of homeless youth in Toronto." *Canadian Journal of Public Health* 100: 36–40.

Li, Peter S. 2008. "The market value and social value of race." In *Daily Struggles: The Deepening Racialization and Feminization of Poverty in Canada*, edited by Maria A. Wallis and Siu-Ming Kwok. Toronto: Canadian Scholar's Press.

Liang, Wenbin, and Tanya Chikritzhs. 2012. "Marital status and alcohol consumption behaviours." *Journal of Substance Use* 17: 84–89.

Lifton, Robert J. 1986. *The Nazi Doctors: Medical Killing and the Psychology of Genocide.* New York: Basic.

Lillard, Lee A., and Waite, Linda J. 1995. "Till death do us part: Marital disruptions and mortality." *American Journal of Sociology* 100: 1131–1156.

Lindo, Jason M. 2011. "Parental job loss and infant health." *Journal of Health Economics* 30: 869–879.

Lindström, Martin. 2009. "Marital status, social capital, material conditions and self-rated health: A population-based study." *Health Policy* 93: 172–179.

Lingard, L., K. Garwood, C. F. Schryer, and M. M. Spafford. 2003. "A certain art of uncertainty: Case presentation and the development of professional identity." *Social Science and Medicine* 56: 603–616.

Link, Bruce G., and Jo Phelan. 1995. "Social conditions as fundamental causes of disease." *Journal of Health and Social Behavior* 35: 80–94.

———. 2002. "McKeown and the idea that social conditions are fundamental causes of disease." *American Journal of Public Health* 92: 730–732.

Lipman, Ellen L., Dan R. Offord, and Michael H. Boyle. 1994. "Relation between economic disadvantage and psychosocial morbidity in children." *Canadian Medical Association Journal* 151: 431–437.

Lippman, Abby. 1991. "Prenatal genetic testing and screening: Constructing needs and reinforcing inequities." *American Journal of Law and Medicine* 17: 15–50.

Liu S., S. W. Wen, D. McMillan, K. Trouton, D. Fowler, and C. McCourt. 2000. "Increased neonatal readmission rate associated with decreased length of hospital stay at birth in Canada." *Canadian Journal of Public Health* 91: 46–50.

Loe, Meika. 2004. *The Rise of Viagra: How the Little Blue Pill Changed Sex in America.* New York: New York University Press.

Loewenberg, Samuel. 2012. "Grassroots project shines hope on Nairobi slum life." *The Lancet* 379: 108–109.

Lonsdale, Susan. 1990. *Women and Disability.* Basingstoke, U.K.: Macmillan.

Low, Carissa A., Rebecca C. Thurston, and Karen A. Matthews. 2010. "Psychosocial factors in the development of heart disease in women: Current research and future directions." *Psychosomatic Medicine* 72: 842–854.

Ludmerer, Kenneth M. 1985. *Learning to Heal: The Development of American Medical Education.* New York: Basic.

Luginaah, Isaac, David Elkins, Eleanor Maticka-Tyndale, Tamara Landry, and Mercy Mathui. 2005. "Challenges of a pandemic: HIV/AIDS-related problems affecting Kenyan widows." *Social Science and Medicine* 60: 1219–1228.

Luhrmann, Tanya M. 2000. *Of Two Minds: The Growing Disorder in American Psychiatry.* New York: Knopf.

Lundberg, George D. 2001. *Severed Trust: Why American Medicine Hasn't Been Fixed.* New York: Basic.

Lynch, Mary E. 2011. "The need for a Canadian pain strategy." *Pain Research and Management: Journal of the Canadian Pain Society* 16: 77–80.

MacDermot, H. E. 1952. "Early medical education in North America." *Canadian Medical Association Journal* 67: 370–375.

Macintyre, Sally. 1997. "The Black Report and beyond: What are the issues?" *Social Science and Medicine* 44: 723–745.

Madi, Nawaf, Helen Zhao and Jerry Fang Li. 2007. "Hospital readmissions for patients with mental illness in Canada." *Healthcare Quarterly* 10: 30–32.

Madill, Anna, and Gary Latchford. 2005. "Identity change and the human dissection experience over the first year of medical training." *Social Science and Medicine* 60: 1637–1647.

Mairs, Nancy. 1986. *Plaintext.* Tucson: University of Arizona Press.

Malacrida, Claudia. 2003. *Cold Comfort: Mothers, Professionals, and Attention Deficit Disorder.* Toronto: University of Toronto Press.

Manning, Nick. 2011. "The reform of health policy in China—Left behind in the race to industrialize?" *Social Policy & Administration* 45: 649–661.

Mannino David M., and A. Sonia Buist. 2007. "Global burden of COPD: risk factors, prevalence, and future trends." *The Lancet* 370: 765–773.

Manuel, Douglas G., Richard Perez, Carol Bennett, Laura Rosella, Monica Taljaard, Melody Roberts, Ruth Sanderson, Meltem Tuna, Peter Tanuseputra, and Heather Manson. 2012. *Seven More Years: The Impact of Smoking, Alcohol, Diet, Physical Activity and Stress on Health and Life Expectancy in Ontario.* An ICES/PHO Report. Toronto: Institute for Clinical Evaluative Sciences and Public Health Ontario.

Marins, Jose Ricardo P., Leda F. Jamal, Sanny Y. Chen, Marilisa B. Barros, Esther S. Hudes, Aristides A. Barbosa, Pedro Chequer, Paulo R. Teixeira, and Norman Hearst. 2003. "Dramatic improvement in survival among adult Brazilian AIDS patients." *AIDS* 17: 1675–1682.

Markle, Gerald E., and Frances B. McCrea. 2008. *What if Medicine Disappeared?* Albany, NY: State University of New York Press.

Markoff, John. 2002. "Technology's toxic trash is sent to poor nations." *New York Times* February 25: C1+.

Marmor, Theodore. 2012. "The unwritten rules of cross-national policy analysis." *Health Economics, Policy and Law* 7: 19–20.

Marmot, Michael G. 2002. "The influence of income on health." *Health Affairs* 21: 31–46.

———. 2004. *The Status Syndrome: How Your Social Standing Directly Affects Your Health and Life Expectancy.* London: Bloomsbury.

Marmot, M. G., H. Bosma, and H. Hemingway. 1997. "Contribution of job control and other risk factors to social variations in coronary heart disease incidence." *The Lancet* 350: 235–239.

Martin, Emily. 1987. *The Woman in the Body.* Boston: Beacon.

Masocco, Maria, Maurizio Pompili, Monica Vichi, Nicola Vanacore, David Lester, and Roberto Tatarelli. 2008. "Suicide and marital status in Italy." *Psychiatric Quarterly* 79: 275–285.

Mate-Kole, C., M. Freschi, and A. Robin. 1990. "A controlled study of psychological and social changes after surgical gender reassignment in selected male transsexuals." *British Journal of Psychiatry* 157, 261–264.

Mathauer Inke, Eleonora Cavagnero, Gabriel Vivas, and Guy Carrin. 2010. *Health Financing Challenges and Institutional Options to Move towards Universal Coverage in Nicaragua.* World Health Report 2010. Health systems financing: The path to universal coverage. Background Paper. No 24. Geneva, Switzerland: World Health Organization.

Mathers, Colin D., Ties Boerma, and Doris Ma Fat. 2009. "Global and regional causes of death." *British Medical Bulletin* 92: 7–32.

Matloff, Ellen T., and Karina L. Brierly. 2010. "The double-helix revealed: The story of the BRCA patent." *The Lancet* 376: 314–315.

Mayes, Rick, Catherine Bagwell, and Jennifer Erkulwater. 2009. *Medicating Children: ADHD and Pediatric Mental Health.* Cambridge, MA: Harvard University Press.

McCarthy, John D., and Mayer N. Zald. 1973. *The Trend of Social Movements in America: Professionalization and Resource Mobilization.* Morristown, NJ: General Learning.

McDonough, Peggy. 2001. "Work and health in the global economy." Pp. 195–222 in *Unhealthy Times: Political Economy Perspectives on Health and Care in Canada,* edited by Pat Armstrong, Hugh Armstrong, and David Coburn. Oxford: Oxford University Press.

McDonough, Peggy, and Pat Berglund. 2003. "Histories of poverty and self-rated health trajectories." *Journal of Health and Social Behavior* 44: 198–214.

McDonough, Peggy, Amanda Sacker, and Richard D. Wiggins. 2005. "Time on my side? Life course trajectories of poverty and health." *Social Science and Medicine* 61: 1795–1808.

McDonough, Peggy, and Lisa Strohschein. 2003. "Age and the gender gap in distress." *Women and Health* 38: 1–20.

McFarland Bentson, Douglas Bigelow, Brigid Zani, Jason Newsom, and Mark Kaplan. 2002. "Complementary and alternative medicine use in Canada and the United States." *American Journal of Public Health* 92: 1616–1618.

McGrail, Kimberlyn M., Eddy van Doorslaer, Nancy A. Ross, and Claudia Sanmartin. 2009. "Income-related health inequalities in Canada and the United States: A decomposition analysis." *American Journal of Public Health* 99: 1856–1863.

McGrail, Kimberlyn M., Margaret J. McGregor, Marcy Cohen, Robert B. Tate, and Lisa A. Ronald. 2007. "For-profit versus not-for-profit delivery of long-term care." *Canadian Medical Association Journal* 176: 57–58.

McIntyre, Lynn, Sarah K. Connor, and James Warren. 2000. "Child hunger in Canada: Results of the 1994 National Longitudinal Survey of Children and Youth." *Canadian Medical Association Journal* 163: 961–965.

McIntyre, Lynn N., Theresa Glanville, Kim D. Raine, Jutta B. Dayle, Bonnie Anderson, and Noreen Battaglia. 2003. "Do low-income lone mothers compromise their nutrition to feed their children?" *Canadian Medical Association Journal* 168: 686–691.

McKendry, Rachael, and Tom Langford. 2001. "Legalized, regulated, but unfunded: midwifery's laborious professionalization in Alberta, Canada, 1975–99." *Social Science and Medicine* 53: 531–542.

McKeown, Thomas. 1979. *The Role of Medicine: Dream, Mirage, or Nemesis?* Princeton, NJ: Princeton University Press.

McKeown, Thomas, R. G. Brown, and R. G. Record. 1972. "An interpretation of the modern rise of population in Europe." *Population Studies* 26: 345–382.

McKeown, Thomas, R. G. Record, and R. D. Turner. 1975. "An interpretation of the decline of mortality in England and Wales during the twentieth century." *Population Studies* 26: 391–422.

McKinlay, John B. 1994. "A case for refocusing upstream: The political economy of illness." Pp. 509–530 in *The Sociology of Health and Illness,* edited by Peter Conrad and Rachelle Kern. New York: St. Martin's Press.

McKinlay, John B., and Sonja J. McKinlay. 1977. "The questionable effect of medical measures on the decline of mortality in the United States in the twentieth century." *Milbank Memorial Fund Quarterly* 55: 405–428.

Mclean, Sheila A. M. 2007. "What and who are clinical ethics committees for?" *Journal of Medical Ethics* 33: 497–500.

McLeod, Christopher B., John N. Lavis, Cameron A. Mustard, and Greg L. Stoddart. 2003. "Income inequality, household income, and health status in Canada: A prospective cohort study." *American Journal of Public Health* 93: 1287–1293.

McLeod, Jane D., and Karen Kaiser. 2004. "Child emotional and behavioral problems and educational attainment." *American Sociological Review* 69: 636–658.

McLeod, Jane D., and Michael J. Shanahan. 1996. "Trajectories of poverty and children's mental health." *Journal of Health and Social Behavior* 37: 207–220.

McNeil, Donald G. 2002. "With folk medicine on rise, health group is monitoring." *New York Times* May 17: A9.

Mechanic, David. 1989. *Mental Health and Social Policy.* 3rd ed. Englewood Cliffs, NJ: Prentice Hall.

———, David. 1995. "Sociological dimensions of illness behavior." *Social Problems* 41: 1207–1216.

———. 2006. *The Truth about Health Care.* New Brunswick, NJ: Rutgers University Press.

Mechanic, David, and David A. Rochefort. 1996. "Comparative medical systems." *Annual Review of Sociology* 22: 239–270.

Melosh, Barbara. 1982. *"The Physician's Hand": Work Culture and Conflict in American Nursing.* Philadelphia: Temple University Press.

Melucci, Alberto. 1995. "The process of collective identity." Pp. 41–63 in *Social Movements and Culture,* edited by Hank Johnston and Bert Klandermans. Minneapolis: University of Minnesota Press.

Mendis, Kamini, Barbara J. Sina, Paola Marchesini, and Richard Carter. 2001. "The neglected burden of plasmodium vivax malaria." *The American Society of Tropical Medicine and Hygiene* 64: 97–106.

Menec, Verena, Lisa Lix, and Leonard MacWilliam. 2005. "Trends in the health status of older Manitobans, 1985–1999." *Canadian Journal on Aging* 24: 5–14.

Messer, Ellen. 1997. "Intra-household allocation of food and health care: Current findings and understandings—Introduction." *Social Science and Medicine* 44: 1675–1684.

Metcalfe, Amy, Jeanne Williams, Jane McChesney, Scott B. Patten, and Nathalie Jetté. 2010. "Use of complementary and alternative medicine by those with a chronic disease and the general population—Results of a national population based survey." *Complementary and Alternative Medicine* 10: 1–6.

Metzl, Jonathan. 2003. "'Mother's little helper': The crisis of psychoanalysis and the Miltown resolution." *Gender and History* 15: 240–267.

Meyerowitz, Beth E., Janice G. Williams, and Jocelyne Gessner. 1987. "Perceptions of controllability and attitudes toward cancer and cancer patients." *Journal of Applied Social Psychology* 17: 471–492.

Midodzi, William K., Brian H. Rowe, Carina M. Majaesic, Leslie Duncan Saunders, and Ambikaipakan Senthilselvan. 2010. "Early life factors associated with incidence of physician-diagnosed asthma in preschool children: Results from the Canadian Early Childhood Development Cohort Study." *Journal of Asthma* 47: 7–13.

Millar, Wayne J. 1996. "Chronic pain." *Health Reports* 7: 47–52.

Millenson, Michael L. 1997. *Demanding Medical Excellence: Doctors and Accountability in the Information Age.* Chicago: University of Chicago Press.

Milloy, John. 2008. *Indian Act Colonialism: A Century of Dishonour, 1869–1969.* Research paper for the National Centre for First Nations Governance. Ottawa: National Centre for First Nations Governance.

Mills, C. Wright. 1959. *The Sociological Imagination*. New York: Grove.

Mintzes, Barbara. 2002. "For and against: Direct to consumer advertising is medicalising normal human experience: For." *BMJ* 324: 908–909.

Mintzes, Barbara. 2009. "Should Canada allow direct-to-consumer advertising on prescription drugs? No." *Canadian Family Physician* 55: 131–133.

Mior, Silvano A., and Audrey Laporte. 2008. "Economic and resource status of the chiropractic profession in Ontario, Canada: A challenge or an opportunity." *Journal of Manipulative and Physiological Therapeutics* 31: 104–114.

Mishler, Elliot G. 1981. "Viewpoint: Critical perspectives on the biomedical model." Pp. 1–23 in *Social Contexts of Health, Illness, and Patient Care*, edited by Elliot G. Mishler. Cambridge, U.K.: Cambridge University Press.

Mizrahi, Terry. 1986. *Getting Rid of Patients: Contradictions in the Socialization of Physicians*. New Brunswick, NJ: Rutgers University Press.

Moen, Phyllis, Erin L. Kelly, Eric Tranby, and Qinlei Huang. 2011. "Changing work, changing health: Can real work-time flexibility promote health behaviors and well-being?" *Journal of Health and Social Behavior* 52: 404–429.

Mohamed, Ahmed D., and Barbara J. Sahakian. 2012. "The ethics of elective psychopharmacology." *International Journal of Neuropsychopharmacology* 15: 559–571.

Monaghan, Lee. F. 1999. "Challenging medicine? Bodybuilding, drugs and risk." *Sociology of Health and Illness* 21: 707–734.

———. 2002. "Vocabularies of motive for illicit steroid use among bodybuilders." *Social Science and Medicine* 55: 695–708.

Mootz, Robert D., Daniel C. Cherkin, Carson E. Odegard, David M. Eisenberg, James P. Barassi, and Richard A. Deyo. 2005. "Characteristics of chiropractic practitioners, patients, and encounters in Massachusetts and Arizona." *Journal of Manipulative and Physiological Therapeutics* 28: 645–653.

Morra, Dante, Sean Nicholson, Wendy Levinson, David N. Gans, Terry Hammons, and Lawrence P. Casalino. 2011. "US physician practices versus Canadians: Spending nearly four times as much money interacting with payers." *Health Affairs* 30: 1–11.

Morris, Jenny. 1991. *Pride against Prejudice: Transforming Attitudes to Disability*. London: Women's Press.

Morrison, Duane R., and Mary J. Coiro. 1999. "Parent conflict and marital disruption: Do children benefit when high-conflict marriages are dissolved?" *Journal of Marriage and the Family* 61: 626–637.

Mossakowski, Krysia N. 2008. "Is the duration of poverty and unemployment a risk factor for heavy drinking?" *Social Science and Medicine* 67: 947–955.

Mousa, Shimaa M., Ibrahim A. Seifeldin, Ahmed Hablas, Eman S. Elbana, and Amr S. Soliman. 2011. "Patterns of seeking medical care among Egyptian breast cancer patients: Relationship to late-stage presentation." *The Breast* 20: 555–561.

Mullan, Fitzhugh. 2002. *Big Doctoring in America: Profiles in Primary Care*. Berkeley: University of California Press.

Mundinger, Mary O., Robert L. Kane, Elizabeth R. Lenz, Annette M. Totten, Wei-Yann Tsai, Paul D. Cleary, William T. Friedewald, Albert L. Siu, and Michael L. Shelanski. 2000. "Primary care outcomes in patients treated by nurse practitioners or physicians: A randomized trial." *Journal of the American Medical Association* 283: 59–68.

Murdocca, Carmela. 2010. "'There is something in that water': Race, nationalism and legal violence." *Law and Social Inquiry* 35 (2): 369–402.

Murphy, Brian, Xuelin Zhang, and Claude Dionne. 2012. *Low Income in Canada: A Multi-line and Multi-index Perspective*. Catalogue No. 75F0002M—No. 001. Ottawa: Minister of Industry.

Murphy, Mike, Karen Glaser, and Emily Grundy. 1997. "Marital status and long-term illness in Great Britain." *Journal of Marriage and Family* 59: 156–164.

Murphy, Timothy F. 2011. "When choosing the traits of children is hurtful to others." *Journal of Medical Ethics* 37: 105–108.

Murray, Christopher J. L., and Alan D. Lopez. 1996. *The Global Burden of Disease*. Cambridge, MA: Harvard University Press.

Musick, Kelly, and Larry Bumpass. 2012. "Reexamining the case for marriage: Union formation and changes in well-being." *Journal of Marriage and Family* 74: 1–18.

Mustard, Cameron A., Amber Bielecky, Jacob Etches, Russell Wilkins, Michael Tjepkema, Benjamin C. Amick, Peter M. Smith, and Kristan J. Aronson. 2010. "Avoidable mortality for causes amenable to medical care, by occupation in Canada, 1991–2001." *Canadian Journal of Public Health* 101: 500–506.

Mustard, Cameron A., Shelley Derksen, Jean-Marie Berthelot, Michael Wolfson, and Leslie L. Roos. 1997. "Age-specific, education and income gradients in morbidity and mortality in a Canadian province." *Social Science and Medicine* 45: 383–397.

Nasca, Philip C., and Harris Pastides. 2001. *Fundamentals of Cancer Epidemiology.* Gaithersburg, MD: Aspen Publishers.

Naylor, C. David. 1995. "Grey zones of clinical practice: Some limits to evidence-based medicine." *The Lancet* 345: 840–842.

———. 1999. "Health care in Canada: Incrementalism under fiscal distress." *Health Affairs* 18: 9–26.

Nestlé, Marion. 2002. *Food Politics: How the Food Industry Influences Nutrition and Health.* Berkeley: University of California Press.

Niccolai, Linda M., Sergei V. Verevochkin, Olga V. Toussova, Edward White, Russel Barour, Andrei P. Kozlov, and Robert Heimer. 2010. "Estimates of HIV incidence among drug users in St. Petersburg, Russia: Continued growth of a rapidly expanding epidemic." *European Journal of Public Health* 21: 613–619.

Nichter, Mark, and Elizabeth Cartwright. 1991. "Saving the children for the tobacco industry." *Medical Anthropology Quarterly* 5: 236–256.

Nomaguchi, Kei M., Melissa A. Milkie, and Suzanne M. Bianchi. 2005. "Time strains and psychological well-being: Do dual-earner mothers and fathers differ?" *Journal of Family Issues* 26: 756–792.

Okiro, Emelda A., Favid Bitira, Gladys Mbabazi, Arthur Mpimbaza, Victor A. Alegana, Ambrose O. Talisuna, and Robert W. Snow. 2011. "Increasing malaria hospital admissions in Uganda between 1999 and 2009." *BMC Medicine* 9: 1–11.

Oldstone, Michael, B. A. 2010. *Viruses, Plagues and History: Past, Present and Future.* New York: Oxford University Press.

Oliver, Lisa N., and Michael V. Hayes. 2005. "Neighbourhood socio-economic status and the prevalence of overweight Canadian children and youth." *Canadian Journal of Public Health* 96: 415–420.

Olshansky, S. Jay, Douglas J. Passaro, Ronald C. Hershow, Jennifer Layden, Bruce A. Carnes, Jacob Brody, Leonard Hayflick, Robert N. Butler, David B. Allison, and David S. Ludwig. 2005. "A potential decline in life expectancy in the United States in the 21st century." *The New England Journal of Medicine* 352: 1138–1145.

Omran, Abdel R. 1971. "The epidemiological transition." *Milbank Memorial Fund Quarterly* 49: 509–538.

O'Neill, Michel, and Ann Pederson, 1994. "Two analytic paths for understanding Canadian developments in health promotion." In *Health Promotion in Canada: Provincial, National and International Perspectives,* edited by Ann Pederson, Michel O'Neill, and Irving Rootman. W. B. Saunders: Toronto.

Ontario Health Quality Council. 2011. *2011 Report on Ontario's Health System.* Ottawa: Author.

Ontario Home Care Association. 2010. Home Care in 2010—Essential for an Aging Population. Ottawa: Author.

Ontario Ministry of Health and Long-Term Care. 2012. *Ontario Wait Times Strategy.* http://www.health.gov.on.ca/en/public/programs/waittimes/strategy.aspx, accessed March 2012.

Or, Zeynep, Chantal Cases, Melanie Lisac, Karsten Vranbaek, Ulrika Winblad, and Gwyn Bevan. 2010. "Are health problems systemic? Politics of access and choice under Beveridge and Bismarck systems." *Health Economics, Policy and Law* 5: 269–293.

O'Reilly, Richard. 2004. "Why are community treatment orders controversial?" *Canadian Journal of Psychiatry* 49: 579–584.

Organisation for Economic Co-operation and Development (OECD). 2011. *Health at a glance 2011: OECD Indicators.* http://www.oecd.org/health/healthataglance, accessed June 2012.

Orr, Robert D., and Eliot Moon. 1993. "Effectiveness of an ethics consultation ser-vice." *Journal of Family Practice* 36: 49–53.

Osborne, Cynthia. 2012. "Further comments on the papers by Marks and Regnerus." *Social Science Research* 41: 779–783.

Osherson, Samuel, and Lorna Amara Singham. 1981. "The machine metaphor in medicine." Pp. 218–249 in *Social Contexts of Health, Illness, and Patient Care,* edited by Elliot G. Mishler. Cambridge, U.K.: Cambridge University Press.

Ostry, Aleck. 2009. "The foundations of national hospital insurance." *Canadian Bulletin of Medical History* 26: 261–281.

Otero, Gerardo, and Kerry Preibisch. 2009. *Farmworker Health and Safety: Challenges for British Columbia.* http://awa-ata.ca/wp-content/uploads/2009/10/farmworker_health_safety2009.pdf, accessed June 2012.

Otto, Mary. 2007. "For want of a dentist." *Washington Post* February 28: B1.

———. 2008. "Md. Praised for Medicaid changes since death." February 15: B1.

Oxfam International. 2010. *The Climate Changes, Threatens and Demands Adaptation: A Look at the Cuban Experience of Protection against Climate Change.* London: Author.

Pampel, Fred. 2007. "National income, inequality and global patterns of cigarette use." *Social Forces* 86: 455–466.

Parsons, Talcott. 1951. *The Social System.* New York: Free Press.

Partridge, Bradley J., Stephanie K. Bell, Jayne C. Lucke, Sarah Yeates, and Wayne D. Hall. 2011. "Smart drugs 'as common as coffee': Media hype about neuroenhancement." *PLoS ONE* 6: 1–8.

Paterson, Stephanie. 2011. "Midwives, women and the state: (De)constructing midwives and pregnant women in Ontario, Canada." *Canadian Journal of Political Science* 44: 483–505.

Patterson, Marian A. 1958. "The cholera epidemic of 1832 in York, Upper Canada." *Journal of the Medical Library Association* 46: 165–184.

Payer, Lynn. 1996. *Medicine and Culture.* Rev. ed. New York: Holt.

Pearlin, Leonard I. 1989. "The sociological study of stress." *Journal of Health and Social Behavior* 30: 241–256.

———. 1992. "Structure and meaning in medical sociology." *Journal of Health and Social Behavior* 33: 1–9.

———. 2010a. "The sociological study of stress." In *The Sociology of Mental Illness: A Comprehensive Reader,* edited by Jane D. McLeod and Eric R. Wright. New York: Oxford University Press.

———. 2010b. "The life course and the stress process: Some conceptual comparisons." *Journal of Gerontology: Social Sciences* 65B: 207–215.

Pearlin, Leonard I., Carol S. Aneshensel, and Allen J. LeBlanc. 1997. "The forms and mechanisms of stress proliferation: The case of AIDS caregivers." *Journal of Health and Social Behavior* 38: 223–236.

Pearlin, Leonard I., M. Lieberman, Elizabeth Menaghan, and J. Mullan. 1981. "The stress process." *Journal of Health and Social Behavior* 22: 337–355.

Peng, Philip, Manon Choiniere, Dominique Dion, Howard Intrater, Sandra Le Forte, Mary Lynch, May Ong, Saifee Rashiq, Gregg Tkachuk, and Yves Veillette. 2007. "Challenges in accessing multidisciplinary pain treatment facilities in Canada." *Canadian Journal of Anesthesia* 54: 977–984.

Percival, John, and Julienne Hanson 2006. "Big brother or brave new world? Telecare and its implications for older people's independence and social inclusion." *Critical Social Policy,* 26: 888–909.

Pescosolido, Bernice A. 1992. "Beyond rational choice: The social dynamics of how people seek help." *American Journal of Sociology* 97: 1096–1138.

Petersen, Alan, and Deborah Lupton. 1996. *The New Public Health: Health and Self in the Age of Risk.* London: Sage Publications.

Phelan, Jo C., Bruce G. Link, and Parisa Tehranifar. 2010. "Social conditions as fundamental causes of disease: Theory, evidence and policy implications." *Journal of Health and Social Behavior* 51: S28–S40.

Phillips, Marilynn J. 1985. "'Try harder': The experience of disability and the dilemma of normalization." *Social Science and Medicine* 22: 45–57.

———. 1990. "Damaged goods: Oral narratives of the experience of disability in American culture." *Social Science and Medicine* 30: 849–857.

Pierret, Janine. 2003. "The illness experience: State of knowledge and perspectives for research." *Sociology of Health and Illness* 25: 4–22.

Pilote, Louise, Lawrence Joseph, Patrick Belisle, and John Penrod. 2003. "Universal health insurance coverage does not eliminate inequities in access to cardiac procedures after acute myocardial infarction." *American Heart Journal* 146: 1030–1037.

Pitters, S. 2002. "Long-term care facilities." Pp. 163–201 in *Continuing the Care: The Issues and Challenges for Long-Term Care,* edited by M. Stephenson and E. Sawyer. Ottawa: CHA Press.

Polakovic, Gary. 2002. "Asia's wind-born pollution a hazardous export to U.S." *Los Angeles Times* April 26: A1+.

Poland, Blake, David Coburn, Ann Robertson, and Joan Eakin. 1998. "Wealth, equity, and health care: A critique of a 'population health' perspective on the determinants of health." *Social Science and Medicine* 46: 785–798.

Population Reference Bureau. 2007. *2007 World Population Data Sheet.* Washington, DC: Author.

———. 2012. *2012 World Population Data Sheet.* Washington, DC: Author.

Powell-Dunford, Nicole C., Amanda S. Cuda, Jeffrey L. Moore, Mark S. Crago, Amanda M. Kelly. 2011. "Menstrual suppression for combat operations: Advantages of oral contraceptive pills." *Women's Health* 21: 86–91.

Power, Elaine M. 2005. "Determinants of healthy eating among low-income Canadians." *Canadian Journal of Public Health* 96: S37–S42.

Prus, Steven G. 2011. "Comparing social determinants of self-rated health across the United States and Canada." *Social Science and Medicine* 73: 50–59.

Public Health Agency of Canada. 2009. *What Mothers Say: The Canadian Maternal Experiences Survey.* Ottawa: Author.

Purewal, Navtej K. 2010. *Son Preference: Sex Selection, Gender and Culture in South Asia.* Oxford: Berg.

Quadagno, Jill. 2005. *One Nation Uninsured: Why The U.S. Has No National Health Insurance.* New York: Oxford University Press.

Quinn, Thomas C., and Julie Overbaugh. 2005. "HIV/AIDS in Women: An expanding epidemic." *Science* 308: 1582–1583.

Raina, Parminder, Steven Dukeshire, Joan Lindsay, and Larry W. Chambers. 1998. "Chronic conditions and disabilities among seniors: An analysis of population-based health and activity limitation surveys." *Annals of Epidemiology* 8: 402–409.

Raising the Roof. 2009. *Youth Homelessness in Canada: The Road to Solutions.* http://www.raisingtheroof.org/Our-Programs/Youthworks.aspx, accessed February 2012.

Ramage-Morin, Pamela L., and Heather Gilmour. 2010. "Chronic pain at ages 12 to 44." *Health Reports* 21: 1–10.

Randhawa, Jean, and Rod Riley. 1996. "Mental Health Statistics, 1982–83 to 1992–93." *Health Reports* 7: 55–61.

Ratcliff, Kathryn Strother. 2002. *Women and Health: Power, Technology, Inequality and Conflict in a Gendered World.* Boston: Allyn and Bacon.

Rawcliffe, Carole. 2006. *Leprosy in Medieval England.* Woodbridge: Boydell Press.

Rawls, John. 1971. *A Theory of Justice.* Cambridge, MA: Harvard University Press.

Reading, Richard. 1997. "Social disadvantage and infection in childhood." *Sociology of Health and Illness* 19: 395–414.

Reaume, Geoffrey. 2002. "Lunatic to patient to person: Nomenclature in psychiatric history and the influence of patients' activism in North America." *International Journal of Law and Psychiatry* 25: 405–426.

Redlich, Fredrick C. 1978. "Medical ethics under National Socialism." Pp. 1015–1019 in *Encyclopedia of Bioethics,* edited by Warren T. Reich. New York: Free Press.

Reid, Jessica L., David Hammond, and Pete Driezen. 2010. "Socio-economic status and smoking in Canada, 1999–2006: Has there been any progress on disparities in tobacco use?" *Canadian Journal of Public Health* 101: 73–78.

Reinhard, Susan, and Allan V. Horwitz. 1996. "Caregiver burden: Differentiating the content and consequences of family caregiving." *Journal of Marriage and the Family* 57: 741–750.

Reinhardt, Uwe E., Peter S. Hussey, and Gerard F. Anderson. 2004. "U.S. health care spending in an international context." *Health Affairs* 23: 10–25.

Renaud, Marc. 1994. "The future: Hygeia or Panakeia?" Pp. 286–317 in *Why are Some People Healthy and Others Not? The Determinants of Health of Populations,* edited by Robert G. Evans, Morris L. Barer, and Theodore R. Marmor. New York: Aldine de Gruyter.

Repetti, R. L., K. A. Matthews, and I. Waldron. 1989. "Effects of paid employment on women's mental and physical health." *American Psychologist* 44: 1394–1401.

Reverby, Susan. 1987. *Ordered to Care: The Dilemma of American Nursing.* New York: Cambridge University Press.

Revkin, Andrew. 2008. "Turning schools from death traps into havens." *New York Times* May 27.

Rhodes, R., and J. J. Strain. 2004. "Whistleblowing in academic medicine." *Journal of Medical Ethics* 30: 35–39.

Ricciardelli, Rosemary, and Kimberley Clow. 2009. "Men, appearance, and cosmetic surgery: The role of self-esteem and comfort with the body." *Canadian Journal of Sociology* 34: 105–134.

Riches, G. 2002. "Food banks and food security: Welfare reform, human rights and social policy. Lessons from Canada?" *Social Policy and Administration* 36: 648–663.

Richmond, Chantal A. M., and Nancy A. Ross. 2009. "The determinants of First Nation and Inuit health: A critical population health approach." *Health and Place* 15: 403–411.

Richter, Linda M., and Chris Desmond. 2008. "Targeting AIDS orphans and child-headed households? A perspective from national surveys in South Africa, 1995–2005." *AIDS Care* 20: 1019–1028.

Riley, James C. 2007. *Low Income, Social Growth, and Good Health: A History of Twelve Countries.* Berkeley: University of California Press.

Riordan, Tim. 2004. *Exploring the Circle: Mental Illness, Homelessness, and the Criminal Justice System in Canada.* Ottawa: Library of Parliament: Parliamentary Information and Research Services.

Risse, Guenter B. 1988. "Epidemics and history: Ecological perspectives and social responses." Pp. 33–66 in *AIDS: The Burdens of History,* edited by Elizabeth Fee and Daniel M. Fox. Berkeley: University of California Press.

Roberts, Les, Riyadh Lafta, Richard Garfield, Jamal Khudhairi, and Gilbert Burnham. 2004. "Mortality before and after the 2003 invasion of Iraq: Cluster sample survey." *The Lancet* 364: 1857–1864.

Robertson, Gerald B. 2008. "A view of the future: Emerging developments in health care liability." *Health Law Journal Special Edition:* 1–12.

Rockwood, Kenneth, Xiaowei Song, and Arnold Mitnitski. 2011. "Changes in relative fitness and frailty across the lifespan: Evidence from the Canadian National Population Health Survey." *Canadian Medical Association Journal* 183: E487–E494.

Rohter, Larry. 2004. "Tracking the sale of a kidney on a path of poverty and hope." *New York Times* May 23: A1+.

Romans, Sarah, Marsha Cohen, and Tonia Forte. 2011. "Rates of depression and anxiety in urban and rural Canada." *Social Psychiatry and Psychiatric Epidemiology* 46: 567–575.

Rooks, Judith. 1997. *Midwifery and Childbirth in America.* Philadelphia: Temple University Press.

Roos, Noralou P., and Cameron A. Mustard. 1997. "Variation in health and health care use by socioeconomic status in Winnipeg, Canada: Does the system work well? Yes and no." *The Milbank Quarterly* 75: 89–111.

Rose, Nikolas. 2003. "Neurochemical selves." *Society* 267: 46–59.

———. 2007. "Molecular biopolitics, somatic ethics and the spirit of biocapital." *Social Theory and Health* 5: 3–29.

Rosenberg, Charles E. 1987. *The Care of Strangers: The Rise of America's Hospital System.* New York: Basic.

Rosenfeld, Dana, and Christopher A. Faircloth (eds). 2005. *Medicalized Masculinities.* Philadelphia: Temple University Press.

Rosenfield, Sarah. 2012. "Triple jeopardy? Mental health at the intersection of gender, race, and class." *Social Science and Medicine* 74: 1791-1801.

———. 1999. "Splitting the difference: Gender, the self, and mental health." In *Handbook of the Sociology of Mental Health,* edited by Carol S. Aneshensel and Jo C. Phelan. London: Kluwer Academic/Plenum Publishers.

Rosenstock, Irwin M. 1966. "Why people use health services." *Milbank Memorial Fund Quarterly* 44: 94–127.

Ross, Catherine E., and Sung Joon Jang. 2000. "Neighborhood disorder, fear and mistrust: The buffering role of social ties with neighbors." *American Journal of Community Psychology* 28: 401–419.

Ross, Catherine E., and John Mirowsky. 2009. "Neighborhood disorder, subjective alienation, and distress." *Journal of Health and Social Behavior* 50: 49–64.

Ross, Catherine E., and Chia-ling Wu. 1995. "The links between education and health." *American Sociological Review* 60: 719–745.

Ross, Nancy A., Heather Gilmour, and Kaberi Dasgupta. 2010. "14-year diabetes incidence: The role of socio-economic status." *Health Reports* 21: 19–28.

Rothman, Barbara K. 2000. *Recreating Motherhood.* New York: Routledge Press.

Rothman, David J. 1991. *Strangers at the Bedside: A History of How Law and Bioethics Transformed Medical Decision-Making.* New York: Basic.

———. 1997. *Beginnings Count: The Technological Imperative in American Health Care.* New York: Oxford University Press.

Ruggeri, Joe, and Yang Zou. 2007. "The fiscal burden of rising dependency rates." *Population Research and Policy Review* 26: 185–201.

Rush, Brian, Karen Urbanoski, Diego Bassani, Saulo Castel, T. Cameron Wild, Carol Strike, Dennis Kimberley, and Julian Somers. 2008. "Prevalence of co-occurring substance abuse and other mental disorders in the Canadian population." *Canadian Journal of Psychiatry* 53: 800–809.

Rutter, Michael. 1989. "Pathways from childhood to adult life." *Journal of Child Psychology and Psychiatry* 30: 23–51.

Safran, Stephen P. 1998. "The first century of disability portrayal in film: An analysis of the literature." *Journal of Special Education* 31: 467–479.

Safriet, Barbara J. 1992. "Health care dollars and regulatory sense: The role of advanced practice nursing." *Yale Journal on Regulation* 9: 417–487.

Sakr, M., J. Angus, J. Perrin, C. Nixon, J. Nicholl, and J. Wardrope. 1999. "Care of minor injuries by emergency NPs or junior MDs: A randomized controlled trial." *The Lancet* 354: 1321–1326.

Sandel, Michael. 2007. *The Case against Perfection: Ethics in the Age of Genetic Engineering.* New York: Harvard University Press.

Scheffler, Richard M., Stephen P. Hinshaw, Sepideh Modrek, and Peter Levine. 2007. "The global market for ADHD medications." *Health Affairs* 26: 450–457.

Scheper-Hughes, Nancy 2001. "Commodity fetishism in organs trafficking." *Body and Society* 72: 31–62.

Schicktanz, Silke. 2007. "Why the way we consider the body matters—Reflections on four bioethical perspectives on the human body." *Philosophy, Ethics and Humanities in Medicine* 2: 30–42.

Schieman, Scott, and Paul Glavin. 2008. "Trouble at the border? Gender, flexibility at work, and the work-home interface." *Social Problems* 55: 590–611.

Schlesinger, Mark. 2010. "Choice cuts: Parsing policymakers' pursuit of patient empowerment from an individual perspective." *Health Economics, Policy and Law* 5: 365–387.

Schneider, Andrew, and David McCumber. 2004. *An Air That Kills: How the Asbestos Poisoning of Libby, Montana, Uncovered a National Scandal.* New York: Putnam's Sons.

Schneider, Joseph W., and Peter Conrad. 1983. *Having Epilepsy: The Experience and Control of Illness.* Philadelphia: Temple University Press.

Schneirov, Matthew, and Jonathan David Geczik. 1996. "A diagnosis for our times: Alternative health's submerged networks and the transformation of identities." *Sociological Quarterly* 37: 627–644.

Schoen, Cathy, Sara R. Collins, Jennifer L. Kriss, and Michelle M. Doty. 2008. "How many are underinsured? Trends among U.S. adults, 2003 and 2007." *Health Affairs* Web Exclusive, June 10, 2008. http://content.healthaffairs.org/content/early/2008/06/10/hlthaff.27.4.w298.citation, accessed August 2012.

Schwartz, Robert, Shawn O'Connor, Nadia Minian, Tracey Borland, Alexey Babayan, Roberta Ferrence, Joanna Cohen, and Jolene Dubray. 2010. *Evidence to Inform Smoking Cessation Policymaking in Ontario: A Special Report by the Ontario Tobacco Research Unit.* Toronto: Ontario Tobacco Research Unit.

Scull, Andrew T. 1976. "The decarceration of the mentally ill: A critical view." *Politics and Society* 6: 173–211.

———. 1977. *Decarceration, Community Treatment and the Deviant: A Radical View.* Englewood Cliffs, NJ: Prentice Hall.

———. 1989. *Social Order/Mental Disorder: Anglo-American Psychiatry in Historical Perspective.* Berkeley, CA: University of California Press.

Sealy, Patricia, and Paul C. Whitehead. 2004. "Forty years of deinstitutionalization of psychiatric services in Canada: An empirical assessment." *Canadian Journal of Psychiatry* 49: 249–257.

Sedgh, Gilda, Stanley Henshaw, Susheela Singh, Elisabeth Åhman, and Iqbal H. Shah. 2007. "Induced abortion: Estimated rates and trends worldwide." *The Lancet* 370: 1338–1345.

Sedgh, Gilda, Susheela Singh, Iqbal H. Shah, Elisabeth Ahman, Stanley K. Henshaw, and Akinrinola Bankola. 2012. "Induced abortion: Incidence and trends worldwide from 1995–2008" *The Lancet* 379: 625–632.

Sen, Amartya. 1999. *Development as Freedom.* New York: Knopf.

Sered, Susan Starr, and Rushika Fernandopulle. 2005. *Uninsured in America: Life and Death in the Land of Opportunity.* Berkeley, CA: University of California Press.

Shann, Frank. 2010. "Warfare and children." *Journal of Paediatrics and Child Health* 46: 217–221.

Shapiro, Martin. 1987. *Getting Doctored: Critical Reflections on Becoming a Physician.* Toronto: Between the Lines.

Shields Margot, Margaret D. Carroll, and Cynthia L. Ogden. 2011. *Adult Obesity Prevalence in Canada and the United States.* National Center for Health Statistics data brief, no 56. Hyattsville, MD: National Center for Health Statistics.

Shields, Margot, and Jiajian Chen. 1999. "Health among older adults." *Health Reports* 11: 47–62.

Shilling, Chris. 2003. *The Body and Social Theory.* London: Sage.

Silversides, Ann. 2009. "Provincial experiments aim to lower public drug plan costs." *Canadian Medical Association Journal* 181: 80–82.

Simen-Kapeu, Aline and Paul J. Veugelers. 2010. "Socio-economic gradients in health behaviours and overweight among children in distinct economic settings." *Canadian Journal of Public Health* 101: S32–S38.

Simonds, Wendy, Barbara Katz Rothman, and Bari Meltzer Norman. 2007. *Laboring On: Birth in Transition in the United States.* London, U.K.: Routledge.

Singh-Setia, M., A. Quesnel-Vallee, S. Curtis, and J. Lynch. 2009. "Assessing the role of individual and neighbourhood characteristics in HIV testing: Evidence from a population based survey." *The Open AIDS Journal* 3: 46–54.

Sinha, Samir K. 2011. "Why the elderly could bankrupt Canada and how demographic imperatives will force the redesign of acute care service delivery." *Healthcare Papers* 11: 46–51.

Skocpol, Theda. 1996. *Boomerang: Clinton's Health Security Effort and the Turn Against Government in U.S. Politics.* New York: Norton.

Smith, Elizabeth A., and Ruth E. Malone. 2007. "'We will speak as the smoker': The tobacco industry's smokers' rights groups." *European Journal of Public Health* 17: 306–313.

Smith, Katherine L. W., Flora I. Matheson, Rahim Moineddin, and Richard H. Glazier. 2007. "Gender, income and immigration differences in depression in Canadian urban centres." *Canadian Journal of Public Health* 98: 149–153.

Smith, Peter M., and Amber Bielecky. 2012. "The impact of changes in job strain and its components on the risk of depression." *American Journal of Public Health* 102: 352–358.

Smith-Spangler, Crystal M., Jay Bhattacharya, and Jeremy D. Goldhaber-Fiebert. 2012. "Diabetes, its treatment, and catastrophic medical spending in 35 developing countries." *Diabetes Care* 35: 319–326.

Smyke, Patricia. 1991. *Women and Health.* London: Zed.

Smylie, Janet, Deshayne Fell, Arne Ohlsson, and the Joint Working Group on First Nations, Indian, Inuit, and Métis Infant Mortality of the Canadian Perinatal Surveillance System. 2010. "A review of Aboriginal infant mortality rates in Canada: Striking and persistent Aboriginal/Non-Aboriginal inequities." *Canadian Journal of Public Health* 101: 143–48.

Sohn, Michael, and Hartmut A. G. Bosinski. 2007. "Gender identity disorders: Diagnostic and surgical aspects." *Journal of Sexual Medicine* 4: 1193–1208.

Soons, Judith P. M., and Matthijs Kalmijn. 2009. "Is marriage more than cohabitation? Well-being differences in 30 European countries." *Journal of Marriage and Family* 71: 1141–1157.

Stack, Carol. 1975. *All Our Kin: Strategies for Survival in a Black Community.* New York: Harper & Row.

Starfield, Barbara. 2009. "Commentary: How does 'insurance' improve equity in health?" *International Journal of Epidemiology* 38: 1551–1553.

Starr, Paul. 1982. *The Social Transformation of American Medicine.* New York: Basic.

———. 1994. *The Logic of Health Care Reform: Why and How the President's Plan Will Work.* New York: Penguin.

Statistics Canada. 1983. *Historical Statistics of Canada.* Ottawa: Minister of Industry, Series B35-50.

———. 2008a. *Aboriginal Peoples in Canada: Inuit, Métis, and First Nations, 2006 Census.* Cat. No. 97-558-XIE. Ottawa: Minister of Industry.

———. 2008b. *Canadian demographics at a glance.* Catalogue No. 91-003-X. Ottawa: Minister of Industry.

———. 2010. *Healthy People, Healthy Places.* Cat. No. 82-229-XWE. Ottawa: Author. http://www.statcan.gc.ca/pub/82-229-x/2009001/demo/int1-eng.htm, accessed August 2012.

———. 2011. *Leading Causes of Death in Canada, 2008.* Cat. No. 84-215-XWE, Tables 1-1 to 1-10 and Table 2. Ottawa: Minister of Industry. http://www.statcan.gc.ca/pub/84-215-x/2011001/tbls-eng.htm, accessed August 2012.

———. 2012a. Health Trends, Cat. No. 82-213-XWE. http://www.statcan.gc.ca/tables-tableaux/sum-som/l01/cst01/health51b-eng.htm, accessed August 2012.

———. 2012b. Health Trends, Cat. No. 82-213-XWE. http://www.statcan.gc.ca/tables-tableaux/sum-som/l01/cst01/health03b-eng.htm, accessed August 2012.

Steingart, Richard M. 1991. "Sex differences in the management of coronary artery disease." *New England Journal of Medicine* 325: 226–230.

Stine, Gerald J. 2005. *AIDS Update 2005.* San Francisco: Benjamin Cummings.

Stolberg, Sheryl Gay. 1999. "The boom in medications brings rise in fatal risks." *New York Times* June 3: A1+.

Straus, Robert. 1957. "The nature and status of medical sociology." *American Sociological Review* 22: 200–204.

Strohschein, Lisa. 2005. "Parental divorce and child mental health trajectories." *Journal of Marriage and Family* 67: 1286–1300.

———. 2010. "Generating heat or light? The challenge of social address variables." *Journal of Marriage and Family* 72: 23–28.

———. 2011a. "A life course approach to studying transitions among Canadian seniors in couple-only households." *Canadian Public Policy* 37: 57–71.

———. 2011b. "Spousal bereavement as a triggering mechanism for a loss of residential independence among Canadian seniors." *Research on Aging* 33: 577–598.

———. 2012. "Parental divorce and child mental health: Accounting for predisruption effects." *Journal of Divorce and Remarriage* 53: 489–502.

Strohschein, Lisa, Peggy McDonough, Georges Monette, and Qing Shao. 2005. "Gender, marital status and mental health: Are there gender differences in the short-term effects of continuity and change in marital status?" *Social Science and Medicine* 61: 2293–2303.

Strong-Boag, Veronica. 1991. "Making a difference: The history of Canada's Nurses." *Canadian Bulletin of Medical History* 8: 231–248.

Suhrcke, Marc, and David Stuckler. 2012. "Will the recession be bad for our health? It depends." *Social Science and Medicine* 74: 647–653.

Sullivan, Daniel, and Till von Wachter. 2009. "Job displacement and mortality: An analysis using administrative data." *Quarterly Journal of Economics* 124: 1265–1306.

Sullivan, Deborah A., and Rose Weitz. 1988. *Labor Pains: Modern Midwives and Home Birth*. New Haven, CT: Yale University Press.

Sullivan, Patrick. 1998. "Progress or neglect? Reviewing the impact of care in the community for the severely mentally ill." *Critical Social Policy* 18: 193–213.

Summerfield, David. 2001. "The invention of post-traumatic stress disorder and the social usefulness of a psychiatric category." *BMJ British Medical Journal* 322: 95–98.

Susser, Mervyn, and Ezra Susser. 1996. "Choosing a future for epidemiology: I. Eras and pardigms." *American Journal of Public Health* 86: 668–669.

Swartz, Donald. 1998. "The limits of health insurance." Pp. 536–548 in *Health and Canadian Society: Sociological Perspectives* (3rd ed.), edited by David Coburn, Carl D'Arcy, and George M. Torrance. Toronto: University of Toronto Press.

Swedish Institute. 1997. *Social Insurance in Sweden*. Stockholm: Author (http://www.si.se).

———. 1999. *The Care of the Elderly in Sweden*. Stockholm: Author (http://www.si.se).

Szasz, Thomas. 1970. *The Manufacture of Madness*. New York: Dell.

———. 1974. *The Myth of Mental Illness*. Rev. ed. New York: Harper & Row.

Tang, Mei, Yue Chen, and Daniel Drewski. 2003. "Gender-related differences in the association between socioeconomic status and self-reported diabetes." *International Journal of Epidemiology* 32: 381–385.

Tang, Nicole K. Y., and Catherine Crane. 2006. "Suicidality in chronic pain: A review of the prevalence, risk factors and psychological links." *Psychological Medicine* 36: 575–586.

Tarasuk, Valerie S., and George H. Beaton. 1999. "Women's dietary intakes in the context of household food insecurity." *Journal of Nutrition* 129: 672–679.

Tarasuk, Valerie, and Naomi Dachner. 2009. "The proliferation of charitable meal programs in Toronto." *Canadian Public Policy* 35: 433–450.

Taylor-Butts, Andrea, and Lindsay Porter. 2011. "Family-related homicides, 2000–2009." *Family Violence in Canada: A Statistical Profile*. Cat. No. 85-224-X. Statistics Canada: Minister of Industry.

Tesh, Sylvia. 1988. *Hidden Arguments: Political Ideology and Disease Prevention Policy*. New Brunswick, NJ: Rutgers University Press.

Tessler, Richard, and Gail Gamache. 1994. "Continuity of care, residence, and family burden in Ohio." *Milbank Quarterly* 72: 149–169.

Thoits, Peggy A. 2010. "Stress and health: Major findings and policy implications." *Journal of Health and Social Behavior* 51: S41–S53.

Thomas, Carol. 2004. "How is disability understood? An examination of sociological approaches." *Disability and Society* 19: 569–583.

Thomas, Carol, and Mairian Corker. 2002. "A journey around the social model." Pp. 18–31 in *Disability/Postmodernity: Embodying Disability Theory*, edited by Mairian Corker and Tom Shakespeare. London: Continuum.

Thomas, Stephen B., and Sandra C. Quinn. 1991. "The Tuskegee Syphilis Study, 1932–1972: Implications for HIV education and AIDS risk education programs in the black community." *American Journal of Public Health* 81: 1498–1504.

Timmermans, Stefan. 1999. *Sudden Death and the Myth of CPR*. Philadelphia: Temple University Press.

———. 2005. "Death brokering: Constructing culturally appropriate deaths." *Sociology of Health and Illness* 27: 993–1013.

Timmermans, Stefan, and Marc Berg. 2003a. *The Gold Standard: The Challenge of Evidence-Based Medicine and Standardization in Health Care*. Philadelphia: Temple University Press.

———. 2003b. "The practice of medical technology." *Sociology of Health and Illness* 25: 97–114.

Timmermans, Stefan, and Hyeyoung Oh. 2010. "The continued social transformation of the medical profession." *Journal of Health and Social Behavior* 51: S94–S106.

Tindle, Hilary A., Roger B. Davis, Russell S. Phillips, and David M. Eisenberg. 2005. "Trends in use of complementary and alternative medicine by U.S. adults: 1997–2002." *Alternative Therapies* 11: 42–49.

Tjepkema, Michael. 2003. "Repetitive strain injury." *Health Reports* 14: 11–30.

Toole, Michael J., and Ronald J. Waldman. 1993. "Refugees and displaced persons: War, hunger, and public health." *Journal of the American Medical Association* 270: 600–605.

Torrance, George M. 1998. "Socio-historical overview: The development of the Canadian health system." Pp. 3–22 in *Health and Canadian Society: Sociological Perspectives* (3rd ed.), edited by David Coburn, Carl D'Arcy, and George M. Torrance. Toronto: University of Toronto Press.

Triggle, David J. 2005. "Vaccines, Viagra, and Vioxx: Medicines, markets, and money—When life-saving meets life-style." *Drug Development Research* 64: 90–98.

Trovato, Frank, and Nirannanilathu Lalu. 2007. "From divergence to convergence: The sex differential in life expectancy in Canada, 1971–2000." *Canadian Review of Sociology and Anthropology* 44: 101–122.

Tse, Carmen, and Valerie Tarasuk. 2008. "Nutritional assessment of charitable meal programmes serving homeless people in Toronto." *Public Health Nutrition* 11: 1296–1305.

Tu, Jack V., Lorelei Nardi, Jiming Fang, Juan Liu, Laila Khalid, and Helen Johansen. 2009. "National trends in rates of death and hospital admissions related to acute myocardial infarction, heart failure and stroke, 1994–2004." *Canadian Medical Association Journal* 180: E120–E127.

Tuohy, Carolyn Hughes. 2002. "The costs of constraint and prospects for health care reform in Canada." *Health Affairs* 21: 32–46.

———. 2012. "Shall we dance? The intricate project of comparison in the study of health policy." *Health Economics, Policy and Law* 7: 21–23.

Tuohy, Carolyn Hughes, Colleen M. Flood, and Mark Stabile. 2004. "How does private finance affect public health care systems? Marshaling the evidence from OECD nations." *Journal of Health Politics, Policy and Law* 29: 359–396.

Turcotte, Martin. 2011. "Intergenerational education mobility: University completion in relation to parents' education level." *Canadian Social Trends* Cat. No. 11-008: 37–43.

Turcotte, Martin, and Grant Schellenberg. 2007. *A Portrait of Seniors in Canada, 2006*. Cat. no. 89-519-XIE. Ottawa: Minister of Industry.

Turner, R. Jay, Blair Wheaton, and Donald Lloyd. 1995. "The epidemiology of social stress." *American Sociological Review* 60: 104–125.

Ubel, Peter A., and Susan Dorr Goold. 1998. "'Rationing' health care: Not all definitions are created equal." *Archives of Internal Medicine* 158: 209–214.

Uecker, Jeremy. 2012. "Marriage and mental health among young adults." *Journal of Health and Social Behavior* 53: 67–83.

UNAIDS/WHO. 2007. *AIDS Epidemic Update*. Geneva, Switzerland: Author.

UNICEF. 2005. "Press Release: Poor feeding for children under two leads to nearly one-fifth of child deaths." http://www.unicef.org/media/media_27814.html, accessed March 2008.

———. 2007. *Child Poverty in Perspective: An Overview of Child Well-being in Rich Countries. A Comprehensive Assessment of the Lives and Well-being of Children and Adolescents in the Economically Advanced Nations.* Innocenti Research Centre Report Card 7. Florence, Italy: UNICEF Innocenti Research Centre.

———. 2011. *Annual Report 2010*. New York: Author.

United Nations. 2011. *The Millennium Development Goals Report 2011*. New York: United Nations.

Väänänen, Ari, Erkko Anttila, Jussi Turtiainen, and Pekka Varje. 2012. "Formulation of work stress in 1960–2000: Analysis of scientific works from the perspective of historical sociology." *Social Science and Medicine* 75: 784–794.

Valenstein, Elliot S. 1986. *Great and Desperate Cures*. New York: Basic.

van den Broek, N. R., and A. D. Falconer. 2011. "Maternal mortality and Millennium Development Goal 5." *British Medical Bulletin* 99: 25–38.

Van den Ent, Maya M. X., David W. Brown, Edward J. Hoekstra, Athalia Christie, and Stephen L. Cochi. 2011. "Measles mortality reduction contributes substantially to reduction of all cause mortality among children less than five years of age, 1990–2008." *The Journal of Infectious Diseases* 204: S18–S23.

van Doorslaer, Eddy, Cristina Masseria, and Xander Koolman. 2006. "Inequalities in access to medical care by income in developed countries." *Canadian Medical Association Journal* 174: 177–183.

Vastag, Brian. 2001. "Pay attention: Ritalin acts much like cocaine." *Journal of the American Medical Association* 286: 905–906.

Veenstra, Gerry. 2000. "Social capital, SES and health: An individual-level analysis." *Social Science and Medicine* 50: 619–629.

Veugelers, Paul J., Angela L. Fitzgerald, and Elizabeth Johnston. 2005. "Dietary intake and risk factors for poor diet quality among children in Nova Scotia." *Canadian Journal of Public Health* 96: 212–216.

Veugelers P. J., and A. M. Yip. 2003. "Socioeconomic disparities in health care use: Does universal coverage reduce inequalities in health?" *Journal of Epidemiology Community Health* 57: 424–428.

Veugelers, Paul J., Alexandra M. Yip, and George Kephart. 2001. "Proximate and contextual socioeconomic determinants of mortality: Multilevel approaches in a setting with universal health care coverage." *American Journal of Epidemiology* 154: 725–732.

Videon, Tammy M. 2002. "The effect of parent-adolescent relationships and parental separation on adolescent well-being." *Journal of Marriage and Family* 64: 489–503.

Vorster, Esté. 2010. "The link between poverty and malnutrition: A South African perspective." *Health SA Gesondheid* 15: 1–6.

Vuckovic, Nancy, and Mark Nichter. 1997. "Changing patterns of pharmaceutical practice in the United States." *Social Science and Medicine* 44: 1285–1302.

Wade, Terrance J., John Cairney, and David J. Pevalin. 2002. "Emergence of gender differences in depression during adolescence: National panel results from three countries." *Journal of the American Academy of Child and Adolescent Psychiatry,* 41: 190–198.

Wadsworth, M. E. J., S. M. Montgomery, and M. J. Bartley 1999. "The persisting effect of unemployment on health and social well-being in men early in working life." *Social Science and Medicine* 48: 1491–1499.

Waite, Linda, and Maggie Gallagher. 2000. *The Case for Marriage: Why Married People are Happier, Healthier and Better Off Financially.* New York: Doubleday.

Waitzkin, Howard. 1981. "The social origins of illness: A neglected history." *International Journal of Health Services* 11: 77–103.

———. 1993. *The Second Sickness: Contradictions of Capitalist Health Care.* Rev. ed. New York: Free Press.

Wall, Martin, Elena Schmidt, Anya Sarang, Rifat Atun, and Adria Renton. 2011. "Sex, drugs, and economic behaviour in Russia: A study of socio-economic characteristics of high risk populations." *International Journal of Drug Policy* 22: 133–139.

Walters, Vivienne, Peggy McDonough, and Lisa Strohschein. 2002. "The influence of work, household structure, and social, personal and material resources on gender differences in health: An analysis of the 1994 Canadian National Population Health Survey." *Social Science and Medicine* 54: 677–692.

Wanberg, Connie R. 2012. "The individual experience of unemployment." *Annual Review of Psychology* 63: 369–396.

Wang, Houli, Tengda Xu, and Jin Xu. 2007. "Factors contributing to high costs and inequality in China's health care system." *Journal of the American Medical Association* 298: 1928–1930.

Wardle, Jane, Yoichi Chida, E. Leigh Gibson, Katriina L. Whitaker, and Andrew Steptoe. 2011. "Stress and adiposity: A meta-analysis of longitudinal studies." *Obesity* 19: 771–778.

Wardwell, Walter I. 1988. "Chiropractors: Evolution to acceptance." Pp. 157–191 in *Other Healers: Unorthodox Medicine in America,* edited by Norman Gevitz. Baltimore: Johns Hopkins University Press.

Watson, Diane E., and Kimberlyn M. McGrail. 2009. "More doctors or better care." *HealthCare Policy* 5: 26–31.

Weinreb, Linda, Cheryl Wehler, Jennifer Perloff, Richard Scott, David Hosmer, Linda Sagor, and Craig Gundersen. 2002. "Hunger: Its impact on children's health and mental health." *Pediatrics* 110: 1–9.

Weitz, Rose. 1991. *Life with AIDS.* New Brunswick, NJ: Rutgers University Press.

Welsh, Sandy, Merrijoy Kelner, Beverly Wellman, and Heather Boon. 2004. "Moving forward? Complementary and alternative practitioners seeking self-regulation." *Sociology of Health and Illness* 26: 216–241.

Werth, Barry. 1991. "How short is too short? Marketing human growth hormone." *New York Times Magazine* June 16: 14+.

Wertz, Richard, and Dorothy Wertz. 1989. *Lying-In*. New Haven, CT: Yale University Press.

Wheaton, Blair. 1990. "Life transitions, role histories and mental health." *American Sociological Review* 55: 209–223.

Whitehouse, Peter J., Eric Juengst, Maxwell Mehlman, and Thomas H. Murray. 1997. "Enhancing cognition in the intellectually intact." *Hastings Center Report* 27 (3): 14–22.

Whittaker, Elvi. 2005. "Adjudicating entitlements: The emerging discourses of research ethics boards." *Health* 9: 513–535.

Wienke, Chris, and Gretchen J. Hill. 2009. "Does the 'marriage benefit' extend to partners in gay and lesbian relationships: Evidence from a random sample of sexually active adults." *Journal of Family Issues* 30: 259–289.

Wilkins, Kathryn and Evelyn Park. 2004. "Injuries." *Health Reports* 15 (3): 43–48.

Wilkins, Russell, Jean-Marie Berthelot, and Edward Ng. 2002. "Trends in mortality by neighbourhood income in urban Canada from 1971 to 1996." *Supplement to Health Reports* 13: 1–27.

Wilkins, Russell, and Gregory J. Sherman. 1999. "Low income and child health in Canada." In *Health and Canadian Society: Sociological Perspectives* (3rd ed.), edited by D. Coburn, C. D'Arcy, and G. M. Torrance. Toronto: University of Toronto Press.

Wilkins, Russell, Sharanjit Uppal, Philippe Finès, Sacha Senécal, Éric Guimond and Rene Dion. 2008. "Life expectancy in the Inuit-inhabited areas of Canada, 1989–2003." *Health Reports* 19: 7–17.

Wilkinson, Richard G. 1996. *Unhealthy Societies: The Afflictions of Inequality*. London: Routledge.

———. 2005. *The Impact of Inequality*. London: New Press.

Wilkinson, Richard G., and Kate E. Pickett. 2006. "Income inequality and population health: A review and explanation of the evidence." *Social Science and Medicine* 62: 1768–1784.

———. 2009. *The Spirit Level: Why More Equal Societies Almost Always Do Better*. London: Penguin.

Willcox, Sharon, Mary Seddon, Stephen Dunn, Rhiannon Tudor Edwards, Jim Pearse, and Jack V. Tu. 2007. "Measuring and reducing waiting times: A cross-national comparison of strategies." *Health Affairs* 26: 1078–1087.

Williams, A. Paul, Raisa Deber, Pat Baranek, and Alina Gildiner. 2001. "From medicare to home care: Globalization, state retrenchment, and the profitization of Canada's health care system." Pp. 7–30 in *Unhealthy Times: Political Economy Perspectives on Health and Care in Canada,* edited by Pat Armstrong, Hugh Armstrong, and David Coburn. Toronto: Oxford University Press.

Williams, Cara. 2006. "Disability in the workplace." Perspectives Catalogue No. 75-001-XIE. Ottawa: Statistics Canada.

Williams, David R., and Chiquita Collins. 1995. "U.S. socioeconomic and racial differences in health: Patterns and explanations." *Annual Review of Sociology* 21: 349–386.

Williams, David R., Mark B. McClellan, and Alice M. Rivlin. 2010. "Beyond the Affordable Care Act: Achieving real improvements in Americans' health." *Health Affairs* 29: 1481–1488.

Williams, Kristi M., 2003. "Has the future of marriage arrived? A contemporary examination of gender, marriage and psychological well-being." *Journal of Health and Social Behavior* 44: 470–487.

Williams, Simon J. 1995. "Theorising class, health and lifestyles: Can Bourdieu help us?" *Sociology of Health and Illness* 17: 577–604.

———. 2003. *Medicine and the Body*. London: Sage.

———. 2005. "Parsons revisited: From sick role to …?" *Health* 9: 123–144.

Willson, Andrea E., Laura M. Shuey, and Glen H. Elder, Jr. 2007. "Cumulative advantage processes as mechanisms of inequality in life course health." *American Journal of Sociology* 112: 1886–1924.

Wilson, Jim, Minoli Amit, William Fitzgerald, Paul Dagg, Graham Bullock, John Steeves, Nicole Robbins, Linda Snell, and Kevin Imrie. 2011. "Generalism: Achieving a balance with specialization: A White Paper prepared for the Royal College of Physicians and Surgeons of Canada, future of medical education in Canada." Royal College of Physicians and Surgeons of Canada Competence by Design-Royal College White Paper Series: Paper 2.

Wilt, Timothy J., Tatyana Shamliyan, Brent Taylor, Roderick MacDonald, James Tacklind, Indulis Rutks, Kenneth Koeneman, Chin-Soo Cho, and Robert L. Kane. 2008. "Comparative effectiveness of therapies for clinically localized prostate cancer." *Comparative Effectiveness Review* No. 13. Rockville, MD: Agency for Healthcare Research and Quality.

Winnick, Terri A. 2005. "From quackery to 'complementary' medicine: The American medical profession confronts alternative therapies." *Social Problems* 52: 38–61.

Wirth, Louis. 1985. "The problem of minority groups." Pp. 309–315 in *Theories of Society: Foundations of Modern Sociological Theory*, edited by T. Parsons, E. Shils, K. D. Naegele, and J. R. Pitts. New York: Free Press.

Wister, Andrew V. 2005. *Baby Boomer Health Dynamics: How Are We Aging?* Toronto: University of Toronto Press.

World Bank. 1998. *Assessing Aid: What Works, What Doesn't, and Why.* New York: Oxford University Press.

World Economic Forum. 2011. *The Global Economic Burden Of Non-communicable Diseases.* Geneva, Switzerland: Author.

World Health Organization (WHO). 1986. *Ottawa Charter for Health Promotion.* Geneva, Switzerland: Author.

———. 2000. *The World Health Report 2000—Health Systems: Improving Performance.* Geneva, Switzerland: Author.

———. 2002. *Patterns of Global Health Expenditures: Results for 191 Countries.* Geneva, Switzerland: Author.

———. 2004. *World Report on Road Traffic Injury Prevention: Prevention.* Geneva, Switzerland: Author.

———. 2005. "Summary of probable SARS cases with onset of illness from 1 November 2002 to 31 July 2003." http://www.who.int/csr/sars/country/table2004_04_21/en/, accessed August 2012.

———. 2006. *SARS: How a global epidemic was stopped.* Geneva, Switzerland: Author.

———. 2008. *The Global Burden of Disease—2004 Update.* Geneva, Switzerland: Author.

———. 2009a. *Global Status Report on Road Safety: Time for Action.* Geneva, Switzerland: Author.

———. 2009b. *Women and Health: Today's Evidence, Tomorrow's Agenda.* Geneva, Switzerland: Author.

———. 2010a. *Trends in Maternal Mortality: 1990 to 2008.* Geneva, Switzerland: Author.

———. 2010b. *The World Health Report, 2005—Health Systems: Health Systems Financing. The Path to Universal Coverage.* Geneva, Switzerland: Author.

———. 2011a. *Global HIV/AIDS Response. Epidemic Update and Health Sector Progress towards Universal Access— Progress Report 2011.* Geneva, Switzerland: Author.

———. 2011b. *Global Status Report on Noncommunicable Diseases.* Geneva: Switzerland: Author.

———. 2011c. *Global Tuberculosis Control—WHO Report 2011.* Geneva, Switzerland: Author.

———. 2011d. *Mental Health Atlas 2011.* Geneva, Switzerland: Author.

———. 2012. *Global Plan for the Decade of Action for Road Safety 2011–2020.* Geneva, Switzerland: Author.

World Health Organization Regional Office for Europe. 2006. *Highlights on Health in the Russian Federation—2005.* http://www.euro.who.int/__data/assets/pdf_file/0003/103593/E88405.pdf, accessed August 2012.

World Health Organization, Reproductive Health and Research Department. 2004. *Low Birthweight: National, Regional, and Global Estimates.* Geneva, Switzerland: Author.

Wu, Tiejian, Maurizio Trevisan, Robert J. Genco, Joan P. Dorn, Karen L. Falkner, and Christopher T. Sempos. 2000. "Periodontal disease and risk of cerebrovascular disease: The First National Health and Nutrition Examination Survey and its follow-up study." *Archives of Internal Medicine* 160: 2749–2755.

Wu, Zheng, Margaret J. Penning, Michael S. Pollard, and Randy Hart. 2003. "In sickness and in health: Does cohabitation count?" *Journal of Family Issues* 24: 811–838.

Xi, Guoliang, Ian McDowell, Rama Nair, and Robert Spasoff. 2005. "Income inequality and health in Ontario." *Canadian Journal of Public Health* 96: 206–211.

Xu, Li, Anne H. Gauthier, and Lisa Strohschein. 2009. "Why are some children left out? Factors barring Canadian children from participating in extracurricular activities." *Canadian Studies in Population* 36: 325–345.

Young, T. Kue, Jeff Reading, Brenda Elias, and John D. O'Neil. 2000. "Type 2 diabetes mellitus in Canada's First Nations: Status of an epidemic in progress." *Canadian Medical Association Journal* 163: 561–566.

Yusuf Salim, Shofi qul Islam, Clara K. Chow, Sumathy Rangarajan, Gilles Dagenais, Rafael Diaz, Rajeev Gupta, Roya Kelishadi, Romaina Iqbal, Alvaro Avezum, Annamarie Kruger, Raman Kutty, Fernando Lanas, Liu Lisheng, Li Wei, Patricio Lopez-Jaramillo, Aytekin Oguz, Omar Rahman, Hany Swidan, Khalid Yusoff, Witold Zatonski, Annika Rosengren, and Koon K. Teo. 2011. "Study investigators use of secondary prevention drugs for cardiovascular disease in the community in high-income, middle-income, and low-income countries (the PURE Study): A prospective epidemiological survey." *The Lancet* 378: 1231–1243.

Zhao, Jun, Li Xue, and Tara Gilkinson. 2010. *Health Status and Social Capital of Recent Immigrants to Canada: Evidence from the Longitudinal Survey of Immigrants to Canada.* Ottawa: Citizenship and Immigration Canada.

Zimmerman, Mary K. 1993. "Caregiving in the welfare state: Mothers' informal health care work in Finland." *Research in the Sociology of Health Care* 10: 193–211.

Ziporyn, Terra D. 1992. *Nameless Diseases.* New Brunswick, NJ: Rutgers University Press.

Zola, Irving K. 1972. "Medicine as an institution of social control." *Sociological Review* 20: 487–504.

———. 1985. "Depictions of disability—Metaphor, message and medium in the media: A research and political agenda." *Social Science and Medicine* 22: 5–17.

———. 1993. "Self, identity and the naming question: Reflections on the language of disability." *Social Science and Medicine* 36: 167–173.

Zoutman, Dick E., and B. Douglas Ford. 2008. "A comparison of infection control program resources, activities, and antibiotic resistant organism rates in Canadian acute care hospitals in 1999 and 2005: Pre- and post-severe acute respiratory syndrome." *American Journal of Infection Control* 36: 711–717.

Zuberi, Daniyal M., and Merlita B. Ptashnick. 2011. "The deleterious consequences of privatization and outsourcing for hospital work: The experiences of contracted-out hospital cleaners and dietary aids in Vancouver, Canada." *Social Science and Medicine* 72: 907–911.

Zussman, Robert. 1992. *Intensive Care: Medical Ethics and the Medical Profession.* Chicago: University of Chicago Press.

———. 1997. "Sociological perspectives on medical ethics and decision-making." *Annual Review of Sociology* 23: 171–189.

Page numbers in *italic* indicate figures or tables. Page numbers in **bold** indicate glossary terms when defined in text.